THE GOOD HOTEL GUIDE 2009

Great Britain & Ireland

Editors:

DESMOND BALMER
AND ADAM RAPHAEL

Editor in Chief:
Caroline Raphael

Founding Editor:
Hilary Rubinstein

Contributing Editors:
Bill Bennett
Nicola Davies

THE GOOD HOTEL GUIDE LTD

Please send reports on hotels to
The Good Hotel Guide
50 Addison Avenue, London W11 4QP
or (if posted in UK)
Freepost PAM 2931, London W11 4BR
Tel/fax: 020-7602 4182
Email: editor@goodhotelguide.com
Website: www.goodhotelguide.com

The Good Hotel Guide Ltd

This edition first published in 2008 by
The Good Hotel Guide Ltd

1 3 5 7 9 10 8 6 4 2

Design: Mick Keates
Production: Hugh Allan
Researcher: Enkeleda Hoti
Text editor: Daphne Trotter
Managing editor: Alison Wormleighton
Computer consultant: Gwyn Evans
Website design and development: HeadChannel Ltd, London

A CIP catalogue record for this book may be found in the British Library.

ISBN: 978-0-9549404-3-0

Typeset from authors' disks by
MATS Typesetters, Southend-on-Sea, Essex
Printed and bound in Great Britain by
Polestar Wheatons, Exeter

Contents

The truly independent guide

This is the leading independent guide to hotels in Great Britain and Ireland. Hotels cannot buy their entry as they do in most rival guides. No money changes hands, and the editors and inspectors do not accept free hospitality on their anonymous visits to hotels. The only vested interest is that of the reader seeking impartial advice on how to find a good hotel.

Our hotels are as independent as we are. Most are small, family owned and family run. They are places of character where the owners and their staff spend time looking after their guests, rather than reporting to an area manager. We look for a warm welcome, with flexible service.

Diversity is the key to our selection. Grand country houses are listed alongside simple B&Bs. Some of our favourite places may not have the full range of hotel-type facilities, but the welcome will be warm. We include a few chain hotels, especially in the larger cities; each one will have met our criteria of high standards of service.

Our new website works in tandem with the printed *Guide*. It carries the entries for many, but not all of our selected hotels (only those which carry a reciprocal web link are included). It has pictures for each entry, and a comprehensive search engine.

Our readers play a crucial role by reporting on existing entries as well as recommending new discoveries. Reader reports, written on the forms at the back of the book or sent by email, bring our entries to life, and give the *Guide* a unique 'word-of-mouth' quality. The editors make a balanced judgment based on these reports, backed where necessary by an anonymous inspection. Many correspondents join our Readers' Club (see page 16).

Annual updates give the *Guide* an added edge. A significant number of hotels fall by the wayside every year, and many new hotels are added. We drop a hotel if there has been a change of owner unless reports after the change are positive, if this year's reports are negative, or in rare cases where there has been no feedback.

Introduction

There has never been a better time for a holiday in Britain. Three key factors point to a resurgence in stays at home: the increasing cost of flying, the rise in the value of the euro, and the growing acceptance of the green agenda. The oil price rise has sent air fares soaring. On long-haul flights, passengers are paying heavy fuel surcharges; on the shorter routes the so-called low-cost airlines have increased the number and cost of 'extras' added to the headline fare. By the time passengers have paid for check-in, luggage, the use of a debit card, and all the other charges, a 'cheap' fare can rise to an alarming level. Travellers to euro-zone countries have been counting the cost of conversion rates that have brought the euro close to parity with the pound. Suddenly, holidays at home don't seem so expensive.

This is where the third factor comes in. As understanding of green issues spreads, we are beginning to change the way we live. Much of the green agenda has become routine for many households: they have adopted recycling measures, low-power light bulbs, dual-flush lavatories, etc. And the rise in air fares will reinforce an acknowledgement that flying damages the environment. An increasing number of *Guide* hoteliers actively pursue green measures. We highlight this in their entry, while Hotelfinder lists ten hotels that we think have outstanding green credentials. John Rowlands, the owner of *Y Goeden Eirin*, the *Guide*'s Green guest house of the year in 2008, has written an article (page 8) explaining why going green is the natural way. (As a matter of course, the *Guide* is printed on paper produced from sustainable forests.)

Only the capriciousness of British weather remains an obstacle. We hope that hotels in Great Britain and Ireland will do everything they can in the coming year to encourage visitors to explore the glories of their home country. An independent guide to the best of these hotels is more important than ever before.

Not in front of the children

Last year we published a mother's lament about discrimination against young children in hotels. She said that just because she had children she had not lowered her standards, nor did she want to stay at 'expensive child-friendly ghettoes'. She would much prefer to stay at the sort of small, personal hotel that the *Guide* seeks to identify, but she found she wasn't always welcomed there with her offspring. We noted that around one in four of the hotels listed in the *Guide* imposed some form of age restriction on children staying, or eating at night in the restaurant. The response from readers was not always sympathetic. Several commented that parents did not always seem to be in control of their children, and said that they would prefer to dine free from such distractions. This has never been an issue in hotels on the Continent, where it is rare to find restrictions on younger visitors. We believe that children will never learn how to behave in hotels and restaurants unless they are given the experience. Good hoteliers know how to handle children. An inspector reported this year on the approach at the *Gumstool* pub at child-friendly *Calcot Manor*, Tetbury. 'The *Gumstool* was vibrant at lunchtime on a Saturday, bursting at the seams with families, toddlers, babes-in-arms. The young staff may sometimes have struggled to stay in control (as did some of the parents), but we liked the way they carefully placed the families to minimise any inconvenience to those without children. It was so much nicer to eat out among all the generations.' The last word must go to our original correspondent who writes: 'My mother-in-law says that at her age she positively seeks out the "no children" hotels.' We shall continue to encourage child-friendly hotels, while listing any restrictions that might be imposed by others.

The absurdity of the service charge

Like many of our readers, we continue to be irritated by the imposition of a 'discretionary' service charge on a hotel bill. This is sometimes included on the original bill, or sometimes by the more insidious means of offering the choice of adding a payment for service as a stage in the processing of a debit or credit card. Our view is that service is the first thing that we expect a hotel to provide. Some hotels justify service charges as a way of helping lower-paid back-of-house staff who rarely receive a tip. Apart from the issue of transparency (how do we know that these payments go to staff?), the imposition of a service charge suggests that hotels are not paying proper wages. Hotelier Alastair Kameen, who reports on page 10 on his experiences staying at hotels across Britain after he sold *Bark House*, Bampton, was infuriated by the imposition of a service charge at a hotel where the service was minimal. 'A 12% service charge was added to my bill. I asked them to deduct this, which played havoc with the computer system.' He adds that he 'leaves a generous gratuity' when he has had a pleasurable stay at a hotel. This is how it should be. The payment of a gratuity should be at the discretion of the guest.

The value of the personal touch

One of the irritations of using Google to find a hotel or restaurant is the placement of hotel booking sites above the actual website you are seeking. A long-standing reader advises against using such sites by instead going directly to the hotel's own website (listed, of course, in the *Guide*). 'Typically, I get better rates than through a booking site,' he says. Hotels pay commission to these third parties, which is why so many advertise that their best online rates will be on their own portals. We suggest that the personal touch might be even better. When you talk to a hotel, especially a small family-run place, you can quickly form an idea of how it treats customers. Even at the more impersonal hotels, you can discover the better deals by this direct approach. One tip is to have the best online rate on your computer screen when you telephone the hotel. If the receptionist fails to match or improve on the screen deal, you can always tell them you'll follow the online route.

John Ardagh

We were saddened, in January 2008, to hear of the death of John Ardagh. He wrote the Irish section of the *Guide* for many years, and the French and German entries in the Continental Europe edition for even longer. His lively style, enthusiasm and deep knowledge of these countries gave real authority to these chapters.

Thank you

One of the best aspects of the email age is that it has encouraged a new generation of readers to write to us about their experiences at hotels. That is reinforced by our new website – please have a look at it (www.goodhotelguide.com). Many readers now use email to send us reports (others write their comments, no less welcome, on the forms at the back of the book). Every report is important to the preparation of an up-to-date hotel guide. They are the bedrock on which the *Good Hotel Guide* is built. They help us capture that elusive 'spirit' that makes the good hotel stand out from the ordinary. Our thanks go to all our correspondents. And, as always, we pay tribute to our intrepid inspectors who travel many miles to check hotels for the *Guide*.

DESMOND BALMER AND ADAM RAPHAEL
July 2008

Why going green is the natural way of living

by John Rowlands

Green doesn't have to be spartan. In its mildest form, it's simply a natural way of living, feeling in tune with the natural and cultural environment, being organically rooted in one's community, and doing all the common-sense things which show respect for the planet.

When awarded a *César* as 'Green guest house of the year' in the 2008 edition of the *Guide*, we felt flattered yet somewhat embarrassed. We thought we simply did what other sensible establishments did: we have installed photovoltaic solar panels, low-power electricity bulbs, water butts, dual-flush toilets, sensor outside lights which come on only when there is someone within their orbit, good insulation. We have strict recycling and composting policies, we use solar-powered radios, eco-friendly toiletries and cleaning materials, and Good Energy electricity. A lot of our vegetables, fruits and herbs are grown in our own kitchen garden in season, and we buy other food locally where possible, much of it organic or at least free-range. We seek the best advice on fish sustainability, and of course we cater for vegetarians. Guests are encouraged to use the excellent public transport which is available around here, and we advise on cycling routes and local walks.

We display a list of hints pertaining to green living in each guest room but these are not prescriptive, and no one has yet complained that they are being treated like a minor. In fact, we aim for a high level of comfort as well as aesthetic taste and try to make guests feel at home, and even pampered. Books in both Welsh and English are to be seen in every nook and cranny, and walls are covered with paintings by Welsh artists of distinction, such as Ceri Richards and Kyffin Williams. It's true that the Bechstein grand in our dining room is obviously German, but it was bought from local suppliers, Pianos Cymru in Porthmadog. The work of local craftsmen is evident all around – in the slate floors and walls of some of our rooms, the oak floors of others. Our granite walls are the work of skilful stonemasons. Oak dressers and dining tables emphasize the traditional aspect of *Y Goeden Eirin*, while other features bring us right up to the present.

Luxury doesn't have to be a product of material wealth, and to live in an area of such outstanding natural beauty, 'twixt mountains and sea, in former farm buildings set in 20 acres of biodiverse land, is in itself a kind of luxury. For us as a family, there is an added dimension to this – the less perceptible cultural heritage of Eryri (Snowdonia). Every mountain peak, river and beach has been shaped by the people living around them from time immemorial. Every small field has its own Welsh name. The very lifeblood of our Welsh communities is the Welsh language itself. Language is not just a way of communicating, but a means of perception, of seeing and of feeling. All the natural beauty of this area has been documented in Welsh – all trees, flowers and birds have their own distinctive Welsh names.

Of course, it would be a tall order to expect worldwide visitors to integrate themselves into this environment by learning Welsh. Some will, but most won't. However, tourism should not be allowed to be a kind of vandalism, although the truth is that that is exactly what it is in many parts of the world, including Wales. Fortunately, the growing green agenda has alerted people to the dangers of commercial tourism, hence the increasing awareness of the need to protect the natural environment, and to respect it in order to enjoy it to the full.

We need to go beyond this. There is not only a natural environment but a cultural and linguistic one, and environmentalism which respects the former while being oblivious of the latter is very short-sighted. We who operate in the tourist industry should alert visitors to the wealth of history and culture all around them. I do not mean that we should be lecturing or hectoring them in any way, but it is our duty to be rooted in our own communities (whether we are natives or newcomers) to such a degree that we should be representatives of those communities, and through this visitors will unconsciously perceive some aspects of the native culture. This might mean simple, straightforward things such as eating local food, or visiting cultural festivals, heritage centres and museums as well as castles and National Trust mansions. Here we make available maps and guides, history books and literature of local interest. More pertinently, we sell books such as John Gwilym Jones's *The Plum Tree*, a translation of *Y Goeden Eirin* from which the name of our house derives, and the anthology of 20th-century Welsh poems in English translation which I co-edited with Menna Elfyn, *The Bloodaxe Book of Modern Welsh Poetry*.

All of us have a long way to go, but let's hope we are going in the right direction. First and foremost, we are in the business of spreading happiness, of making people get away from it all and enjoy some peace and quiet in a natural environment where there are real people going around their daily lives, and inhabited by natural species which are worthy of respect. Going on holiday should be an enjoyable experience, and greening our business has certainly been that.

(*With his wife, Eluned, John Rowlands runs* Y Goeden Eirin, *which won its* César *as 'Green guest house of the year' in the 2008 edition of the* Good Hotel Guide.)

The spirit that sets apart good hotels

by Alastair Kameen

In late summer 2007, I sold my hotel in Devon (*Bark House*, Bampton). Having been 'confined to barracks' for 11 years, I found the chance to travel and savour British hospitality too good to miss. The following is a brief personal sketch on the state of British hotel-keeping, based on what was necessarily a limited and eclectic sample.

Travelling the highways and byways of Britain set me thinking once again on the question of what makes for a really good hotel. Is it just the 'eat, drink, sleep' experience that contemporary marketing jargon would have us believe? Or is there some other factor that sets apart a good hotel, be it small or large, simple or plush? My experience on my travels confirmed my long-held view that the single factor that sets apart a pleasurable hotel experience from the mediocre is the spirit in which a hotel is run. This emanates from the proprietor/manager who influences its every aspect.

The 'spirit' factor is neglected by too many professional hotel inspectors who have boxes to tick and percentage scores to mark. I can best illustrate this by my experience at a Scottish hotel (not in the *Good Hotel Guide*). I arrived at 5.15 pm to receive a welcome that was anything but warm. Afternoon tea, I was informed, was served at 4 pm and was now over. The lounge and dining room had the ambience of a doctor's waiting room. When I checked out, I told the proprietor what I thought. His reply: 'The AA rates me at 85%.' The fact that I had not enjoyed my stay seemed irrelevant as long as his hotel was rated at 85%, 'mission accomplished'.

The infuriating thing about hotels is that you have to commit to spending hundreds of pounds before finding out if you like the place and enjoy what it has to offer. You test-drive a car before you buy it, and try on clothing to see if it fits; but you can't try out a hotel before you stay in it. This is why I find the *Good Hotel Guide* such an invaluable reference book. It is also the reason why readers must continue to send feedback forms which are vital to keep reports up to date and to identify the best hotels. I believe that comments on the manner in which a hotel is run are as important as the comfort of the rooms and the standard of the food.

The first clue about the spirit in which a hotel is run comes with the letter confirming the booking. If it is spontaneous and welcoming, it will be a fairly safe bet that you will enjoy your stay. If it is a standard computer printout or, worse still, contains draconian threats of what will happen if you dare to cancel, you will probably not enjoy your experience. The tone of the letter will tell you how the hotel is run.

I was reassured by the number of hotels run by vocational hoteliers with flair and a sense of pride in their hotel. I was troubled by a number run by accountant/hoteliers, which tended to be cold, formulaic, joyless. Those that kept things relatively simple generally offered the best hospitality and engendered a sense of well-being. The important elements include staff chosen for the warmth of their personality. The offer of a pot of tea and home-made cake on arrival is so much more welcoming than telling visitors that there are tea- and coffee-making facilities in the room. Those earning their living through hospitality should be prepared to be hospitable. This seems self-evident, yet occasionally I did wonder at the lack of hospitality.

I found that service charges were generally added only by hotels giving second-rate, even third-rate, service. I consider the addition of service charges bad mannered and high handed. They smack of greed. Has the hotelier not heard of the Minimum Wage Act? Is there transparency to ensure that the charges actually go to the staff? The worst example of this was at a hotel (which will remain nameless) where the service was poor. Indeed, breakfast was self-service except for the cooked dish which was plonked on the table before I'd started my muesli. Yet a 12% service charge was added to my bill. I asked them to deduct this, which played havoc with the computer system (this appealed to my wicked sense of humour).

Call me old-fashioned, but I thought a service charge implied receiving service. This stems from hoteliers engaging staff with a feel for what they do, and training them to carry out their duties with sensitivity to each and every guest's requirements. Whenever I have had a pleasurable stay at a hotel, I always leave a generous gratuity. It seems natural. Of course, these are never the hotels which impose a service charge.

THE 2009 CÉSAR AWARDS

Our *César* award, named after César Ritz,
the most celebrated of all hoteliers, is the accolade
that hoteliers most want to win. Every year we
nominate ten places that stand out for their
excellence. But our laurel wreaths are not given for
grandeur. We champion independent hotels of all
types. The following special places caught our eye
this year. Each has a distinct character;
what they have in common is an attitude
to service that puts the customer first. Previous
César winners, provided that they are still in the
same hands and as good as ever, are indicated in the
text by the symbol of a small laurel leaf.

ENGLISH COUNTRY HOTEL OF THE YEAR
Lindeth Fell, Bowness-on-Windermere

For more than 20 years, Diana and Pat Kennedy have maintained high standards at their traditional country hotel. It has a happy blend of formality and informality without a hint of pretension, and a beautiful setting above Lake Windermere.

RESTAURANT-WITH-ROOMS OF THE YEAR
The Great House, Lavenham

In a historic English building in a lovely wool town, Régis and Martine Crépy run their restaurant-with-rooms in true Gallic style. The superb modern cooking of Enrique Bilbault is served with winning warmth by a young French staff.

NEWCOMER OF THE YEAR
Hotel TerraVina, Netley Marsh

Experienced hoteliers Gérard and Nina Basset have created a stylish contemporary hotel in the New Forest. They make great efforts to care for their guests. Their staff are enthusiastic, and the cooking is refined and imaginative.

ISLAND HOTEL OF THE YEAR
Star Castle, St Mary's

In a commanding position above the main harbour of the Isles of Scilly, this star-shaped Tudor fortress has a real family-run feel. Owner Robert Francis co-manages with his son, James. Their staff are professional yet friendly.

CUMBRIAN INN OF THE YEAR
The Bay Horse, Ulverston

Once a staging post for coaches crossing the sands of Morecambe Bay, this 18th-century building is run as a good, honest inn by owner Robert Lyons and manageress Lesley Wheeler. Their charm disguises a deep attention to detail.

DINING PUB OF THE YEAR
The Gurnard's Head, Zennor

On the wild north Cornish coast, Charles and Edmund Inkin
have struck the right note in their conversion of this old pub.
Locals and visitors enjoy the congenial atmosphere, and the
excellent modern cooking of Robert Wright.

LUXURY HOTEL OF THE YEAR
Tresanton, St Mawes

In a seaside village, Olga Polizzi has combined the best of the
old and the new at her luxurious yet informal hotel. It is self-
assured, elegant, and well managed by Federica Bertolini. Paul
Wadham's cooking is delicious.

SCOTTISH GUEST HOUSE OF THE YEAR
Bealach House, Duror

Surrounded by woods and mountains, this small guest house is
run to the highest standards by Jim and Hilary McFadyen. The
welcome is warm, the housekeeping exemplary, the cooking
excellent. A very special enterprise.

WELSH COUNTRY HOTEL OF THE YEAR
Gliffaes, Crickhowell

Susie and James Suter, the third generation of her family to own
this smart sporting hotel on the banks of the River Usk, have an
unaffected approach that creates a happy atmosphere. The staff
are friendly, and the cooking of Stephan Trinci is much praised.

IRISH HERITAGE HOME OF THE YEAR
Ballyvolane House, Castlelyons

Justin and Jenny Green offer a taste of country house living in
the Irish way at their elegant Georgian home. They welcome
guests in house-party style, with relaxed aplomb. Dinner, around
a huge table, is an event; breakfast is served until midday.

Join the *Good Hotel Guide* Readers' Club

Send us a review of your favourite hotel.

As a member of the club, you will be entitled to:

1. A pre-publication discount offer

2. Personal advice on hotels

3. Advice if you are in dispute with a hotel

The writers of the 12 best reviews will each win a free copy of the *Guide* and an invitation to our launch party.

Send your review via:

our website: www.goodhotelguide.com

or email: editor@goodhotelguide.com

or fax: 020-7602 4182

or write to:

Good Hotel Guide
Freepost PAM 2931
London W11 4BR
(no stamp is needed in the UK)

or, from outside the UK:

Good Hotel Guide
50 Addison Avenue
London W11 4QP
England

Hotelfinder

A visit to a hotel should be a special occasion.
This section will help you find a good hotel that
matches your mood, whether for romance or sport,
or to entertain the children. Don't forget to turn
to the full entry for the bigger picture.

DISCOVERIES

There are 59 new hotels in the *Guide* this year. Here are some of the most interesting of our finds

The Abbey Country Restaurant, Byland

By the ruins of Byland Abbey, this old inn has been given an elaborate make-over by English Heritage. The 'intrinsic history of the building' has been retained; much of the furniture has been made locally. Lots of extras in the bedrooms: two face the abbey ruins (floodlit at night), the third a 'lovely' garden. Meals are 'suited to the surroundings'.
Read more: page 134.

Timberstone, Clee Stanton

In a peaceful setting in the hills above Ludlow, Alex Read and Tracey Baylis welcome guests to their family home. Bedrooms in the main house have original beams, old pine furnishings; two bedrooms in a new extension have 'beautifully crafted oak fittings'. Communal meals (many organic ingredients) are taken in a 'lovely, light connecting room'.
Read more: page 145.

Plantation House, Ermington

On the sunny side of the River Erme valley, this cream-painted former rectory has been renovated by Richard and Magdalena Hendey, 'charming, talented owners'. Bedrooms are 'furnished with flair'. He is a 'talented chef', and the service is attentive, effective. 'Everything showed meticulous attention to detail and seemed to be delivered with effortless panache.'
Read more: page 164.

The Bath Arms, Horningsham

Christoph Brooke and his wife Sarah Montague (of the *Today* programme) lease this handsome old inn on the edge of the Longleat estate from the Marquis of Bath. They have created an 'informal, happy atmosphere' in a building filled with Indian furniture and fabrics. The bedrooms, all different, have an oriental theme. The pub is packed at night with locals.
Read more: page 193.

The Kingham Plough, Kingham

Emily Watkins, former *sous-chef* at the celebrated *Fat Duck* in Bray, serves 'outstanding food at keen prices' at her new dining pub, a conversion of an old inn in an attractive Cotswold village.

Bedrooms in the old house have quirky features; simpler annexe rooms are 'good value'. 'Exceptional' dishes are enjoyed in the bar and dining room (original beams, stripped wood). *Read more: page 197.*

Hotel TerraVina, Netley Marsh

Gérard and Nina Basset, co-founders of the Hotel du Vin group, are hands-on owners of this stylish contemporary hotel in the New Forest. No stuffiness in the tastefully converted building: open, modern, top-quality fittings, glass panels, natural wood or slate flooring. Organic produce is preferred for the 'delicious, refined' cooking. *Read more: page 243.*

The Neptune Inn & Restaurant, Old Hunstanton

Near the north Norfolk coast, Kevin (the chef) and Jacki Mangeolles are refurbishing this 18th-century coaching inn as an 'excellent restaurant-with-rooms'. Bedrooms are thoughtfully equipped (digital radio, TV and Wi-Fi). The smart, attractive restaurant is 'the centre of the action'; interesting dishes, carefully presented. *Read more: page 251.*

Broad House Hotel, Wroxham

In peaceful gardens close to Wroxham Broad, this beautiful

Queen Anne house has been modernised 'in a careful way' by Philip and Caroline Search. Bedrooms have attractive fabrics, antique furniture, good lighting. Books and games in the library; friendly, informal service in the restaurant (large windows, red walls, contemporary cutlery and china). *Read more: page 329.*

The New White Lion, Llandovery

In a small town near Brecon, this Grade II listed former pub has been transformed into a 'stylish guest house' by Gerald and Sylvia Pritchard. 'They are natural hosts, unpretentious, with plenty of time to spend with their guests.' They have created a sophisticated ambience with chandeliers, fine fabrics, smart wallpaper. 'Satisfying' dinners (pre-booked) have 'no frills, but good raw materials'. *Read more: page 413.*

Hafod Elwy Hall, Pentrefoelas

A 'characterful house with an Edwardian feel' which stands 'far from anywhere' on a working farm in Denbighshire. Roger and Wendy Charles-Warner give a 'personal, unforced' welcome. They are 'very green': everything is home grown or home made; the cooking is country style, authentic. The bedrooms have 'everything one could wish for'. *Read more: page 424.*

GREEN

Enjoy a guilt-free stay at
these hotels which take
active measures to protect
the environment

One Aldwych, London

Gordon Campbell Gray's ultra-
modern conversion of the old
Morning Post offices is 'one of the
UK's most eco-friendly hotels'.
Paper, plastic and cardboard are
recycled, and long-life light
bulbs are used. Bio-active bath
products (with recyclable
containers) are provided in the
bathrooms. Organic ingredients
are used in the two restaurants.
Read more: page 71.

Paskins Town House, Brighton

In a conservation area 100 yards
from the sea, this stylish town
house is a holder of a Green
Tourism Business Gold Award.
Low-energy light bulbs are used;
soap and shampoo are synthetic-
free, animal produce-free.
Organic local ingredients are
used for breakfast; vegetarian
dishes a speciality; fair trade tea
and coffee.
Read more: page 127.

Milden Hall, Milden

Near historic Lavenham, this
'much-loved Georgianised 16th-
century farmhouse' is run on
eco-friendly lines by Juliet and
Christopher Hawkins. They

promote 'the environmental
benefits of sensitively farmed
Suffolk countryside and the
real value of good local produce'
at their listed 16th-century
farmhouse. They promise to buy
goods 'that are not over-
packaged', to recycle and
compost as much as possible,
to be energy-efficient, and to
'minimise the use of the car'.
Read more: page 236.

Primrose Valley Hotel, St Ives

The owners of this Edwardian
villa place 'a huge emphasis
on sustainability'. An optional
charge of £1 is added to the
bill to go towards marine
conservation initiatives. Local
and fair trade food is used, and
waste is recycled where possible.
The website lists '20 things that
make us more sustainable', and
'50 things to do without a car'.
Read more: page 279.

Innsacre Farmhouse, Shipton Gorge

'Idyllically' set in a small valley
of fields, orchards and woodland,
this 17th-century Dorset
farmhouse is run in 'highly
individual' style by Sydney and

Jayne Davies. They are committed to using local produce, organic when possible. They promise: 'Injunctions in the rooms about waste and recycling are authentic rather than formulaic.' 'Hair shirts are entirely absent,' say visitors. *Read more: page 288.*

Strattons, Swaffham

A comprehensive environmental policy has long been followed by Vanessa and Les Scott at their Palladian-style villa in a Norfolk market town. They give a discount of 10% on the B&B rate to visitors who arrive by public transport; they rewrite their environmental policy annually; staff are encouraged to come up with new ideas.
Read more: page 298.

Eaglescairnie Mains, Gifford

On a working farm in deepest country in the East Lothians, this 'quiet and tranquil', white-painted Georgian house is run on ecological lines by Michael and Barbara Williams. Their farming methods seek to 'unite wildlife and landscape conservation with profitable modern agriculture'. Guests 'feel more like family friends than paying residents'.
Read more: page 354.

Argyll Hotel, Iona

Daniel Morgan and Claire Bachellerie have a strong ecological ethos at their small hotel in a row of 19th-century houses on the 'mystical' island of Iona. Most of their produce is organically home grown, local or fair trade. They are committed recyclers and users of environmentally friendly products. Corridor lights are dimmed in the evening.
Read more: page 359.

Y Goeden Eirin, Dolydd

Very Welsh, John and Eluned Rowlands's small guest house near Caernarfon is also very green. They follow recycling and composting policies, serve locally sourced organic food, fair trade tea and coffee, and have installed solar panels. Guests arriving by train are met at Bangor, and advice is given about the 'excellent local transport'. They have joined the Slow Food movement.
Read more: page 408.

Hafod Elwy Hall, Pentrefoelas

Roger and Wendy Charles-Warner have won awards for sustainability at their 'characterful house with an Edwardian feel' on a working farm on the Denbighshire mountains. They produce their own lamb, pork and beef. 'Eggs from our own hens, nothing bought in.' Everything is home made; vegetables and fruit are organically grown. The welcome is 'personal, natural, unforced'.
Read more: page 424.

ROMANCE

Get in the mood for love by spiriting your chosen one away to one of these romantic hotels

Lovelady Shield, Alston

In a secluded location in wooded grounds on the River Nent, this Cumbrian country hotel is loved for the silence and the unspoilt setting ('an oasis from modern life'). A 'romantic package' includes champagne, chocolates and a bouquet of flowers in the bedroom; Room 9 has a four-poster bed.
Read more: page 81.

Hell Bay Hotel, Bryher

This contemporary hotel is the only one on Bryher, the smallest of the inhabited Scilly Isles, which has few inhabitants, no made-up roads. 'Lovely, relaxed, relaxing', it is on the wilder western coast: next stop America. Most of the accommodation is in suites. You can walk straight to the beach from the decked patio of a ground-floor studio.
Read more: page 131.

The Abbey Country Restaurant, Byland

In 'one of the most romantic settings in England', by the ruins of Byland Abbey, this old inn has been refurbished by English Heritage. The Byland suite has a four-poster bed, a seating area,

and a modern bathroom with a roll-top bath; two windows to enjoy the view of the Abbey, which is floodlit at night.
Read more: page 134.

Tor Cottage, Chillaton

Four of the bedrooms at Maureen Rowlatt's upmarket B&B are in the gardens in large wooded grounds in a secluded mid-Devon valley; each has a private patio. Try Laughing Waters, a clapboard cabin by a stream, in a private corner: it has a log fire, a terrace, a hammock and a gypsy caravan. A trug with sparkling wine, home-made truffles and fresh fruit is presented to arriving guests.
Read more: page 144.

Le Manoir aux Quat'Saisons, Great Milton

'Well worth while for the occasional treat', Raymond Blanc's famous *domaine* stands in beautiful gardens. M. Blanc believes in romance, and all bedrooms are individually designed: try Dovecote, on two levels, with a freestanding bath with glass surround and full-body water jets. Three menus to

choose from in the conservatory restaurant (two *Michelin* stars), including the ten-course *Menu Découverte*.
Read more: page 179.

Lavenham Priory, Lavenham

The five spacious bedchambers at this sympathetically restored 13th-century priory, later an Elizabethan merchant's house, have sloping, beamed ceiling, an oak floor. There are unusual beds (four-poster, polonaise or sleigh). The suite has a ribboned four-poster, a slipper bath and a private sitting room.
Read more: page 207.

Swinton Park, Masham

There are stunning views from many of the spacious bedrooms at this creeper-clad 17th-century castle in huge landscaped grounds. It is now a luxury hotel with a spa. Sleep in the circular Turret suite with rooms on three floors linked by a steep curved staircase: the shower room has the views; there's a freestanding rain bath on the top floor.
Read more: page 229.

The Old Railway Station, Petworth

Enjoy all the romance of a Pullman railway car without any of the attendant discomfort at this disused Victorian railway station which has been restored with flair. The biggest bedrooms are in the station building, but the most romantic are in the converted Pullman carriages: 'beautifully restored, well designed, with a comfortable bed'.
Read more: page 259.

Isle of Eriska, Eriska

Beppo and Chay Buchanan-Smith 'cannot control the weather but they faultlessly deliver everything else' at their Scottish baronial mansion on a 300-acre private island. In the house, the tower room has a 'fantastic view, well worth climbing 54 stairs'; each of the spa suites in the grounds has a conservatory and private garden with hot tub.
Read more: page 351.

Ardanaiseig, Kilchrenan

Voted 'Scotland's most romantic hotel', this baronial mansion stands remotely in a beautiful garden on Loch Awe. An old boat house on the loch shore has been converted into a suite: double-height windows open on to a deck above the water. The bedroom is on a mezzanine level; a balustrade allows uninterrupted views across the loch to Ben Lui.
Read more: page 361.

FAMILY

All too rare in Britain, these are places where parents can relax knowing that their children are welcomed

Woolley Grange, Bradford-on-Avon

Parents pay by the room, sharing with as many children as they can tolerate at this Jacobean stone manor house, part of the von Essen Luxury Family Hotels division. The very young are looked after in the Ofsted-approved Woolley Bears' Den; older children have the run of the unsupervised Hen House (with games galore). 'Just the right blend of luxury and informality for families,' said a parent. There is a pool, badminton, croquet and trampoline in the grounds.
Read more: page 118.

The Trout at Tadpole Bridge, Buckland Marsh

Children of all ages are welcomed at Gareth and Helen Pugh's old Cotswold pub in a large garden that slopes down to the Thames. Parents themselves, they have made it 'as child-friendly as possible'. They promise 'decent children's menus (no nuggets), games, toys, plenty of space outdoors'. The atmosphere is informal, the decor contemporary, unfussy.
Read more: page 133.

The Evesham Hotel, Evesham

Children are charged according to age and amount of food eaten at John and Sue Jenkinson's quirky hotel which has lots to keep younger guests happy. 'Our children had a really good time; they loved the swimming pool and play area.' 'Fun things' in the garden include a trampoline and slides. There's a junior *à la carte* menu, and a games room.
Read more: page 165.

Augill Castle, Kirkby Stephen

'Parents can kick off their shoes and relax knowing that their children are having an equally good time,' say Simon and Wendy Bennett who entertain guests in informal house-party style at their family home, a Victorian Gothic folly. Bedrooms are big enough to take extra beds; some are interconnecting. There are cots, high chairs, baby-listening; a cookery school for the over-7s.
Read more: page 198.

Bedruthan Steps Hotel, Mawgan Porth

At this large, purpose-built family hotel above a golden sandy north

Cornwall beach, there is much for children to do: an indoor play area, an Ofsted-registered nursery, a soft play and ball pool for toddlers, a junior assault course, and a teenagers' room. Baby-sitters and nannies are available. *Read more: page 231.*

Calcot Manor, Tetbury

'We don't just accept children, we love having them,' say Richard Ball, managing director of this Cotswold hotel. It has extensive facilities for children: baby-listening, an Ofsted-registered crèche, and a Playzone in a converted tithe barn. Suites have a bedroom for parents and a sitting room with bunk beds or sofa beds for the young. Children are allowed access at designated times to the spa and swimming pool. *Read more: page 303.*

Glenfinnan House, Glenfinnan

Fans of the Harry Potter movies will recognise Glenfinnan Viaduct which is a ten-minute walk from this family-friendly Victorian mansion on the shores of Loch Shiel. Children under 12 are accommodated free: they have a playground, and special menus in the 'relaxed' dining room, and 'good value' bar menu choices. *Read more: page 356.*

Porth Tocyn Hotel, Abersoch

Parents can relax on sunbeds in the pretty garden while the children enjoy the many activities ptovided at Nick and Louise Fletcher-Brewer's family-friendly hotel. 'We have three sons of our own; we reckon we know quite a bit about the joys and pitfalls of children in hotels,' they say. Children have their own area with TV, table tennis, etc. Interconnecting bedrooms are available, and child-minding is offered. Excellent beaches close by. *Read more: page 397.*

The Druidstone, Broadhaven

'Our policy is to look after families without making them feel uncomfortable about children; this does mean the place suffers wear and tear,' writes Jane Bell, who presides with her husband, Rod, over this informal 'family holiday centre' on a clifftop above a huge deserted beach. The children's high tea is 'always interesting'. *Read more: page 401.*

Sychnant Pass House, Conwy

'It is run very much as a home that takes guests,' say Bre and Graham Carrington-Sykes whose Edwardian house is in the foothills of Snowdonia national park. Children are welcomed and can enjoy swings and the swimming pool, and indoor games. There are three resident cats and two dogs. *Read more: page 404.*

SEASIDE

Pack your buckets and spades and be ready to get sand in your shoes at these coastal places

Hell Bay Hotel, Bryher

On the western side of the island, this is the only hotel on the smallest of the inhabited Scilly Isles. You can walk straight down to a beach at the end of the garden; other good beaches are around the island which has no made-up roads. Accommodation is mainly in suites, decorated in seaside colours.
Read more: page 131.

Treglos Hotel, Constantine Bay

In landscaped gardens overlooking Constantine Bay, this traditional hotel is liked for its 'quiet, professional atmosphere'. It is five minutes' walk from a safe, sandy beach and the coastal path. In the gardens are a children's play area, secluded sitting places.
Read more: page 148.

Bedruthan Steps Hotel, Mawgan Porth

Popular with families, this large, purpose-built hotel stands above a golden, sandy north Cornish beach which has Atlantic waves for surfers, and sandy coves and rock pools for explorers. If children tire of the beach, they can enjoy 'fantastic play areas', children's clubs, swimming pools indoors and out, and 'water fun sessions'. There are 'amazing sea views', coastal walks, and a spa.
Read more: page 231.

driftwood hotel, Portscatho

'A tranquil haven', this contemporary hotel stands above a quiet cove. Steep steps through woodland lead down to a private beach; there is good walking on the coastal paths. The modern interiors with a 'simple white background and shades of blue' are in keeping with the seaside theme. Superb coastline views from most bedrooms.
Read more: page 263.

St Martin's on the Isle, St Martin's

By a white sandy beach on the western shore of a charming Scilly island (just 30 houses and a population of 100), this smart hotel was built in the 1980s to resemble a row of fishermen's cottages. Many other sandy stretches can be found on the island. Most bedrooms face the sea; the best views are from the dining room on the first floor.
Read more: page 281.

The Tides Reach, Salcombe

The Edwards family's traditional hotel, which faces south over the Salcombe estuary, has its own boat house on South Sands

beach: guests enjoy safe bathing and many water sports. You can catch a ferry from here to the centre, or across the estuary to other fine beaches. For damp days, there is a swimming pool in an 'exotic' conservatory.
Read more: page 284.

Soar Mill Cove Hotel, Soar Mill Cove

Surrounded by National Trust land, this single-storey stone and slate hotel stands in grounds that slope down to an isolated cove with a beautiful beach. Glorious views from the restaurant; sea-facing rooms, with patio, get the afternoon sun. Children are genuinely welcomed: there are small swimming pools, a play area, activity packs.
Read more: page 290.

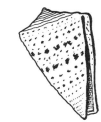

The Island Hotel, Tresco

On a promontory by a large sandy beach on this small private island, this sprawling single-storey hotel is owned by Robert Dorrien-Smith. It is popular with families in the summer: buckets, spades, pushchairs, high teas are provided. The decor reflects the colours of the sea and the beach; most bedrooms have a sea view, some have a balcony.
Read more: page 308.

The Wellington Hotel, Ventnor

'An excellent base for a seaside break', this 'smart, stylish' hotel on the south side of the Isle of Wight is built into cliffs above a safe, sandy beach. The decor is contemporary (bare floorboards in public areas). All but two bedrooms face the sea: 'It was a delight to sit on our balcony in the sun and take in the view.' 'The only noise at night is the sound of the waves.'
Read more: page 313.

Kylesku Hotel, Kylesku

'What a beautiful location.' Louise and Struan Lothian's former 17th-century coaching inn stands on the shoreline where lochs Glendhu and Glencoul meet in glorious north-west Sutherland. There are many magnificent beaches in the area: Oldshoremore beach, flanked by rocky cliffs, is recommended for a family picnic. Children are welcomed.
Read more: page 368.

GOURMET

Savour the pleasures of the
table at these hotels and
restaurants-with-rooms
without having to drive home

Hipping Hall, Cowan Bridge

A spectacular 15th-century Great
Hall is 'a fitting setting' for the
'impressive' cooking of the
talented young chef, Jason 'Bruno'
Birkbeck, at Andrew Wildsmith's
'faultless' small hotel/restaurant
in a village near Kirkby Lonsdale.
'Seared foie gras with quail's
breast and a sauterne jelly was a
conversation stopper.'
Read more: page 150.

Combe House, Gittisham

At this extended Grade I listed
Elizabethan manor house, chef
Hadleigh Barratt provides
'confident, unfussy' cooking on a
locally sourced seasonal menu
(many vegetables and herbs from
the walled kitchen garden).
Sample dishes: roast Devon
quail, shallot confit tart, smoked
bacon; roast fillet and crispy belly
pork, spiced sweet potatoes.
Read more: page 175.

The Star Inn, Harome

'A watering hole for foodies', this
converted medieval cruck-framed
longhouse is run by charming
owners Jacquie and Andrew Pern.
It 'buzzes with visitors' attracted
by his Yorkshire-influenced
modern cooking, 'local sourcing
and fish to the fore'. He promises
'spiced-up old favourites' in
dishes like terrine of ham
knuckle with pineapple pickle,
fried quail egg; North Sea fish pie
with melting Montgomery
cheddar and herb topping.
Read more: page 183.

Northcote Manor, Langho

Chef/*patron* Nigel Haworth
presides at this informal
restaurant-with-rooms, a
renovated late Victorian/
Edwardian residence in rolling
Lancashire farmland. Inspectors
thought his five-course tasting
menu was 'impressive, well
balanced': it included carpaccio
of lamb; an organic porridge of
shrimps 'with a refreshing
sharpness'; unpasteurised British
cheese in 'perfect condition'.
Read more: page 204.

Mr Underhill's, Ludlow

At his restaurant-with-rooms by
the River Teme below Ludlow
Castle, the cooking of
Christopher Bradley 'goes from
strength to strength'. Guests are
told of the proposed set menu

(alternatives can be offered). Dinner kicks off with 'three Hobbit-sized dishes' (perhaps marinated salmon, pea velouté, duck liver custard); 'delicious pavé of halibut with crunchy vegetables; rhubarb crumble 'worth every calorie'. The wine list is a 'winner'.
Read more: page 221.

Morston Hall, Morston

'This is how it should be done,' say visitors to Tracy and Galton Blackiston's hotel/restaurant in an area of outstanding natural beauty on the north Norfolk coast. His four-course dinner menu changes daily: 'Interesting use of herbs, a tiny serving of delicious garlic and parsley soup, wonderful lamb with such variety of fresh flavours.'
Read more: page 241.

West Stoke House, West Stoke

'Relaxed and unstuffy', this white-painted Georgian mansion is run informally by Rowland and Mary Leach. Darren Brown's modern French-influenced cooking is thought 'superb'. Sample dishes: ravioli of lobster, samphire, shellfish foam; pan-fried fillet of sea trout, trout tartare, crushed peas, confit potatoes.
Read more: page 319.

The Three Chimneys, Dunvegan

On a single-track road in beautiful north-west Skye, Eddie and Shirley Spear's restaurant-with-rooms is 'excellent in every respect'. Michael Smith's three- or four-course menu (much local fish and meat) wins praise: 'Fresh ingredients, perfectly cooked and presented; wonderful home-made breads.'
Read more: page 345.

Plas Bodegroes, Pwllheli

In lovely wooded grounds on the Lleyn pensinula, this Georgian manor house is run as a restaurant-with-rooms by Chris Chown (the chef) and his Faroese wife, Gunna (front-of-house). He uses local ingredients for his classically based dishes served in the lovely dining room, eg, foie gras with fig jelly; turbot with lime hollandaise and star anise. 'Utterly charming' staff.
Read more: page 427.

The Crown at Whitebrook, Whitebrook

'Residents are no less important than guests at table' at this former 17th-century drovers' inn in a small village near Monmouth. The chef, James Sommerin (modern British 'with French flair'), is 'faultless at every course': perhaps seared and carpaccio scallops, artichoke and lemon verbena; fillet of rabbit with leg-meat lasagne, carrot, fennel and confit garlic. 'A splendid place.'
Read more: page 432.

GASTROPUBS

Interesting cooking and a
lively atmosphere can be
expected at these revitalised
old inns and pubs

The Devonshire Arms at Beeley, Beeley

On the Chatsworth estate, this
17th-century coaching inn has
been renovated, blending ancient
with modern, by the Duke and
Duchess of Devonshire. 'Good
fun if you recognise that it's a
pub.' A buzzing atmosphere in
the contemporary brasserie
where Alan Hill's dinner menu
uses local produce, perhaps
Beeley lamb with green chilli,
ginger and potato curry.
'Excellent wines by the glass.'
Read more: page 102.

The Horse and Groom, Bourton-on-the-Hill

At the top of the hill in a
Cotswold village, this Georgian
coaching inn is run by brothers
Tom (front-of-house) and Will
(the chef) Greenstock, who are
'engaging hosts'. It has ancient
beams, wooden floors and tables,
sisal matting, stools around the
bar. Local ingredients are cooked
'with passion' on a modern
menu, perhaps risotto cakes with
spinach and ricotta; slow-roasted
pork belly, apple compote; pear
and almond tart with home-
grown raspberries.
Read more: page 113.

The Royal Oak, East Lavant

Charles Ullmann, the new owner
of this flint-stone Georgian inn,
on the edge of the South Downs,
says he is making no changes.
'Same good food, same winning
formula,' says an inspector. In the
restaurant, Sam Baker's modern
carte (with blackboard specials)
might include seared black
pudding, fried duck's egg; beer
battered fish with hand-cut chips.
Read more: page 162.

The Chequers Inn, Froggatt Edge

Below rugged Froggatt Edge in
some of the Peak District's finest
scenery, this 17th-century inn
has an attractive bar/restaurant
(heavy lintels, dark beams,
library chairs). Phil Ball blends
traditional and modern for his
dishes that are a 'cut above
normal pub fare'. Typical dishes:
belly pork with saffron and red
pepper; homity pie with
Henderson's Relish.
Read more: page 173.

The Angel Inn, Hetton

In the Yorkshire Dales, this old
drovers' inn has been a popular
dining pub for more than

20 years. In a series of panelled and beamed rooms, you can choose from a bar menu (with blackboard specials, perhaps seared plaice fillets with queen scallops) and a *carte* with dishes like Little Moneybags (sea food in crispy pastry); rare breed suckling pig.
Read more: page 187.

The Lord Poulett Arms, Hinton St George

This 17th-century pub in a pretty Somerset village has been sensitively renovated by Steve Hill and Michelle Paynton. In the busy bar, popular with locals, Gary Coughlan (promoted to head chef this year) has a short menu of local organic produce: dishes might include char-grilled Merguez sausage, puy lentils, fetta cheese.
Read more: page 188.

The Kingham Plough, Kingham

In a pretty Cotswolds village (voted England's favourite by *Country Life*), Emily Watkins has renovated an old pub opposite the green. Former *sous-chef* at the celebrated *Fat Duck* in Bray, she serves 'outstanding food at keen prices'. Her short menu (four choices for each course) changes for every meal (sometimes during meals). Inspectors enjoyed crisp duck egg, bacon and watercress sauce; sea trout with sea shore vegetables in a wild garlic pancake.
Read more: page 197.

The Peat Spade Inn, Longstock

'Simple, fresh, classic dishes' are presented in the dining rooms of Lucy Townsend and Andy Clark's unpretentious old inn and 'rooming house' in a village in the Test valley. 'All you could wish for in a country pub; hands-on management, cheerful and efficient service, straightforward food [eg, potted shrimp with toasted sourdough; ribeye steak with chips]; reasonable prices.'
Read more: page 218.

The Felin Fach Griffin, Felin Fach

Charles and Edmund Inkin's 'civilised' inn, between the Brecon Beacons and the Black Mountains, is liked for its 'relaxed atmosphere'. In the popular restaurant, chef Ricardo Van Ede uses home-grown organic ingredients in dishes like ragout of boudin blanc and langoustines; Welsh saddle of lamb, fondant potatoes, garden peas.
Read more: page 409.

The Bell at Skenfrith, Skenfrith

Beside an old stone bridge across the River Monnow, Janet and William Hutchings's 17th-century coaching inn has flagstone floors and an inglenook fireplace. Chef David Hill serves modern dishes like confit of duck leg, herb mashed potato, asparagus, redcurrant jus.
Read more: page 429.

COUNTRY HOUSE

These bastions of old-fashioned service provide plenty of pampering

Hartwell House, Aylesbury

'Beautifully restored, full of antiques yet with all mod cons', this stately home, with Jacobean front and Georgian rear, is a 'perfect blend of the 18th and the 21st centuries'. Magnificent public rooms are 'flooded with light'. 'Nothing forbidding or gloomy'; antiques, 'to be used not just admired'.
Read more: page 90.

Farlam Hall, Brampton

Run by the Quinion and Stevenson families since 1975, this manorial house, approached up a sweeping drive, stands in an 'immaculate' landscaped garden with a large ornamental lake. 'A sense of humour abounds alongside proper service.' Public rooms are ornate, with patterned wallpaper, open fires; bedrooms are traditionally furnished.
Read more: page 121.

Gravetye Manor, East Grinstead

'The template for country house hotels' (says a *Guide* reader): a creeper-covered Elizabethan manor standing amid woodland in grounds designed by William Robinson, pioneer of the English natural garden. The 'aroma of polish and pot-pourri' pervades the oak-panelled hall and staircase; there are leaded windows, open fires, antique furniture. Visitors like the 'personal touches' and 'the genuine care and attention to detail'.
Read more: page 161.

Summer Lodge, Evershot

In large grounds in an attractive Dorset village, this former dower house has 'a relaxing country house atmosphere'. It is owned by the Red Carnation group; the staff 'greet guests by name, are always on hand, but never overbearing'. The pretty bedrooms are traditionally furnished with fine fabrics, heavy drapes. In an 'elegant' dining room, Steven Titman serves 'excellent' modern dishes.
Read more: page 165.

Stock Hill House, Gillingham

'Luxurious comfort, very good food' was enjoyed in Peter and Nita Hauser's small luxury hotel, a Victorian building in

landscaped, tree-lined grounds, with terraced lawns, herbaceous borders and a small lake fed by a stream. 'We were welcomed like family friends.' The bedrooms have antiques and curios. In the formal dining room, Peter Hauser's cooking reflects his Austrian heritage.
Read more: page 174.

Hambleton Hall, Hambleton

'A rarity, a luxury hotel which does things well and is comfortable with itself', Tim Hart's Victorian mansion has an 'idyllic' setting on a peninsula jutting into Rutland Water. His wife, Stefa, designed the classic interiors with Nina Campbell: fine fabrics, antiques, good paintings, open fires. The atmosphere is 'formal but friendly, just right'. The cooking of Aaron Patterson 'never disappoints'.
Read more: page 181.

Hotel Endsleigh, Milton Abbot

The restoration of Olga Polizzi's luxury hotel, a Victorian shooting and fishing lodge, has created a 'modern, comfortable country house'. It stands in 'huge, wonderful grounds' where the only noise comes 'from birds, and streams and waterfalls cascading down to the wide River Tamar'. The bedrooms are 'beautifully kept'. At night, candles provide much of the lighting.
Read more: page 237.

Sharrow Bay, Ullswater

In a spectacular setting on the eastern shore of Lake Ullswater, this is the original country house hotel, 60 years old this year. Traditional decor: swagged curtains, cherubs, ornaments, open fires; chintzy, cosy bedrooms. Colin Akrigg has a *Michelin* star for his 'richly flavoured classic English cooking'.
Read more: page 311.

Gilpin Lodge, Windermere

The Cunliffe family run their Edwardian country house in hands-on but informal style. 'Like being in someone's lovely home, with discreet but attentive family members to look after you.' Some bedrooms in the main house have a four-poster. The cooking of Chris Meredith 'gets better all the time'.
Read more: page 323.

Kinnaird, Dunkeld

Sumptuously furnished, this creeper-covered mansion has family portraits, a grand piano, antiques, flowers, billiards. Most bedrooms are large, with a view of the valley. Men wear a jacket at dinner in the elegant restaurant where Jean-Baptiste Bady uses home-produced or local ingredients for his three-course dinner menu. A chambermaid brings early morning tea to the bedroom on a tray.
Read more: page 344.

CITY CHIC

Cutting-edge urban style allied to high levels of service can be expected at these contemporary hotels

One Aldwych, London

Even the smaller bedrooms are stylish at Gordon Campbell Gray's modern conversion of the Edwardian offices of the *Morning Post*. Muted tones, white pillars and a giant statue of an oarsman in the double-height lobby, with huge arched windows; trendy flower arrangements and 400 pieces of contemporary art. 'Outstandingly attentive service from young, friendly staff.' *Read more: page 71.*

The rockwell, London

Two Victorian terrace houses on the Cromwell Road have been turned 'with flair' into a modern hotel by architect Michael Squire and Tony Bartlett. It has a bright facade and, inside, a modern decor, interesting patterns and colours. 'Exciting' mezzanine suites have a lounge and sleeping area down a curved staircase. *Read more: page 74.*

The Zetter, London

A glass door leads to a white-walled lobby with a pink Murano chandelier at this converted 19th-century warehouse in trendy Clerkenwell. A striking contemporary decor: bright colours, raindance shower in bathrooms. Bedrooms have lighting with a pink option; roof studios a patio with panoramic views. Informal restaurant. *Read more: page 76.*

Hotel du Vin, Brighton

A collection of Gothic revival and mock-Tudor buildings between the Lanes and the seafront forms the du Vin Brighton outpost. Original features include a carved wooden staircase with gargoyles, double-height hall (now the lively bar). Bedrooms are modern and well equipped with big 'retro-look' bathrooms. 'Good moules marinère and charcoal grilled steak' in the busy bistro. *Read more: page 126.*

Hotel Barcelona, Exeter

The city's former Victorian eye infirmary near the cathedral has been cleverly converted into a contemporary hotel by Alias Hotels. A huge marble fireplace, 'big old radiators, fat old pipes' have been retained. 'The feel is quirky and the spirit is fun.' Excellent pizzas, locally caught fish, West Country meat served in *Café Paradiso*. *Read more: page 166.*

42 The Calls, Leeds

A 'fabulous' conversion of a grain mill on the River Aire in the city centre, now part of the Eton Collection. It has hundreds of original paintings and drawings, bold fabrics, stylish public rooms.

Many bedrooms are spacious; they are 'fully kitted out for the business traveller' with (expensive) Wi-Fi, etc. Beds are 'supremely comfortable'.
Read more: page 208.

Hope Street Hotel, Liverpool

On a Georgian street linking the two cathedrals, a conversion of an old carriage works built in the style of an Italian *palazzo*. It was liked this year for the 'modern style and enthusiastic young staff'. Original iron columns, beams and exposed brickwork have been retained. Dramatic floor-to-ceiling glass sculptures in the restaurant.
Read more: page 216.

Hart's Hotel, Nottingham

'Every city should have one,' says a visitor to Tim Hart's purpose-built hotel on the site of a medieval castle. The 'well-thought-out' building has curved buttresses, lots of glass, limestone floors. 'Comfortable' bedrooms (most have 'breathtaking' views), 'efficient' bathrooms. Light meals, and wine and champagne by the glass are served in the bar; excellent meals in the restaurant.
Read more: page 250.

Old Bank, Oxford

Opposite All Souls on the High, Jeremy Mogford's striking hotel is an elegant conversion of three buildings, one a former bank. His abundant collection of modern art is displayed in the public rooms and bedrooms. 'Stylish without being too cutting-edge; modern but relaxing.' The old banking hall houses *Quod*, a lively bar and restaurant.
Read more: page 255.

The Scotsman, Edinburgh

Many baroque features of a 'fascinating' Edwardian building, once the offices of the *Scotsman* newspaper, have been retained in its conversion to a modern luxury hotel (part of the Eton Collection). These include a black-and-white marble staircase, intricate stained-glass windows, turrets and ornate ceilings. 'Fiendishly complicated' technology in the bedrooms. Meals are served in a brasserie/bar in the newspaper's old entrance hall.
Read more: page 349.

GARDENS

A glorious garden and beguiling landscape make each of these hotels a destination in its own right

Barnsley House, Barnsley

The Cotswolds home of the late Rosemary Verey, acclaimed garden designer and author, has been 'propelled into the 21st century' as a luxury hotel. The gardens remain true to her creation; her bold approach has an eclectic mix of features including a laburnum walk, a temple with a pool, a *potager* and a knot garden.
Read more, page 92.

Lindeth Fell, Bowness-on-Windermere

'Superbly set amid lovely grounds', Diana and Pat Kennedy's Edwardian house has views over Lake Windermere. Laid out by Thomas Mawson (a renowned Windermere landscape gardener), the gardens are filled with rhododendrons, azaleas and specimen trees, best in spring and early summer, when open to the public. Lawns are laid for bowls and croquet.
Read more: page 116.

Gravetye Manor, East Grinstead

William Robinson, who bought this 16th-century manor house (now a luxury hotel) and its 1,000-acre grounds in 1884 from the profits of his garden design and writing, was helped by his close friend Gertrude Jekyll in the planting of a naturalistic garden filled with bulbs, wild flowers and indigenous varieties. When wheelchair-bound in the 1930s, Robinson would still go out to scatter bulbs and seeds.
Read more: page 161.

Lewtrenchard Manor, Lewdown

Walter Sorel and Gertrude Jekyll designed the gardens of this Devon manor house (mentioned in the Domesday Book), now a small hotel run by chef/*patron* Jason Hornbuckle for the von Essen group. The grounds have walkways, an avenue of beech trees, fountains and statuary and sunken lawns. There's a large rustic dovecote and a restored walled garden.
Read more: page 210.

Hob Green, Markington

With wide views across a valley, the Hutchinson family's traditional hotel is set in 800-acre grounds with award-winning gardens, a farm, and woodlands. Walkways and paths lead through extensive herbaceous borders to feature lawns, a rockery and a pergola. There's a large greenhouse and a walled kitchen garden.
Read more: page 226.

Meudon, Mawnan Smith

At the head of a wooded valley leading to a private beach, the Pilgrim family's traditional hotel has a fine example of a Cornish 'hanging garden' (designed by Robert Were Fox *c.* 1800), with specimens from early RHS expeditions to the Yangtze and the Himalayas; rare shrubs, plants, trees. Giant Australian tree ferns were brought as ballast by packet ships to Falmouth, and thrown overboard in the bay. *Read more: page 232.*

Hotel Endsleigh, Milton Abbot

Olga Polizzi's luxurious hotel was built as a shooting lodge by the Duchess of Bedford who commissioned Humphry Repton to design the gardens in the 108-acre wooded estate overlooking the River Tamar. He created forested walks, wild meadows, a rose and jasmine walkway. There are rare and grand trees, a parterre beside the veranda, and a shell-covered summer house. *Read more: page 236.*

Burleigh Court, Minchinhampton

'Superb, and well tended', the gardens of this 18th-century Cotswold stone manor house were remodelled by Clough Williams-Ellis. His compartmentalised design has hidden pathways, terraces, ponds and a Victorian plunge pool. In

spring the tulip display is dazzling; among the trees are a purple beech and mature cedars. *Read more: page 237.*

Stone House, Rushlake Green

Visitors to Jane and Peter Dunn's 15th-century house (with 18th-century modifications) are encouraged to enjoy the 'wonderful' five-and-a-half-acre garden, which has an ornamental lake, gazebos, a rose garden, a 100-foot herbaceous border, a walled herb and a vegetable and fruit garden. A 'quintessentially English country experience'. *Read more: page 274.*

Ladyburn, Maybole

In a beautiful Ayrshire valley, Jane Hepburn's former dower house ('guests are treated as members of family') has large wild and formal gardens with several authenticated National Rose collections. Rhododendrons, bluebells, azaleas grow in spring. Guests may also walk in the grounds of the 'magnificent' neighbouring Kilkerran estate. *Read more: page 373.*

GOLF

Golfers and golf widows alike can enjoy these hotels, well placed for some of the best courses on these islands

The Mount, Bideford

Guests at this popular B&B, an imposing Georgian property near the town centre, qualify for a discount at the Royal North Devon course at nearby Westward Ho. This course, the oldest links in England (commissioned in 1864), is never more testing than when the wind blows; the fast greens 'will test your nerve'.
Read more: page 104.

Budock Vean, Mawnan Smith

The country club at the Barlow family's traditional hotel on the south-facing bank of the Helford River, has plenty of activities for golfers and non-golfers alike. An attractive nine-hole parkland course is a good place to brush up your game. David Short runs three- and four-day golf schools, and competition weeks for all handicaps over five local courses.
Read more: page 231.

Gilpin Lodge, Windermere

Golfing breaks with tuition are available at this Edwardian country house hotel which is 200 yards from the entrance of Windermere golf club (described as 'the miniature Gleneagles'). The undulating course may be relatively short but it is a tough test with narrow fairways, natural water hazards and blind second shots into greens.
Read more: page 323.

Coul House, Contin

With stunning views over the Strathconon valley, this Georgian hunting lodge has been refurbished by Stuart and Susannah Macpherson. It is within easy reach of three fine courses designed by the legendary Old Tom Morris in the late 19th century: Strathpeffer, a scenic hilly challenge; Tain, a fine links course; and the championship links at Royal Dornoch.
Read more: page 342.

Eaglescairnie Mains, Gifford

In deepest country south-east of Edinburgh, this impeccable Georgian B&B is well placed for golfers seeking to explore the East Lothians, an area steeped in golfing history. Among the famous local links are Muirfield,

Gullane and North Berwick. The nine-hole Musselburgh Old Course claims to be the oldest playing links in the world.
Read more: page 354.

The Inn at Lathones, Largoward

An extended old coaching inn in a hamlet five miles from St Andrews, the home of golf. All seven of the links courses in St Andrews are open to public play. If you fail to win a tee time in the ballot for the famous Old Course, try the most recently built, The Castle which has views back to the town.
Read more: page 369.

The Dower House, Muir of Ord

Robyn and Mena Aitchison are friendly hosts at their gabled *cottage-orné* in a large, wooded garden bordered by two rivers. He is a keen golfer and can advise on the 25 courses that are within an hour's drive. Try the championship links at Nairn, which has hosted the Walker Cup. You can see the Moray Firth from every hole, and it is possible to strike the ball into the sea on the first seven.
Read more: page 374.

Stella Maris, Ballycastle

Terence McSweeney, who runs this converted 19th-century coastguard station in north Mayo with his wife, Frances Kelly, works for the US PGA in Florida

during the winter. He can guide golfers to the world-class links at Enniscrone and Carne and, further afield, Rosses Point and Westport. Golf memorabilia and photographs adorn the walls.
Read more: page 443.

St Ernan's House, Donegal

The magnificent Donegal course at Murvagh is a short drive from this Georgian building on a tranquil wooded tidal island. The fifth hole, known as the Valley of Tears, is a vicious 200-yard par-3, with high banks to the left of the hole, pot bunkers on the right.
Read more: page 458.

Admiralty Lodge, Miltown Malbay

Pat and Aoifa O'Malley's much-extended Georgian country house is in good golfing country on the coast of Clare. Greg Norman's course along the beach and dunes at Doonbeg is close. For a genuine links experience at a fraction of the cost (and no need for a handicap certificate), try the nine-hole Spanish Point just minutes away.
Read more: page 472.

FISHING

No need to cast around for
the best beats; these hotels
all have private access to
rivers and lakes

The Arundell Arms, Lifton

An experienced fly-fisher herself,
Anne Voss-Bark has 20 miles of
fishing (salmon and brown trout
in season) on the Tamar and its
four tributaries, 'wild' rivers
which rise on Dartmoor. There is
a three-acre stocked lake with
rainbow trout all year round.
Fishing courses for all levels.
The creeper-covered sporting
hotel has a 'lovely atmosphere,
friendly staff, brilliant food'.
Read more: page 213.

The Peat Spade Inn, Longstock

In a village in the Test valley
('fly-fishing capital of the
world'), this old inn has 'bags of
character'. Fly-fishing can be
arranged at the chalk stream
rivers nearby. 'We also have
access to a spring-fed private
estate, perfect for beginners and
improvers alike; a super fishing-
stalking water,' say the owners,
Lucy Townsend and Andy Clark.
Read more: page 218.

The Inn at Whitewell, Whitewell

Charles Bowman manages this
old inn in a lovely setting in the
Forest of Bowland, high above
the River Hodder. Liked for its
quirky style and food, it has four
rods on the Hodder for trout, sea-
trout, and salmon in season, and
seven miles of river with 14 pools
('lots of interesting runs'). Ghillie
available.
Read more: page 320.

Kinnaird, Dunkeld

On a vast sporting estate this
listed mansion is run as a luxury
hotel, 'friendly without being
overbearing'. Guests may fish for
salmon and trout on the River
Tay which flows through the
estate, and for trout in *Kinnaird*'s
three lochs. The hotel has its
own smokehouse.
Read more: page 344.

Culdearn House, Grantown-on-Spey

On the edge of a pretty market
town in the Spey valley, William
and Sonia Marshall's Victorian
granite house has been given a
major refurbishment. Fishing can
be arranged on the Spey, a
productive salmon and sea-trout
river with formidable currents.
There are private beats with
ghillie service.
Read more: page 357.

Ardanaiseig, Kilchrenan

Bennie Gray's stone baronial mansion stands in a beautiful garden on Loch Awe, noted for its wild brown trout. Boats are available for fishing on the loch where perch and pike abound (also rogue rainbow trout, escapees from fish farms). There is a small trout lochan for fly-casting.
Read more: page 361.

Gliffaes, Crickhowell

Susie and James Suter's smart sporting hotel (a 19th-century Italianate building) stands in wooded grounds on a private stretch of the trout- and salmon-laden River Usk. They own a stretch of 2½ miles; ghillies are available, and three-day fly-fishing courses for beginners are offered. The best bedrooms have a river view and balcony. Only fish from sustainable fisheries is served in the dining room.
Read more: page 405.

Ballyvolane House, Castlelyons

Justin and Jenny Green have four beats on a 24-mile stretch of the Blackwater, the best salmon fishing river in Ireland; these are available at all times in season, others can be arranged. When conditions on the river are impossible, there is fly-fishing for rainbow trout on three lakes in the grounds. The Greens give a taste of country house living Irish-style at their Georgian house in glorious grounds.
Read more: page 455.

Newport House, Newport

Overlooking the Newport estuary in a village above Clew Bay, Thelma and Kieran Thompson's Georgian mansion is liked for its unstuffy atmosphere. They have eight miles of fishing on the River Newport, for spring salmon, grilse and sea trout; also fishing on Lough Beltra West, one of the few fisheries in Ireland where salmon can be fished from a boat. 'All our fish are wild,' they say.
Read more: page 474.

Currarevagh House, Oughterard

In a 'glorious setting of lake, lawns and woodland', this early Victorian manor house is run with 'easy Irish charm' by the Hodgson family. They have their own boats and ghillies on Lough Corrib, 'probably the best wild brown trout lake in Europe' (also pike, perch, and a small run of salmon from May to July).
Read more: page 475.

WALKING

Your boots are meant for walking at these hotels which cater for ramblers and casual walkers alike

Biggin Hall, Biggin-by-Hartington

High in the Peak District, this small hotel in a small village is popular with walkers for its simple, unfussy style. Footpaths lead in all directions from the grounds. Disused railway tracks nearby provide flat walking. The 17th-century stone house has antiques, inviting public rooms. Bedrooms in a barn conversion have an outdoor porch.
Read more: page 107.

Seatoller House, Borrowdale

Long popular with walkers and climbers for the easy access to the lakes and hills, this guest house is at the head of the Borrowdale valley. It has a homely atmosphere, and absence of 'modern intrusions' like television and radio. There is non-stop coffee (can be taken out in flasks) and an honesty bar.
Read more: page 111.

The George, Hathersage

On the River Derwent in the Peak District, Hathersage, surrounded by moorland and spectacular tors, is a busy centre for outdoor sport enthusiasts. This 600-year-old grey stone inn is 'a happy place' popular with walkers and rock climbers.
Read more: page 185.

Underleigh House, Hope

There is 'amazing value' and good walking from the door at this barn and cottage conversion in the Hope valley. Maps and packed lunches are provided for walks. A 'delicious' breakfast is served around a large oak table in the flagstoned hall.
Read more: page 191.

Overwater Hall, Ireby

In a relatively unspoilt part of the northern Lake District, this

castellated Georgian mansion stands beside Overwater tarn, close to Bassenthwaite Lake. There is good walking (and climbing) in every direction. Lovers of wildlife will enjoy seeing red squirrels in the grounds and watching breeding osprey fish in the tarn. Breakfast is a full Cumbrian affair.
Read more: page 196.

Heddon's Gate Hotel, Martinhoe

On the steep slopes of the 'magnificently wooded' Heddon valley, this former Victorian hunting lodge has old-fashioned comfort, a warm welcome. 'Superb' walking from the door, and on Exmoor. An 'excellent' afternoon tea (complimentary on arrival). Modern and traditional cooking in the dining room. 'Very friendly hosts'.
Read more: page 228.

Hazel Bank, Rosthwaite

In a 'stunning' Borrowdale location, this intimate hotel is 'very personally run' by Glen and Brenda Davies who treat guests 'generously and attentively'. The area 'is hard to beat for a walker'. There is immediate access from the grounds to many well-known peaks; for easier days there are pleasant walks along the River Derwent, up the Langstrath or over to Watendlath. Good traditional cooking.
Read more: page 272.

Howtown Hotel, Ullswater

Jacquie and son David Baldry's simple guest house, on the 'idyllic' eastern shore of Lake Ullswater, has fields and garden on one side, wooded hills on the other. Visitors like the lack of frills (no TV or telephone in the bedroom). Traditional cooking and generous breakfasts. Substantial picnics provided.
Read more: page 310.

Deeside Hotel, Ballater

In the 'delightful mountainous countryside' of the Cairngorm national park, this Victorian house is run as a home from home by Gordon Waddell and Penella Price. There are hour-long strolls along the river and through woodland, and strenuous uphill hikes for the more serious walker. Drying facilities and packed lunches are available.
Read more: page 336.

Pen-y-Gwryd Hotel, Nant Gwynant

In a spectacular location at the foot of Mount Snowdon, Brian and Jane Pullee's low-priced, 'delightfully eccentric' inn 'oozes atmosphere'; it was the training base for Hillary's 1953 Everest expedition. The slate-floored bar is filled with climbing gear. There's a panelled lounge with log fire, and a natural swimming pool in the garden. Substantial packed lunches.
Read more: page 420.

DOGS

No need to leave your best friend at home when visiting these hotels where dogs command special treatment

The Regent by the Lake, Ambleside

'We are a family of dog lovers and we welcome dogs,' says Christine Hewitt whose hotel is opposite a slipway on Lake Windermere. 'Your dog can run tail-waggingly free' on Borrans Park and Bird House Meadow, a short stroll from the door. Courtyard rooms allow dog owners to come and go as they please. 'We can prepare food for dogs the same as their owners; special requests and diets are no problem.'
Read more: page 82.

Blagdon Manor, Ashwater

Dogs are 'very welcome' at this 17th-century manor house. The resident chocolate Labradors 'always look forward to meeting new friends'. Visiting dogs are given a fleece blanket, towel, dog bowl and treats. Good walking in 17 acres of open fields leading from the garden.
Read more: page 87.

Corse Lawn House, Corse Lawn

Dogs are allowed in the bedrooms and the drawing rooms of this 'unfussy, comfortable' Queen Anne building set back from the green and road in a village near Tewkesbury. They can be exercised in fields within the extensive grounds. The house black Labradors are an added attraction for visitors.
Read more: page 149.

Knocklayd, Dartmouth

Visiting dogs sleep in the 'doggie dormitory (the utility room) or by the Aga in the kitchen of this large, rambling house at the highest point of Kingswear village. 'Very much a home', it is 'strongly recommended for dog lovers'. The owners have Molly, a retired hearing dog for the deaf.
Read more: page 157.

Overwater Hall, Ireby

'Dogs are genuinely welcomed' at this Georgian mansion in 18-acre grounds flanked by Skiddaw and surrounding fells. They are allowed to enjoy unleashed the grounds, including a woodland boardwalk. In the house, well-behaved canines may sit with their owners in one of the lounges and the bar. 'Cumbria is a walker's paradise; your dog will love it, too.'
Read more: page 196.

Pen-y-Dyffryn, Oswestry

Four bedrooms in a coach house at this 'attractive' country hotel are popular with dog owners. Each has a patio leading to a garden with 'lovely views'. There is a dog-walking area in the five-acre grounds. The listed Georgian rectory stands peacefully on the last hill in Shropshire close to the Welsh border. Good walking from the door, including the Offa's Dyke circular path.
Read more: page 253.

The Boar's Head, Ripley

At Sir Thomas and Lady Ingilby's old inn in a model village on their castle estate 'dogs are welcome providing they bring with them well-trained owners'. Dogs are allowed (£10 charge) in two courtyard rooms, which may be smallish, but a 'turn-down Bonio is placed in their basket, and water bowls are provided'.
Read more: page 268.

Willowburn Hotel, Clachan Seil

The resident dogs and cat at Jan and Chris Wolfe's homely small hotel on a little island on the shores of Clachan Sound send a card to prospective canine guests. Sisko a 'food-guided' Labrador, Tussock, a German hoverwart ('a real character'), and Odo the cat explain the set-up. Doggy treats await visiting pets, who are welcome in bedrooms but not in the lounge.
Read more: page 341.

Kilcamb Lodge, Strontian

'The beauty and outdoor life of the Highlands has to be shared with your best pal,' say the owners of this lodge on the shores of Loch Sunart. Dogs enjoy 'the wonderful freedom' in the grounds (no flowerbeds to worry about) and on the shore. Towels are provided for drying after swimming.
Read more: page 387.

Rathmullan House, Rathmullan

The Wheeler family's handsome mansion has a room for dog lovers in a courtyard extension opening on to the garden. The dog has its own room within a room, with a bed and toys, and a doormat decorated with patterns of paws. Pets can roam on a two-mile sandy beach (pooper-scoopers provided).
Read more: page 476.

COTSWOLDS

Enjoy beautiful landscapes and explore towns and villages whose wealth was built on the wool trade

Barnsley House, Barnsley

In a village near Cirencester, the former home of garden designer Rosemary Verey has been transformed into a luxury hotel by Tim Haigh and Rupert Pendered. The interiors are contemporary, with high-tech gadgets in the bedrooms (and a fridge with complimentary champagne). The style is discreet, the setting secluded.
Read more: page 92.

The Horse and Groom, Bourton-on-the-Hill

Old Cotswolds coaching inn at the top of a steep hill in pretty honey-stone village. Brothers Tom (front-of-house) and Will (chef) Greenstock are 'engaging hosts'. Good-sized bedrooms, refurbished in modern style, with well-equipped bathroom. Modern meals on blackboard menu, served by enthusiastic young staff. Generous breakfasts.
Read more, page 113.

Dial House, Bourton-on-the-Water

The River Windrush runs through this pretty town (busy with coach parties by day, quieter

in the evening). Under new owners, Martyn and Elaine Booth, the 17th-century building is set back from street, with quiet rear garden. Sophisticated cooking served in candlelit dining rooms with stone windows, wooden floor.
Read more, page 114.

The Malt House, Broad Campden

In a pretty honey-stoned hamlet, this 16th-century listed building is an upmarket B&B run by owner Judi Wilkes. 'The quality of the fabrics and furnishings would put most hotels to shame.' All bedrooms overlook the garden; three have their own entrance. Breakfast has a 'vast choice'. In warm weather, teas and evening drinks are served in the summer house or outdoors. From the gate you can walk on to the Cotswold Way.
Read more: page 128.

Russell's Restaurant, Broadway

On the wide main street, lined with period houses and cottages, of this lovely village, this listed building is run as a restaurant-with-rooms with a contemporary look by Barry Hancox and Andrew Riley. Original features blend with modern gadgets and paintings. In the stylish L-shaped dining room Matthew Laughton's modern cooking is 'first class'.

Read more, page 129.

The Rectory Hotel, Crudwell

In a village near Malmesbury, Julian Muggridge and Jonathan Barry have given this 16th-century former rectory in a Victorian garden a contemporary feel. 'A pleasant place to stay', it has a large hall with soft chairs and magazines. A 'miscellany of furniture', and a new king-size bed, in a 'spacious bedroom'; 'magnificent bathroom'. Peter Fairclough, the chef, serves classic British dishes on a seasonal menu.

Read more: page 156.

At the Sign of the Angel, Lacock

On the southern edge of the Cotswolds in an ancient National Trust village much used by film-makers (*Cranford, Harry Potter*), this 15th-century half-timbered inn is a welcoming place. Rooms in the old house may be small but have 'bags of character'; four newer rooms are in a cottage 'through a garden and over a brook'. 'High-quality English cooking' in the medieval candlelit dining rooms.

Read more: page 201.

The Grey Cottage, Leonard Stanley

Rosemary Reeves 'continues to amaze with her attention to detail' at her little stone guest house near Stroud. Extra touches include help with luggage, leaf tea and biscuits on arrival; fruit, fresh milk, even a torch in the immaculate bedrooms. The no-choice dinners are 'sumptuous'; bring your own bottle (no corkage charge). *Read more: page 209.*

Burleigh Court, Minchinhampton

In an 'impressive setting' on a steep hillside facing the western-most ridge of the Cotswolds, this creeper-covered 18th-century stone manor house is owned by Louise Noble. The 'superb' grounds were designed by Sir Clough Williams-Ellis. The staff are 'attentive but unobtrusive'.

Read more: page 237.

The Redesdale Arms, Moreton-in-Marsh

On the main street of this attractive market town, Robert Smith's old coaching inn has been welcoming travellers on the Fosse Way since the reign of Charles II. Visitors find it 'good value for the Cotswolds'. It has a 'pleasant, informal atmosphere', and 'courteous, cheerful' staff. Six new bedrooms are in a converted stable yard. The bar is popular with locals; the cooking is thought 'excellent'.

Read more: page 240.

EAST ANGLIA

Whether you are seeking a seascape or a country hideaway, the *Guide* has a wide choice in East Anglia

The Wentworth, Aldeburgh

Sea-facing bedrooms have binoculars at the Pritt family's traditional seaside hotel that overlooks fishing huts and Aldeburgh's shingle beach. There are antiques, books, plants, Russell Flint prints in the lounges; sea views from the best bedrooms. Chef Graham Reid serves 'good, unfussy' dishes in the conservatory restaurant.
Read more: page 80.

The Blakeney Hotel, Blakeney

With 'inspiring' views across a tidal estuary and salt marshes, Michael Stannard's large traditional hotel stands 'four-square to the quayside'. The public rooms face the estuary, as do many bedrooms. Traditional cooking in the dining room with 'high standards of presentation and service'.
Read more: page 109.

The White Horse, Brancaster Staithe

'Informal but with a sense of decorum', Cliff Nye's popular inn has a spectacular location, looking over the sea and salt marshes of Brancaster Bay. The interior has 'character and style': the lounge, restaurant, and bedrooms have been redecorated in contemporary rustic style. 'Delicious local fish dishes.' Children and dogs are welcomed.
Read more: page 122.

Byfords, Holt

A 'delightful' conversion of old houses on the main square of this charming market town is run by Iain and Clair Wilson as an unusual combination of 'posh' B&B, café by day, bistro by night, and deli. Tables and chairs on the pavement; old beams, exposed brickwork in a series of eating rooms. A warm welcome, chic, clean rooms. 'Cheerful bistro food, very friendly service.'
Read more: page 190.

Morston Hall, Morston

In a designated area of outstanding natural beauty on the north Norfolk coast, this

brick Jacobean house is run as a restaurant-with-rooms by Tracy (front-of-house) and Galton (chef/*patron*) Blackiston. He has a *Michelin* star for his accomplished cooking on a four-course menu. 'Impeccable housekeeping', beds turned down in evening.
Read more: page 241.

Beechwood, North Walsham

'Everything runs like clockwork' at Lindsay Spalding and Don Birch's creeper-clad Georgian house (with Victorian character), once Agatha Christie's Norfolk hideaway. Service is 'charming, attentive'. Bedrooms are well proportioned; Wi-Fi and flat-screen TVs are new. Steven Norgate's modern cooking reflects 'a real interest in local ingredients'.
Read more: page 247.

The Neptune Inn & Restaurant, Old Hunstanton

Kevin and Jacki Mangeolles are updating this 18th-century coaching inn a short walk from the sea. Bedrooms are 'thoughtfully equipped' with digital radio, TV and Wi-Fi. The bar and lounge have a nautical feel. The 'smart' restaurant is 'the centre of the action': he cooks interesting dishes, carefully presented. 'Good value' half-board.
Read more: page 251.

The Crown and Castle, Orford

Cookery writer and TV presenter Ruth Watson and her husband, David, run this 'feel-good' red brick inn in a peaceful Suffolk village. Bedrooms are 'stylish, well equipped'; each of the garden rooms has a terrace. In the bistro-style restaurant, Ruth Watson and Max Dougal have a *Michelin Bib Gourmand* for their unfussy seasonal dishes.
Read more: page 252.

The Rose & Crown, Snettisham

Opposite the cricket pitch in a pleasant Norfolk village, Jeannette and Anthony Goodrich's 'lovely' old country pub (14th century) has twisting passages, hidden corners, low ceilings and old beams. The bars and dining areas are popular with locals; residents have their own lounge. Older bedrooms are decorated in the contemporary style of five newer rooms. 'Delightful' staff; 'delicious' cooking.
Read more: page 289.

Broad House Hotel, Wroxham

'Homely yet smart', this Queen Anne house has been extensively modernised by Philip and Caroline Search. Bedrooms have attractive fabrics, antique furnishings. Books and games in the library which opens on to the garden. Friendly, informal service in the restaurant.
Read more: page 329.

LAKE DISTRICT

In the magnificent setting of lakes and mountains, these are some of the *Guide*'s favourite hotels

Rothay Manor, Ambleside

'Always welcoming and comfortable', Nigel Nixon's white Regency house has 'real country house style without pretension'. The service is 'professional yet relaxed'. Many of the 'well-furnished' bedrooms are large; the quietest rooms face the attractive gardens; four are in an annexe. You can walk across fields to the head of Lake Windermere from the attractive grounds. Jane Binns's daily-changing menus of French/British dishes are imaginative.
Read more: page 83.

The Pheasant, Bassenthwaite Lake

In woodland between lakes and fells in the unspoilt northern Lake District, this 400-year-old inn has oak beams, open log fires, antiques, old prints and paintings. 'It exudes warmth, comfort and an air of confidence.' Matthew Wylie is the 'extremely good' manager for the trustees of the Inglewood estate. Most bedrooms are large and comfortable. There is good walking in all directions.
Read more: page 95.

Fayrer Garden House Hotel, Bowness-on-Windermere

In five-acre grounds overlooking Lake Windermere, Claire and Eric Wildsmith's Edwardian mansion is 'comfortable and friendly'. 'Everything was done to make our stay enjoyable.' The lounge, restaurant, and some bedrooms face the water; other rooms look over award-winning gardens. Eddie Wilkinson serves modern English dishes, using local produce where possible, on a daily-changing menu.
Read more: page 115.

Lindeth Fell, Bowness-on-Windermere

In a superb setting among lovely gardens, Pat and Diana Kennedy's traditional hotel stands on the hills above Lake Windermere. 'Good traditional establishment.' 'Such a friendly welcome.' 'Standards never falter.' Bedrooms are 'well lit and warm', turn-down during dinner. There are 'gorgeous views' from the dining room (with conservatory-style extension) where Philip Taylor serves a 'copious daily-changing menu'.
Read more: page 116.

The Cottage in the Wood, Braithwaite

On Whinlatter Pass, looking down the valley to the Skiddaw mountain range, this 17th-century Lakeland inn is run by Liam and Kath Berney as a restaurant-with-rooms. They are 'genuinely caring' hosts; she is front of house ('excellent personal service'); his cooking is 'superb'.

Read more: page 120.

Aynsome Manor, Cartmel

Run by the Varley family for 28 years, this traditional Lakeland hotel between the fells and the sea has a loyal following. 'Food, service, management, value, faultless as ever,' says a regular. Smart casual dress is required in the evening in oak-panelled restaurant where ingredients are sourced within Cumbria for Gordon Topp's five-course dinner.

Read more: page 136.

Overwater Hall, Ireby

'Away from the bustle of more touristy areas', this castellated Georgian mansion stands in large grounds below Skiddaw and Uldale Fells. Stephen Bore is the 'gentle front-of-house'. All bathrooms have been refurbished; there are double-ended baths and walk-in showers. Adrian Hyde cooks 'well balanced' modern dishes. Children and dogs are welcome.

Read more: page 196.

Ees Wyke Country House, Near Sawrey

Richard (the 'most hospitable' chef) and Margaret Lee run this attractive Georgian house with panoramic views over Esthwaite Water. It is liked for the 'cosy English decor', and the 'unpretentious atmosphere'. Expect a warm greeting from the owner and his two Old English sheepdogs. In a lovely dining room, dinner is 'beautifully cooked, well presented'.

Read more: page 242.

Howtown Hotel, Ullswater

In an idyllic setting on the eastern shore of Lake Ullswater, this simple guest house is run by Jacquie Baldry and her son, David. 'Pure gold, no ostentation,' is a typical comment. No phones, TV, or radios in the bedrooms. A gong summons guests to dinner.

Read more: page 310.

Holbeck Ghyll, Windermere

Built as a Victorian hunting lodge, David and Patricia Nicholson's luxurious hotel stands in large grounds that slope down to the lake. The welcome is warm, the staff are friendly. The impeccable public rooms have stained glass, open fires, wood panelling, antiques. David McLaughlin's refined cooking is served in two dining rooms.

Read more: page 324.

WEST COUNTRY

Dorset, Devon and Cornwall are hot spots for good *Guide* establishments

Blagdon Manor, Ashwater

In rolling country towards Dartmoor ('perfect for a quiet stay'), this rambling manor house is run in 'a friendly, easy manner but with the highest standards' by Liz and Steve Morey. She is front-of-house; his imaginative cooking is much enjoyed. Fresh flowers and open fires in the bar and lounge.
Read more: page 87.

Bridge House, Beaminster

'Welcoming and comfortable', Mark and Joanna Donovan's small hotel/restaurant is a former priest's house with thick walls, mullioned windows and old beams. The quietest rooms overlook a large walled garden. The atmosphere is 'relaxed', the staff are 'friendly'. In a panelled dining room with conservatory extension, chef Linda Paget serves dishes with an emphasis on local organic produce.
Read more: page 100.

The Henley, Bigbury-on-Sea

'Ideal for recharging your batteries', this small, unpretentious hotel stands on a cliff above the tidal Avon estuary. In the evening in the lounge, with its spectacular views, Petra Scarterfield recites the short menu; the cooking of her husband, Martyn, is much admired. 'Every meal was a delight, freshly cooked food, perfectly served.'
Read more: page 106.

Mill End Hotel, Chagford

The owner, Keith Green, is 'busy keeping everyone happy' at his white-walled former mill (the wheel still revolves 'with much splashing'). There are large grounds to explore; the River Teign runs at the bottom of the garden. The lounges, with log fires, have a 'homely feel'. Christophe Ferraro cooks modern French dishes. Sympathetic modernisation is ongoing.
Read more: page 139.

Combe House, Gittisham

On a vast country estate of woodland, meadows and pastures, this extended Elizabethan manor house is informally run by Ken and Ruth Hunt. Visitors are greeted by 'a roaring fire rather than a reception desk'. Grand public rooms have oak panelling, antiques, fresh flowers. Bedrooms, 'unpretentious rather than sumptuous', have rich fabrics, 'extra touches'. Hadleigh

Barrett has a rising *Michelin* star for his modern dishes on a locally sourced seasonal menu. *Read more: page 175.*

Molesworth Manor, Little Petherick

In an attractive garden in a tiny village near Padstow, this 17th-century rectory is now a B&B run by Jessica Clarke and Geoff French. 'Plenty of sitting room and bedroom space', a 'friendly atmosphere'. Breakfast has 'imaginative options, home-made muffins and marmalades'. *Read more: page 214.*

Meudon, Mawnan Smith

'Traditional standards are still our cornerstone,' say Harry Pilgrim and his son, Mark, of their red-brick hotel in gardens that run down to a private beach. Service is 'personal and attentive'. A dress code of jacket and tie for men is encouraged in the restaurant where chef Alan Webb's 'inspirational' cooking uses local produce, including fish from Newlyn. *Read more: page 232.*

Heasley House, North Molton

Wooded slopes and water meadows surround this Georgian dower house in a pretty hamlet on the southern edge of Dartmoor. Jan and Paul Gambrill's warm welcome comes with tea and 'excellent fruitcake'.

Peaceful bedrooms are in pastel colours. Paul Gambrill, 'passionate about cooking', serves a 'first-class' three-course menu. *Read more: page 246.*

Ennys, St Hilary

A 'tranquil place', this 17th-century manor house is surrounded by fields that lead to the River Hayle. It is run as a B&B by travel writer Gill Charlton. 'You can tell she is well travelled by the little comforts in the bedrooms' (big waffle bathrobes, books and magazines, good toiletries, as well as flat-screen TVs and free Wi-Fi). *Read more: page 279.*

Talland Bay Hotel, Talland-by-Looe

Sheltered by ancient pines in subtropical gardens 150 feet above a quiet bay, this old manor house is a 'very fine family-run hotel'. George and Mary Granville and their staff are 'courteous, obliging and efficient'. In the wood-panelled dining room, Steven Buick's modern cooking is 'outstanding'. The best bedrooms have 'smart draperies and great views'. *Read more: page 299.*

VALUE

Limit the damage to your
wallet at these hotels;
each provides value in its
own category

Abbey House, Abbotsbury

'Beautifully situated' by a
remaining fragment of an 11th-
century abbey, this 15th-century
building is liked for its 'informal
warmth'. The 'friendly and
attentive' owners, Jonathan and
Maureen Cooke, 'run it
impeccably yet find time to chat'.
Original windows, flagstones; lots
of chintz and knick-knacks in
cosy lounge and cottagey
bedrooms. B&B £35–£45 per
person. Evening meals available
for house parties only. The sea is
a 15-minute walk away.
Read more: page 80.

The Rosemary, Falmouth

There are good sea views from
the lounge and dining room of
Suzanne and Geoff Warring's
white-walled ten-room B&B
near the Coast Path, in a quiet
residential road. 'Welcoming,
clean and comfortable', it has
paintings by contemporary
artists, a small bar and a pretty
garden with a sun deck. 'Each
bedroom is excellent'; a 'great'
breakfast. B&B from £32.50
per person.
Read more: page 168.

The Old Store, Halnaker

Once the village store and
bakery, this 18th-century red
brick and flint house is run as an
unpretentious guest house by
Patrick and Heather Birchenough,
'model hosts'. There are beamed
ceilings and a small, newly
decorated lounge. Some
bedrooms look across fields to
Chichester cathedral. A 'perfect'
breakfast has free-range eggs,
local sausages; packed lunches
are available, and there is a pub
across the road for evening meals.
B&B £32.50–£45 per person.
Read more: page 180.

Aspen House, Hoarwithy

In a village in the Wye valley,
this pink 18th-century farmhouse
is run as a guest house by Sally
Dean and Rob Elliott, liked
for their 'enthusiasm and
dedication'. No frills; 'real rooms,
real comfort'. 'Ingredients are
allowed to speak for themselves'
in the cooking, which shows
Polish influences (the host is
half-Polish). Excellent home-
made bread. B&B £36–£43 per
person. Dinner £24.
Read more: page 189.

The Mistley Thorn, Mistley

'Excellent; good food, good value.' Sherri Singleton runs this old inn on the Stour estuary as a restaurant-with-rooms. It has a 'seasidey freshness', uncluttered bedrooms, modern bathrooms. Seafood and seasonal local produce are on the menus. D,B&B from £52.50 per person. *Read more: page 238.*

The Gurnard's Head, Zennor

In a 'thrilling setting' on the wild north Cornish coast, this yellow-painted inn has been modernised by Charles and Edmund Inkin. 'They have struck just the right note; a congenial atmosphere, a welcome for locals and visitors alike.' Nothing fancy in the bedrooms; admired cooking in the bar with old tables and chairs, rugs on stone floors. B&B £40–£70 per person; dinner £24. *Read more: page 332.*

Bealach House, Duror

Up a forestry track among woods and mountains (much wildlife), Jim and Hilary McFadyen's handsome small guest house is beautifully decorated, well maintained. The bedrooms, not large, are 'extremely comfortable'. The hostess is an 'excellent' cook: 'well-chosen ingredients, well-balanced flavours, attractively served'. B&B £40–£65 per person; dinner £25. *Read more: page 346.*

The Steam Packet Inn, Whithorn

In a pretty sea-faring village, this 'delightful' quayside inn has comfortable rooms and a popular restaurant. 'Consistently good' blackboard menus are offered in the small, busy bars and the 'bright, cheerful' dining room. Dishes for a hearty appetite. D,B&B £50–£60 per person. *Read more: page 394.*

The Manor Town House, Fishguard

'A genuine warmth of welcome, a simple, quiet room and delicious bistro-style food' win admirers for Gail and James Stewart's Georgian town house near the main square. A group of visitors enjoyed 'cosseting and home cooking'. In the restaurant in a homely basement, local organic ingredients are used: 'Everything was meticulously prepared.' B&B £35–£45 per person; dinner £25. *Read more: page 410.*

The Hand at Llanarmon, Llanarmon Dyffryn Ceiriog

'Terrific value for money', this down-to-earth and 'charming' old inn at the head of a pretty valley beneath the Berwyn mountains is 'a very pleasant place to stay'. Housekeeping is 'immaculate'. Good 'straightforward hearty fare' is served in the restaurant. 'Everyone is so friendly.' D,B&B £55–£85 per person. *Read more: page 412.*

HISTORIC

Step back in time at these magnificent buildings which are part of our national heritage

Hartwell House, Aylesbury

'Beautifully restored' by Richard Broyd's Historic House Hotels, this stately home was built in the early 17th-century for the Hampden family. King Louis XVIII held his court in the house during his five-year exile from France. Today it is 'a perfect blend of the 18th and 21st centuries'. The 'elegant' public rooms have 'priceless antiques there to be used, not just admired'. Some bedrooms are in a converted stable block. Dinner is served by candlelight with silver and damask.
Read more: page 90.

Augill Castle, Kirkby Stephen

John Bagot Pearson, a Victorian 'gentleman of leisure', commissioned this Gothic-style castle in 1837 as a weekend retreat to entertain friends in the style of a medieval banquet. Today it is run in informal house-party style by Simon and Wendy Bennett. Lavishly restored, the house has a panelled hall, vaulted ceilings, turrets, stained-glass windows and ticking clocks.
Read more: page 198.

At the Sign of the Angel, Lacock

In the centre of an ancient National Trust village, this 15th-century half-timbered inn has oak panels, creaking doors, low ceilings and old beams. Bedrooms in the old inn may be small (and sound-proofing is 'not 21st century') but they are 'full of character' with antiques; one has a four-poster bed, another a French tented bed.
Read more: page 201.

Lavenham Priory, Lavenham

Tim and Gilli Pitt have sympathetically restored their half-timbered medieval house, once a Benedictine priory, later an Elizabethan merchant's house. The 13th-century Great Hall has a beamed ceiling and a huge inglenook fireplace. The 'bedchambers' have sloping beamed ceilings, mullioned windows and unusual beds (four-poster, sleigh, polonaise).
Read more: page 207.

Lewtrenchard Manor, Lewdown

'Wonderfully romantic', this 17th-century manor house on an

estate that is mentioned in the Domesday Book was lovingly transformed into a Victorian/Elizabethan fantasy by Sabine Baring Gould (who wrote 'Onward, Christian Soldiers'). It has ornate plaster ceilings, oak panelling, huge fireplaces and family portraits.
Read more: page 210.

Swinton Park, Masham

The Cunliffe-Lister family run their ancestral home as a luxury hotel with a wide range of activities in the grounds. The creeper-covered 17th-century house became a 'castle' in the 19th century when a tower, turrets and battlements were added. The large reception rooms have antiques and polished floors.
Read more: page 229.

Moccas Court, Moccas

One of Herefordshire's great houses, this Georgian mansion is the family home of Ben and Mimi Chester-Master who offer visitors 'the chance to live the landed lifestyle for a weekend'. Original designs by the Adam brothers are incorporated in the building, in particular the ornate classical decoration in the public rooms.
Read more: page 239.

Stone House, Rushlake Green

Peter and Jane Dunn, whose family built this 15th-century

manor house, offer visitors an 'authentic English experience'. The original Tudor timber frame, built around a chimney, faces north; the south face has a sandstone multi-gabled face, while the west wing is Georgian. The largest bedrooms are in the Georgian section (two have a four-poster); those in the Tudor wing have beams, sloping ceilings, antiques.
Read more: page 274.

Viewfield House, Portree

Hugh Macdonald entertains guests in house-party style at his family's home for more than 200 years, a baronial pile which began as a modest Georgian house with ambitious Victorian additions. Visitors enjoy the 'faded grandeur' and 'Gothic' air of the public rooms which have family portraits, stag's antlers, Indian brass and other imperial relics.
Read more: page 382.

Bodysgallen Hall and Spa, Llandudno

In a fine situation in a large park outside Llandudno, this mansion was built over 600 years; the main block dates from the 17th century (a 13th-century lookout tower is retained). Restored and run as a luxury hotel by Historic House Hotels, it has fine panelled public rooms, splendid fireplaces and stone mullioned windows; 'great old-fashioned luxury.'
Read more: page 414.

DISABLED FACILITIES

Each of these hotels has at least one bedroom equipped for a visitor in a wheelchair

We advise phoning to discuss individual requirements.

London
One Aldwych; Zetter.

England
Wentworth, Aldeburgh; Rothay Manor, Ambleside; Callow Hall, Ashbourne; Hartwell Hs, Aylesbury; Leathes Head, Borrowdale; Millstream, Bosham; White Horse, Brancaster Staithe; du Vin, Brighton; Frogg Manor, Broxton; Hell Bay, Bryer; Blackmore Fm, Cannington; Brockencote Hall, Chaddesley Corbett; Gidleigh Pk, Chagford; Beech Hs & Olive Branch, Clipsham; Treglos, Constantine Bay; Clow Beck Hs, Croft-on-Tees; Coach Hs at Crookham, Crookham; Summer Lodge, Evershot; Evesham, Evesham; Angel Inn, Hetton; Bath Arms, Horningsham; Dashwood, Kirtlington; Northcote Manor, Langho; 42 The Calls, Leeds; Lewtrenchard Manor, Lewdown; Cottage in the Wood, Malvern Wells; Swinton Pk, Masham; Bedruthan Steps, Mawgan Porth; Meudon, Mawnan Smith; Redesdale Arms, Moreton-in-Marsh; Cleeve Hs, Mortehoe; Jesmond Dene Hs, Newcastle upon Tyne; Beechwood, North Walsham; Hart's, Nottingham; Grange at Oborne, Oborne; Malmaison, Oxford; Old Bank, Oxford; Old Parsonage, Oxford; Seafood Restaurant, Padstow; Old Railway Station, Petworth; Bourgoyne, Reeth; St Michael's Manor, St Albans; Seaview, Seaview; Rose & Crown, Snettisham; Titchwell Manor, Titchwell; Royal, Truro; Nare, Veryan-in-Roseland; Windy Ridge, Whitstable; Holbeck Ghyll, Windermere; Old Vicarage, Worfield; Middlethorpe Hall, York.

Scotland
Dornoch Castle, Dornoch; Three Chimneys and House Over-By, Dunvegan; Scotsman, Edinburgh; Ardeonaig, Killin; Corsewall Lighthouse, Kirkcolm; Lynnfield, Kirkwall; New Lanark Mill, Lanark; Plockton, Plockton; Viewfield Hs, Portree; Skirling Hs, Skirling; Cleaton Hs, Westray.

Wales
Jolyon's, Cardiff; Gliffaes, Crickhowell; Bodysgallen Hall, Llandudno; Hafod Elwy Hall, Pentrefoelas.

Ireland
Dunbrody Country Hs, Arthurstown; Stella Marris, Ballycastle; Seaview Hs, Ballylickey; Cromleach Lodge, Castlebaldwin; Rayanne Hs, Holywood; Sheedy's, Lisdoonvarna; Rathmullan Hs, Rathmullan; Barberstown Castle, Straffan.

TENNIS AND SWIMMING

Each of these hotels has a tennis court (T) and/or swimming pool (S)

London
One Aldwych (S).

England
Regent by the Lake, Ambleside (S); Hartwell Hs, Aylesbury (T,S); Bath Priory, Bath (S); Park Hs, Bepton (T,S); West Coates, Berwick-upon-Tweed (S); Burgh Island, Bigbury-on-Sea (T,S); Blakeney, Blakeney (S); Woolley Grange, Bradford-on-Avon (S); Frogg Manor, Broxton (T); Hell Bay, Bryer (S); Brockencote Hall, Chaddesley Corbett (T); Gidleigh Pk, Chagford (T); Tor Cottage, Chillaton (S); Treglos, Constantine Bay (S); Corse Lawn Hs, Corse Lawn (T,S); Cloth Hall Oast, Cranbrook (S); Rectory, Crudwell (S); Summer Lodge, Evershot (T,S); Evesham, Evesham (S); Moonfleet Manor, Fleet (T,S); Stock Hill Hs, Gillingham (T); Hambleton Hall, Hambleton (T,S); Pheasant, Harome (S); Feversham Arms, Helmsley (S); Esseborne Manor, Hurstbourne Tarrant (T); Bindon Country House, Langford Budville (T,S); Feathers, Ledbury (S); Bedruthan Steps, Mawgan Porth (T,S); Budock Vean, Mawnan Smith (T,S); Milden Hall, Milden (T); Ennys, St Hilary (T,S); St Martin's on the Isle, St Martin's (S); Star Castle, St Mary's (S); Tides Reach, Salcombe (S); Soar Mill Cove, Soar Mill Cove (T,S); Stoke Lodge, Stoke Fleming (T,S); Plumber Manor, Sturminster Newton (T); Talland Bay, Talland-by-Looe (S); Calcot Manor, Tetbury (T,S); Island, Tresco (T,S); Nare, Veryan-in-Roseland (T,S); Gilpin Lodge, Windermere (S); Holbeck Ghyll, Windermere (T); Broad Hs, Wroxham (S); Middlethorpe Hall, York (S).

Scotland
Kinloch Hs, Blairgowrie (S); Kinnaird, Dunkeld (T); Greshornish Hs, Edinbane (T); Scotsman, Edinburgh (S); Isle of Eriska, Eriska (T,S); Eaglescairnie Mains, Gifford (T); Ardanaiseig, Kilchrenan (T); New Lanark Mill, Lanark (S); Kirroughtree Hs, Newton Stewart (T); Skirling Hs, Skirling (T).

Wales
Port Tocyn, Abersoch (T,S); Sychnant Pass Hs, Conwy (S); Glangrwyney Ct, Crickhowell (T); Gliffaes, Crickhowell (T); Bodysgallen Hall and Spa, Llandudno (T,S); St Tudno, Llandudno (S); Lake, Llangammarch Wells (T,S); Llangoed Hall, Llyswen (T); Portmeirion, Portmeirion (T,S).

(continued overleaf)

Channel Islands

White Hs, Herm (T,S); **Atlantic**, St Brelade (T,S); **St Brelade's Bay**, St Brelade (T,S); **Longueville Manor**, St Saviour (T,S); **Petit Champ**, Sark (S).

Ireland

Cashel Hs, Cashel Bay (T); **Glin Castle**, Glin (T); **Marlfield Hs**, Gorey (T); **Shelburne Lodge**, Kenmare (T); **Rosleague Manor**, Letterfrack (T); **Currarevagh Hs**, Oughterard (T); **Rathmullan Hs**, Rathmullan (T,S); **Coopershill**, Riverstown (T); **Ballymaloe Hs**, Shanagarry (T,S); **Foxmount Country House**, Waterford (T).

How to use the *Good Hotel Guide*

Hotelfinder is for those looking for ideas: we suggest hotels to match your mood or interests, perhaps romance or sport, for a family or for gourmets. We highlight hotels in a wide range of categories, giving a short profile and a cross-reference to the main entry.

Main entries carry our considered judgments, based on anonymous inspections and reader reports, of those hotels that we consider to be the best of their type. Hotels are listed alphabetically by country, under the name of the town or village. If you remember a hotel's name but not where it is, consult the alphabetical hotel list at the end of the book.

Italic entries These short entries describe hotels which are worth considering, but for various reasons – lack of information, recent change of ownership, mixed reports – do not merit a full entry.

The Shortlist suggests alternatives, especially in areas where we have a limited choice. These short entries have not been subjected to the same rigorous tests as the main entries; standards may be variable.

The maps Each hotel's location is marked. A small house indicates a main entry, a triangle a Shortlist one. We give the map number and grid reference at the top of the hotel's entry.

Reading the entries

Information panels We give the number of bedrooms without detailing the type of room (the distinction between a single room and a small double for single use, a standard or a superior double, a junior or a senior suite varies widely between hotels). We give the geographical location, but not detailed driving directions. As with room types, these are best discussed with the hotel when booking; directions are usually found on a hotel's website.

Prices We give each hotel's estimated prices for 2009, or the 2008 prices, which applied when the *Guide* went to press. The figures indicate the range from off-season to high season. A 'set lunch/dinner' can be no-choice or *table d'hôte*. The 'full alc' price is the cost per person of a three-course meal with a half bottle of wine; 'alc' indicates the price excluding wine. These figures cannot be guaranteed. *You should always check prices when booking.*

Symbols The label 'New' at the top of an entry identifies a hotel making its first appearance in the *Guide*, or one returning after an absence. We say 'Unsuitable for ♿' when a hotel tells us that it cannot accommodate wheelchair-users. We do not have the resources to inspect such facilities or to assess the even more complicated matter of facilities for the partially disabled. We suggest that you discuss such details directly with the hotel.

Names We give the names of the readers who have nominated or endorsed a hotel in brackets at the end of each entry. We do not name inspectors, correspondents who ask to remain anonymous, or those who have written critical reports.

Facilities We give an outline of the facilities offered by each hotel. We suggest that you check in advance if specific items (tea-making equipment, trouser press, sheets and blankets instead of a duvet) are important to you.

Changes We try to ensure that the details we provide are correct, but inevitably they are subject to change. Small hotels sometimes close at short notice off-season. Some change hands after we have gone to press.

Vouchers Hotels which join our voucher scheme – identified by a *V* – have agreed to give readers a discount of 25% off their normal bed-and-breakfast rate for one night only. You will be expected to pay the full price for other meals and all other services. *You should request a voucher reservation at the time of booking,* but a hotel may refuse to accept it at busy times. The six vouchers in the centre of the book are valid until the publication of the next edition of the *Guide*.

Traveller's tales These horror stories are taken from reports from readers. None of the hotels mentioned is included in the *Guide*; and the stories have *no connection* with the entry immediately above.

Report of the Year competition

Readers' contributions are the lifeblood of the *Good Hotel Guide*. Everyone who writes to the *Guide* is a potential winner of the Report of the Year competition. Each year a dozen correspondents are singled out for the helpfulness and generosity of their reports. They win a copy of the *Guide*, and an invitation to our annual launch party in October. The following generous readers are winners this year.

Kathy Armes of Sheffield
Michael Blanchard of Broadway
Elisabeth Biggs of Chichester
Liz and Phil Donnelly of Winchester
Alec Franks of Lewes
Christine Hughes of Churton
Sue Lyon of London
Tom Mann of London
Ann Morrison of Reading
David Nicholls of Ipswich
Roderic Rennison of Ickleford
Tara and Rick Varco of St Paul, Minnesota

Hotel reports

The report forms on the following pages may be used to endorse or criticise an existing entry or to nominate a hotel for inclusion in the *Guide*. But it is not essential that you use our forms or restrict yourself to the space available. Many readers email their reports to us.

All reports (*each on a separate piece of paper, please*) should include your name and address, the name and location of the hotel, and the date and length of your stay. Please nominate only places that you have visited in the past 12 months, unless friends tell you that standards have been maintained. Please be as specific as possible, and critical where appropriate, about the building, the public rooms and bedrooms, the meals, the service, the nightlife, the grounds.

If you describe the location as well as the hotel, particularly in less familiar regions, that is helpful. In the case of B&B hotels it is useful if you can recommend any restaurants.

We want the *Guide* to convey the special flavour of its hotels, and any details that you provide will give life to the description. If the report is too brief we may not be able to follow it up. Do not bother to give prices and routine information about number of rooms and facilities; we get such details from the hotels. We want readers to supply information that is not accessible elsewhere. In the case of a new nomination, it helps if you include a brochure or mention a website.

Please never tell a hotel that you intend to file a report. Anonymity is essential to objectivity.

The 2010 edition of the *Guide* will be written between mid-March and the end of May 2009, and published in early October 2009. Nominations should reach us not later than 15 May 2009. The latest date for comments on existing entries is 1 June 2009.

Please let us know if you would like us to send you more report forms. Our address for UK correspondents (no stamp needed) is: *Good Hotel Guide*, Freepost PAM 2931, London W11 4BR.

Reports can be emailed to editor@goodhotelguide.com or faxed to us on 020-7602 4182.

Reports posted outside the UK should be stamped normally and addressed to: *Good Hotel Guide*, 50 Addison Avenue, London W11 4QP, England.

LONDON

It is still possible to find hotels of character amid the swathe of branded, corporate hotels in London. As in other chapters, the *Guide*'s selection is led by hotels where the family owners show a keen personal interest: the Miller family at *Durrants*; David Levin at *The Capital* and its sister hotel, *The Levin*; the Goring family at *The Goring*; and Henry Togna at *22 Jermyn Street*.

Twenty Nevern Square, London

LONDON   Map 2:D4

The Capital	*Tel* 020-7589 5171
22–24 Basil Street	*Fax* 020-7225 0011
London SW3 1AT	*Email* reservations@capitalhotel.co.uk
	Website www.capitalhotel.co.uk

❧ *César award in 2008*

Admired as a 'successful attempt to produce a grand hotel in miniature', this luxurious place is owned by David Levin; Henrik Muehle
is manager. It stands on a busy little Knightsbridge street, but inside,
it is 'an oasis of civilised calm'. Visitors write of 'seriously high standards', and praise the staff ('attentive without obsequiousness'). But
some found Reception 'cool'. The decor is traditional (perhaps 'old-
fashioned') and understated. The comfortable bedrooms have heavy
fabrics, flowers, double glazing, air conditioning, marble bathroom;
'big, firm' beds have thick cotton sheets (no duvets). In the intimate
restaurant, 'service is efficient' and Eric Chavot has two *Michelin* stars
for French-inspired cooking which had reporters 'purring' this year.
Sample dishes: fricassée of frogs' legs, veal sweetbread and cèpe
purée; grilled turbot with mushroom ravioli. 'Superb food; extensive
wine list.' 'Good breakfasts', and 'afternoon tea of impeccable
country house standard'. Guests can also eat at the brasserie, *Le Metro*,
in *The Levin* (*qv*), the sister hotel next door but one, and they have
access to a nearby health club (£10 per person). A 'personal shopper'
(Harrods and Harvey Nichols are near) can be provided.

Bedrooms: 49. *Open*: all year, restaurant closed 25 Dec evening. *Facilities*: lift,
sitting room, bar, restaurant, brasserie/bar nearby, 2 private dining rooms,
business facilities, only restaurant suitable for ♿. *Background music*: 'modern'
in bar. *Location*: central, underground Knightsbridge, private car park (£6 an
hour, £30 a day). *Smoking*: not allowed. *Children*: all ages welcomed. *Dogs*: not
allowed. *Credit cards*: all major cards. *Prices*: [2008] room £210–£455, breakfast
£14–£18.50, set dinner £58–£70 (*plus 12½% discretionary service charge*).

Charlotte Street Hotel

	Tel 020-7806 2000
15 Charlotte Street	*Fax* 020-7806 2002
London W1T 1RJ	*Email* charlotte@firmdale.com
	Website www.charlottestreethotel.com

Just north of Soho, near many theatres and 'in an area densely populated with good restaurants', this member of Tim and Kit Kemp's
small Firmdale group (see also *The Pelham*) has a 'Bloomsbury Set'

decor. The entrance lobby is 'elegant but not pompous'; two 'comfortable, quite large' lounges are 'in the spirit of Vanessa Bell and Duncan Grant'. There is artwork from the period, and the bar/restaurant, *Oscar*, has a mural of contemporary London. Its open-plan kitchen serves a short menu of modern dishes (eg, lobster ravioli; soba noodle ramen with king prawns). 'We liked it a lot,' said recent visitors. 'Staff attentive and friendly. Our quiet, air-conditioned bedroom had sitting area, good storage, beautiful, well-heated bathroom.' The 'excellent' buffet breakfast has fresh fruit, cereals, etc, cooked English. There is a 64-seat screening room. The manager is Jakob Hansen. (*WS*)

Bedrooms: 52. *Open*: all year, restaurant closed Sun noon–5 pm. *Facilities*: lift, ramps, drawing room, library, bar/restaurant, 3 private dining/meeting rooms, screening room, limited access for &. *Background music*: none. *Location*: West End, N of Soho, underground Goodge Street. *Smoking*: allowed in all bedrooms. *Children*: all ages welcomed. *Dogs*: not allowed. *Credit cards*: all major cards. *Prices*: [to 31 Jan 2009] room (*excluding VAT*) £220–£1,150, breakfast £19, set dinner £21.50 (£35 on Sun including movie of the week), full alc £45, special breaks.

Durrants

26–32 George Street
London W1H 5BJ

Tel 020-7935 8131
Fax 020-7487 3510
Email enquiries@durrantshotel.co.uk
Website www.durrantshotel.co.uk

'The type of old-fashioned but well-run hotel that is so typically British (but difficult to find).' Praise this year for the Miller family's conversion of four terraced houses with a Georgian facade, just north of Oxford Street and near the Wallace Collection. Other praise: 'Great location, helpful staff; a welcoming, comfortable country house hotel feel.' 'We loved it, felt relaxed and pampered.' Managed by Ian McIntosh, it has small panelled lounges with leather settees and chairs; original paintings, prints and engravings; antique furniture; a 'comfortable' bar. 'The brass at the front is polished every day, and the public areas are well kept.' Renovation of the bedrooms continues. The larger rooms at the front may get some traffic noise; quieter rooms at the back might sometimes hear early-morning deliveries. Some rooms have antiques; all have broadband Internet access. The restaurant serves 'generous portions' of international dishes, eg, rack of lamb; roast breast of guinea fowl. 'At breakfast there was nice yogurt and prunes but nasty sliced-bread toast; efficient and pleasant service.' (*Wolfgang Stroebe, Marilyn Frampton, Ellin Osmond*)

Bedrooms: 92, 7 on ground floor. *Open*: all year, restaurant closed 25 Dec. *Facilities*: lifts, ramp, bar, restaurant, lounge, 5 function rooms. *Background music*: none. *Location*: off Oxford Street, underground Bond Street, Baker Street. *Smoking*: not allowed. *Children*: all ages welcomed. *Dogs*: only guide dogs allowed. *Credit cards*: Amex, MasterCard, Visa. *Prices*: single room £125, double £225, breakfast £11.50–£14.50, full alc £50 (*excluding 'optional' 12½% service charge*).

Egerton House

17–19 Egerton Terrace
London SW3 2BX

Tel 020-7589 2412
Fax 020-7584 6540
Email bookeg@rchmail.com
Website www.egertonhousehotel.com

Overlooking two tree-lined garden squares, this conversion of two Victorian town houses in Knightsbridge has been refurbished by the Red Carnation group. It is managed by Sandra Anido. Returning visitors were 'warmly welcomed' and found 'front desk impressive; all staff helpful; housekeeping spot on'. Original artworks abound. Traditional afternoon tea (with freshly baked scones with clotted cream and fruit preserves) is taken in the drawing room. The 'skilful, chatty' barman, Antonio (famed for his Martinis), presides in the bar ('a watering hole for local residents'). The bedrooms are 'attractive and outstandingly well equipped', though 'one doesn't get a lot of square footage for the money: our superior garden-facing room (£300) was peaceful, but we had occasionally to avoid collision when moving around'. At the evening turn-down, a scented candle is lit in the bathroom. Breakfast is available round the clock: between 7 and 11 am it is served in a pretty room where there is a large buffet (fruit, ham, 'excellent' bread rolls, pastries and fresh orange juice) and cooked dishes. Snacks and meals are available all day, and you can order a picnic to take to a park. There is free Wi-Fi throughout, and 'many good restaurants are nearby'. (*K and DW*)

Bedrooms: 29, some on ground floor, all air conditioned. *Open*: all year. *Facilities*: lift, drawing room, bar, breakfast room, private dining/meeting room, 24-hour butler service. *Background music*: 'soft classical' in bar in evening. *Location*: central, valet parking, underground Knightsbridge, South Kensington. *Smoking*: not allowed. *Children*: all ages welcomed (must be accompanied by an adult). *Dogs*: allowed. *Credit cards*: Amex, MasterCard, Visa. *Prices*: [2008] room (*excluding VAT*) £255–£495, breakfast £17–£24.50.

Please always send a report if you stay at a *Guide* hotel, even if it's only to endorse the existing entry.

The Goring
Beeston Place
Grosvenor Gardens
London SW1W 0JW

Tel 020-7396 9000
Fax 020-7834 4393
Email reception@goringhotel.co.uk
Website www.goringhotel.co.uk

❧ *César award in 1994*

Owned and managed for four generations by the Goring family, this traditional city hotel is close to Victoria Station and Buckingham Palace (some royal visitors to the palace are said to prefer the comforts of *The Goring*). It was the first hotel in the world to offer central heating and private facilities for every bedroom. Jeremy Goring now runs it with David Morgan-Hewitt as managing director. Many of the staff are long serving. 'Forever excellent, really upmarket,' was one comment. The restaurant was recently redesigned by David Linley: it has quirky glass chandeliers which are lowered in the evening, no background music and a ban on mobile phones. Derek Quelch's much-admired seasonal cooking uses 'painstakingly sourced British produce' (eg, whisky-marinated salmon with fennel salad; roast best end of Devonshire lamb with a brioche crust). Breakfast has 'a mind-boggling selection of fruits'; 'the best kipper this fan of fish has tasted'. The 'clubby' bar has a light veranda facing the hotel's private garden (open to guests). Drinks and cream teas are served on a terrace in summer. Many bedrooms face the garden; some have a private terrace. Eccentric touches include large replica sheep which migrate around the building. (*BP, MF*)

Bedrooms: 71, 2 suitable for &. *Open*: all year, restaurant closed Sat lunch. *Facilities*: lift, ramps, lounge bar (pianist in evening), terrace room, restaurant, function facilities. *Background music*: none. *Location*: near Victoria Station, garage, mews parking, underground Victoria. *Smoking*: allowed in some bedrooms. *Children*: all ages welcomed. *Dogs*: not allowed. *Credit cards*: Amex, Diners, MasterCard. *Prices*: [2008] room (*excluding VAT*) £114.50–£362.50 per person, breakfast £23, set lunch £35, dinner £45, Christmas/New Year packages.

Hazlitt's
6 Frith Street
London W1D 3JA

Tel 020-7434 1771
Fax 020-7439 1524
Email reservations@hazlitts.co.uk
Website www.hazlittshotel.com

❧ *César award in 2002*

Occupying three historic houses in Soho, this stylish B&B hotel, owned by Peter McKay, is named after the essayist, who lived here. 'In many ways charming and interesting,' said a visitor this year.

'Delightful staff.' Others wrote: 'A small but opulent and quirky room with our very own illuminated bust in the fireplace. The bed was very comfortable.' The bedrooms, named after friends of Hazlitt, vary in size: all are furnished with antiques; many have original panelling and a four-poster or half-tester bed; some have freestanding Victorian bath. Plumbing and other facilities are modern: there is air conditioning, Wi-Fi and flat-screen LCD television. The quietest rooms are at the back; in 2008 those overlooking Frith Street, which is busy with revellers especially at weekends, were given triple glazing. The only public room is a small lounge. No lift (listed building): some stairs are steep. A continental breakfast (freshly baked bread, freshly squeezed juice, etc) is brought to the bedroom on a tray, and a simple room-service menu is available from 11 am to 10.30 pm. *Hazlitt's* is popular with people in film, fashion, music and publishing: writers who stay here leave signed copies of their books. (*PR, Mr and Mrs J Anderson*)

Bedrooms: 23. *Open*: all year. *Facilities*: sitting room, 3 small courtyard gardens, unsuitable for &. *Background music*: none. *Location*: Soho (front windows triple glazed, rear rooms quietest), NCP nearby, underground Tottenham Court Road, Leicester Square. *Smoking*: allowed in 16 bedrooms. *Children*: all ages welcomed. *Dogs*: allowed. *Credit cards*: all major cards. *Prices*: [2008] room (*excluding VAT*) £175–£500, breakfast £9.75, special breaks.

The Levin   NEW

28 Basil Street
London SW3 1AS

Tel 020-7589 6286
Fax 020-7823 7826
Email reservations@thelevinhotel.co.uk
Website www.thelevinhotel.co.uk

'It couldn't be faulted for service, room, facilities and location, but prices are high.' Next door but one to its bigger sister, *The Capital* (*qv*), the former *L'Hotel* reopened in 2007 after a major facelift. Named after its owner, David Levin, it is managed by Henrik Muehle who also manages *The Capital*. Sophisticated bedrooms have a '1930s-inspired' decor, air conditioning, champagne bar, high-speed Internet access, 'state-of-the-art audio and video system', 24-hour room service. But the 'rackety old lift' survives, inspectors tell us. 'The welcome was charming: luggage carried into the spacious lobby, elegant with easy chairs, tables, long windows, formal flower arrangements. Our large superior room overlooking Basil Street had huge bed with massive headboard, deliciously soft pillows and duvet, well-lit bathroom with everything you could need.' Continental breakfast ('very good orange juice, muesli, proper butter and conserves, leaf tea, above-average toast') is included in the room rate (cooked dishes cost extra). It is available between 7.30 and 11.30 am in the basement brasserie, *Le Metro*: open to the public, it also serves lunch and dinner (noon to 9.30) and afternoon tea. 'We chose a simple meal of steak and kidney pie and quiche; exceptionally good house wines from David Levin's French vineyard.'

Bedrooms: 12. *Open*: all year. *Facilities*: lobby, library, honesty bar, bar/brasserie (*Le Metro*), access to nearby health club/spa, unsuitable for &. *Background music*: modern, in *Le Metro*. *Location*: Central, underground Knightsbridge (Harrods exit), private car park (£30 a night). *Smoking*: not allowed. *Children*: all ages welcomed, under-12s must be accompanied by an adult, cot £30 per night. *Dogs*: not allowed. *Credit cards*: all major cards. *Prices*: [2008] b&b £117.50–£222.50, full alc £45.50, seasonal offers, Christmas/New Year packages.

One Aldwych

1 Aldwych
London WC2B 4RH

Tel 020-7300 1000
Fax 020-7300 1001
Email reservations@onealdwych.com
Website www.onealdwych.com

❦ *César award in 2005*

The 'courteous, outstandingly attentive service from young, friendly staff' impressed a visitor in 2008 to this modern, eco-friendly hotel opposite Waterloo Bridge. Originally the Edwardian offices of the old *Morning Post*, it was converted by owner Gordon Campbell Gray; Simon Hirst is the manager. Over 400 pieces of contemporary art are displayed throughout. The double-height lobby/bar has huge arched windows, a giant statue of an oarsman, 'trendy flower arrangements'. 'Ground-floor and lift decor is impressive, my room was less so, some of the furniture starting to look its age. Efficient triple glazing: total silence overnight.' Bedrooms have digital TV, modem socket, etc. 'Luxurious bed; plump pillows. Huge windows looked over rooftops.' The 'well-appointed, spotless' bathrooms have granite surfaces, 'green' toiletries, a 'vacuum-based waste water system'. The 'relaxed' *Indigo* restaurant, on a balcony, has a contemporary European menu using organic ingredients where possible. Classic European dishes are served in the more formal *Axis at One Aldwych*, on the lower ground floor. The *Cinnamon Bar* provides soups, sandwiches, fruit juice cocktails, wine by the glass. Breakfast is continental, healthy or English. There is a basement swimming pool and a spa offering various treatments. Children are welcomed. *Dukes Hotel*, St James, is under the same ownership (see Shortlist). (*Robert Gower*)

Bedrooms: 105, 6 adapted for ♿, all air conditioned. *Open*: all year, *Axis at One Aldwych* closed Sat midday, Sun, Easter, Christmas. *Facilities*: lifts, 2 bars (live DJ Sat evening), 2 restaurants, private dining rooms, function facilities, civil wedding licence, screening room, newsagent, florist, health club (18-metre swimming pool, spa, sauna, gym). *Background music*: at certain hours. *Location*: Strand (windows triple glazed), valet parking, underground Covent Garden, Charing Cross, Waterloo. *Smoking*: allowed in 36 bedrooms. *Children*: all ages welcomed (some interconnecting rooms). *Dogs*: only guide dogs allowed. *Credit cards*: all major cards. *Prices*: [2008] room/suite (*excluding VAT*) £380–£1,160, English breakfast £22, set lunch £15.50–£17.50, full alc £70, promotional offers, 1-night bookings sometimes refused in high season.

Parkes Hotel
41 Beaufort Gardens
London SW3 1PW

Tel 020-7581 9944
Fax 020-7581 1999
Email info@parkeshotel.com
Website www.parkeshotel.com

Guests at this much-liked hotel in a tree-lined Knightsbridge cul-de-sac are welcomed by a hand-written note from the managing director, Susan Shaw (the owner, Bertil Nygren, is Swedish). 'The staff make a point of learning your name, and using it,' said a recent visitor. 'You enter into an oak-panelled reception area. My decent-sized room had big bed, sofa and chairs, and a separate dressing room.' The elegant bedrooms are traditionally furnished with bold colours, chandeliers, tapestry curtains, sofas and oriental rugs. Modern amenities include Wi-Fi, flat-screen plasma TV with movies on demand, and under-floor heating and 'rain-effect' shower in the green marble bathroom. Each of the 14 suites has a sitting room and kitchenette. Some rooms have a large balcony facing a garden square. An 'excellent' breakfast (continental or cooked) is served until 10.30 am. No restaurant, but 'a thoughtful information folder lists some excellent local restaurants which deliver'. More reports, please.

Bedrooms: 33, some on ground floor. *Open*: all year. *Facilities*: lobby, lounge, breakfast room, access to nearby health club, unsuitable for ♿. *Background music*: classical. *Location*: Knightsbridge (windows double glazed), meter parking, underground Knightsbridge. *Smoking*: not allowed. *Children*: all ages welcomed. *Dogs*: not allowed. *Credit cards*: all major cards. *Prices*: [2008] room (*excluding VAT*) £135–£525, breakfast £12.50–£30.

The terms printed in the *Guide* are only a rough indication of the size of the bill to be expected at the end of your stay. Always check the tariffs when booking.

The Pelham

15 Cromwell Place
London SW7 2LA

Tel 020-7589 8288
Fax 020-7584 8444
Email pelham@firmdale.com
Website www.pelhamhotel.co.uk

Visitors in 2008 had a 'great stay' of a week at Tim and Kit Kemp's large, white, Victorian terraced hotel. With its yellow-and-white-striped awnings, it stands opposite South Kensington underground station. It is managed by Lisa Brooklyn. 'We were upgraded from a superior to a deluxe room. A legion of friendly and helpful staff was present.' Both the lounge and the library have an open fireplace. The smallest bedrooms are in the eaves; larger rooms have big bed and antique furnishings; the spacious suites have high ceilings and original features. All rooms have plasma TV, Wi-Fi, business facilities and 24-hour room service. 'Courtesy newspapers were outside the door every morning; free shoe-shine.' *Kemps*, the candle-lit basement restaurant, is 'good for a reasonably priced lunch; and peaceful'. Chef Rachel Hitchcock's dishes might include steak and ale pie; confit lamb shoulder with roast vegetables. But there is no obligation to eat in: 'The concierge suggested good dining spots', and if you want a cheaper breakfast, 'there are several tasty places nearby'. Children are welcomed. Hyde Park is near; so are the Knightsbridge shops. (*Scott Atkins, and others*)

Bedrooms: 52. *Open*: all year. *Facilities*: lift, drawing room, library, bar, restaurant/bar, 3 private dining/meeting rooms, gym, access to nearby health club, limited access for &. *Background music*: none. *Location*: South Kensington, opposite underground station (windows double glazed), meter parking, public car park nearby. *Smoking*: allowed in all bedrooms. *Children*: all ages welcomed. *Dogs*: not allowed. *Credit cards*: all major cards. *Prices*: [2008] room (*excluding VAT*) £180–£2,500, breakfast £17.50, set menus £12.95–£17.95, full alc £30, special b&b rates Christmas/New Year, Easter, end July–beginning Sept.

The Portobello

22 Stanley Gardens
London W11 2NG

Tel 020-7727 2777
Fax 020-7792 9641
Email info@portobellohotel.co.uk
Website www.portobellohotel.co.uk

'Informal, relaxed, full of character; nothing anonymous here.' An inspector's comment in 2008 on this bohemian little hotel which stands discreetly in a Victorian terrace on a Notting Hill residential street. It has been owned for many years by Tim and Cathy Herring with partner Johnny Ekperigin, who manages it with Hanna Turner.

Its 'special rooms' are liked for their quirky features. The Japanese room on the lower ground floor has a large ornamental bed and a small outside area with a shell grotto. Other rooms include 'Indian' and 'Pacific Rim'. 'Our third-floor room had garden view, supremely comfortable four-poster bed, quality bedlinen and towels, good bathroom (though shower and loo were in a tiny sectioned-off area). It was very peaceful.' Standard rooms may be very small. The 'charming' garden-facing drawing room has gilt mirrors, military pictures, marble fireplaces, potted palms, Edwardiana. A simple continental breakfast is included in the room rate; full English is available at extra cost, and the *à la carte* breakfast menu includes smoked salmon with scrambled eggs, champagne, fresh fruit, yogurt. It can be taken in the drawing room or in the bedroom. There is free Wi-Fi and 24-hour room service menu, and a hydraulic lift services all floors. *The Portobello*'s residents get a discount at *Julie's*, the owners' restaurant/bar/café in nearby Clarendon Cross.

Bedrooms: 21. *Open*: all year, except 24–29 Dec. *Facilities*: lift, small bar, foyer/lounge, access to nearby health club, unsuitable for &. *Background music*: 'soft' at breakfast, evenings. *Location*: Notting Hill, meter parking, underground Notting Hill Gate. *Smoking*: allowed in 3 bedrooms. *Children*: all ages welcomed. *Dogs*: allowed by prior arrangement. *Credit cards*: Amex, MasterCard, Visa. *Prices*: b&b (continental) £97.50–£175 per person, English breakfast £16.

The rockwell
181 Cromwell Road
London SW5 0SF

Tel 020-7244 2000
Fax 020-7244 2001
Email enquiries@therockwell.com
Website www.therockwell.com

'Bright, modern, with well-trained staff': two Victorian terrace houses have been turned 'with flair' into a hotel by architect Michael Squire with Tony Bartlett. Its bright facade 'shines like a beacon of light on a dreary stretch of Cromwell Road'. Visitors like the 'well-ventilated' bedrooms and 'sophisticated' decor: 'interesting wallpaper, patterns and colour'. The 'fine, high-ceilinged' lounge has an open fire; the small bar opens on to a garden with plants in huge pots, where drinks and meals can be served. Spacious garden bedrooms have a patio; 'exciting' mezzanine suites have a lounge and sleeping area down a curved staircase. 'Our compact fourth-floor standard double made good use of space: built-in light oak wardrobe, matching bedhead, minibar, flat-screen TV; well-lit bathroom with bathrobes and powerful shower. Double glazing kept out road noise. 24-hour room service.' In the restaurant, overlooking the garden, contemporary English dishes (eg,

organic corn-fed chicken supreme stuffed with herbs and Parmesan)
are accompanied by a 'wide-ranging' wine list. Breakfast is served until
10 am: it has a buffet with 'the freshest of orange juice; home-made
muesli; big jars of preserves' and various cooked dishes. 'Reasonable
prices for central London.' Ocky Paller is the manager.

Bedrooms: 40, some on ground floor. *Open*: all year. *Facilities*: lift, ramps, lobby,
lounge, bar, restaurant, conference room, garden. *Background music*: in public
rooms. *Location*: 1 mile W of West End, opposite Cromwell Hospital, underground Earls Court. *Smoking*: not allowed. *Children*: all ages welcomed. *Dogs*:
not allowed. *Credit cards*: Amex, MasterCard, Visa. *Prices*: [2008] room £120–
£200, breakfast £9.50–£12.50, alc £30.

Twenty Nevern Square   NEW

20 Nevern Square
London SW5 9PD

Tel 020-7565 9555
Fax 020-7565 9444
Email hotel@twentynevernsquare.co.uk
Website www.twentynevernsquare.co.uk

Owned by the Mayflower group, this converted red brick Victorian
town house faces a garden square. Inspectors found it 'surprisingly
peaceful, given the location between two busy roads'. It has some
exotic bedrooms, 'with a mix of European and Asian influences'. The
best ones, which face the square, include the Pasha Suite (lots of gold
silk); the Chinese Double (cream silk curtains, black silk bedspread,
pagoda-style armoire). Rococo Double has silk curtains in blue, gold
and purple. 'Our small room (No. 7) overlooked a side street. It was
clean, well equipped, comfortable. A four-poster bed took up most of
the space. Blankets, not duvet, to our delight. The compact shower
room had good towels and toiletries, a basin that favoured design over
utility.' All rooms have free Wi-Fi, CD-player, wide-screen TV and
safe. Complimentary afternoon tea is served in a small lounge with
armchairs and two exotic birdcages, each housing a parakeet. A
'generous' continental breakfast (cold meats, fruit salad, etc), served
in the conservatory-style *Café Twenty*, is included in the room price;
cooked costs extra. 'Service was excellent (staff mainly oriental).
Prices for London (which unusually include VAT) are reasonable.' A
'South-African-style' barbecue is sometimes held. Leisure facilities
are available nearby courtesy of Soho Gyms.

Bedrooms: 20. *Open*: all year. *Facilities*: lounge, restaurant, small garden,
unsuitable for &. *Background music*: in public rooms. *Location*: central, underground Earls Court. *Smoking*: not allowed. *Children*: all ages welcomed (under-
5s accommodated free). *Dogs*: not allowed. *Credit cards*: all major cards. *Prices*:
b&b £49.50–£119 per person, cooked breakfast £9, barbecue from £18.

22 Jermyn Street

22 Jermyn Street
London SW1Y 6HL

Tel 020-7734 2353
Fax 020-7734 0750
Email office@22jermyn.com
Website www.22jermyn.com

♙ *César award in 1996*

'A superb little hotel, very well run', Henry Togna's Victorian town house provides 'a sense of privacy' close to Piccadilly Circus. Laurie Smith has long been the manager. 'Like staying in a private, but serviced apartment,' say inspectors in 2008. No public rooms, but much of the accommodation is in suites. 'The welcome begins when you book: help offered with transport, theatre tickets, restaurant reservations.' The entrance is discreet; tapestries hang in a panelled hall. 'We were welcomed by a charming Italian receptionist. Our suite (we were upgraded) had an elegant living room with sofa, chairs, traditional furnishings; well-equipped bathroom with thoughtful extras; enormous bed, good lighting and storage space. Everything of the highest quality, demonstrating great attention to detail; excellent information pack. A short story is left on the bed at turn-down.' Some suites can be turned into two or three bedrooms. Children and pets are welcomed. No restaurant, but there is a good 24-hour room service menu. Breakfast, brought on a tray, has 'a basket of warm pastries, freshly squeezed juice, excellent tea and coffee'; cooked dishes *à la carte* ('tasty bacon', porridge, etc). There might be late-night noise from passers-by. Guests may use the sporting facilities at a nearby club.

Bedrooms: 18. *Open*: all year. *Facilities*: lift, reception, small conference facilities, 24-hour room service, access to health club (£15). *Background music*: classical in reception. *Location*: West End (St James's), car park nearby, valet parking (expensive), underground Piccadilly Circus. *Smoking*: allowed in 4 bedrooms. *Children*: all ages welcomed. *Dogs*: allowed. *Credit cards*: all major cards. *Prices*: room (*excluding VAT*) £220–£350, breakfast £13.20, full alc £30–£45.

The Zetter

86–88 Clerkenwell Road
London EC1M 5RJ

Tel 020-7324 4444
Fax 020-7324 4445
Email info@thezetter.com
Website www.thezetter.com

The staff are 'exceptionally friendly' at this converted 19th-century warehouse which has been given a contemporary look by owners Mark Sainsbury and Michael Benyan. Justin Pinchbeck is manager.

A glass door leads to a white-walled lobby with a pink Murano chandelier. The crescent-shaped restaurant has floor-to-ceiling windows, tables well spaced, 'good atmosphere'. The 'interesting' Mediterranean menu of chef Diego Jacquet might include smoked eel and grilled tuna with horseradish cream; charcoal-grilled lamb with caponata. 'Good puddings. Portions not over-large; reasonable prices.' On Sunday there is a brunch menu and a short *carte*. The bedrooms have bright colours, comfortable beds with duck-down duvet, modern bathroom with raindance shower, free Wi-Fi. 'We were upgraded to a roof studio with patio and panoramic views.' A 'superior' room was 'small, a bit stark, but stylish. Great lighting, with a pink option; smart, if awkward, oblong granite basin.' The bedrooms and hallways have new carpets this year; the building has been repainted throughout. Breakfast can be express (a basket of pastries), continental, classic English, vegetarian, or *à la carte* (perhaps pear vanilla compote with crunchy muesli). Vending machines on each floor produce drinks, disposable cameras, champagne, etc. *The Zetter* 'has an environmental conscience' (sustainable materials, energy-efficient technology). (*ML, and others*)

Bedrooms: 59, 1 suitable for &. *Open*: all year. *Facilities*: 2 lifts, ramps, cocktail bar, restaurant, 2 function/meeting rooms. *Background music*: modern eclectic mix. *Location*: Clerkenwell, by St John's Sq, NCP garage 5 mins' walk, underground Farringdon. *Smoking*: allowed in 13 bedrooms. *Children*: all ages welcomed. *Dogs*: only guide dogs allowed. *Credit cards*: Amex, MasterCard, Visa. *Prices*: [2008] room £188–£399.50, breakfast £6.50–£16.50, full alc £50.

See also SHORTLIST

****

Traveller's tale *Hotel in the Lake District* After a seven-hour drive, we were looking forward to a hot bath and a delicious home-cooked dinner. We were greeted by the news that the owner had hurt her back playing with her grandchild and wouldn't be able to cook the dinner that we had arranged weeks before. She assumed we wouldn't mind driving another 20 minutes for a meal in a pub. I thought she was joking. When we objected, she finally agreed to put together a cold platter of whatever was in the fridge (a couple of hard-boiled eggs and some bread). OK for a picnic, but not what we had been hoping for.

****

ENGLAND

Our selection of English hotels is as varied as ever, ranging from smart city establishments to simple country guest houses and affordable B&Bs. The common denominator is hands-on ownership (sometimes carried out by a good manager), creating an overriding concern for the comfort and well-being of the guest. We like to find places that are distinctly un-hotel-like; perhaps restaurants-with-rooms or dining pubs where the pleasures of the table are accompanied by decent overnight facilities and good service. Readers sometimes ask why we include B&Bs alongside more illustrious full-service hotels. The answer is found in the warmth of the welcome and some of the best breakfasts we've enjoyed.

Lindeth Fell, Bowness-on-Windermere

ABBOTSBURY Dorset   Map 1:D6

Abbey House   *Tel* 01305-871330
Church Street   *Fax* 01305-871088
Abbotsbury DT3 4JJ   *Email* info@theabbeyhouse.co.uk
                          Website www.theabbeyhouse.co.uk

Ever popular, 'good value', and commended again in 2009 for its 'informal warmth', this 15th-century building is 'beautifully situated' by a remaining fragment of an 11th-century abbey. Owned by the 'friendly, attentive' Jonathan and Maureen Cooke, who 'run it impeccably, yet find time to chat', it has flagstone floors, panelled doors, original windows. There is a 'cosy lounge with plenty of books'; 'lots of chintz and knick-knacks'. Light lunches and cream teas are served in summer in the 'lovely large garden'; it has flowerbeds in wide lawns that slope down to a millpond. Beyond is Abbotsbury's huge, ancient tithe barn. The 'cottagey' bedrooms vary in size and style: 'Ours, inside the main roof gable on the second floor, had a sitting area and a big brass bed; good modern TV. The decor seemed obsessed with teddy bears.' 'Good breakfasts', served with damask tablecloths, have a cold buffet, 'croissants worth a mention', and a wide choice of cooked dishes using local produce. Evening meals are available only for house parties. *Abbey House* has a comprehensive list of local eating places, but most involve a drive and some may be closed on Sunday and Monday. The village is famed for its swannery (established by monks over 600 years ago), and its subtropical gardens. (*PJK, Richard and Catriona Smith, and others*)

Bedrooms: 5. *Open*: all year, tea room open for lunches Apr–Oct, dinners for house parties only. *Facilities*: reception, lounge, breakfast/tea room, 1½-acre garden (stage for opera), sea 15 mins' walk, unsuitable for &. *Background music*: sometimes. *Location*: village centre. *Smoking*: not allowed. *Children*: not under 12. *Dogs*: not allowed. *Credit cards*: none. *Prices*: b&b £35–£45 per person, New Year package, 1-night bookings sometimes refused.

ALDEBURGH Suffolk   Map 2:C6

The Wentworth   *Tel* 01728-452312
Wentworth Road   *Fax* 01728-454343
Aldeburgh IP15 5BD   *Email* stay@wentworth-aldeburgh.co.uk
                          Website www.wentworth-aldeburgh.com

Michael Pritt is the third generation of his family to run this traditional seaside hotel. It faces fishing huts and boats on Aldeburgh's shingle beach. Visitors in 2008 found it 'clean, comfortable, with good, unfussy food and pleasant service', though one thought it 'a bit strange to be allocated one table throughout the stay'. Another was 'delighted by the relaxed atmosphere'. Sea-facing bedrooms have binoculars: 'Ours was fairly compact, but the comfortable chairs were a boon. Sheets and blankets on bed; stylish modern bathroom.' Second-floor rooms are up a 'steep, narrow' staircase (no lift). The annexe, *Darfield House*, has large rooms and a garden, but no sea view. Each room has a copy of Kathleen Hale's *Orlando the Marmalade Cat* (her 'Owlbarrow' is Aldeburgh). The lounges have 'comfy sofas', log fires, antiques, books, plants, flowers and Russell Flint prints. In the conservatory restaurant, chef Graham Reid serves generous dishes on a daily-changing menu. 'Refreshing to see lamb's liver, rather than the ubiquitous calf's, on offer; profiterole cake the best ever. When mistakes were made, staff seemed genuinely concerned to put things right.' Light lunches and cream teas are served under white parasols on a terrace. Dogs are welcomed. Musicians and actors stay here during the Aldeburgh Festival. (*Sarah Hollowell, Janet Austin*)

Bedrooms: 35, 7 in *Darfield House*, opposite, 5 on ground floor, 1 suitable for ♿. *Open*: all year. *Facilities*: ramps, 2 lounges, bar, restaurant, private dining room, conference room, small sunken terrace, shingle beach 200 yds. *Background music*: none. *Location*: seafront, 5 mins' walk from centre, car park, train Saxmundham 8 miles. *Smoking*: not allowed. *Children*: all ages welcomed. *Dogs*: not allowed in restaurant. *Credit cards*: all major cards. *Prices*: b&b £46.50–£117 per person, d,b&b £56.50–£132, set dinner £19.50, weekend/midweek breaks, Christmas/New Year packages, 1-night bookings refused Sat.

ALSTON Cumbria   Map 4:B3

Lovelady Shield
Nenthead Road
nr Alston CA9 3LF

Tel 01434-381203
Fax 01434-381515
Email enquiries@lovelady.co.uk
Website www.lovelady.co.uk

'A grand old house converted to a small hotel', Peter and Marie Haynes's white-fronted Georgian building has 'a beautiful, secluded position' on the River Nent and 'a pleasing blend of elegance, simplicity and style'. 'Our welcome was warm, the staff were helpful, so was the owner when we saw him,' say visitors this year. Others wrote: 'Up to standard in every department.' The silence is appreciated, both in the wooded grounds and indoors ('blissfully free from muzak'). Guests have the use of a sitting room and a 'cosy library full of books and games for rainy days'. Bedrooms are 'comfortably furnished' (some are small). 'Our bathroom was a squeeze.' Early morning tea is brought to the room (for a charge), or tea-making equipment can be provided. Barrie Garton, the long-serving chef, serves a daily-changing four-course *table d'hôte* menu, 'on a three-day cycle'. 'Good but not great cooking': British dishes with continental influence include twice-baked lobster soufflé; slow-braised haunch and rare roasted loin of venison, prune purée. 'We enjoyed the meals and the wines. Breakfasts were excellent, with lots of choice. The waiting staff were enthusiastic and helpful.' Good walking from the door. (*Clair and David Stevens, and others*)

Bedrooms: 12. *Open*: all year. *Facilities*: 2 lounges, bar, restaurant, conference facilities, civil wedding licence, 3-acre grounds (river, fishing, croquet, woodland walks), unsuitable for &. *Background music*: none. *Location*: 2 miles N of Alston on A689. *Smoking*: not allowed. *Children*: all ages welcomed. *Dogs*: not allowed in public rooms. *Credit cards*: Amex, MasterCard, Visa. *Prices*: b&b £80–£150 per person, d,b&b £100–£170, set dinner £42.50, reductions for 2/3 nights, Christmas/New Year packages. *V*

AMBLESIDE Cumbria   Map 4: inset C2

The Regent by the Lake
Waterhead Bay
Ambleside LA22 0ES

Tel 015394-32254
Fax 015394-31474
Email info@regentlakes.co.uk
Website www.regentlakes.co.uk

'Our over-riding memory is of the warm welcome at reception, breakfast and dinner.' Praise from returning visitors this year to Christine Hewitt's hotel in a 'great location', opposite a slipway on to Lake Windermere (her son Andrew is manager). Other comments: 'Total relaxation guaranteed.' 'Service could not be faulted.' In the split-level restaurant, the daily-changing menus of chef John Mathers are commended: 'Our favourites were vegetarian mushrooms and peppers; pink trout with crayfish tails and lobster sauce; delicious fruit platters.' Breakfast, served until midday, is 'varied and innovative: notable scrambled egg laced with bacon; wide choice of omelettes'. 'By jingo, the kippers were good.' The public rooms have a modern decor of pale browns and cream. Bedrooms come in 'all shapes and sizes'. A courtyard room was 'packed with wonderful features including music centre and DVD-player; its modern bathroom had a spa bath'. These rooms are recommended for children (near the swimming pool), and for dogs: both are welcomed ('special requests and diets no problem'). Being 'a family of keen motorcyclists', the Hewitts welcome motorcycling guests (secure garaging). (*Frank G Millen, Carol Pendlebury, Gwyn Morgan*)

Bedrooms: 30, 10 in courtyard, 5 in garden, 7 on ground floor. *Open*: all year, except 19–27 Dec. *Facilities*: ramp, lounge, sun lounge, bar, restaurant, 17-metre indoor swimming pool, courtyard, ¼-acre garden, on Lake Windermere (sailing, waterskiing, fishing). *Background music*: in public rooms in evening. *Location*: on A591, S of centre, at Waterhead Bay, train Windermere 5 miles. *Smoking*: not allowed. *Children*: all ages welcomed. *Dogs*: not allowed in public rooms. *Credit cards*: MasterCard, Visa. *Prices*: [2008] b&b £42.50–£95 per person, d,b&b £50–£110, New Year package, 1-night bookings refused weekends. *V*

Rothay Manor
Rothay Bridge
Ambleside LA22 0EH

Tel 015394-33605
Fax 015394-33607
Email hotel@rothaymanor.co.uk
Website www.rothaymanor.co.uk

♛ *César award in 1992*

'Always welcoming and comfortable', this white Regency house near the head of Lake Windermere has been run by the Nixon family for over 40 years. Stephen and Colette Nixon retired in 2008 but his brother Nigel remains at the helm; Peter Sinclair has been appointed to a new position of manager. Returning visitors found 'high standards maintained'. Other comments: 'Real country house style without pretension.' 'We cannot fault the professional yet relaxed service.' 'No canned music anywhere, thank goodness.' 'Well-furnished' bedrooms (many are large) have 'proper coat-hangers'. Quietest rooms face the 'well-laid-out' garden ('ours was bright and sunny'); four are in an annexe joined to the main building by a covered walkway. 'Sitting in the sun on our balcony was idyllic.' One couple would have liked 'more pictures on the walls'. Children are welcomed (family rooms, special menus, cots, etc). Chef Jane Binns provides a daily-changing traditional British/French menu: 'Particularly good, with imaginative choices.' It might include Cartmel valley oak-smoked salmon; Holker Hall wild mallard braised with damson gin. Breakfasts have freshly squeezed orange juice, 'eggs perfectly cooked', 'very good toast and marmalade'. From the garden you can walk across fields to the lake. (*Brenda and Bob Halstead, Stephen and Pauline Glover, Jill and Mike Bennett, and others*)

Bedrooms: 19, 2 in annexe, 2 suitable for &. *Open*: all year except 4–22 Jan. *Facilities*: ramp, 2 lounges, bar, 2 dining rooms, meeting/conference facilities, 1-acre garden (croquet), free access to local leisure centre. *Background music*: none. *Location*: ¼ mile SW of Ambleside. *Smoking*: not allowed. *Children*: all ages welcomed. *Dogs*: not allowed. *Credit cards*: all major cards. *Prices*: [2008] b&b £70–£175 per person, set menus £19–£45, special breaks (winter, bridge, walking, etc), Christmas/New Year packages, 1-night bookings refused Sat.

AMPLEFORTH North Yorkshire   Map 4:D4

Shallowdale House   *Tel* 01439-788325
West End, Ampleforth   *Fax* 01439-788885
nr York, YO62 4DY   *Email* stay@shallowdalehouse.co.uk
                           Website www.shallowdalehouse.co.uk

Ω *César award in 2005*

'Remains a haven of civilisation.' At their small guest house on a sheltered south-facing slope of the Hambleton hills, Phillip Gill and Anton van der Horst 'welcome you like family'. 'They greeted us as we got out of the car and insisted on carrying our luggage,' one couple wrote. 'Immaculate housekeeping, lovely food,' is another comment this year. The architect-designed building (1963) has panoramic views of the surrounding countryside on the edge of the North York Moors national park. Complimentary afternoon tea with home-made biscuits is served in the ground-floor drawing room, which has an open fire in winter. Two bedrooms are large; the third, slightly smaller, has a private bathroom across a corridor. 'Everything was provided in our spacious room including bathrobes and newspapers.' Bathrooms are 'smart and well stocked'; beds are turned down during dinner. A four-course set meal is served by arrangement (48 hours' notice) at separate candlelit tables; the cooking is 'domestic eclectic', perhaps fennel and potato pancakes with smoked salmon; slow-roasted cushion of lamb. The menu is 'always imaginative, well cooked and presented'. Wine by the glass is 'well chosen'. Breakfast includes dry-cured bacon, Whitby kippers, home-made preserves. (*Andrew Warren, Gordon Franklin, Elizabeth Brice, Christine Moore, Richard Creed*)

Bedrooms: 3. *Open*: all year except Christmas/New Year, occasionally at other times. *Facilities*: drawing room, sitting room, dining room, 2½-acre grounds, unsuitable for &. *Background music*: none. *Location*: edge of village. *Smoking*: not allowed. *Children*: not under 12. *Dogs*: not allowed. *Credit cards*: MasterCard, Visa. *Prices*: b&b £47.50–£85 per person, d,b&b £80–£120, set dinner £35, 1-night bookings often refused weekend.

ARUNDEL West Sussex   Map 2:E3

Arundel House
11 High Street
Arundel BN18 9AD

Tel 01903-882136
Fax 01903-881179
Email mail@arundelhouseonline.co.uk
Website www.arundelhouseonline.com

Opposite the castle, at the foot of the steep High Street of this attractive town, this bow-windowed 19th-century merchant's house has been turned into a 'comfortable' restaurant-with-rooms by Luke Hackman (the chef) and Billy Lewis-Bowker. 'An amazing find,' wrote one reader, 'the food is extraordinary.' The 'pleasing' decor is by Mr Lewis-Bowker's wife, Emma, whose paintings hang throughout. Meals are served in two 'attractive' rooms, one on each side of the entrance hall. 'Wild, local and seasonal' ingredients are used in the 'British-led, modern cuisine', eg, smoked haddock brandade with Melba toast; breast and braised leg of Barbary duck. Dessert lovers find it difficult to resist the 'Arundel House Assiette', miniatures of five desserts for two people to share. On Tuesday evenings guests may bring their own wine, no corkage charge. No residents' lounge; bedrooms have flat-screen TV, free wireless Internet access and power shower. There is a choice between duvet and blankets (best specify when you book). 'Our room was well appointed, with all the latest fads in the bathroom.' The house is on a short one-way system: no car park, but you can draw up outside to unload, and vouchers are given for the large, safe municipal car park close by. (*PA, MH, and others*)

Bedrooms: 5. *Open*: all year except 24–26 Dec, 2 weeks early April, 2 weeks end Oct, restaurant closed Sun except bank holidays. *Facilities*: restaurant, unsuitable for &. *Background music*: in restaurant. *Location*: town centre. *Smoking*: not allowed. *Children*: not under 16. *Dogs*: only assistance dogs allowed. *Credit cards*: Amex, MasterCard, Visa. *Prices*: b&b £60–£100 per person, set dinner £16–£28, 1-night bookings refused Sat. *V*

The Town House
65 High Street
Arundel BN18 9AJ

Tel 01903-883847
Email enquiries@thetownhouse.co.uk
Website www.thetownhouse.co.uk

Opposite Arundel castle, at the top of the steep High Street, Lee Williams and his wife, Katie, manage their restaurant-with-rooms in a Grade II listed Regency building. 'We aim to attract a relaxed clientele,' they say, 'where children are welcome and stuffiness is taboo.' The dining room has an 'amazing' 16th-century carved Florentine ceiling, acquired in Italy by Lord Maltravers, son of an earl of Arundel (he once lived here). Typical dishes: tiger prawn and langoustine risotto; roasted fillet of wild boar with braised oxtail. Bread is home baked. The suite has a four-poster bed and a private balcony facing the castle; Rosemary, on the second floor, is decorated in beige and white; it has a short lobby and an 'amazing amount of original intricate plasterwork and furniture mouldings; plenty of storage; house-keeping faultless'. Breakfast is continental or 'full English with additions'. 'Excellent scrambled eggs and smoked salmon.' No lounge or grounds, so probably best for a short stay. On Sunday, when the restaurant is closed, guests are asked to check in before 1 o'clock (they are then given a key). More reports, please.

Bedrooms: 4. *Open*: all year except 25 Dec, 2 weeks Jan, 2 weeks Oct, restaurant closed Sun/Mon. *Facilities*: restaurant unsuitable for &. *Background music*: in restaurant. *Location*: top end of High Street. *Smoking*: not allowed. *Children*: all ages welcomed. *Dogs*: not allowed. *Credit cards*: all major cards. *Prices*: [2008] b&b £42.50–£85 per person, d,b&b (midweek) £60–£75, set dinner £28.50, 1-night bookings refused weekends in high season. *V*

ASHBOURNE Derbyshire   Map 3:B6

Callow Hall
Mappleton
Ashbourne DE6 2AA

Tel 01335-300900
Fax 01335-300512
Email enquiries@callowhall.co.uk
Website www.callowhall.co.uk

Owned by the Spencer family (David, Dorothy, Anthony and Emma), this Grade II listed Victorian house with tall chimneys stands in large grounds which overlook the Bentley Brook and the valley of the River Dove. The Peak District national park is nearby. The Spencers, admired for their 'warmth and professionalism', tell us they have completed their programme of bedroom refurbishment, includ-ing the installation of flat-screen TVs and a broadband connection in the building. The 'lovely old house' has 'beautifully furnished' public rooms; there are rugs on polished floors, stags' heads, large flower arrangements. Mrs Spencer and her daughter run front-of-house; son Anthony and his father are in the kitchen. Butchery, curing and baking are done on site; salmon and bacon are home smoked. In the candlelit, red-walled restaurant, a five-course dinner menu, with extensive choice, changes daily (main courses like fillet of beef baked en croûte, with mushrooms and baby spinach). The bedrooms vary greatly: elderly visitors were pleased with their 'excellent ground-floor room with walk-in shower'; a ground-floor suite near the kitch-ens was less liked. Children are welcomed. (*Anne Laurence, and others*)

Bedrooms: 16, 2 on ground floor, 1 suitable for ⅎ. *Open*: all year except 25/26 Dec, restaurant closed for lunch except Sun. *Facilities*: lounge, bar, 3 dining rooms, function/conference facilities, 42-acre grounds (walled garden, woodland, farm, stables, river, fishing). *Background music*: none. *Location*: ¾ mile from Ashbourne. *Smoking*: not allowed. *Children*: all ages welcomed. *Dogs*: by prior arrangement, not allowed in public rooms. *Credit cards*: all major cards. *Prices*: [2008] b&b £75–£155 per person, set dinner £42, full alc £42, weekend/midweek breaks. *V*

ASHWATER Devon   Map 1:C3

Blagdon Manor   *Tel* 01409-211224
Ashwater EX21 5DF   *Fax* 01409-211634
                                     Email stay@blagdon.com
                                     Website www.blagdon.com

🏵 *César award in 2006*

'A highlight of my two-month sabbatical. Our three days here were a joy.' A fellow *Guide* hotelier praises Liz and Steve Morey's rambling, 17th-century manor house (Grade II listed) which looks across rolling countryside towards Dartmoor. 'While *Blagdon* may be furnished traditionally, it is run in a friendly, easy manner, but with the highest standards in all respects.' Many original features of the building are retained (oak beams, slate flagstones, etc). 'Spotless' bedrooms vary in size and style: garden-facing ones have the best views. 'Our very comfortable room had some surprises – a box of home-made chocolates, complimentary sherry.' Fresh flowers and open fires are in the bar and lounge. Books, ornaments and striped fabrics abound. In the bright dining room, Steve Morey's 'imaginative dishes were a real experience. Pan-fried John Dory with green herb risotto, tomatoes, olives and capers was an incredible combination. With so many hotels treating breakfast with disdain it was good to sit back and savour the pleasures here.' This year a Cornish slate terrace has been added outside the conservatory, to enable summer wining and dining. The Moreys have two 'gorgeous' chocolate Labradors, Nutmeg and Cassia, and a cat. Guests' dogs 'are positively welcomed'. (*Alastair Kameen, Steven Hur*)

Bedrooms: 8. *Open*: all year except 31 Dec–2 Jan, 2 weeks Jan, 2 weeks Oct. *Facilities*: ramps, lounge, library, bar, conservatory, restaurant, private dining room, 20-acre grounds (3-acre gardens, croquet, giant chess, gazebo, pond), unsuitable for ⅎ. *Background music*: none. *Location*: 8 miles NE of Launceston. *Smoking*: not allowed. *Children*: not under 12. *Dogs*: not allowed in restaurant, conservatory. *Credit cards*: MasterCard, Visa. *Prices*: b&b £67.50–£90 per person, set lunch £20, dinner £35, 1-night bookings refused at Christmas. *V*

ATCHAM Shropshire   Map 3:B5

The Mytton & Mermaid Hotel
Atcham, nr Shrewsbury
SY5 6QG

Tel 01743-761220
Fax 01743-761292
Email info@myttonandmermaid.co.uk
Website www.myttonandmermaid.co.uk

'Lovely setting. Good value. Comfortable room. Good food. A gem.'
Enthusiasm in 2008 for Ann and Danny Ditella's small hotel named
after Jack Mytton, an eccentric local squire who ended up in a debt-
ors' prison. Other visitors wrote of 'friendly, polite service'. With the
17th-century church of St Eata behind and Attingham Park (National
Trust) opposite, the early 18th-century Grade II listed building
stands by the River Severn. An earlier owner was the architect Sir
Clough Williams-Ellis of *Portmeirion* fame. The best bedrooms are in
the main house (the Mytton suite has a four-poster bed and bay
windows). 'Our large superior room had fab views.' Ground-floor
courtyard bedrooms are suitable for people with limited mobility.
Afternoon tea is served in the lounge, which faces garden and river;
decor is a blend of modern and traditional. The 'lively' bar (open all
day) has log fire and sofas. It serves meals, and holds a jazz evening
every Sunday. In the candlelit restaurant, with antique oak tables and
fresh flowers, chef Adrian Badland cooks in modern British style (eg,
risotto of crab and clams; roast lamb with garlic and cumin crust).
There are menus for vegetarians and for children. (*David Sefton*)

Bedrooms: 18, 6 on ground floor in courtyard, also 4-bedroom cottage. *Open*:
all year except 25 Dec. *Facilities*: ramps, drawing room with TV, *Mad Jack's
Bar*, restaurant, civil wedding licence, 1-acre garden on River Severn
(fishing rights), unsuitable for &. *Background music*: 'quiet jazz' in bar.
Location: 3 miles SE of Shrewsbury. *Smoking*: not allowed. *Children*: all ages
welcomed. *Dogs*: allowed in some bedrooms, not in public rooms. *Credit
cards*: all major cards. *Prices*: b&b £55–£90 per person, set meal £28.50, full
alc £42, New Year package.

****

Traveller's tale *Hotel in Sussex* The breakfasts were the
worst we have tasted for many years: sausages underdone,
fried bread and fried egg were charred, everything was
greasy beyond belief. The manager spent most of his time
flapping around and complaining that he had to do
everything, but in fact he seemed to do very little: think
Basil in *Fawlty Towers*. The receptionist doubled as
breakfast waitress and was fairly clueless.

****

AUSTWICK North Yorkshire   Map 4:D3

The Austwick Traddock

Austwick, via Lancaster
LA2 8BY

Tel 01524-251224
Fax 01524-251796
Email info@austwicktraddock.co.uk
Website www.austwicktraddock.co.uk

Two generations of one family now run this small hotel, a substantial
Georgian house in a peaceful village in the Yorkshire Dales national
park. Bruce and Jane Reynolds have been joined by their son, Paul,
and his wife, Jenny, who are joint managers. They have taken the
hotel off the market and are continuing with 'rolling redecoration'.
Visitors this year praised the 'homely' welcome: 'Our spirits were
lifted on a dull day by the warm and well-lit entrance hall/sitting room
with its blazing fire.' The bedrooms are 'comfortably furnished in
restrained country style' (patterned wallpaper, plain fitted carpets,
'fine country antiques'; also sherry, magazines, fresh milk, home-
made biscuits). 'Ours had pleasantly faded elegance, comfort married
to good taste. The staff were efficient, with a gentle, mainly East
European smile; a receptionist drew on her local knowledge to give
us useful information.' A new chef was being appointed as we went to
press; we would welcome reports on the cooking. The kitchen is
certified as 100% organic by the Soil Association. 'This was evident in
the wide and lavish choice for breakfast' (porridge, eggs Benedict,
kippers and much else). Good walking from the door. (*David Nicholls,
and others*)

Bedrooms: 10. *Open*: all year. *Facilities*: large lounge, front lounge, bar, dining
room, breakfast room, function facilities, 1-acre grounds (sun deck), only
public rooms accessible to &. *Background music*: 'if needed' in lounge and
dining room. *Location*: 4 miles NW of Settle, train Settle, bus. *Smoking*: not
allowed. *Children*: all ages welcomed. *Dogs*: not allowed in public rooms. *Credit
cards*: MasterCard, Visa. *Prices*: [2008] b&b £70–£95 per person, d,b&b
£85–£105, full alc £46, Christmas/New Year packages, 1-night bookings
refused weekends in season. *V*

Readers' contributions, written on the forms at the back of the
book or sent by email, are the lifeblood of the *Good Hotel Guide*.
Our readers play a crucial role by reporting on existing entries
as well as recommending new discoveries. Everyone who
writes to the *Guide* is a potential winner of the Report of the
Year competition (page 63), in which a dozen correspondents
each year win a copy of the *Guide* and an invitation to our
annual launch party in October.

AYLESBURY Buckinghamshire   Map 2:C3

Hartwell House
Oxford Road
nr Aylesbury HP17 8NR

Tel 01296-747444
Fax 01296-747450
Email info@hartwell-house.com
Website www.hartwell-house.com

🦢 *César award in 1997*

'A perfect blend of the 18th and 21st centuries', this stately home is run as a luxury hotel by Richard Broyd's Historic House Hotels (see also *Middlethorpe Hall*, York, *Bodysgallen Hall*, Llandudno). It is 'beautifully restored, full of antiques, yet with all mod cons'; 'unobtrusive' air conditioning has been fitted to many rooms this year, and all have been given a flat-screen TV. Other comments: 'Very enjoyable; tremendous architecture, comfortable, friendly, good food.' 'A visit is refreshing and restorative.' The long-serving manager, Jonathan Thompson, 'keeps an eagle eye on everything; his staff are unfailingly polite, helpful'. The four 'elegant' drawing rooms are furnished with 'priceless antiques, there to be used, not just admired'. Bedrooms in the main house vary (some are large and grand). Those in a 'sensitively' converted stable block are 'attractively decorated' (some are split-level). The dress code for dinner (served by candlelight with silver and damask) is smart casual (jacket and tie not obligatory). Chef Daniel Richardson's 'excellent' cooking 'was discreetly adapted for my special dietary requirements'. A new café and bar was due to replace the spa buttery in September 2008. (*Jane and Martin Bailey, Richard Mayou, C and MD*)

Bedrooms: 46, 16 in stable block, some on ground floor, 2 suitable for &. *Open*: all year. *Facilities*: lift, ramp, 4 drawing rooms, bar, 3 dining rooms, pianist in vestibule Fri/Sat evening, conference facilities, civil wedding licence, spa (18-metre swimming pool, whirlpool, sauna, beauty salon, café/bar), 90-acre grounds (tennis, croquet, lake fishing), jogging track, woodlands). *Background music*: none. *Location*: 2 miles W of Aylesbury. *Smoking*: not allowed. *Children*: not under 6. *Dogs*: allowed in ground-floor suites and *Hartwell Court*. *Credit cards*: Amex, MasterCard, Visa. *Prices*: [2008] b&b £130–£180 per person, cooked breakfast £7, set dinner £38, special breaks, Christmas/New Year packages. *V* (Sun–Thurs)

If you dislike piped music, why not join Pipedown, the campaign for freedom from piped music? It is at 1 The Row, Berwick St James, Salisbury SP3 4TP. *Tel* 01722-690622, www.pipedown.info.

BAMBURGH Northumberland   Map 4:A3

The Victoria Hotel   *Tel* 01668-214431
Bamburgh NE69 7BP   *Fax* 01668-214404
Email enquiries@thevictoriahotelbamburgh.co.uk
Website www.thevictoriahotelbamburgh.co.uk

In a 'scenically superb area', this 'good-value' hotel stands opposite
the green of this village (known for its magnificent castle) on the
North Sea coast facing Farne Island. Fronted by potted plants and a
coat of arms, it is managed by Graham Young. It is 'strongly recommended' for its 'pleasant and helpful' staff, and 'excellent' food. In
the smart brasserie, with its glass-domed ceiling, 'pheasant, game pie,
rack of lamb were all good; very good budget wines'. Other dishes
include smoked haddock and salmon fish stew; chicken breast stuffed
with basil and mozzarella. The bar area has mirrors, pictures, board
games, and an extensive menu (eg, baguettes; steak with chips;
pasta). It also serves afternoon teas. 'Our room was comfortable, if
small; good bathroom facilities.' Another guest had a 'large, well-
appointed bedroom, with two armchairs, sofa, desk, etc, large bathroom'. Eight bedrooms are new this year (three face the castle).
Young children and babies are welcomed (family accommodation and
special menus). 'Generous breakfast.' (*Andrew Hillier, and others*)

Bedrooms: 37, some on ground floor. *Open*: all year except 10 days Jan. *Facilities*:
ramp, 2 lounges, bar area, brasserie, conference facilities, civil wedding
licence. *Background music*: in bar. *Location*: village centre. *Smoking*: not allowed.
Children: all ages welcomed (under-5s stay free in parents' room). *Dogs*: allowed
by arrangement. *Credit cards*: all major cards. *Prices*: b&b £40–£90 per
person, d,b&b £70–£120, full alc £35, group rates, Christmas/New Year
packages. **V***

BARNARD CASTLE Co. Durham   Map 4:C3

Homelands Guest House   *Tel* 01833-638757
85 Galgate   *Email* enquiries@homelandsguesthouse.co.uk
Barnard Castle DL12 8ES *Website* www.homelandsguesthouse.co.uk

'Impeccable. The hostess is so sweet, helpful and welcoming, and
great with food.' A warm endorsement this year for Irene Williamson.
She wins many friends for her B&B in a spacious Victorian town
house in a residential area of this historic Teesdale market town. It
stands on a road that is busy by day but quiet at night (windows are
double glazed). The quietest bedroom, in the 'exquisitely tended'

garden, is 'blissful'. Some rooms are 'compact', with a small shower room. 'After a 300-mile journey followed by 18 holes of golf, we were shattered. Mrs Williamson settled us in our bedroom with cheese and biscuits and a large glass of wine each' (the premises are licensed). The 'delicious' breakfast, served in a 'spotless' room, has cereals, fruit, etc, from a buffet; and 'a large choice of well-cooked dishes' including 'brilliant bacon, herby sausages, fresh mushrooms and black pudding from Stornaway'. No evening meals, but advice is offered on local restaurants. (*Myrtle Allen, Ann Duncan*)

Bedrooms: 5, 1 in garden. *Open*: all year except 24 Dec–1 Jan. *Facilities*: lounge, breakfast room, small garden, unsuitable for &. *Background music*: 'easy listening' in breakfast room. *Location*: town centre. *Smoking*: not allowed. *Children*: not under 7. *Dogs*: not allowed. *Credit cards*: MasterCard, Visa. *Prices*: b&b £32.50–£50 per person, 1-night bookings refused bank holidays.

BARNSLEY Gloucestershire   Map 3:E6

Barnsley House   NEW   *Tel* 01285-740000
Barnsley, nr Cirencester   *Fax* 01285-740925
GL7 5EE   *Email* info@barnsleyhouse.com
                               Website www.barnsleyhouse.com

'A beautiful house in the illustrious gardens created by the late Rosemary Verey in the 1950s and 1960s, propelled into the 21st century by owners Tim Haigh and Rupert Pendered.' It has a contemporary interior, with high-tech gadgets in the bedrooms (also a fridge containing complimentary champagne, orange juice, water, chocolates). It is 'a haven of relaxation and pure delight', say visitors this year. 'Staff were most welcoming. Our beautiful stable yard suite had six-foot bed, plasma-screen TV and lounge area.' There is a 'minimalist modern chrome and perspex' decor in public areas, and a red 1970s-style bar. One suite has a terrace and grotto with waterfall, another a glittering disco ball and a spa bath; some rooms have two freestanding baths, side by side. Chef Graham Grafton serves modern European cooking with an Italian influence. 'Dinner was excellent: starter of fresh langoustines; local rib-eye of beef with roast beetroot and lentils. Breakfast had home-made yogurt; stewed rhubarb from the garden.' There is a 'stunning' new spa in a sunken garden. Visitors include film stars and other glitterati, who appreciate the discreet style and secluded setting. The 17th-century *Village Pub* opposite, under the same ownership, has seven 'rustic bedrooms' (from £95), and is recommended for its food. (*Liz and Phil Donnelly*)

Bedrooms: 18, 12 in stables, etc, 1 with ramp on ground floor. *Open*: all year. *Facilities*: sitting room, bar, restaurant, cinema, meeting room, civil wedding licence, 11-acre garden (spa with hydrotherapy pool). *Background music*: pop and jazz. *Location*: 5 miles NE of Cirencester. *Smoking:*: not allowed. *Children*: all ages welcomed. *Dogs*: allowed in 2 bedrooms only, not in public rooms. *Credit cards*: Diners, MasterCard, Visa. *Prices*: b&b double £295–£390, English breakfast £12, set dinner £39.50 (*excluding 12½% service charge*), Christmas/New Year packages, 1-night bookings generally refused weekends. ***V*** (Sun–Thurs)

BARWICK Somerset   Map 1:C6

Little Barwick House   *Tel* 01935-423902
Barwick, nr Yeovil   *Fax* 01935-420908
BA22 9TD   *Email* reservations@barwick7.fsnet.co.uk
                                  Website www.littlebarwickhouse.co.uk

❧ *César award in 2002*

In lovely countryside near the Somerset/Dorset border, this Georgian dower house is a restaurant-with-rooms run by its owners, Tim and Emma Ford. She is 'a gem', say fans, a 'welcoming front-of-house'; his 'excellent' cooking has long won praise from readers. The large, airy dining room (with conservatory extension) was re-decorated in early 2008; tables now have a full-length skirt topped with a white linen tablecloth, and a hessian-style wool carpet has been laid. 'Delightful modern English dishes using locally sourced ingredients' are served on a short menu with daily changes, perhaps Lyme Bay scallops, crispy bacon and truffle oil; rump of lamb, aubergine caviar. 'The staff are lovely', service is 'well organised'. Bedrooms vary in size (some are small). 'Our large room had king-size bed, turned down during dinner; functional bathroom with good power shower.' 'Our high-ceilinged room was tastefully decorated; we liked the fresh milk and home-made shortbread.' Housekeeping is 'excellent'. Breakfast, 'stylishly arranged', has fresh juices, fruit compote, 'melt-in-the-mouth croissants'. Visitors are welcomed with complimentary tea and 'fabulous' fruitcake. 'What impressed us most was the absolute quiet.' 'As good as ever.' 'Our eighth visit, it feels like a home from home.' (*Bryan and Mary Blaxall, Jennifer Davis, and others*)

Bedrooms: 6. *Open*: all year except Christmas, 2 weeks Jan, restaurant closed Sun evenings, midday on Mon and Tues. *Facilities*: ramp, 2 lounges, restaur-ant, conservatory, 3½-acre garden (terrace, paddock), unsuitable for &. *Background music*: none. *Location*: ¼ mile outside Yeovil. *Smoking*: not allowed. *Children*: not under 5. *Dogs*: not allowed in public rooms. *Credit cards*: MasterCard, Visa. *Prices*: [2008] b&b £69–£126 per person, d,b&b £100–£162.95, set dinner £36.95, 2-night breaks, 1-night bookings sometimes refused.

BASLOW Derbyshire   Map 3:A6

The Cavendish	*Tel* 01246-582311
Church Lane	*Fax* 01246-582312
Baslow DE45 1SP	*Email* info@cavendish-hotel.net
	Website www.cavendish-hotel.net

꙳ *César award in 2002*

'Staff are great [most are local]; service good as the food.' Praise again for Eric Marsh's 'remarkable' hotel on the edge of the Chatsworth estate. Another comment: 'The receptionists are the nicest we know in any hotel.' Also valued: help with luggage on arrival, and a telephone call to the bedroom after half an hour 'to ensure everything is in order'. The hotel stands on a busy road, but the bedrooms are at the back, and quiet at night. 'Ours had two large windows facing Chatsworth park, large, comfortable bed, very good bathroom and shower.' Chris Allison's modern cooking has 'lifted a notch; more global influences'. Meals can be 'nearly formal' in the *Gallery* restaurant ('pressed ham hock and foie gras terrine was a delicious concoction'). The 'more casual' *Garden Room* now has a 'more sophisticated' menu. Breakfast, served until midday and not included in the room price, is 'excellent'. Mr Marsh's lease with the Chatsworth estate has expired, but he continues to run *The Cavendish* on a management contract; its 'exceptionally helpful' general manager, Philip Joseph, also manages Mr Marsh's other hotel, *The George*, in nearby Hathersage (*qv*). (*Gill Holden, Padi Howard, John and Annette Linton*)

Bedrooms: 24, 2 on ground floor. *Open*: all year, restaurant closed to non-residents 25 Dec. *Facilities*: lounge, bar, 2 restaurants, 2 private dining rooms, ½-acre grounds (putting), river fishing nearby, unsuitable for &. *Background music*: classical CDs in *Gallery*. *Location*: on A619, in Chatsworth grounds. *Smoking*: not allowed. *Children*: all ages welcomed. *Dogs*: not allowed. *Credit cards*: all major cards. *Prices*: [2008] room £121–£230, breakfast alc £14.95–£22, set menus £38.50 (5% '*service levy*' *added to all accounts*), midweek breaks, 1-night bookings sometimes refused weekends. *V*

Prices may change – always check them when booking.

Fischer's Baslow Hall

Calver Road
Baslow DE45 1RR

Tel 01246-583259
Fax 01246-583818
Email reservations@fischers-baslowhall.co.uk
Website www.fischers-baslowhall.co.uk

♕ *César award in 1998*

Built in 1907 in the style of a 17th-century Derbyshire manor house (wood panelling, beams, leaded casements), Max and Susan Fischer's restaurant-with-rooms near the Chatsworth estate is 'highly recommended' again this year. 'He is a cheerful soul, very much a hands-on owner/chef. Food, accommodation and efficiency of the staff are truly exceptional.' Residents must book for the elegant dining room where 'smart casual' dress is required. Mr Fischer and Rupert Rowley, the head chef, have a *Michelin* star for dishes like ravioli of English lobster and Scottish salmon; roast saddle of wild venison. There is a standard dinner menu, a three-course *menu du jour*, and a 'Prestige' tasting menu (served to a whole table). 'Max was very understanding when we found the food too rich: he allowed us to create our own menu.' 'Service is correct but friendly.' The absence of background music is much appreciated. The garden rooms are 'the best', 'no frills but plenty of space and a good bathroom'. Breakfast has freshly squeezed juice, a wide range of teas, and 'good fruit salad' (cooked dishes cost extra). The gastropub, *Rowley's Restaurant & Bar*, down the road, is under the same ownership. (*Robert Wardell, Anne and Denis Tate*)

Bedrooms: 11, 5 in *Garden House*. *Open*: all year except 25/26 and 31 Dec, 1 Jan, restaurant closed Mon lunch. *Facilities*: lounge/bar, breakfast room, 3 dining rooms, function facilities, civil wedding licence, 5-acre grounds, unsuitable for ⅍. *Background music*: none. *Location*: edge of village. *Smoking*: not allowed. *Children*: no under-12s in restaurant after 7 pm. *Dogs*: not allowed. *Credit cards*: Amex, MasterCard, Visa. *Prices*: [2008] b&b £70–£140 per person, set dinner £45–£75, 1-night bookings refused at weekends in season.

BASSENTHWAITE LAKE   Map 4: inset C2
Cumbria

The Pheasant   **NEW**

Bassenthwaite Lake
nr Cockermouth
CA13 9YE

Tel 017687-76234
Fax 017687-76002
Email info@the-pheasant.co.uk
Website www.the-pheasant.co.uk

A 'pleasant', long, low, L-shaped 400-year-old inn behind a beech hedge. It stands amid woodland in an unspoilt northern part of the Lake District. Matthew Wylie has long been the 'extremely good' manager for the trustees of the Inglewood estate. 'It remains our favourite Lakeland hotel,' one visitor writes. 'It exudes warmth, comfort and an air of confidence.' Oak beams and open log fires have been preserved. There are antiques, old prints and paintings, and a 'most attractive' oak-panelled bar. The lounges, where afternoon teas are served, have parquet flooring and potted plants. 'No background music, to our delight.' Most bedrooms are 'large and comfortable', though two above the kitchen hear the early morning refuse collection. 'Ours had a roomy, quite modern bathroom. Good to excellent food, welcoming service.' Chef Malcolm Ennis serves modern dishes in the beamed dining room, eg, calf's liver with butternut squash, Parma ham, red onion marmalade. 'On a recent visit we were well pleased with the quality.' Four courses; the menu changes daily. The wine list, though not vast, is 'well thought out', and has good choice by the glass. Lighter meals are served in the lounges and bar. Good walking in all directions. (*Robert Cooper, A and P Goda*)

Bedrooms: 15, 2 on ground floor in lodge. *Open*: all year except 25 Dec. *Facilities*: 3 lounges, bar, dining room, 10-acre grounds, lake 200 yds (fishing), unsuitable for &. *Background music*: none. *Location*: 5 miles E of Cockermouth, ¼ mile off A66 to Keswick. *Smoking*: not allowed. *Children*: not under 8. *Dogs*: allowed in lodge bedrooms and public rooms. *Credit cards*: MasterCard, Visa. *Prices*: b&b £73–£100 per person, d,b&b £100–£130, set dinner £33.95–£37.50, New Year package, 1-night bookings refused Fri and Sat.

BATH Somerset   Map 2:D1

Apsley House
141 Newbridge Hill
Bath BA1 3PT

Tel 01225-336966
Fax 01225-425462
Email info@apsley-house.co.uk
Website www.apsley-house.co.uk

'Charming, elegant, airy, with the luxurious feel of a hotel', this Georgian guest house is five minutes' drive from the city centre. Built by the Duke of Wellington in 1830 for his mistress, it is furnished with fine antiques and paintings. Its owners, Nicholas and Claire Potts, have been joined by managers Duncan and Anél Neville, 'smart, friendly, welcoming'. The 'delightful' lounge has 'a log fire that is hard to resist', a piano that guests may play, and an honesty bar. 'Each bedroom is sumptuous in its own way. Our attic room, with richly coloured decor and spacious bathroom, was a gem, peaceful and quiet.' Two rooms can be a family suite. On the ground floor, a four-poster room with walk-in shower is suitable for visitors with limited

mobility. A refurbished basement room (with window
has a new limestone bathroom. A coach house has been tui
an apartment for families. Breakfast has fresh fruit, marmalade in a
and 'Duncan's cooked feasts' (eg, pancakes with maple syrup). Soup
and sandwiches can be provided, and a light supper is available by
arrangement during the week in the quieter months. (*Anna
Wormleighton and Bill Brewer, D and PK*)

Bedrooms: 12, 1 on ground floor. *Open*: all year except 3 days over Christmas.
Facilities: drawing room, bar, dining room, ⅓-acre garden. *Background music*:
Classic FM in public rooms. *Location*: 1¼ miles W of city centre. *Smoking*: not
allowed. *Children*: all ages welcomed (under-2s free). *Dogs*: only guide dogs
allowed. *Credit cards*: Amex, MasterCard, Visa. *Prices*: [2008] b&b £35–£140
per person, 1-night bookings refused Sat and bank holidays. *V*

The Bath Priory

Weston Road
Bath BA1 2XT

Tel 01225-331922
Fax 01225-448276
Email mail@thebathpriory.co.uk
Website www.thebathpriory.co.uk

Built as a private residence in 1835, this listed mansion, owned by
Andrew and Christine Brownsword, is now a luxurious 'hotel, restaurant and spa' in 'super' landscaped gardens. Its staff are 'formal but
helpful'; the atmosphere is 'quiet, people speaking in hushed tones
as though in a church'; the lack of muzak is 'a bonus'. A collection of
early 20th-century and contemporary paintings hangs throughout.
The main lounge is 'a superb example of Victorian opulence: plush
sofas, pot-pourri, gently ticking grandfather clock'. Bedrooms vary in
size; 'premier deluxe' ones are 'seriously comfortable'; all have
antiques and the latest technology, but some hear traffic. 'Ours,
Begonia, had everything one could wish for, especially the garden
view.' Children are welcomed and might find a basket of toys in their
room, but under-8s may not join their parents in the restaurant in the
evening. The chef, Chris Horridge, has a *Michelin* star for his modern
British cooking served in two dining rooms (one 'romantic', the other
'more modern'). 'Delicious, imaginative, inventive; portions just the
right size,' said a visitor this year. Breakfast, however, was thought
'mediocre'. The city centre is reached by a short walk through Royal
Victoria Park. *Gidleigh Park*, Chagford (*qv*), is under the same ownership. (*Gilbert Hall, Sarah Curtis, and others*)

Bedrooms: 27, 3 on ground floor. *Open*: all year. *Facilities*: ramps, library, drawing
room, 2 dining rooms, private dining rooms, wine room, conference facilities,
civil wedding licence, spa (indoor heated swimming pool (10 by 5 metres),

.s), 4-acre grounds (heated outdoor pool (12 by
und music: none. *Location*: 1½ miles W of centre.
lren: no under-8s in restaurant at night. *Dogs*: only
it cards: all major cards. *Prices*: [2008] b&b £107.50–
...er £55, special breaks, Christmas/New Year packages,
...ed weekends.

Number

30 Crescent Gardens
Bath BA1 2NB

Tel/Fax 01225-337393
Email david.greenwood12@btinternet.com
Website www.numberthirty.com

'Spotless and comfortable', this airy B&B is a short walk from the historic centre; the on-site parking is a bonus. The owners, David and Caroline Greenwood, 'went out of their way to help and advise us', one couple wrote. They have renovated the house in pastel colours (much blue and white). 'Our bedroom had crisp cotton sheets, blankets (we hate duvets but they are also available), flat-screen TV, CD-player, free Wi-Fi connection, natural toiletries from New Zealand.' Bathrooms are 'impeccable' though one visitor found towels 'slightly abrasive'. Three rooms have facilities *en suite*; the fourth has an adjacent private bathroom. The 'expertly prepared' breakfast has an 'amazing range', including fresh fruit, fruit compote, leaf tea, home-made muesli, organic toast, full English. 'A vegetarian option was a sumptuous English muffin spread with pesto, topped with avocado, tomato, mozzarella, then grilled. All this, and home-made marmalade and hedgerow jam.' Help is given with luggage and with restaurant reservations. (*WJ Webster, and others*)

Bedrooms: 4. *Open*: all year except Christmas/New Year. *Facilities*: dining room, patio garden, unsuitable for &. *Background music*: none. *Location*: 5 mins' walk from centre, parking. *Smoking*: not allowed. *Children*: not under 12. *Dogs*: not allowed. *Credit cards*: MasterCard, Visa. *Prices*: b&b £37.50–£85 per person, 1-night bookings refused weekends.

The Queensberry

4–7 Russel Street
Bath BA1 2QF

Tel 01225-447928
Fax 01225-446065
Email reservations@thequeensberry.co.uk
Website www.thequeensberry.co.uk

In 'one of Bath's handsomest streets', this is a conversion of four adjoining town houses designed by John Wood for the Marquis of Queensberry in 1771. Though near the Assembly Rooms and Royal Crescent, 'it is very quiet'. Since buying it six years ago, Laurence and

Helen Beere have renovated in understated contemporary style, with the aim of providing 'affordable luxury'. Lauren McCann is the manager; staff are 'welcoming and helpful', say visitors. The 'easy-going atmosphere' is liked. There are 'three nice public rooms'. A glass roof creates a light feel, and 'a warren of stairs and corridors' leads to bedrooms of varying sizes. All have now been refurbished ('muted beige, brown and fawn, square leather-covered pouffes'); suites have an iPod docking station and a wet room. In the subterranean *Olive Tree* restaurant, in three rooms with oak floors, white linen and large abstract paintings, Marc Salmon cooks in modern British style, eg, Cornish red mullet with lemon thyme crushed potatoes, black olive beignet and sun-dried tomatoes. Breakfast, 'an appetising affair' (which costs extra), is served here or in the bedrooms. The four 'charming' terraced gardens, on different levels, are connected by stone arches. (*M and ED, and others*)

Bedrooms: 29, some on ground floor. *Open*: all year, restaurant closed Mon lunch. *Facilities*: lift, 2 drawing rooms, bar, restaurant, meeting room, 4 linked courtyard gardens, unsuitable for &. *Background music*: in restaurant. *Location*: near Assembly Rooms. *Smoking*: not allowed. *Children*: all ages welcomed. *Dogs*: not allowed. *Credit cards*: Amex (*2% handling charge*), MasterCard, Visa. *Prices*: [2008] room £110–£425, breakfast £10–£15, full alc £45, 1-night bookings refused Sat. *V*

Tasburgh House

Warminster Road
Bath BA2 6SH

Tel 01225-425096
Fax 01225-463842
Email hotel@bathtasburgh.co.uk
Website www.bathtasburgh.co.uk

In 'lovely grounds' that slope down to the Kennet and Avon canal, this red brick Victorian house is run in a personal way by Sue Keeling, 'an elegant and kind hostess'. She is 'very much around', says an inspector, 'and presides at breakfast with her girls (who wear white gloves)'. The house is a three-minute taxi ride from the city centre. 'In good weather you can walk along the canal past fields with sheep.' The bedrooms, each named after an English author (Wordsworth, Shelley, etc), vary in size: some have a super-king-size bed. The house faces a busy road: 'But it is in a dip and I wasn't bothered by traffic noise in my immaculate small front room (Dickens).' Sheets and blankets can be provided instead of a duvet but you should ask for these when booking. Drinks, a sandwich lunch ('delicious') and a light supper (eg, lamb tagine; chicken tarragon) are available. Breakfast, served in a 'pretty conservatory with a chandelier', has a 'small buffet of cereals, croissants, fruit and jams in little jars'. Charlie, the parrot in Reception, provides entertainment. 'There is a nice sitting room.' Only criticism: 'Such a pity that they play Classic FM all day.'

Bedrooms: 12, 2 on ground floor. *Open*: 14 Jan–21 Dec. *Facilities*: drawing room, dining room, conservatory, terrace, 7-acre grounds (canal walks, mooring), unsuitable for &. *Background music*: all day in public rooms. *Location*: on A36 to Warminster, 1 mile E of centre. *Smoking*: not allowed. *Children*: all ages welcomed ('well-behaved, with well-behaved parents'). *Dogs*: only allowed in grounds, on lead. *Credit cards*: MasterCard, Visa. *Prices*: b&b £47.50–£75 per person, full alc £26.60, 1-night bookings refused Sat.

See also SHORTLIST

BATHFORD Somerset   Map 2:D1
See SHORTLIST

BEAMINSTER Dorset   Map 1:C6

Bridge House   *Tel* 01308-862200
3 Prout Bridge   *Fax* 01308-863700
Beaminster DT8 3AY   *Email* enquiries@bridge-house.co.uk
                              Website www.bridge-house.co.uk

'Welcoming and comfortable. Two very good meals.' By a bridge in a pretty old market town, this former priest's house dates back to the 13th century. Visitors like its 'relaxed' atmosphere, 'very friendly staff', led by owners Mark and Joanna Donovan, and 'high standards'. Its 'unusual, pleasing' interior has thick walls, mullioned windows, old beams, open fires in inglenook fireplaces, and a priest's hole. The quietest bedrooms face the large walled garden at the back; front ones face a road that is busy by day. All rooms have now been refurbished. 'Ours was bright, well furnished, spacious.' Some small rooms and a family suite are in a coach house at the rear (baby-listening, cots, etc, provided). In the candlelit, oak-beamed dining room, with conservatory extension, the long-serving chef, Linda Paget, serves dishes 'with emphasis on the finest local, seasonal, organic produce available', eg, pan-seared Lyme Bay scallops with red pesto butter; breast of Sydling Brook free-range chicken stuffed with spinach and brie. Breakfast and light lunches are taken in another conservatory;

summer meals can be served in the garden. Tea is taken by a fire in winter. Nearby are Abbotsbury (with its famous swannery), the Jurassic Coast, Mapperton Garden. (*Mary Milne-Day, PQ*)

Bedrooms: 14, 5 in coach house, 4 on ground floor. *Open*: all year. *Facilities*: hall/reception, lounge, bar, conservatory, brasserie, restaurant, civil wedding licence, ¼-acre walled garden. *Background music*: modern/classical in bar and dining areas. *Location*: 100 yards from centre. *Smoking*: not allowed. *Children*: all ages welcomed. *Dogs*: allowed in coach house (not unattended), in bar except during service. *Credit cards*: Amex, MasterCard, Visa. *Prices*: b&b £58–£108 per person, d,b&b £83–£158, set dinner £37, special breaks, Christmas/New Year packages, 1-night bookings refused weekends and bank holidays. *V*

BEAULIEU Hampshire   Map 2:E2

Montagu Arms   NEW   *Tel* 01590-612324
Palace Lane   *Fax* 01590-612188
Beaulieu SO42 7ZL   *Email* reservations@montaguarmshotel.co.uk
                     Website www.montaguarmshotel.co.uk

In a New Forest riverside village, this sprawling, 'elegantly restored', much-extended 18th-century building is managed by Philip Archer. One visitor wrote of 'a good welcome (luggage taken without our asking) and a pleasant, quiet garden-facing room'. The bedrooms vary greatly: 'Ours was a little dark but well furnished.' Many suites have a four-poster. The director of cooking, the renowned chef Shaun Hill, is 'aided and abetted by a professional, enthusiastic young staff'. 'The food is excellent,' say regular *Guide* correspondents in 2008. The *Terrace Restaurant* has 'beautiful views of the formal garden' and a 'smart dress code (no trainers or denim)'; dishes include John Dory with pepper mousse, shrimps and saffron potatoes; Berkshire pork with pease pudding and deep-fried sage. *Monty's*, the informal bar/brasserie, serves 'home-cooked classics' like sausage and mash; children under eight have supper here. Lavish afternoon teas include Fairtrade teas, scones with clotted cream. 'Excellent breakfasts' have 'a wide choice of home-made pastries, etc, and well-cooked hot dishes'. (*Ian and Barbara Dewey, EJT Palmer, and others*)

Bedrooms: 22. *Open*: all year. *Facilities*: lounge, conservatory, bar/brasserie, restaurant, conference/function facilities, civil wedding licence, garden, access to nearby spa, only public rooms suitable for &. *Background music*: none. *Location*: village centre. *Smoking*: not allowed. *Children*: all ages welcomed (under-3s stay free). *Dogs*: not allowed. *Credit cards*: Amex, MasterCard, Visa. *Prices*: b&b £89–£169 per person, d,b&b £129–£209, set menu £45, special breaks all year, Christmas/New Year packages, 1-night bookings refused Sat. *V*

BEELEY Derbyshire   Map 3:A6

The Devonshire Arms at Beeley   *Tel* 01629-733259
Devonshire Square   *Fax* 01629-734542
Beeley, nr Matlock   *Email* enquiries@devonshirebeeley.co.uk
DE4 2NR   *Website* www.devonshirebeeley.co.uk

'Good fun provided you recognise that it's a pub, not a hotel.' On the
Chatsworth estate, this 17th-century coaching inn has been given a
make-over, blending ancient and modern, by the Duke and Duchess
of Devonshire. Iain Shelton is the manager. The original bar area
'remains cosy', said inspectors. The brasserie is contemporary: bright
colours, large windows facing the village; modern round tables with
cast iron legs, simply laid ('white china, decent cutlery, good glass').
Four bedrooms are in the main building. Colours are bright. The
family suite, up a steepish staircase, has a white and turquoise bedroom, and a pink sitting room with sofa bed. 'Bathroom smallish,
narrow bath but excellent shower.' Another room has a double bathtub. 'Exquisite botanical watercolours' by the duke's sister, Emma
Tennant, hang throughout. In 2008, four more rooms opened in an
adjacent house. Alan Hill's dinner menu uses local produce when possible, eg, Beeley lamb with green chilli, ginger and potato curry; Mr
Pursglove's beef fillet with tomato ketchup and port wine glaze. 'The
atmosphere was buzzing, staff were informally dressed, service was
good-humoured, the meal well paced. Excellent wines by the glass.'
Breakfast included cereals and cooked items 'but no fruit or yogurt'.

Bedrooms: 8, 4 in annexe, some ground floor. *Open*: all year. *Facilities*: bar,
2 brasseries, malt vault. *Background music*: 'easy listening' in brasserie. *Location*:
5 miles N of Matlock, off B6012. *Smoking*: not allowed. *Children*: all ages welcomed. *Dogs*: not allowed in public rooms. *Credit cards*: Amex, MasterCard,
Visa. *Prices*: [2008] b&b £72.50–£82.50 per person, full alc £35.40, Christmas
package.

BELFORD Northumberland   Map 4:A3
See SHORTLIST

'Set menu' indicates a fixed-price meal, with ample, limited or
no choice. 'Full alc' is the hotel's estimated price per person of
a three-course *à la carte* meal, with a half bottle of house wine.
'Alc' is the price of an *à la carte* meal excluding the cost of wine.

BEPTON West Sussex   Map 2:E3

Park House   *Tel* 01730-819000
Bepton, nr Midhurst   *Fax* 01730-819099
GU29 0JB   *Email* reservations@parkhousehotel.com
                                  Website www.parkhousehotel.com

Liked for its 'unfussy atmosphere', this small country hotel is in a
sleepy village at the foot of the South Downs. An inspector enjoyed a
'memorable stay' thanks to the 'tranquillity, first-rate staff, immaculate housekeeping and superb scenery'. Owned by the O'Brien
family since 1948, the imposing Victorian house is managed by
Rebecca Crowe and James Coonon. Downstairs is an 'unusually well-
stocked' honesty bar, overlooking the terrace and fine garden. The
huge drawing room has 'plenty of comfortable seating'. Dinner is
taken in the formal dining room or in a conservatory; no background
music; good table linen. 'Our bedroom was large, elegantly furnished
(some antique pieces), a two-seater settee under a bay window, a
large, comfortable bed; really good bathroom lighting. Turn-down
service while we dined. Breakfast was perfect: a buffet, comprehensive choice of cooked dishes, no silly little pots of preserves.'
There is a small converted barn for conferences and functions. The
hotel is popular with polo players and visitors to nearby Cowdray
Park. More reports, please.

Bedrooms: 15, some in two cottages, 1 on ground floor. *Open*: all year. *Facilities*:
lounge, bar, dining room, conservatory, civil wedding licence, 9-acre grounds
(tennis, croquet, heated 13-metre swimming pool, pitch-and-putt golf).
Background music: none. *Location*: 2½ miles SW of Midhurst. *Smoking*: not
allowed. *Children*: all ages welcomed. *Dogs*: allowed. *Credit cards*: MasterCard,
Visa. *Prices*: b&b £62.50–£147.50 per person, d,b&b £100–£175, set dinner £30,
winter breaks.

BERWICK-UPON-TWEED   Map 4:A3
Northumberland

West Coates   *Tel/Fax* 01289-309666
30 Castle Terrace   *Email* karenbrownwestcoates@yahoo.com
Berwick-upon-Tweed TD15 1NZ   *Website* www.westcoates.co.uk

Recommended 'without hesitation' this year, Karen Brown's 'wonderfully comfortable' Georgian house is close to the centre of this
historic border town. Set in an attractive, mature garden, it has a large
indoor swimming pool and hot tub (the changing room has been

refurbished this year). The bedrooms are 'beautifully furnished, with everything one could want, including home-made cake on the hospitality tray each day'. 'My room had a spacious dressing room/ bathroom.' Mrs Brown also runs a cookery school, and serves 'excellent food', using local ingredients for her 'fabulous' no-choice three-course dinners, served by candlelight; dishes might include split langoustines with garlic and herb butter; chicken with sherry and tarragon. The 'wonderful' breakfast has smoked salmon and scrambled eggs, porridge, yogurt, home-made preserves, etc. (*Dr JT Roberts, and others*)

Bedrooms: 3. *Open*: all year except 2 weeks Christmas. *Facilities*: sitting/dining room, 2½-acre garden, 12-metre indoor swimming pool, hot tub, croquet, unsuitable for &. *Background music*: 'easy listening'. *Location*: 10 mins' walk from centre. *Smoking*: not allowed. *Children*: not allowed. *Dogs*: not allowed. *Credit cards*: MasterCard, Visa. *Prices*: b&b £45–£60 per person, set dinner £35, special breaks.

See also SHORTLIST

BEVERLEY East Yorkshire   Map 4:D5
See SHORTLIST

BIDEFORD Devon   Map 1:C4

The Mount   *Tel* 01237-473748
Northdown Road   *Fax* 01237-373813
Bideford EX39 3LP   *Email* andrew@themountbideford.co.uk
                         Website www.themountbideford.co.uk

Fronted by creepers and plants in pots, this imposing Georgian house was built at the turn of the 19th century. Now a B&B, it is near the town centre and the quay where fishing boats unload their catches by the medieval bridge (it is said that Sir Walter Raleigh landed his first shipment of tobacco here). Readers say that it is 'well run, spotless'; the owners, Andrew and Heather Laugharne, are 'very friendly'. Inside are bright colours: red walls to the white-painted, winding staircase, pink in the lounge which has an open fire and a licence to sell alcohol, blue in the room where the 'excellent breakfasts' are served. 'The bedrooms are tastefully furnished, the beds are large and comfortable,' writes one of many fans. Guests have access to the pretty, partly walled garden. Discounts are available at the Royal North Devon Golf Club. Guests arriving by train can be met at Barnstaple. More reports, please.

Bedrooms: 8, some family, 1 on ground floor. *Open*: all year except Christmas. *Facilities*: ramp, lounge, breakfast room, garden. *Background music*: classical sometimes. *Location*: town centre. *Smoking*: not allowed. *Children*: all ages welcomed. *Dogs*: not allowed. *Credit cards*: all major cards. *Prices*: b&b £32–£37.50 per person.

BIGBURY-ON-SEA Devon   Map 1:D4

Burgh Island Hotel
Burgh Island
Bigbury-on-Sea TQ7 4BG

Tel 01548-810514
Fax 01548-810243
Email reception@burghisland.com
Website www.burghisland.com

Liked for its 'fabulous location' (a private tidal island in Bigbury Bay), 'great atmosphere' and 'good food', this Grade II listed Art Deco building opened as a hotel in 1929. Early guests included Edward and Mrs Simpson, Agatha Christie, Noël Coward. At high tide, visitors arrive on a sea tractor; at low tide by four-wheel-drive vehicle. Tony Orchard and Deborah Clark, owners since 2001, have refurbished throughout in period style. 'Mementos of the Jazz Age abound,' they write; 'relaxed glamour' is their aim. 1920s cocktails are served in the Palm Court bar (with magnificent peacock dome); meals are taken in the Ganges Room, decorated in black and white; dinner dances are held in the ballroom (diners in full evening dress). Conor Heneghan serves modern British seasonal dishes, eg, white truffle, Jerusalem artichoke and watercress risotto; chicken breast, sweetcorn cream, chorizo, Madeira reduction. Many bedrooms have a sea view: most have a balcony. There are ten suites (one on stilts above the beach). Open-plan bathrooms have a roll-top bath. There is a natural swimming pool in the rocks, and a private beach. Non-residents are not admitted unless they have booked lunch or dinner. The island's *Pilchard Inn* is under the same ownership. (*GH*)

Bedrooms: 24, 1 suite in beach house, apartment above *Pilchard Inn*. *Open*: all year. *Facilities*: lift, sun lounge, Palm Court bar, dining room, ball room (live 1930s music Wed and Sat nights), children's games room, spa (treatment room, gym, sauna), dinner/dance Wed and Sat, civil wedding licence, 12-acre grounds on 26-acre island (natural sea swimming pool, beach, water sports, tennis, helipad). *Background music*: 1930s music in bar. *Location*: 5 miles S of Modbury, private garages on mainland. *Smoking*: not allowed. *Children*: not under 5, no under-13s at dinner. *Dogs*: not allowed. *Credit cards*: MasterCard, Visa. *Prices*: d,b&b £192.50–£300 per person, special events, Christmas/New Year packages, 1-night bookings sometimes refused Sat.

The Henley
Folly Hill
Bigbury-on-Sea TQ7 4AR

Tel/Fax 01548-810240
Email thehenleyhotel@btconnect.com
Website www.thehenleyhotel.co.uk

♔ *César award in 2003*

'The warm welcome and relaxing atmosphere are ideal for recharging your batteries.' Fresh praise this year for Martyn and Petra Scarterfield's popular, small, unpretentious hotel. On a cliff above the tidal Avon estuary (spectacular views), it was built as a holiday cottage in Edwardian days. The public rooms have dark red walls, well-polished old furniture, Lloyd Loom chairs; books, magazines and binoculars are provided. Renovation of the bedrooms continues: the two smallest rooms have been amalgamated into a superior room with a new bathroom. A shower room has been expanded in another bedroom. Guests gather in the lounge at 7 pm for drinks and canapés before dinner: Mrs Scarterfield recites the short menu (two choices for each course). 'Every meal was a delight, freshly cooked food, perfectly served.' Typical dishes: tian of crab with avocado; baked halibut with cabbage, smoked bacon, tarragon sauce. At breakfast ('tasty and unhurried') 'you are asked when you want toast; good coffee and tea are replenished as you wish; excellent bacon and sausages'. The 'delightfully unfussy' garden, 'spectacularly precipitous', has 'many sheltered nooks with seating'. 'Our three dogs were made most welcome by our hosts and by Kaspar, the resident black Labrador.' (*Jenny Morgan*)

Bedrooms: 5. *Open*: all year except Nov–mid-Mar. *Facilities*: 2 lounges, bar, conservatory dining room, small garden (steps to beach, golf, sailing, fishing), coastal path nearby, unsuitable for &. *Background music*: evenings in lounge, dining room. *Location*: 5 miles S of Modbury. *Smoking*: not allowed. *Children*: not under 12. *Dogs*: not allowed in public rooms. *Credit cards*: Amex, MasterCard, Visa. *Prices*: [2008] b&b £51–£64 per person, d,b&b (4 nights min.) £81–£94, set dinner £31, 1-night bookings sometimes refused weekends.

Hotels often try to persuade you to stay two nights at the weekend. Resist this pressure if you want to stay only one night.

BIGGIN-BY-HARTINGTON   Map 3:B6
Derbyshire

Biggin Hall   *Tel* 01298-84451
Biggin-by-Hartington   *Fax* 01298-84681
Buxton SK17 0DH   *Email* enquiries@bigginhall.co.uk
                                   Website www.bigginhall.co.uk

High in the Peak District national park, this historic house in a small
village is popular with walkers (especially groups of doctors) for its
simple, unfussy style. Close by are 'footpaths in all directions over
beautiful countryside': one starts from the grounds, and disused
railway tracks nearby provide flat walking and cycling. 'Altogether
first class,' writes a guest this year. 'Good value.' The 17th-century
Grade II* listed building has antiques, narrow mullioned windows,
and 'warm and inviting' public rooms. The lounge, with its massive
stone fireplace, can get crowded when guests gather at 6.30 for pre-
dinner drinks. An 'excellent' dinner is served to everyone at 7 in the
'chintzy' small dining room. Mark Wilton's 'traditional English'
dishes are hearty and 'well cooked', eg, braised beefsteak with red
wine and mushrooms; treacle sponge and custard. Breakfast is a
'comprehensive hot and cold buffet'. Packed lunches are available.
The master suite (beamed, with four-poster) is in the main house.
Some rooms are in buildings in the courtyard or across the lawn. 'My
small room was clean, with good bathroom and small fridge, but poor
soundproofing.' The owner, James Moffett, is 'semi-retired'; his
manager is Steven Williams. (*A Melville, and others*)

Bedrooms: 20, 12 in annexes, some on ground floor. *Open*: all year. *Facilities*:
sitting room, library, dining room, meeting room, 7-acre grounds (croquet),
River Dove 1½ miles, unsuitable for &. *Background music*: in dining room.
Location: 8 miles N of Ashbourne. *Smoking*: not allowed. *Children*: not under 12.
Dogs: allowed in some bedrooms, not in public rooms. *Credit cards*: Amex,
MasterCard, Visa. *Prices*: [2008] b&b £37–£65 per person, d,b&b £50–£78,
Christmas/New Year packages, 1-night bookings sometimes refused. ***V***

Readers' contributions, written on the forms at the back of the
book or sent by email, are the lifeblood of the *Good Hotel Guide*.
Our readers play a crucial role by reporting on existing entries
as well as recommending new discoveries. Everyone who
writes to the *Guide* is a potential winner of the Report of the
Year competition (page 63), in which a dozen correspondents
each year win a copy of the *Guide* and an invitation to our
annual launch party in October.

BIRMINGHAM West Midlands   Map 2:B2

Simpsons   *Tel* 0121-454 3434
20 Highfield Road, Edgbaston   *Fax* 0121-454 3399
Birmingham B15 3DU   *Email* info@simpsonsrestaurant.co.uk
                                   Website www.simpsonsrestaurant.co.uk

At his Georgian mansion in leafy Edgbaston, Andreas Antona's restaurant-with-rooms has Birmingham's only *Michelin* star – for classic French cooking. He now concentrates on running the business, leaving executive chef, Luke Tipping, and head chef, Adam Bennett, to 'take the heat in the kitchen'. They can be watched (behind glass) from one of the 'relaxed' dining areas which give on to a terrace. Dishes on the seasonal menu might include tartare of sashimi tuna, avocado purée, soft-boiled quail's egg, aubergine, marinated mooli, caviar d'Aquitaine; slow-cooked corn-fed poussin, asparagus, potato and pancetta terrine, morel à la crème. The petits fours trolley is 'laden with treats like chocolate lollipops'. Children and vegetarians are catered for. The four bedrooms are themed: French (the largest), done in primrose and blue, has ornate cream and gold furniture, a sleigh bed, plaster mouldings. Venetian has velvet, reds and gold, a bed 'reminiscent of a gondola'; the 'lavish' Oriental, in red and gold, has dark lacquered furniture; Colonial, done in cream, has wooden blinds, 'empire' decor, dark wood furniture. Bathrooms are 'state of the art'. All rooms have digital TV and DVD-player. Breakfast is continental. More reports, please.

Bedrooms: 4. *Open*: all year, except Christmas/New Year, bank holidays, restaurant closed Sun evening. *Facilities*: lounge, 3 restaurant areas, private dining room, cookery school, garden (alfresco dining), only restaurant suitable for &. *Background music*: none. *Location*: 1 mile from centre. *Smoking*: not allowed. *Children*: all ages welcomed ('no special facilities'). *Dogs*: only guide dogs allowed. *Credit cards*: Amex, MasterCard, Visa. *Prices*: [2008] £80–£112.50 per person, set dinner £30–£40, full alc £50.

See also SHORTLIST

BLACKBURN Lancashire   Map 4:D3
See SHORTLIST

BLACKPOOL Lancashire   Map 4:D2
See SHORTLIST

BLAKENEY Norfolk   Map 2:A5

The Blakeney Hotel   *Tel* 01263-740797
Blakeney   *Fax* 01263-740795
nr Holt NR25 7NE   *Email* reception@blakeney-hotel.co.uk
                    Website www.blakeney-hotel.co.uk

'The scene never ceases to please,' say fans of Michael Stannard's large, traditional hotel which stands 'four-square to the quayside' and has 'inspiring' views across the tidal estuary and salt marshes to Blakeney Point. Anne Thornalley is the manageress; staff are 'friendly, reliable, unobtrusive'. In a post-Christmas visit, 'once again it came up trumps; cheerful, efficient service, excellent food'. The public rooms face the estuary, as do many bedrooms; others face the garden (some have a patio). Regular visitors who 'have tried many of the rooms' find them all 'adequately appointed and maintained, with first-class housekeeping'. Six more have been refurbished this year. The traditional cooking in the dining room may not be 'showy' (though a double cheese soufflé is 'something special'), but 'high standards of presentation and service are maintained' along with 'a relaxed feeling'. There are light lunches on weekdays; a choice of roasts on Sunday. 'All you could want for breakfast' (including local smoked kippers). The *Blakeney* is busy with families at weekends and in school holidays – there is much for children to do (see below). It makes 'a good base for walking in all directions'; in winter you can 'watch the changing Norfolk skies'. (*David Nicholls, and others*)

Bedrooms: 64, 16 in *Granary* annexe opposite, some on ground floor. *Open*: all year. *Facilities*: lift, ramps, lounge, sun lounge, bar, restaurant, function facilities, indoor heated swimming pool (12 by 5 metres), spa bath (steam room), mini-gym, games room (table tennis, pool, darts), ¼-acre garden, sailing, fishing, water sports, golf, tennis nearby. *Background music*: none. *Location*: on quay. *Smoking*: not allowed. *Children*: all ages welcomed. *Dogs*: allowed in some bedrooms, not in public rooms. *Credit cards*: all major cards. *Prices*: [2008] b&b £72–£134 per person, d,b&b £84–£152, set dinner £27.50, full alc £50, activity breaks, Christmas/New Year packages, 1-night bookings sometimes refused Fri/Sat, bank holidays.

BONCHURCH Isle of Wight   Map 2:E2
See SHORTLIST

BORROWDALE Cumbria   Map 4: inset C2

The Leathes Head Hotel
Borrowdale
Keswick CA12 5UY

Tel 017687-77247
Fax 017687-77363
Email enq@leatheshead.co.uk
Website www.leatheshead.co.uk

High up in wooded grounds, set back from the road above Borrowdale, this gabled Edwardian house, built of local slat, is a traditional ('perhaps slightly dated') hotel, popular with serious walkers and climbers. The owners, Roy and Janice Smith, 'work hard to make sure guests have an enjoyable stay', all agree. Tea and drinks (complimentary on arrival) are served in a sunroom with wicker armchairs. It is 'worth paying extra' for a double-aspect superior bedroom: 'Ours was large, with sofa, coffee table and new plasma TV'; other visitors had a 'very small bathroom, with a tiny basin'. A wheelchair-dependent guest found 'the entire ground floor accessible, and my bedroom and bathroom fine for manoeuvrability'. Pre-dinner drinks are taken in the 'well-stocked' bar and lounge. The chef, David Jackson, serves a 'well-balanced' daily-changing four-course menu of modern dishes, eg, oak-smoked trout fillet; grilled Ullswater lamb noisettes. The packed lunches are commended. Breakfast ranges from healthy to full English. 'Two red squirrels scampering in the grounds put the seal on a wonderful holiday.' The Smiths have put the hotel on the market but do not anticipate an early sale: check before booking. (*Frank G Millen, Dr JMR Irving, and others*)

Bedrooms: 12, 3 on ground floor, 1 suitable for &. *Open*: mid-Feb–end Nov. *Facilities*: ramp, lounge, sun lounge, bar lounge, restaurant, sun terrace, 3-acre grounds (woodland). *Background music*: none. *Location*: 3½ miles S of Keswick. *Smoking*: not allowed. *Children*: not under 10. *Dogs*: not allowed. *Credit cards*: MasterCard, Visa. *Prices*: [2008] d,b&b £82.50–£93 per person, special breaks, 1-night bookings refused at weekends. *V*

We ask for more reports on a hotel if we haven't received feedback from readers for some time. Please send an endorsement if you think a hotel should remain in the *Guide*.

Seatoller House
Borrowdale
Keswick CA12 5XN

Tel 017687-77218
Fax 017687-77189
Email seatollerhouse@btconnect.com
Website www.seatollerhouse.co.uk

'Still very good,' says a visitor this year to this popular, unpretentious guest house at the head of the beautiful Borrowdale valley. Owned by a private company, The Lake Hunts Ltd, it is managed by Daniel Potts and Lynne Moorehouse. It has long been popular with walkers and ramblers for its easy access to lakes and hills. They welcome the lack of 'modern intrusions' like television and radio, and love its 'homely atmosphere'. It has creaky floorboards, an oak-panelled sitting room, cosy chairs, cushioned window seats and a piano. In the tea bar, non-stop coffee is available (it can be taken out in flasks); there is an honesty bar, and a self-help fridge. The simple bedrooms all have new hand-made double-glazed windows. All have private facilities, though six are not *en suite*. Lynne Moorehouse serves a no-choice, daily-changing menu at 7 pm; her style is traditional 'with a twist', eg, twice-baked Gruyère, spinach and potato soufflé; home-made wild boar, apple and prune meatballs. On Tuesday, there is a light supper of soup, bread and cheese. Breakfast, between 8 and 8.30 am, is hearty. (*Graham Child*)

Bedrooms: 10, 2 on ground floor, 1 in garden bungalow, all with shower. *Open*: 13 Mar–23 Nov, dining room closed midday, Tues night (light supper available). *Facilities*: lounge, library, tea bar, dining room, drying room, 1-acre grounds (beck), unsuitable for &. *Background music*: none. *Location*: on B5289, 7 miles S of Keswick. *Smoking*: not allowed. *Children*: not under 6 (unless in a private group). *Dogs*: not allowed in public rooms. *Credit cards*: MasterCard, Visa. *Prices*: b&b £41–£55 per person, d,b&b £53–£67, set dinner £18, reductions for longer stays, 1-night bookings sometimes refused weekends.

BOSCASTLE Cornwall   Map 1:C3

The Old Rectory
St Juliot, nr Boscastle
PL35 0BT

Tel/Fax 01840-250225
Email sally@stjuliot.com
Website www.stjuliot.com

Near the north Cornish coast, this historic rectory, immortalised in Thomas Hardy's novel *A Pair of Blue Eyes*, is the home of the 'warm-hearted' Chris and Sally Searle, who run it as a B&B. Hardy, then an architect, met the rector's sister-in-law, Emma Gifford, here in 1870 and married her in 1874; the conservatory that he described still stands. Three bedrooms are in the main house. Mr Hardy's has an antique carved double bed and a power shower. Emma's has a shower and the original thunderbox loo. The Rector's room has a whirlpool bath with shower, and a super-king-size bed. The fourth room, with wood stove, bath and shower, is in stables linked to the main house by the conservatory. The 'good breakfast', served until 10 am, has Fairtrade tea and coffee, free-range chicken and duck eggs, locally produced bacon and sausages; also locally smoked salmon, mackerel and kipper, and 'the best produce we have in the garden', eg, peaches, figs, loganberries and gooseberries. The comfortable guests' sitting room, with fireplace, looks over terrace and garden. 'Sally, who clearly loves company, makes a point of stressing that you can come and go throughout the day.' (*BR, and others*)

Bedrooms: 4, 1 in stables (linked to house). *Open*: mid-Feb–mid-Nov. *Facilities*: sitting room, breakfast room, 3-acre garden (croquet lawn, 'lookout'), unsuitable for &. *Background music*: none. *Location*: 2 miles NE of Boscastle. *Smoking*: not allowed. *Children*: not under 12. *Dogs*: only allowed in stables. *Credit cards*: MasterCard, Visa. *Prices*: [2008] b&b £40–£54 per person, 1-night bookings sometimes refused weekends, bank holidays.

See also SHORTLIST

BOSHAM West Sussex   Map 2:E3

The Millstream	*Tel* 01243-573234
Bosham Lane	*Fax* 01243-573459
Bosham, nr Chichester	*Email* info@millstream-hotel.co.uk
PO18 8HL	*Website* www.millstream-hotel.co.uk

In a manicured garden with millstream and gazebo, this converted manor house stands in an attractive village on the West Sussex coast. The long-serving general manager, Antony Wallace, 'is ever-present and has a close eye on detail'. Smiles are 'much in evidence from the attentive young staff'. 'A very happy weekend,' one guest wrote. 'Our fourth visit; all bedrooms are comfortable and well equipped,' said others. The rooms, with conventional decor, vary in size. 'Ours, overlooking the front garden, had all we needed: we liked the fresh milk and bottled water in its fridge.' Room 18, over the kitchen, was 'large, with sofa and two armchairs, sheets and blankets on bed', but it suffered from noise (an extractor fan); 'luckily no cooking smells; good bathroom, with powerful shower, plenty of towels'. A wheelchair-dependent visitor found the Garden Room 'ideal: wide doors and room to manoeuvre'. Public rooms are 'pleasant' and spacious. Comments on the food are mixed: 'Good, but standards varied.' 'Sauces masked the flavour of fish and meat dishes.' A pianist accompanies dinner on Friday and Saturday. Breakfast includes kippers, comb honey, fruit compotes. Bar lunches are available. Guests attending the Chichester theatre can have an early supper. (*Roger and Lesley Everett, Mollie and Bob Sullivan, and others*)

Bedrooms: 35, 2 in cottage, 7 on ground floor, 1 suitable for &. *Open*: all year. *Facilities*: lounge, bar, restaurant (pianist Fri and Sat), conference room, civil wedding licence, 1½-acre garden (stream, gazebo), Chichester Harbour (sailing, fishing) 300 yards. *Background music*: classical 10.30 am–10.30 pm. *Location*: 4 miles W of Chichester. *Smoking*: not allowed. *Children*: all ages welcomed. *Dogs*: not allowed. *Credit cards*: all major cards. *Prices*: [2008] b&b £71–£107.50 per person, d,b&b (min. 2 nights) £85–£134, full alc £39, Christmas/New Year packages, 1-night bookings refused Sat.

BOURNEMOUTH Dorset   Map 2:E2
See SHORTLIST

BOURTON-ON-THE-HILL   Map 3:D6
Gloucestershire

The Horse and Groom   *Tel/Fax* 01386-700413
Bourton-on-the-Hill   *Email* greenstocks@horseandgroom.info
nr Moreton-in-Marsh   *Website* www.horseandgroom.info
GL56 9AQ

'Engaging hosts', brothers Will (the chef) and Tom (front-of-house) Greenstock run this Grade II listed Georgian coaching inn as a dining pub. It stands at the top of a hill in a honey-stone Cotswold village. 'It's just how an old inn should be,' said our inspector, 'with ancient beams, wooden floors and tables, sisal matting, and stools around the bar.' Service is by a 'young, enthusiastic team'. 'We were addressed by name from the moment we checked in.' Meals, chosen from a blackboard menu, are served in four seating areas, or alfresco: the garden has a 'splendid view down the valley'. The menu is modern, local ingredients cooked 'with passion', eg, herb-crusted rack of lamb, parsnip purée; Mrs G's toffee meringue. All bedrooms have been refurbished in modern style; all are of good size and have a well-equipped bathroom, but light sleepers may hear traffic. 'Our room at the back was lovely and light; well thought out with good storage space; a most comfortable bed. Glazed doors opened on to the garden. Excellent preserves, good toast, tea and coffee, and a generous helping of bacon at breakfast, but packaged juice.'

Bedrooms: 5. *Open*: all year except 25/26/31 Dec, 1 Jan, restaurant closed Sun eve, Mon lunch. *Facilities*: bar/restaurant, 2-acre garden, unsuitable for &. *Background music*: none. *Location*: village centre. *Smoking*: not allowed. *Children*: all ages welcomed. *Dogs*: allowed in garden only. *Credit cards*: MasterCard, Visa. *Prices*: [2008] b&b £50–£70 per person, d,b&b (min. 2 nights) £67.50–£90.50, full alc £37, 1-night bookings refused weekends.

BOURTON-ON-THE-WATER   Map 3:D6
Gloucestershire

Dial House	*Tel* 01451-822244
High Street	*Fax* 01451-810126
Bourton-on-the-Water GL54 2AN	*Email* info@dialhousehotel.com
	Website www.dialhousehotel.com

In January 2008, Martyn and Elaine Booth, owners of the *Royal Adelaide Hotel*, Windsor, bought this 17th-century building. With a well-kept rear garden, it stands back from the street in this pretty if busy Cotswold town. Carmelo Alfano is the manager. 'No obvious changes,' say returning inspectors. 'We were well looked after by friendly staff. The food is excellent. The delightful atmosphere in the lounge/bar, with its mix of modern and antique furniture, is spoiled only by intrusive background music, played also in the restaurant.' The two small dining rooms have stone windows, wooden floor, candles on wooden tables. Chef Jamie Forman has stayed on from the previous regime. 'Sophisticated cooking; delicate flavours. Shellfish soup with fennel; pot-roast lamb with wild garlic; brill on a delicious lobster risotto; memorable champagne and elderflower jelly. Well-judged portions, served at the right pace.' The 'excellent' breakfast, served at table, includes freshly squeezed juices. The bedrooms vary greatly. 'Our front room in the main house, decorated in dark reds, had black bedspread and bedhead; tiny badly lit bathroom with noisy fan and macerator. Refurbishment much needed.' Five more modern bedrooms are in a converted building to the side: a ground-floor room here had 'huge bed; French grey trimmings; tea-making kit, fruit, mineral water; bright modern bathroom'.

Bedrooms: 13, 5 in coach house, 4 on ground floor. *Open*: all year. *Facilities*: lounge, 2 dining rooms, 1½-acre garden. *Background music*: 'easy listening' in lounge and dining rooms. *Location*: town centre. *Smoking*: not allowed. *Children*: not under 13. *Dogs*: allowed in 1 bedroom. *Credit cards*: all major cards. *Prices*: [2008] b&b £60–£115 per person, full alc £40, Christmas/New Year packages, 1-night bookings refused weekends.

BOWNESS-ON-WINDERMERE   Map 4: inset C2
Cumbria

Fayrer Garden House Hotel

Lyth Valley Road
Bowness-on-Windermere
LA23 3JP

Tel 015394-88195
Fax 015394-45986
Email lakescene@fayrergarden.com
Website www.fayrergarden.com

'Everything was done to make our stay enjoyable,' says a visitor returning this year to this 'comfortable and friendly place'. 'Hotel and staff as good as ever.' Owned by Claire and Eric Wildsmith, the former Edwardian gentleman's residence stands in large grounds with award-winning gardens. It looks towards Lake Windermere (through groups of trees) and the surrounding countryside: the lounge (with original oil paintings and flowers), the *Terrace Restaurant* and some bedrooms face the water; other bedrooms have a garden view. Earlier praise: 'We were pampered; amenities very good. Our room was serviced with professionalism, though we never saw a cleaner.' Head chef Eddie Wilkinson serves a daily-changing menu of modern English dishes, using local produce when possible, eg, tart of Thornby Moor goat's cheese, with basil pesto; breast of Lakeland pheasant, puy lentils and a rich game sauce. 'Good, though not top-notch cooking.' The dining room and four bedrooms have been updated this year. The manager, Mark Jones, is 'very helpful'. (*Trevor B Lee, Ellin Osmond, and others*)

Bedrooms: 29, 5 in cottage in grounds, 7 on ground floor. *Open*: all year except first 2 weeks Jan. *Facilities*: 2 lounges, lounge bar, restaurant, civil wedding licence, 5-acre grounds. *Background music*: none. *Location*: 1 mile S of Bowness on A5074. *Smoking*: not allowed. *Children*: not under 6. *Dogs*: allowed in cottage rooms only. *Credit cards*: MasterCard, Visa. *Prices*: d,b&b £71–£150 per person, Christmas/New Year packages, 1-night bookings sometimes refused Sat.

Deadlines: nominations for the 2010 edition of this volume should reach us not later than 15 May 2009. Latest date for comments on existing entries: 1 June 2009.

Lindeth Fell
Lyth Valley Road
Bowness-on-Windermere
LA23 3JP

Tel 015394-43286
Fax 015394-47455
Email kennedy@lindethfell.co.uk
Website www.lindethfell.co.uk

César award: English country hotel of the year

'Superbly set amid lovely gardens', this Edwardian gentleman's
residence above Lake Windermere has been owned since 1984 by Pat
and Diana Kennedy. 'A good, traditional establishment,' say visitors
this year. 'They don't take themselves too seriously.' 'How good hotels
used to be.' Other praise: 'Our third visit, standards never falter.' 'Such
a friendly welcome; important to a single traveller.' 'The pleasantness
and cheerfulness of the staff, led by Mrs Kennedy, made it a happy
experience.' She is assisted by the 'charming, long-standing'
manageress, Linda Hartill. Guests enter into a panelled hall. The 'cosy'
main lounge has 'deep sofas' and Victorian watercolours; the blue
lounge has 'masses of books' and memorabilia from Mr Kennedy's time
in the RAF. Bedrooms (which are serviced during dinner) are 'well lit
and warm'; bathrooms are being updated: 'Ours was spanking new and
immaculate.' The dining room, with conservatory-style extensions, has
'gorgeous views until blinds are pulled down after dark'. Chef Philip
Taylor serves a 'copious' daily-changing menu: 'Filling tomato soup;
potted shrimps; steak rare as requested and tender; a well-filled side
dish of vegetables. Good wine list; several decent bottles at about £20.'
'No hurry between courses; timings to suit the diners.' Breakfast (a self-
service buffet; cooked dishes brought to the table) was 'entirely
satisfactory'. (*Francine and Ian Walsh, Sue and Colin Raymond, Ken and
Mildred Edwards, Dorothy Brining*)

Bedrooms: 14, 1 on ground floor. *Open*: all year except 3 weeks Jan. *Facilities*:
ramp, hall, 2 lounges, dispense bar, 3 dining rooms, 7-acre grounds (gardens,
croquet, putting, bowls, tarn, fishing permits). *Background music*: none.
Location: 1 mile S of Bowness on A5074. *Smoking*: not allowed. *Children*: all ages
welcomed. *Dogs*: only assistance dogs allowed. *Credit cards*: MasterCard, Visa.
Prices: [2008] b&b £50–£85 per person, d,b&b £78–£115, set dinner £35,
Christmas/New Year packages, 1-night bookings sometimes refused Sat. *V*

The *V* sign at the end of an entry indicates a hotel that has
agreed to take part in our Voucher scheme and to give *Guide*
readers a 25% discount on their room rates for a one-night stay,
subject to the conditions on the back of the vouchers and page 62.

Linthwaite House

Crook Road
Bowness-on-Windermere
LA23 3JA

Tel 015394-88600
Fax 015394-88601
Email stay@linthwaite.com
Website www.linthwaite.com

Run by owner Mike Bevans with manageress Sarah Wilcock, this timbered, creeper-covered, white and stone house has 'amazing views' over landscaped gardens to Lake Windermere. Its decor is 'a successful combination of traditional and contemporary'. Public rooms have oriental rugs, potted plants, cabin trunks, memorabilia, and an enclosed veranda faces the lake. A recent visitor who had a 'really enjoyable stay' with her family said: 'Staff young, informal but professional.' The bedrooms, which have a 'calm, chintzless' decor and Wi-Fi, vary greatly: 'Our small suite was well furnished and equipped; good storage, firm mattress, good lighting.' Rooms 14 and 15 (each with king-size bed and lake views) are liked. But one visitor considered his room 'cramped, the bathroom small and in need of refurbishment'. Three new rooms, one a 'star-gazing' suite, were being added as the *Guide* went to press. A new chef, Paul Peters, arrived in 2008. His modern cooking uses local produce where possible, eg, roasted scallop with caramelised cauliflower; seared venison with roasted parsnip, beetroot and chocolate. 'Our four-year-old son was made very welcome, and was served good suppers in the bedroom. Good choice of cold and hot dishes at breakfast, and delicious scones at teatime.' More reports, please.

Bedrooms: 27, some on ground floor. *Open*: all year. *Facilities*: ramp, lounge/bar, conservatory, 3 dining rooms, function facilities, civil wedding licence, 14-acre grounds (croquet, tarn, fly-fishing). *Background music*: in bar all day, dining room during meals. *Location*: ¾ mile S of Bowness off B5284. *Smoking*: not allowed. *Children*: no under-7s in dining rooms after 7 pm. *Dogs*: allowed in grounds only. *Credit cards*: Amex, MasterCard, Visa. *Prices*: [2008] b&b £90–£165 per person, d,b&b £115–£190, set dinner £50, Christmas/New Year packages, 1-night bookings refused weekends, bank holidays. ***V***

See also SHORTLIST

The more reports we receive, the more accurate the *Guide* becomes. Please don't hesitate to write again about an old favourite, even if it is only to endorse the entry. New reports help us keep the *Guide* up to date.

BRADFORD-ON-AVON Wiltshire   Map 2:D1

The Swan Hotel
1 Church Street
Bradford-on-Avon
BA15 1LN

Tel 01225-868686
Fax 01225-868681
Email theswan-hotel@btconnect.com
Website www.theswan-hotel.com

In the centre of a 'picture-perfect' small town, this Grade II listed building has been renovated with a 'sensitive blend' of the old and the new by owner Stephen Ross. Exposed beams and polished wooden floors (sloping and 'wonky' in places) are complemented by muted modern-coloured walls and stylish furniture. The lounge areas in front are 'cosy, charming'; the dining room at the back has wooden tables and chairs. 'Our room was lovely, simple, airy and light,' reported inspectors. 'The staff were warm, and seemed to care that you had a good time.' Chef Tom Bridgeman (also the manager) serves 'straightforward English cooking', eg, slow roast belly pork with spring greens and apple sauce. The bar, which stocks real ales, is popular with locals; there may be noise in some bedrooms until closing time. 'Excellent breakfast: buffet with cereals, fruit, juices; thick-cut home-made bread, National Trust jams; cooked dishes included eggs Florentine, delicious full English. Newspapers on a side table. A great stay. Good value.'

Bedrooms: 12. *Open*: all year. *Facilities*: bar, sitting room, 2 restaurant areas, private dining room, terrace, unsuitable for &. *Background music*: in bar. *Location*: town centre. *Smoking*: not allowed. *Children*: all ages welcomed. *Dogs*: not allowed in bedrooms, only guide dogs in restaurant. *Credit cards*: MasterCard, Visa. *Prices*: [2008] b&b £42.50–£120 per person, set lunch £10.50–£14, full alc £32, winter breaks, 1-night bookings refused weekends, Christmas, Easter. *V*

Woolley Grange
Woolley Green
Bradford-on-Avon
BA15 1TX

Tel 01225-864705
Fax 01225-864059
Email info@woolleygrangehotel.co.uk
Website www.woolleygrangehotel.co.uk

On the edge of the medieval wool town, this Jacobean stone manor house is part of the von Essen group's Luxury Family Hotels division; it is managed by Clare Hammond. Guests pay by the room, sharing with as many children as they can tolerate. There are many activities for families in the 'beautiful' grounds (see below). The very young are catered for in the Ofsted-approved Woolley Bears' Den; older children have the run of the unsupervised Hen House (with games galore). 'We loved it: just the right blend of luxury and informality for families with young children,' one parent wrote. Mark Bradbury was appointed head chef in 2008: he serves 'modern British dishes with European and Asian flavours'. Small children are given high tea. More reports, please.

Bedrooms: 26, 9 in courtyard, 3 in pavilion in grounds, 1 on ground floor. *Open*: all year. *Facilities*: ramps, 2 lounges, TV room, 2 restaurants, dispense bar, conservatory, children's nursery, games rooms, civil wedding licence, 14-acre grounds (heated swimming pool, 13 by 7 metres, badminton, croquet, trampoline, children's play area), cycling, riding, golf, tennis, fishing, hot-air ballooning nearby. *Background music*: none. *Location*: 1 mile NE of Bradford-on-Avon on B3105. *Smoking*: not allowed. *Children*: all ages welcomed. *Dogs*: not allowed in dining rooms. *Credit cards*: all major cards. *Prices*: [2008] b&b £85.50–£369 per person, d,b&b £103–£404.50, set dinner £40, special Christmas/New Year packages, 1-night bookings refused weekends.

BRADPOLE Dorset   Map 1:C6

Orchard Barn
Bradpole
nr Bridport DT6 4AR

Tel/Fax 01308-455655
Email enquiries@lodgeatorchardbarn.co.uk
Website www.lodgeatorchardbarn.co.uk

The River Asker runs at the foot of the peaceful garden of Nigel and Margaret Corbett's home on the site of an old Dorset farm. Living in a separate wing, they run it, 'with genuine warmth', as a B&B. Their large collection of cheese dishes has come with them from their earlier, much-loved hotel, *Summer Lodge* at Evershot (*qv*). 'Attention to our needs was exemplary,' one visitor wrote. 'Nigel ushered us into a large, vaulted, high-ceilinged lounge with an open log fire burning on a deep bed of ashes; tea quickly arrived with home-made cake and shortbread.' The comfortable bedrooms 'are simple, but have fine linen, good lighting, free-range coat-hangers and individual temperature control'. One bedroom has a private bathroom adjacent. The ground-floor bedroom has a separate entrance. Breakfast, in a room with a log fire or on the patio, has 'unbelievable quality and choice'; it includes free-range eggs cooked in many ways, local bacon and sausages, 'delicious, unusual yogurts', organic wholemeal toast, home-made marmalade and jams. A snack supper (soup, sandwiches, quiches, salads) can be served. (*A and AM, and others*)

Bedrooms: 3, 1 on ground floor. *Open*: all year except Christmas/New Year. *Facilities*: lounge, dining room. *Background music*: none. *Location*: off A35, via Lee Lane, in village adjoining Bridport, train Dorchester, bus to Bridport. *Smoking*: not allowed. *Children*: all ages welcomed. *Dogs*: allowed in public rooms subject to other guests' approval. *Credit cards*: none in 2008, will reconsider in 2009. *Prices*: b&b £60–£80 per person, snack supper £5–£15, 1-night bookings sometimes refused Sat.

BRAITHWAITE Cumbria   Map 4: inset C2

The Cottage in the Wood   *Tel* 017687-78409
Whinlatter Pass   *Email* relax@thecottageinthewood.co.uk
Braithwaite CA12 5TW   *Website* www.thecottageinthewood.co.uk

In a 'marvellous setting' on Whinlatter Pass, looking down the valley to the Skiddaw mountain range, this 17th-century Lakeland coaching inn is run 'with dedication' by Kath and Liam Berney. They are 'genuinely caring' hosts, say visitors; she offers 'excellent personal service'; his cooking is thought 'superb'. This year, they have refurbished the restaurant, added a conservatory and extended the terrace. 'From 2008 we will be trading as a restaurant-with-rooms,' they tell us. Their new menus offer a choice of five dishes for each course, using seasonal, local produce, eg, terrine of Sillfield Farm ham hock; confit of Goosnargh duck, winter vegetable stew. Vegetarians are catered for. In the small garden, residents 'can take a drink or have a nap'. Two of the 'cottagey' bedrooms have a sleigh bed; 'what used to be our family attic' has a roll-top bath and a separate shower *en suite*. Other rooms are smaller. 'We were made to feel welcome with our dog. Wet clothes taken to the drying room.' There are walking magazines, books, games and an open fire in the 'cosy' sitting room. Breakfast includes fresh grapefruit, yogurts, fruit, and a Cumbrian cooked platter. (*Mrs M McCartney, Robert Ellis*)

Bedrooms: 9, 1 on ground floor. *Open*: Feb–Dec, restaurant closed Mon night. *Facilities*: lounge, bar, restaurant, 4½-acre grounds (terraced garden). *Background music*: light classical/'easy listening'. *Location*: 5 miles NW of Keswick. *Smoking*: not allowed. *Children*: not under 10. *Dogs*: not allowed. *Credit cards*: MasterCard, Visa. *Prices*: b&b £45–£60 per person, d,b&b £65–£72.50, set dinner £35, midweek breaks, Christmas/New Year packages, 1-night bookings refused weekends.

> Most hotels have reduced rates out of season, and offer breaks throughout the year. It is always worth checking for special deals on the hotel's website or by telephone.

BRAMPTON Cumbria   Map 4:B3

Farlam Hall   *Tel* 01697-746234
Brampton CA8 2NG   *Fax* 01697-746683
                            Email farlam@farlamhall.co.uk
                            Website www.farlamhall.co.uk

César award in 2001

'The Quinion and Stevenson families clearly take great pride in their
country hotel and the service they provide.' Praise from American
visitors this year for this traditional hotel (Relais & Châteaux), which
has been run by the two families since 1975 (and has had an entry in
every edition of the *Guide*). 'A sense of humour abounds alongside
proper service, which we appreciated when we arrived muddy and
frazzled.' The old manorial house, which takes it character from a
Victorian renovation, stands in an 'immaculate' landscaped garden
with a large ornamental lake, tall trees, a stream and a paddock.
Ornate public rooms have open fires, patterned wallpaper, fresh
flowers, lots of knick-knacks and Victoriana. Drinks are served in the
lounge (there is no bar). Barry Quinion's country house cooking is
thought 'delicious', 'especially the old-fashioned way of serving
vegetables'. Typical dishes: cream of watercress and pear soup; breast
of guinea fowl on pak choi, plum and orange sauce. Bedrooms are
priced according to size (best ones have a whirlpool bath). 'Our
beautiful room had a huge new bathroom, and an American-size bed;
couldn't have been more comfortable. Breakfasts were lovely.
Expensive, but well worth it.' (*Tara and Rick Varco; also Martin Wyatt*)

Bedrooms: 12, 1 in stables, 2 on ground floor. *Open*: all year except 24–30 Dec,
restaurant closed midday (light lunches for residents by arrangement).
Facilities: ramps, 2 lounges, restaurant, 10-acre grounds (croquet lawn),
unsuitable for &. *Background music*: none. *Location*: on A689, 2½ miles SE of
Brampton (*not* in Farlam village). *Smoking*: not allowed. *Children*: not under 5.
Dogs: not allowed unattended in bedrooms. *Credit cards*: Amex, MasterCard,
Visa. *Prices*: [2008] d,b&b £145–£180 per person, set dinner £40–£42, special
breaks, New Year package. *V*

****

Traveller's tale *Hotel in Devon* The food was truly awful.
When I complained to the owner, I got the answer: 'Oh, I
had it myself this evening.' Obviously a graduate of the Basil
Fawlty school of hotel management. I won't go back there
in a hurry.

****

BRANCASTER STAITHE Norfolk   Map 2:A5

The White Horse   *Tel* 01485-210262
Brancaster Staithe   *Fax* 01485-210930
PE31 8BY   *Email* reception@whitehorsebrancaster.co.uk
                     Website www.whitehorsebrancaster.co.uk

With panoramic views over sea and salt marshes, Cliff Nye's unpretentious inn is popular with walkers and birdwatchers. 'Informal, but
with a degree of decorum; extremely friendly staff', 'relaxing,
enjoyable,' say visitors this year. The interior has 'character and style'.
The lounge, restaurant and bedrooms were redecorated in January
2008; furnishings are 'contemporary rustic'. There are spacious bedrooms upstairs in the pub; the split-level Room at the Top (£15
supplement) has a viewing balcony with telescope. The ground-floor
annexe bedrooms (where dogs may stay) each have a private terrace.
Some rooms have a sofa bed; all have Wi-Fi. An open-plan public area
includes the bar (often busy with locals) and the restaurant in a large
conservatory. Chef Nicholas Parker, who has worked for the Roux
brothers, serves 'excellent' modern dishes. 'Local oysters in tempura
batter a delight; halibut with buttered samphire on creamed potato a
main course to be savoured.' Children have their own menu (and
colouring books and crayons in the lounge). A visitor in 2008 found
breakfast 'uninspiring, with sliced white toast', but other guests
praised the 'well-presented' cooked dishes; 'eggs done to perfection,
good smoked haddock with spinach and poached egg'. (*Simon
Rodway, Richard Mayou, Roger and Lesley Everett, Fredina Minshall*)

Bedrooms: 15, 8 in annexe, 2 suitable for &. *Open*: all year. *Facilities*: 2 lounge
areas, public bar, conservatory restaurant, dining room, ½-acre garden (covered
sunken garden), harbour sailing. *Background music*: 'easy listening' at quiet
times. *Location*: centre of village just E of Brancaster. *Smoking*: not allowed.
Children: all ages welcomed. *Dogs*: allowed in annexe rooms (£10) and bar.
Credit cards: Diners, MasterCard, Visa. *Prices*: [2008] b&b £50–£89 per person,
d,b&b £68, full alc £36, off-season breaks, Christmas/New Year packages.

How to contact the *Guide*
By mail: From anywhere in the UK, write to Freepost PAM
2931, London W11 4BR (no stamp is needed)
From outside the UK: *Good Hotel Guide*, 50 Addison Avenue,
London W11 4QP, England
By telephone or fax: 020-7602 4182
By email: editor@goodhotelguide.com
Via our website: www.goodhotelguide.com

BRANSCOMBE Devon   Map 1:C5

The Masons Arms   *Tel* 01297-680300
Branscombe EX12 3DJ   *Fax* 01297-680500
                           Email reception@masonsarms.co.uk
                           Website www.masonsarms.co.uk

'Beautifully located', an 'undemanding stroll' from Branscombe's
shingle beach, this creeper-covered 14th-century inn (Grade II listed)
stands at the centre of this attractive National Trust village. Many of
the bedrooms are in cottages across a terrace from the pub. During the
'buzz' of the summer season, when the inn was 'busy with diners and
drinkers of all ages', visitors 'enjoyed peace and quiet' in their cottage
room 'with four-poster bed, *chaise longue*, and a table and chairs in the
secluded, flower-filled garden. Green hills with sheep and even a
glimpse of the sea were in the background.' All bathrooms in the main
building have been upgraded this year. The owners, Carol and Colin
Slaney, were 'very much in evidence, friendly and helpful', say
Christmas visitors (Scott Wain is their manager). In 2007 reports on
the food were mixed ('we would go back for the location, the rooms,
the breakfast and the pub lunch, and put up with dinner'). Andrew
Deam was promoted to head chef in 2008 and we would welcome
comments on his cooking. 'Staff, mainly central European, were
attentive, polite and professional.' 'Breakfast was excellent.' Booking
is advised for both restaurant and pub. (*Pat Harman, BB*)

Bedrooms: 21, 14 in cottages. *Open*: all year. *Facilities*: ramps, lounge, 2 bars,
2 dining rooms, large terraced gardens, pebble beach ½ mile, unsuitable for &.
Background music: none. *Location*: village centre. *Smoking*: not allowed. *Children*:
all ages welcomed. *Dogs*: allowed in some bedrooms, bar. *Credit cards*:
MasterCard, Visa. *Prices*: [2008] b&b £40–£170 per person, d,b&b £67.50–
£197.50, full alc £37.50, Christmas/New Year packages, 1-night bookings
refused weekends.

BRAY Berkshire   Map 2:D3

The Waterside Inn   *Tel* 01628-620691
Ferry Road   *Fax* 01628-784710
Bray SL6 2AT   *Email* reservations@waterside-inn.co.uk
                           Website www.waterside-inn.co.uk

Idyllically set on the bank of the River Thames, Michel Roux's
renowned restaurant-with-rooms (Relais & Châteaux) has held
three *Michelin* stars for 23 years for its top-of-the-range French *haute*

cuisine. Under the direction of M. Roux's son Alain, new head chef Fabrice Uhryn serves dishes such as velouté of Granny Smith apples with a tartare of scallop and slices of truffle; moistly cooked breasts of pigeon and quail on a bed of crushed potato and cabbage. 'A cosseting dining experience.' A five-course *menu exceptionnel* (to be ordered by the whole table) is available at £93.50 per person. Drinks can be taken in a summer house or on an electric launch. For the 'sybaritic overnight stay', there are bedrooms upstairs and in a nearby cottage. Designed by Roux's wife, Robyn, they have an 'elegant French feel', linen sheets, Wi-Fi, flat-screen TV, flowers and access to a kitchenette. The two best rooms, La Terrasse and La Tamise, open on to a terrace with 'stunning views of the river'. Breakfast, served after 8 am in the bedroom, is a large wicker tray with fresh orange juice, yogurt, croissants, etc, 'good coffee' and a newspaper. Diego Masciaga is the 'dedicated', long-serving general manager.

Bedrooms: 9, 3 in nearby cottage, plus 2 apartments. *Open*: all year except 26 Dec 2008–mid-Feb 2009, Mon/Tues (except Tues evening June–Aug). *Facilities*: restaurant, private dining room (with drawing room and courtyard garden), civil wedding licence, riverside terrace (launch for drinks/coffee), unsuitable for &. *Background music*: none. *Location*: 3 miles SE of Maidenhead. *Smoking*: not allowed. *Children*: not under 12. *Dogs*: not allowed. *Credit cards*: all major cards. *Prices*: b&b £90–£290 per person, apartment £450–£675, full alc £120–£150, (*excluding 'optional' 12½% service charge on meals*).

BRIDPORT Dorset   Map 1:C6

The Bull Hotel
34 East Street
Bridport DT6 3LF

Tel 01308-422878
Fax 01308-426872
Email info@thebullhotel.co.uk
Website www.thebullhotel.co.uk

In the centre of this historic market town, Richard and Nikki Cooper have turned a Grade II listed coaching inn into a boutique hotel/gastropub. 'Lovely atmosphere,' said inspectors, 'though trendily done, it attracts locals of all ages.' Walls have been demolished to open up the interior. Decor is a combination of antiques, vintage mirrors, modern paintings, bold colours. Public areas have an 'understated' style. Bedrooms (on first and second floors), more dashing, include Black and White (metallic and black flock wallpaper, seven-foot four-poster); Red (red walls, carved wood four-poster, roll-top claw-footed bath); Gold (six-foot brass bed; tiny antique gilt sofa).

All have fine Egyptian cotton linen, bathrobes, slippers, flat-screen TV, free Wi-Fi. Front rooms hear street noise, particularly on market days (Wednesday and Saturday). The dining room has 'stylish wooden-topped tables, grey/green-painted chairs, panelled walls and stripped wood floor'. The new chef, Matt Cook, serves modern English dishes like lamb carpaccio with mustard and rosemary dressing; chicken with black paella. Wednesdays have a 'Moules Frites Night'. Breakfast had 'delicious mueslis; wonderful, creamy milk; real bread as toast'. The Coopers, parents themselves, welcome children (cots, high chairs, toys, a Sunday lunch crèche). In the huge first-floor Georgian ballroom, civil weddings, parties and conferences are held.

Bedrooms: 14. *Open*: all year. *Facilities*: bar, restaurant, private dining room, ballroom, civil wedding licence, courtyard, children's play area, unsuitable for &. *Background music*: all day, also occasional live music. *Location*: town centre. *Smoking*: not allowed. *Children*: all ages welcomed. *Dogs*: not allowed in restaurant. *Credit cards*: Amex, MasterCard, Visa. *Prices*: [2008] b&b £35–£125 per person, full alc £36, 1-night bookings refused weekends, Christmas/New Year packages.

BRIGHTON East Sussex   Map 2:E4

drakes   *Tel* 01273-696934
43/44 Marine Parade   *Fax* 01273-684805
Brighton BN2 1PE   *Email* info@drakesofbrighton.com
                           Website www.drakesofbrighton.com

On the seafront between the marina and the town, this design hotel is a conversion ('with a touch of the orient') of two 19th-century town houses. It has 'expensive, lovely bedrooms': the better ones face the sea; others have a 'city view', mainly of the back gardens of other houses. A circular suite has a freestanding bath in front of floor-to-ceiling windows. A second-floor room, up a steep hanging staircase, was 'smallish, well designed, done in cream, shades of brown and natural wood; it had air conditioning, flat-screen TV, DVD-player, Internet access, etc. Excellent lighting; but not much storage space.' There are 'very comfortable beds, good linen; water everywhere in the wet room'. Breakfast has fruit, yogurt, porridge, kippers, etc. There is 24-hour service in the ground-floor lounge bar. Hotel guests should reserve a table for the basement *Gingerman* restaurant: separately owned by Ben McKellar, it has a new head chef, Andrew McKenzie, this year. (*JW, and others*)

Bedrooms: 20, 2 on ground floor. *Open*: all year, restaurant closed midday. *Facilities*: ramp, lounge/bar/reception, restaurant (separately owned), meeting room, civil wedding/partnership licence, unsuitable for &. *Background music*: 'easy listening' in lounge and bar. *Location*: 3 miles from centre, station 20 mins' walk. *Smoking*: not allowed. *Children*: all ages welcomed. *Dogs*: only guide dogs allowed. *Credit cards*: Amex, MasterCard, Visa. *Prices*: room £100–£325, breakfast £5–£12.50, full alc £42.50, 1-night bookings refused Sat, 3-night minimum stay bank holidays. *V*

Hotel du Vin Brighton

2–6 Ship Street
Brighton BN1 1AD

Tel 01273-718588
Fax 01273-718599
Email reception@brighton.hotelduvin.com
Website www.hotelduvin.com

Between the Lanes conservation area and the seafront, this branch of the Hotel du Vin chain is in a collection of Gothic revival and mock-Tudor buildings. It is managed by Lora Strizic. Original features include a carved wooden staircase with gargoyles, and the original double-height, vaulted-ceilinged hall (now the wine bar). It was 'greatly liked' by a trusted *Guide* correspondent this year. The bedrooms, each named after, and sponsored by, a wine company, are modern, well equipped. 'We had a sizeable superior room on the top floor (no lift but help with luggage). Extremely comfortable bed, big, trendy retro-look bathroom with shower as big as a football field. Nice views over the roofs of Brighton. The bar was full and lively; we very much enjoyed dinner in the busy bistro: good moules marinière, and a charcoal-grilled steak.' There is a 'huge and enticing' wine list. 'Staff were friendly and efficient. The reasonably priced continental breakfast was excellent: a great buffet of cereals, cakes, fruit salad, yogurt, jams, etc.' Cooked dishes (charged extra) are brought to the table. Cots and beds for children are supplied. Private parking is no longer available, but there are several multi-storey car parks nearby. (*Wolfgang Stroebe*)

Bedrooms: 37, 6 in courtyard, 2 on ground floor suitable for &. *Open*: all year. *Facilities*: lounge/bar, bistro. *Background music*: 'easy listening' all day. *Location*: 50 yds from beachfront. *Smoking*: not allowed. *Children*: all ages welcomed. *Dogs*: not allowed in public rooms. *Credit cards*: all major cards. *Prices*: [2008] room £150–£410, breakfast £9.95–£13.50, full alc £47, New Year package, 1-night bookings refused weekends.

Report forms (Freepost in UK) are at the end of the *Guide*.

| Paskins Town House | NEW | *Tel* 01273-601203 |

Paskins Town House NEW   *Tel* 01273-601203
18–19 Charlotte Street,   *Fax* 01273-621973
Brighton BN2 1AG   *Email* welcome@paskins.co.uk
                                Website www.paskins.co.uk

'Amazing peace. Very friendly staff. A 1920/30s museum,' say visitors this year to Susan and Roger Marlowe's 'stylish' and environmentally friendly B&B, holder of a Green Tourism Business Gold Award. In two Grade II listed buildings in a conservation area 100 yards from the sea, it has an Art Nouveau Reception and breakfast room, and an 'imaginative' modern Japanese-style decor in its 'smallish' bedrooms (all are different). These are supplied with synthetic-free, animal produce-free soap and shampoo. Organic locally produced ingredients are used for the 'excellent' breakfast, served in a basement room next to the small lounge. Organic porridge with whisky; boiled duck's eggs, organic mushrooms, vegetarian sausages, Fairtrade tea and coffee, fish dishes on a blackboard menu, breads from a local independent baker and much else are on the menu. 'Butter in a little dish; home-made marmalade.' But the Mackintosh-style chairs were thought uncomfortable. Sandwiches and local beers are served in the lounge or bedroom. (*Alan and Val Green, and others*)

Bedrooms: 19. *Open*: all year. *Facilities*: lounge, breakfast room, unsuitable for &. *Background music*: none. *Location*: 10 mins' walk from centre. *Smoking*: not allowed. *Children*: all ages welcomed. *Dogs*: allowed. *Credit cards*: all major cards. *Prices*: b&b £37.50–£55 per person, 3-night breaks, 1-night bookings sometimes refused.

See also SHORTLIST

BRISTOL *See SHORTLIST*   Map 1:B6

****

Traveller's tale *Hotel in Wales* The restaurant is 'fancy' without being any good. On arrival, guests are conducted to their table and napkins placed on their laps with a flourish, but this attention is quite unnecessary, and the staff would do better to spend the time ensuring that the food is good and the crockery clean.

****

BROAD CAMPDEN Gloucestershire   Map 3:D6

The Malt House	
Broad Campden	*Tel* 01386-840295
nr Chipping Campden	*Fax* 01386-841334
GL55 6UU	*Email* info@malt-house.co.uk
	Website www.malt-house.co.uk

In a pretty honey-stoned Cotswold hamlet, this 'beautiful old building' (a conversion of a Grade II listed malt house with two adjacent
cottages) is a 'pleasant B&B', run by owner Judi Wilkes. 'The quality
of the fabrics and furnishings would put most hotels to shame,' says a
visitor this year. The sitting rooms have low-beamed ceilings, log
fires, antiques, *objets trouvés* and flowers. All the bedrooms overlook
the 'lovely' garden; three have a private entrance. One room has a
fireplace, one a small sitting room. 'Our garden suite of two bedrooms
and a shower room was nicely decorated, and had a cottagey feel.'
Rooms are well equipped, with umbrella, spare toothbrush, torch,
fresh milk for tea-making, and current magazines. Breakfast has 'a
vast choice of buffet items', freshly squeezed orange juice, home-
made preserves, and cooked dishes. In warm weather, teas (with
home-made biscuits) and evening drinks are served in the summer
house in the garden. Meals may be provided, by arrangement, for
groups of 12 or more, and house parties are catered for. 'There are lots
of excellent gastropubs within a short drive', and a map with
recommendations is in each room. From the gate you can walk on to
the Cotswold Way. (*Bianca Emberson, Michael and Eithne Dandy*)

Bedrooms: 7, 2 on ground floor, 3 with own entrance. *Open*: all year except
Christmas. *Facilities*: ramp, 2 lounges, dining room, 3-acre garden (croquet,
orchard, stream), unsuitable for &. *Background music*: none. *Location*: 1 mile S
of Chipping Campden. *Smoking*: not allowed. *Children*: all ages welcomed.
Dogs: allowed in 1 bedroom only. *Credit cards*: Amex, MasterCard, Visa. *Prices*:
[2008] b&b £67.50–£85 per person, 1-night bookings refused weekends high
season. *V*

BROADWAY Worcestershire   Map 3:D6

The Olive Branch	
78 High Street	*Tel* 01386-853440
	Email davidpam@theolivebranch-broadway.com
Broadway WR12 7AJ	*Website* www.theolivebranch-broadway.com

David and Pam Talboys are the friendly owners of this B&B in a
Grade II listed 16th-century house in the centre of this lovely old
Cotswold village. Arriving guests are helped with luggage, and given

a glass of sherry in the 'cosy lounge' (wood floors, rugs, squashy sofas, books and magazines); there are 'large vases of flowers, freshly picked from the garden' here and in the dining room. The nominator liked her bedroom, 'elegant and comfortable: king-size bed with plump pillows, mini-fridge, chocolates, teddy bear; spotless shower room with lovely towels'. But one couple this year were disappointed with a small garden room where noise was audible from a bedroom above. Breakfast, in a room with inglenook fireplace and original stone floor, has home-made smoothies, fresh juices, home-made muesli. And 'David cooks an excellent English, with delicious herby mushrooms'. Guests may use the barbecue in the pretty walled garden. More reports, please.

Bedrooms: 8, 1 on ground floor. *Open*: all year. *Facilities*: lounge, breakfast room, ¼-acre garden. *Background music*: in breakfast room. *Location*: village centre. *Smoking*: not allowed. *Children*: all ages welcomed (reduction for children under 10). *Dogs*: allowed in 1 bedroom only. *Credit cards*: MasterCard, Visa. *Prices*: b&b £37.50–£65 per person, 1-night bookings sometimes refused weekends. *V*

Russell's Restaurant

The Green, 20 High Street
Broadway WR12 7DT

Tel 01386-853555
Fax 01386-853964
Email info@russellsofbroadway.co.uk
Website www.russellsofbroadway.co.uk

❦ *César award in 2006*

On the wide main street of this honey-stoned Cotswold village, this listed building (former home of Sir Gordon Russell, the Arts and Crafts furniture designer) has been turned into a restaurant-with-rooms with a chic, contemporary look, by Barry Hancox and Andrew Riley. Original features (beams, inglenook fireplaces, an oak stair-case) were retained while modern gadgets and paintings were added. The L-shaped bistro-style dining room is 'very stylish; china, glass, all top quality, modern cutlery', wooden tables with grey slate mats. 'Our beautiful bedroom (No. 4), on two levels, was exciting and comfortable. Plenty of space and colour, large double bed, two comfortable armchairs, a window on almost every wall: light flooded in during the day.' Some rooms face the village, but windows are double glazed, and 'all is quiet at night'. A supermarket car park is visible from the rear windows and patio. 'Dinners were first class.' Matthew Laughton serves a seasonal set menu at midday and from 6 to 7 pm; later, guests eat *à la carte*. The style is modern, eg, escabeche of gurnard; grilled faggots with glazed carrots. Staff are 'friendly, efficient'. There is a 'parasol-covered patio with metal chairs and tables'. (*P and JH, TM*)

Bedrooms: 7, 3 in adjoining building, 2 on ground floor. *Open*: all year, restaurant closed Sun night. *Facilities*: ramp, residents' lobby, bar, restaurant, private dining room, patio (heating, meal service). *Background music*: 'ambient', in restaurant. *Location*: village centre. *Smoking*: not allowed. *Children*: all ages welcomed. *Dogs*: not allowed. *Credit cards*: Amex, MasterCard, Visa. *Prices*: [2008] b&b £60–£162.50 per person, set dinner £40, 1-night bookings refused weekends. *V*

BROCKENHURST Hampshire   Map 2:E2
See SHORTLIST

BROXTON Cheshire   Map 3:A5

Frogg Manor   *Tel* 01829-782629
Nantwich Road (A594)   *Fax* 01829-782459
Broxton, Chester CH3 9JH   *Email* info@froggmanorhotel.co.uk
      Website www.froggmanorhotel.co.uk

César award in 1997

'Eccentric and interesting', 'quintessentially English', this Georgian manor house in hamlet south of Chester is dedicated to frogs. Visitors this year, greeted by the owner, John Sykes, 'in his dressing gown, wearing a trilby', enjoyed the 'weird adventure'. Returning guests found it 'excellent as ever'. There is 'a hint of an Agatha Christie whodunit' in the 'cluttered' public rooms, with their antique furniture and ceramic, brass and straw frogs. The 1930s/40s background music was found 'acceptable' by a Pipedown member normally averse to muzak (there is a dance floor off the dining room). Well-equipped if 'quirky' bedrooms are themed (Wellington, Sherlock Holmes, Nightingale, etc). For a 'real special occasion' there is the 'fantastic' Lady Guinevere tree house in the garden, with its Arthurian murals. James Powell and Sion Newton cook 'wonderful food' on an extensive menu (eg, duck breast with an orange and cardamom glaze) between 7 and 10 pm in the conservatory restaurant; after-dinner coffee comes with chocolate frogs. Continental breakfast is included in the price; other breakfast dishes are *à la carte* (up to £15 for full English). The large grounds, floodlit at night, look across Cheshire to the Welsh mountains. (*Helen Dewar, Mrs Roberts, Susan Davies*)

Bedrooms: 8, 1 in tree house, 1 suitable for &. *Open*: all year except 1 Jan. *Facilities*: ramp, lounge, bar lounge, restaurant, private dining room, conference/function facilities, civil wedding licence, 12-acre grounds (tennis). *Background music*: 1930s/40s CDs in lounge and bar. *Location*: 12 miles SE of Chester. *Smoking*: allowed in 4 bedrooms. *Children*: all ages welcomed. *Dogs*: allowed in bedrooms, bar. *Credit cards*: all major cards. *Prices*: b&b £37–£175 per person, set dinner £32–£42. *V*

BRYHER Isles of Scilly   Map 1: inset C1

Hell Bay Hotel   NEW
Bryher, Isles of Scilly
Cornwall TR23 0PR

Tel 01720-422947
Fax 01720-423004
Email contactus@hellbay.co.uk
Website www.hellbay.co.uk

'Lovely, in an isolated location. Relaxed, relaxing,' say inspectors in 2008. Built like a group of cottages, this is the only hotel on Bryher (the smallest of the inhabited Scilly Isles), which is owned by Robert Dorrien-Smith who also owns Tresco, a five-minute boat ride away. Philip Callan is the manager. Guests are collected from the quay in a Land Rover. Accommodation is in suites, some with two bedrooms and a lounge, in buildings around a courtyard and in the garden. 'Our delightful studio, light, bright, with seaside colours, had the best view we've had in a hotel. A door led on to a decking patio; you can walk straight to the beach.' The spacious Emperor has 'huge bed with baldachin, large private terrace'. First-floor rooms have a balcony. In the enormous lounge, modern, mainly Cornish artworks (Barbara Hepworth, Ivon Hitchens and others) are displayed 'to great effect', and there is a large collection of art books. Huge paintings by local artist Richard Pearce are in the panoramic dining room where Glenn Gatland serves a daily-changing *table d'hôte* menu. 'Well balanced, three choices for each course. Memorable dishes: field mushrooms with hollandaise; seared scallops with pancetta. Good service from friendly, mostly Polish girls.' Breakfast 'has a superior buffet; cooked dishes included three kinds of fish'. Bar meals are available much of the day. *Hell Bay* has facilities for disabled visitors but 'Bryher has no made-up roads and no dedicated transport system'. (*RC, and others*)

Bedrooms: 25 suites, in 5 buildings, some on ground floor, 1 suitable for &. *Open*: Feb–Oct. *Facilities*: lounge, games room, bar, 2 dining rooms, gym, sauna, large grounds (heated swimming pool, 15 by 10 metres, giant chess, boules, croquet, children's playground, par 3 golf course), beach 75 yds. *Background music*: none. *Location*: W coast of island, boat from Tresco (reached by boat/helicopter from Penzance) or St Mary's, hotel will make travel arrangements. *Smoking*: not allowed. *Children*: all ages welcomed (high tea at 5.30). *Dogs*: not allowed in public rooms. *Credit cards*: MasterCard, Visa. *Prices*: [2008] d,b&b £130–£300 per person, 4-night breaks. *V*

BUCKDEN Cambridgeshire   Map 2:B4

The George
High Street
Buckden PE19 5XA

Tel 01480-812300
Fax 01480-813920
Email mail@thegeorgebuckden.com
Website www.thegeorgebuckden.com

'Strongly commended' this year ('lovely restoration, excellent dinner, delightful staff'), this Georgian coaching inn stands on the main street of a historic village near Huntingdon. Owners Anne, Richard and Becky Furbank have created a 'fashionably stylish' decor of neutral colours (taupe, chocolate, grey-green), leather tub chairs and sofas. 'Furnishings are well chosen, comfortable and eye-catching,' said earlier visitors. The themed bedrooms, dedicated to Georges, are up a polished staircase. Hanover and Gershwin (premiere) have mahogany furniture and a 'very comfortable' bed with brass bedhead. A standard room (Mallory, 'perhaps because of the climb') has a patchwork counterpane. Handel is twin bedded. The busy brasserie, where breakfast, light lunch and dinner are served, has 'chic nightlight holders, quirky prints', wooden tables and an 'orangerie' extension. Summer meals can be served in the courtyard. The chef, Ray Smikle, serves modern dishes like teriyaki-marinated Gloucestershire Old Spot pork belly, warm noodle salad. The wine list is well priced ('plenty in the £15–£16 range'). Waiters wear grey shirt and tie. Breakfast includes brown bread toast, croissants, fruit, cheese, etc, and any variation of a standard fry-up. 'Good coffee. Plenty of free newspapers.' Anne Furbank runs a smart clothing boutique next door. (*K Salway*)

Bedrooms: 12. *Open*: all year. *Facilities*: lift, bar, lounge, restaurant, private dining room, civil wedding licence, courtyard. *Background music*: jazz/ contemporary planned for all public areas. *Location*: village centre. *Smoking*: not allowed. *Children*: all ages welcomed, baby-changing facilities. *Dogs*: allowed in bedrooms and foyer. *Credit cards*: all major cards. *Prices*: b&b £50–£130 per person, d,b&b £35 added, Christmas package. *V*

We asked hotels to quote their 2009 tariffs. Many had yet to fix these rates as we went to press. Prices should always be checked on booking.

BUCKLAND MARSH Oxfordshire   Map 2:C2

The Trout at Tadpole Bridge
Buckland Marsh
SN7 8RF

Tel 01367-870382
Fax 01367-870912
Email info@trout-inn.co.uk
Website www.trout-inn.co.uk

In a large garden sloping down to the Thames, this 17th-century stone Cotswold pub-with-rooms stands by a bridge. Floods in July 2007 caused severe damage: the bar (frequented by locals) reopened within a week, but the rooms and restaurant were closed for four months. 'We have completely refurbished, ironically for the second time in a year,' say the owners, Gareth and Helen Pugh, who came here in 2006. 'They are efficient and friendly,' wrote inspectors. The atmosphere is informal and the decor is 'unfussy'; contemporary colour schemes combined with traditional materials. Children of all ages are welcomed: there is a 'decent children's menu (no nuggets), games, toys, plenty of space outdoors'. The 'immaculate' bedrooms (all different) are equipped with flat-screen digital TV, DVD- and CD-player and quality toiletries, and there is free Wi-Fi throughout. 'The bar at night is busy, but the dining areas have an intimate feel. Service is friendly.' A new chef, Robert Skuse, came in 2008. He has introduced more slow-cooked and braised dishes, eg, beef and mushroom steamed pudding. 'Breakfast had fresh orange juice, home-made bread, a well-stocked sideboard, and the usual full English.' Guests are asked to check in before 3 pm or after 6 pm.

Bedrooms: 6, 3 in courtyard. *Open*: all year except 25/26 Dec, restaurant closed Sun night in winter. *Facilities*: bar, dining area, breakfast area, 2-acre garden (river, moorings), unsuitable for &. *Background music*: none. *Location*: 2 miles N of A420, halfway between Oxford and Swindon. *Smoking*: not allowed. *Children*: all ages welcomed. *Dogs*: allowed. *Credit cards*: MasterCard, Visa. *Prices*: [2008] b&b £55–£75 per person, d,b&b £85–£105, full alc £33.85, 1-night bookings refused weekends.

BUDE Cornwall *See SHORTLIST*   Map 1:C3

BUDLEIGH SALTERTON Devon   Map 1:D5
See SHORTLIST

BUNGAY Suffolk *See SHORTLIST*   Map 2:B6

BURY ST EDMUNDS Suffolk   Map 2:B5
See SHORTLIST

BUXTON Derbyshire *See SHORTLIST*   Map 3:A6

BYLAND North Yorkshire   Map 4:D4

The Abbey Country Restaurant   `NEW`   *Tel* 01347-868204
Byland Abbey, nr Coxwold   *Fax* 01347-868678
YO61 4BD   *Email* paultatham@english-heritage.org.uk
                                       Website www.bylandabbeyinn.com

In 'one of the most romantic settings in England', by the ruins of
Byland Abbey, this old inn, dating from the 12th century, is owned by
English Heritage. They recently gave it an elaborate make-over
'without losing the intrinsic history of the building', say inspectors.
Managed by Paul Tatham, it is filled with 'Mouseman' furniture
made in the nearby village of Kilburn. Its three bedrooms, Byland and
Mouseman (abbey view) and Kilburn (which faces the 'lovely garden
with trees, shrubs and a patio for outside eating'), are done 'with great
attention to detail'. 'Excellent information folder, lots of extras
(sherry, sweets, flowers), lovely old wardrobe with proper hangers;
well-lit bathroom, white and blue, with window. Access from outside:
umbrellas and torches provided.' Meals (John Malia is the chef) are
served in *The Piggery* (main dining area), and two smaller rooms,
Coxwold and *Wass* ('slate floors, plain wood tables, bare stone walls,
views of the abbey, floodlit at night'). 'We thought the food very
good, highly suited to the surroundings, fairly unsophisticated and
natural. Local asparagus; lovely tian of Whitby crab; hearty main
courses of "posh fish and chips"; goujons of local whiting. Breakfast,
pre-ordered at dinner, was fine: freshly squeezed orange juice,
smoked salmon with scrambled eggs.'

Bedrooms: 3. *Open*: all year except Christmas/New Year, closed Sun night/Mon/
Tues. *Facilities*: 3 dining rooms, patio, 2-acre grounds, unsuitable for &.
Background music: in dining rooms. *Location*: 2 miles W of Ampleforth. *Smoking*:

not allowed. *Children*: not welcomed. *Dogs*: not allowed. *Credit cards*: MasterCard, Visa. *Prices*: [2008] b&b £42–£99.50 per person, set Sun lunch £24, full alc £35.

CAMBER East Sussex *See SHORTLIST* Map 2:E5

CAMBRIDGE Cambridgeshire   Map 2:B4
See SHORTLIST

CANNINGTON Somerset   Map 1:B5

Blackmore Farm   *Tel* 01278-653442
Blackmore Lane   *Fax* 01278-653427
Cannington   *Email* dyerfarm@aol.com
nr Bridgwater TA5 2NE   *Website* www.dyerfarm.co.uk

'Very welcoming and helpful, especially to children,' says a report in 2008. On their working farm, Ann and Ian Dyer welcome B&B visitors to their large 14th-century manor house, 'great for lovers of historical buildings, and for children'. 'Younger visitors,' said inspectors, 'will love the quirky rooms, the nooks and crannies, the lack of formality and the farm animals.' Entry is through the Great Hall with its long oak refectory table and large open fireplace. The small sitting room has books, board games and brochures. 'Our bedroom, The Gallery, had original wall panelling, wide, comfortable bed, sitting room up a steep flight of steps, small bathroom (lavatory in a medieval garderobe).' A family room, The Solar, has a large double bedroom, a single bed in a closet leading off it, and *en suite* bathroom. 'My two-year-old daughter was provided with cot, bedding and breakfast at no extra charge.' Tea and 'delicious home-made cake' are served free to arriving guests. Guests take breakfast ('particularly good'; 'lots of local ingredients') together around a refectory table: fresh fruit salad, cereals, toast, croissants and any combination of full English. The *Maltshovel* pub nearby has a friendly atmosphere and 'pretty basic pub grub'; there are plenty of restaurants within easy driving distance. (*Avril Campbell, and others*)

Bedrooms: 5, 2, in ground-floor barn, suitable for &. *Open*: all year. *Facilities*: lounge/TV room, hall/breakfast room, 2-acre garden (stream, coarse fishing). *Background music*: none. *Location*: 3 miles NW of Bridgwater. *Smoking*: not allowed. *Children*: all ages welcomed. *Dogs*: not allowed. *Credit cards*: all major cards. *Prices*: b&b £37.50–£55 per person, 1-night bookings refused bank holiday weekends.

CANTERBURY Kent *See SHORTLIST* Map 2:D5

CARTMEL Cumbria   Map 4: inset C2

Aynsome Manor   *Tel* 01539-536653
Cartmel   *Fax* 01539-536016
nr Grange-over-Sands   *Email* aynsomemanor@btconnect.com
LA11 6HH   *Website* www.aynsomemanorhotel.co.uk

Ⓠ *César award in 1998*

Between fells and the sea in the Vale of Cartmel, this Lakeland hotel has a loyal following: readers staying for the fourth time were 'positively the junior veterans; others were on their 20th-plus visit'. The Varley family ('excellent hoteliers') have owned and run it for 28 years: Christopher and Andrea Varley are helped by his parents, Tony and Margaret, 'assured and pleasant as ever', now in their 80s. 'One of them is always front of house.' Regular visitors returning this year found 'everything as it should be; food, service, management, value faultless as ever'. 'How a successful hotel should be run.' Dog-owners thought this 'an excellent place'. The decor is traditional: one guest found it 'dated'. Bedrooms vary in size; some are suitable for a family, two are in a cottage across the cobbled courtyard. A smaller room at the top was 'comfortable, with a good view across rolling fields'. 'Smart casual' dress is required in the oak-panelled restaurant where ingredients are sourced within Cumbria for Gordon Topp's 'very pleasing', daily-changing five-course dinner menu (four choices for each course, 'always with a lighter option'). At busy times there are two sittings for dinner. (*Christopher Beadle, David Reed, and others*)

Bedrooms: 12, 2 in cottage (with lounge) across courtyard. *Open*: all year except 25/26 Dec, 2–30 Jan, lunch served Sun only, Sun dinner for residents only. *Facilities*: 2 lounges, bar, dining room, ½-acre garden, unsuitable for ♿. *Background music*: none. *Location*: ½ mile outside village. *Smoking*: not allowed. *Children*: no under-5s at dinner. *Dogs*: not allowed in public rooms. *Credit cards*: Amex, MasterCard, Visa. *Prices*: b&b £50–£85 per person, set dinner £26, 1-night bookings sometimes refused Sat, bank holidays. *V*

See also SHORTLIST

CASTLE COMBE Wiltshire   Map 2:D1

The Castle Inn	*Tel* 01249-783030
Castle Combe	*Fax* 01249-782315
Chippenham SN14 7HN	*Email* enquiries@castle-inn.info
	Website www.castle-inn.info

In the market place of one of England's prettiest villages, this 'old-world inn' is 'cobbled together from several dwellings, some of them 12th-century'. It is owned by Ann and Bill Cross who 'run it well', say fans. 'She is a charming front-of-house, friendly, with just the right manner.' It is managed by Jo Worsley. It has 'fireside nooks, antiques and cosy corners, rambling corridors, different levels, low beams'. Bedrooms vary: a standard room at the back was 'smallish, but attractively furnished. Its huge bathroom had a spa bath. Some noise from kitchen fans, but they were turned off between 11 pm and 7 am.' Earlier visitors were upgraded to a superior room. 'We slept well: the comfortable bed had cotton sheets and a duvet. The village is quiet at night.' A single room was 'minuscule, not good value'. In the elegant green candlelit dining room, Jamie Gemell serves traditional English dishes ('delicious, with plentiful vegetables'). Bar meals include cod in beer batter; baguettes, etc. Breakfast, in a conservatory ('squeaky floor'), has 'good granary toast', smoked salmon with scrambled eggs. Parking can be difficult during the day in summer, 'but in the evening, when restrictions are relaxed, you can move your car to within a sensible distance'. (*CLH, KS*)

Bedrooms: 11. *Open*: all year except 25 Dec. *Facilities*: 2 lounges, bar, dining room, conservatory breakfast room, small courtyard garden, unsuitable for &. *Background music*: in bar, restaurant, conservatory. *Location*: Village centre, 7 miles NW of Chippenham. *Smoking*: not allowed. *Children*: all ages welcomed. *Dogs*: not allowed. *Credit cards*: Amex, MasterCard, Visa. *Prices*: b&b £55–£87.50 per person, set dinner £32.50, full alc £30, special breaks, New Year package.

'Set menu' indicates a fixed-price meal, with ample, limited or no choice. 'Full alc' is the hotel's estimated price per person of a three-course *à la carte* meal, with a half bottle of house wine. 'Alc' is the price of an *à la carte* meal excluding the cost of wine.

CHADDESLEY CORBETT   Map 3:C5
Worcestershire

Brockencote Hall   *Tel* 01562-777876
Chaddesley Corbett   *Fax* 01562-777872
nr Kidderminster DY10 4PY   *Email* info@brockencotehall.com
                              Website www.brockencotehall.com

'My favourite hotel, they get everything right.' Praise in 2008 from a
frequent visitor to this 19th-century, white-fronted mansion which
stands in landscaped parkland south-west of Birmingham.
'Everyone, from the owners [Joseph and Alison Petitjean] to the
chambermaids, is friendly. When I visited for my 70th birthday I
found in my bedroom a card and a bottle of vintage port. Everyone
wished me a happy day and a cake was produced at coffee time.'
Other comments: 'We liked our bedroom, spacious and slightly
eccentric.' 'Our superior room had a huge four-poster and a double-
aspect view over the lawns. Its bathroom had a shower cabinet and a
good-sized bath.' The sitting rooms are 'very pretty'. Tables in the
three-part restaurant are 'well spaced, each with a nice flower
arrangement'. Didier Philipot is head chef, and 'the food is
sensational'. The *table d'hôte* dinner menu might include pickled
Brixham mackerel and new potato salad; slow-cooked shank of lamb
with roasted root vegetables. A six-course *dégustation* menu suggests
a wine for each course, and there are separate menus for vegetarians
and for children. In the grounds are all-weather tennis courts, a
croquet lawn, a half-timbered Tudor dovecote, gatehouse and an
ornamental lake. (*Gordon Hands, and others*)

Bedrooms: 17, some on ground floor, 1 suitable for &. *Open*: all year except
1–17 Jan, restaurant closed Sat midday. *Facilities*: lift, ramp, hall, 3 lounges,
bar, conservatory, restaurant, function facilities, civil wedding licence, 70-acre
grounds (gardens, lake, fishing, croquet, tennis.) *Background music*: in restaurant, lounges. *Location*: 3 miles SE of Kidderminster. *Smoking*: not allowed.
Children: all ages welcomed. *Dogs*: not allowed in bedrooms. *Credit cards*: all
major cards. *Prices*: b&b £60–£125 per person, d,b&b £96.50–£161.50, set
dinner £36.50, full alc £54.50, Christmas/New Year packages. ***V***

The ***V*** sign at the end of an entry indicates a hotel that has
agreed to take part in our Voucher scheme and to give *Guide*
readers a 25% discount on their room rates for a one-night stay,
subject to the conditions on the back of the vouchers and
explained in 'How to use the *Good Hotel Guide*' (page 62).

CHAGFORD Devon   Map 1:C4

Gidleigh Park   `NEW`   *Tel* 01647-432367
Chagford TQ13 8HH   *Fax* 01647-432574
                          Email gidleighpark@gidleigh.co.uk
                               Website www.gidleigh.com

Andrew and Christina Brownsword are co-owners with head chef
Michael Caines (one *Michelin* star) of this luxurious country house hotel
(Relais & Châteaux); it is managed by Sue Kendall. The group also
owns *The Bath Priory* in Bath (*qv*) and the ABode 'lifestyle' hotels. The
heavily beamed mock-Tudor building stands in a large estate up a
narrow lane from the village. In its 'stunning' gardens are marked walks
with bridges over the River Teign (narrow at this point) and much else
(see below). Major refurbishment took place in 2006. A visitor who had
stayed under the previous regime found it 'just as good now;
comfortable rooms, food first rate, service both friendly and efficient'.
Another comment: 'Excellent staff, except Reception, who were cool.'
The bedrooms, all different, have antiques, paintings, prints, flowers,
fruit, a decanter of port, and Wi-Fi. 'Our splendid suite, the most
expensive, had two big sofas, desk, wide balcony with armchairs facing
the lovely garden and the moor beyond.' Another, smaller room was
'also comfortable with an equally wide bed'. But several readers were
critical of the design of the 'expensively done' marble bathrooms.
Courtyard-facing rooms are the cheapest. The thatched pavilion in the
garden is good for a family. (*Conrad Dehn, and others*)

Bedrooms: 24, 2 in annexe, 75 yds, 2 in cottage, some on ground floor suitable
for &. *Open*: all year. *Facilities*: ramps, 2 lounges, bar, 2 dining rooms, civil
wedding licence, 52-acre grounds (gardens, croquet, tennis, 18-hole putting
course, river, fishing). *Background music*: none. *Location*: 2½ miles from
Chagford. *Smoking*: not allowed. *Children*: no under-8s at dinner. *Dogs*: allowed
in some bedrooms, not in public rooms. *Credit cards*: all major cards. *Prices*: b&b
£155–£577.50 per person, d,b&b £240–£662.50, set dinner £41, full alc £125,
Christmas/New Year packages, 1-night bookings sometimes refused.

Mill End Hotel   *Tel* 01647-432282
Sandy Park   *Fax* 01647-433106
nr Chagford TQ13 8JN   *Email* info@millendhotel.com
                            Website www.millendhotel.com

By a bridge over the River Teign, this white-walled former corn mill
was 'greatly enjoyed' by visitors this year. 'We were greeted by two
Labradors; our bags were carried to our room.' 'Nice big bed, staff

lovely, food superb.' The owner, Keith Green, 'is busy keeping everyone happy, lighting fires, delivering drinks, mowing the lawn'. The lounges, with log fires, 'have a homely feel rather than a smart country house look'. Three bedrooms have been refurbished this year. The rooms vary from a large first-floor suite to standard ones that face the road; there are three south-facing ground-floor rooms, each with private patio. 'Our pretty, light bedroom, in the extension, had large bathroom, lots of hot water. No turn-down service or bathrobes. The window alcove faced a rather scruffy back garden, but there is a nice front garden on the river. You can walk upstream to Chagford and downstream to a wooded gorge below Castle Drogo.' Non-residents frequent the bar. The mill wheel, which 'revolves with much splashing at the back of the building', is visible from the restaurant. Chef Christophe Ferraro serves modern French dishes (eg, braised shin of beef cannelloni with ox tongue and thyme jus). (*Nigel and Jennifer Jee, and others*)

Bedrooms: 14, 3 on ground floor. *Open*: all year. *Facilities*: 3 lounges, bar, restaurant, 15-acre grounds (river, fishing, bathing), unsuitable for &. *Background music*: in 1 lounge. *Location*: village on A382, 2¼ miles NE of Chagford. *Smoking*: not allowed. *Children*: all ages welcomed, no under-12s in restaurant in evening. *Dogs*: not allowed in public rooms. *Credit cards*: MasterCard, Visa. *Prices*: b&b £45–£110 per person, d,b&b £75–£165, Christmas/New Year packages, 1-night bookings sometimes refused. *V*

Parford Well   *Tel* 01647-433353
Sandy Park   *Email* tim@parfordwell.co.uk
nr Chagford TQ13 8JW   *Website* www.parfordwell.co.uk

'A simple concept, but beautifully done': this smart little B&B, in a walled garden in a village in the Dartmoor national park, is owned and run by Tim Daniel, once co-owner of *Number Sixteen* in South Kensington, London (see Shortlist); he lives in an adjoining small cottage. 'Each time, something good gets better,' said a reader on his fifth visit. Another returning guest wrote of 'the most accommodating host'. Named after the village well, the house overlooks meadows. It has a comfortable lounge with original paintings, sculptures, fresh flowers, books and a fire. The 'immaculate' small bedrooms upstairs 'have everything you might possibly expect'. One has its bathroom across the hall. Breakfast is 'varied, all cooked to order, nothing packaged, all fresh local produce', and with blue and white china. It is normally served communally, round a farmhouse table, but guests wanting privacy may eat at a table for two across the hall, in a small room hung with luxurious drapes that once belonged to the Queen Mother. There are good walks from the door, on the moor and in the wooded Teign valley. (*DC, KA*)

Bedrooms: 3. *Open*: all year except Christmas. *Facilities*: sitting room, 2 breakfast rooms, ⅕-acre garden, unsuitable for &. *Background music*: none. *Location*: in hamlet 1 mile N of Chagford. *Smoking*: not allowed. *Children*: not under 8. *Dogs*: not allowed. *Credit cards*: none. *Prices*: b&b £35–£85 per person.

CHELTENHAM Gloucestershire   Map 3:D5
See SHORTLIST

CHESTER Cheshire   Map 3:A4

Green Bough
60 Hoole Road
Chester CH2 3NL

Tel 01244-326241
Fax 01244-326265
Email luxury@greenbough.co.uk
Website www.greenbough.co.uk

'Unexpectedly sumptuous', this conversion of two Victorian town houses, a mile from Chester's historic centre, is owned by Janice and Philip Martin; Laura Currie is the manageress. Inspectors were given an 'exemplary' welcome: 'The charming young receptionist explained everything in detail; the owner insisted on carrying our heavy suitcase.' Bedrooms vary. 'Our suite at the top faced the back and was quiet. It had a small sitting room, bedroom with medium-sized double bed, good bathroom. Large teddy on the bed, plastic ducks in the bath. Free Wi-Fi. A card offered choice of pillows and type of bedding.' A 'large, light' deluxe room had 'antique brass bed, two armchairs, squashy sofa, luxurious fabrics'. Traditional afternoon tea is served in the lounge. Muzak plays all day in the public rooms. In the *Olive Tree* restaurant, head chef Tim Seddon's modern European menu might include bay shrimps with griddled brioche; wild partridge with confit oxtail. A five-course *menu gourmand* (£95) includes all accompanying wines. Breakfast had 'a wonderful buffet of fruit compotes, salads, yogurt and comb honey'. There is a rooftop garden with water feature. Buses can be taken into the centre from the busy, tree-lined street. More reports, please.

Bedrooms: 15, 8 in lodge linked by 'feature bridge'. *Open*: all year except 25 Dec–2 Jan. *Facilities*: ramp, lounge, champagne bar, 2 dining rooms, banqueting room, theatre/conference room, rooftop garden, small front garden. *Background music*: classical/jazz in public rooms. *Location*: 1 mile from centre. *Smoking*: not allowed. *Children*: not under 14. *Dogs*: only guide dogs allowed. *Credit cards*: all major cards. *Prices*: b&b £87.50–£172.50 per person, d,b&b £110–£195, set dinner £47.50, full alc £67.50, special breaks.

See also SHORTLIST

CHESTERFIELD Derbyshire   Map 4:E4

Buckingham's Hotel

85–87 Newbold Road, Newbold
Chesterfield S41 7PU

Tel 01246-201041
Fax 01246-550059
Email info@buckinghams-table.com
Website www.buckinghams-table.com

Originally a pair of Victorian semi-detached houses, these old buildings in a residential area of the city have been sympathetically converted by Nick and Tina Buckingham into an unusual hotel with two restaurants. It is managed by daughters Vicci and Emma; son Will is co-chef. Inspectors reported: 'A warm welcome, attractive decor, a well-stocked bar; our spacious bedroom was well equipped.' In *The Restaurant with One Table*, ten guests (a group or unconnected visitors) eat together off a 'surprise menu'. 'You give a list of likes and dislikes, and choose the level of meal, Bronze, Silver, Gold or Platinum' (the last one at £120 per person including wine). *Clowns* conservatory restaurant, open all day, has separate tables. The cooking ('spontaneous modern British') 'uses the best local ingredients'. Our inspectors' meal was 'inventive, the atmosphere was fun, Nick whipped in and out of the kitchen, explaining the dishes. We could not fault the service. Portions are large.' There are 'stunning afternoon teas', award-winning breakfasts and Wi-Fi. And, says the brochure, 'children are more than welcome'.

Bedrooms: 10. *Open*: all year except Christmas/New Year. *Facilities*: stair lift, 2 lounges, bar, 2 restaurants, small conference facilities, courtyard, small Japanese garden. *Background music*: none. *Location*: 1 mile NW of centre. *Smoking*: not allowed. *Children*: all ages welcomed (under supervision). *Dogs*: allowed by arrangement. *Credit cards*: Amex (*5% surcharge*), MasterCard, Visa (*3% surcharge*). *Prices*: [2008] b&b £47.50–£85 per person, d,b&b £72.50–£110, full alc £37.50–£120 (*plus 10% 'discretionary' service charge*), special breaks.

CHETTLE Dorset   Map 2:E1

Castleman   NEW

Chettle
nr Blandford Forum
DT11 8DB

Tel 01258-830096
Fax 01258-830051
Email enquiry@castlemanhotel.co.uk
Website www.castlemanhotel.co.uk

In one of England's few remaining feudal villages (in Cranbourne Chase), this Queen Anne dower house is run as an informal restaurant-with-rooms by Barbara Garnsworthy and Edward Bourke (his family has owned the estate for over 150 years). 'Friendly, with no frills', it has many fans. One writes this year: 'Like being in one's home, delightfully understated, warm and embracing. No sense of hotelier/guest relationship.' Other comments: 'Very reasonable prices.' 'Slightly faded gentility; haphazard decor.' The building, enlarged and remodelled in Victorian days, has a porticoed doorway, galleried hall, carved staircase, plasterwork ceilings, Jacobean fireplace, 'much dark wood'. 'Both lounges have deep armchairs and sofas, plenty of reading matter.' The bar has 'a welcoming fire and warm atmosphere'. In the 'softly elegant', yellow-walled dining room, Mrs Garnsworthy and Richard Morris serve 'excellent' dinners: 'Beef and crab for starters; partridge and scallops for main course; all beyond reproach.' 'Good-value wines.' 'The view from the bedroom was rural; silence is absolute.' 'Our room, with four-poster bed, was very comfortable.' But inspectors thought their bathroom needed renovation. Breakfast is cooked to order: 'Faultless scrambled eggs.' 'Staff universally pleasant and helpful (but don't expect hotel service).' (*Air Vice-Marshal Bobby Robson, Dr and Mrs John Lunn, and others*)

Bedrooms: 8 (1 family). *Open*: all year except 25/26 Dec, 1 Jan, Feb, restaurant closed midday except Sun. *Facilities*: 2 drawing rooms, bar, restaurant, 2-acre grounds (stables for visiting horses), riding, fishing, shooting, cycling nearby, only restaurant suitable for &. *Background music*: none. *Location*: village, 1 mile off A354 Salisbury–Blandford, hotel signposted. *Smoking*: not allowed. *Children*: all ages welcomed. *Dogs*: not allowed. *Credit cards*: MasterCard, Visa. *Prices*: b&b £40–£55, set Sun lunch £21 (child £10.50), full alc from £40, discount for 3 or more nights.

CHICHESTER West Sussex   Map 2:E3
See SHORTLIST

CHIDDINGFOLD Surrey   Map 2:D3
See SHORTLIST

CHILLATON Devon   Map 1:D3

Tor Cottage   *Tel* 01822-860248
Chillaton, nr Lifton   *Fax* 01822-860126
PL16 0JE   *Email* info@torcottage.co.uk
                         Website www.torcottage.co.uk

'Beautifully set', up a bridle path in a secluded mid-Devon valley, this upmarket B&B stands in large wooded grounds with abundant flowers and wildlife. It is run by the 'warm and generous' owner, Maureen Rowlatt. 'Attention to detail is incredible,' say visitors this year. 'She greeted us warmly, gave us a drink while she explained the operation.' Guests are welcomed with a trug containing sparkling wine, home-made truffles, fresh fruit. Four bedrooms, each with private terrace, are in the garden. 'We had Deco, a museum of Art Deco, with a cabinet full of collectibles to which many guests have contributed, and a splendid tiled fireplace.' Laughing Waters has Shaker furniture, a gypsy caravan, a hammock and a barbecue. All rooms have CD- and DVD-player. Reading lights have been upgraded and the pool house has been refurbished; guests are now allowed to use the pool all day and in the evening (bring towels). 'Wonderful' breakfasts, ordered the evening before, are taken in the conservatory or on a terrace. 'We asked for a modest portion of smoked salmon and scrambled eggs. I hate to think what a full portion must do to your figure.' A light supper tray can be ordered in advance (soup and pasty, salads, etc). (*Mr and Mrs MB Gowers, Mrs EM Ludlow, Sonia Coates*)

Bedrooms: 5, 4 in garden. *Open*: mid-Jan–mid-Dec, do not arrive before 4 pm. *Facilities*: sitting room, large conservatory, breakfast room, 28-acre grounds (2-acre garden, heated swimming pool, 13 by 6 metres, barbecue, stream, bridleway, walks), river (fishing ½ mile), unsuitable for &. *Background music*: in breakfast room. *Location*: ½ mile S of Chillaton. *Smoking*: not allowed. *Children*: not under 14. *Dogs*: only guide dogs allowed. *Credit cards*: MasterCard, Visa. *Prices*: b&b (min. 2 nights) £70–£94 per person, tray supper £24, autumn and spring breaks, 1-night bookings sometimes refused.

Make sure the hotel has included VAT in the prices it quotes.

CHRISTCHURCH Dorset   Map 2:E2
See SHORTLIST

CLEE STANTON Co. Shropshire   Map 3:C5

Timberstone   NEW   *Tel* 01584-823519
Clee Stanton   *Email* enquiry@timberstone1.co.uk
nr Ludlow SY8 3EL   *Website* www.timberstoneludlow.co.uk

In a hamlet in the hills above Ludlow, this 'charming house in a peaceful setting' is run as a B&B by Alex Read and Tracey Baylis, 'a delightful couple'. In June 2008, they completed an extension with two extra bedrooms, and a 'lovely, light connecting room', with comfy sofas and chairs, and a large dining table; kilim rugs on oak floorboards; lots of books, TV, DVDs, games. 'Alex greeted us warmly, brought us tea and biscuits, and lent us the house phone to sort out a problem with our car,' said an inspector. 'We loved our large bedroom in the main house, with original beams, old pine furniture, sofa, window seat, big comfortable bed; the attractive bathroom has a long claw-foot bath.' The new bedrooms, have 'beautifully crafted oak fittings'; one has a free-standing bath in the room, and a small balcony. Breakfast, served communally, has 'big jars of organic cereals and muesli, fresh fruit, yogurt, home-made preserves. Lovely chunky toast, tasty bacon and sausages, eggs from their own hens.' The hostess, who once worked with the chef Shaun Hill in Ludlow, cooks dinner, by arrangement: 'Good country dishes, local pork and lamb, delicious summer pudding.' A qualified reflexologist and Bowen therapist, she offers treatments. A green agenda is followed, with an underground heat pump, solar panels. Children and dogs are welcome; they have two young sons and two outdoor dogs.

Bedrooms: 4 (plus summerhouse retreat in summer). *Open*: all year. *Facilities*: lounge/dining room, ½-acre garden, treatment room, unsuitable for &. *Background music*: in lounge/dining room ('but guests may turn it off'). *Location*: 5 miles NE of Ludlow. *Smoking*: not allowed. *Children*: all ages welcome. *Dogs*: allowed (£4). *Credit cards*: Amex, MasterCard, Visa. *Prices*: b&b £40–£70 per person, set dinner £22.

Report forms (Freepost in UK) are at the end of the *Guide*. If you need more, please ask. We welcome email reports, too: send these to editor@goodhotelguide.com.

CLIPSHAM Rutland   Map 2:A3

Beech House & Olive Branch

Main Street
Clipsham LE15 7SH

Tel 01780-410355
Fax 01780-410000
Email beechhouse@theolivebranchpub.com
Website www.theolivebranchpub.com

'Strongly recommended; an enjoyable stay, a comfortable room, an interesting dinner at a reasonable price,' says a visitor this year. In an attractive village near Stamford, Sean Hope (chef) and Ben Jones, formerly of *Hambleton Hall* (*qv*), have a *Michelin* star for their pub/ restaurant; opposite they provide accommodation in honey-coloured Georgian *Beech House*. Facing rolling fields, it has a 'cheerful' hall, with a checked carpet and contemporary hunting prints. The colourful bedrooms combine antiques with a contemporary feel. Aubergine has an Art Deco theme; Biscuit, on the ground floor, has a lounge area and seating on a patio; Double Cream has 'a stunning bathroom, claw-footed bath positioned so you get nice views while soaking'. The only public area is the landing, which has a fridge, CDs, DVDs, magazines, books, local information. The *Olive Branch* has a rustic ambience: stone-flagged floors and wooden floors, plain wooden tables, pews, an open fire. Dishes might include shallot Tatin, smoked duck breast; organic salmon, bhaji rösti, curried cauliflower sauce. Breakfast, in the *Barn*, adjacent, has fresh juice, a buffet of fresh fruit, muesli, yogurt, smoothies, etc; cooked dishes include boiled eggs with soldiers, kippers. Service was thought 'a little casual' this year. (*MB Griffith, ANR, and others*)

Bedrooms: 6, 2 on ground floor, family room (also suitable for &) in annexe. *Open*: all year except 25/26 Dec, 1 Jan. *Facilities*: ramps, pub, dining room, breakfast room, small front garden. *Background music*: in pub. *Location*: in village 7 miles NW of Stamford. *Smoking*: not allowed. *Children*: all ages welcomed. *Dogs*: allowed in downstairs bedrooms and bar. *Credit cards*: MasterCard, Visa. *Prices*: [2008] b&b £55–£160 per person, full alc £39, 1-night bookings refused bank holidays.

How to contact the *Guide*
By mail: From anywhere in the UK, write to Freepost PAM 2931, London W11 4BR (no stamp is needed)
From outside the UK: *Good Hotel Guide*, 50 Addison Avenue, London W11 4QP, England
By telephone or fax: 020-7602 4182
By email: editor@goodhotelguide.com
Via our website: www.goodhotelguide.com

COLWALL Worcestershire   Map 3:D5

Colwall Park Hotel	*Tel* 01684-540000
Colwall, nr Malvern	*Fax* 01684-540847
WR13 6QG	*Email* hotel@colwall.com
	Website www.colwall.com

'Far removed from the world of chain hotels.' In a pretty village below the western slopes of the Malvern hills, this mock-Tudor building is run as a traditional hotel by owners Iain and Sarah Nesbitt with manager Peter Dann. Their staff are 'efficient, friendly and caring', says a report in 2008. 'Service was the correct balance between professional and friendly,' says a visitor in a party of eight. The bedrooms, 'spotlessly clean, with ample space', vary in size: bathrooms have been renewed this year, and rooms have flat-screen TV with Freeview channels. 'Ours had fresh flowers, books, table games.' A standard double 'had repro Edwardian furniture, large bed, lovely soft pillows'. Some bedrooms face the garden but some others hear traffic; some singles have a shower only; some attic rooms have limited head room. One winter visitor complained of a cold room. In the oak-panelled *Seasons* restaurant, everyone liked James Garth's modern cooking; local suppliers are named on a menu that might include terrine of spiced pig's cheek and white beans; steamed sea trout on a herb and pea risotto. The *Lantern* bar, popular with locals, serves sandwiches, soups, and dishes like fish cakes; lamb's liver and streaky bacon. There is good walking from the door on to the Malvern hills. A good base for exploring Elgar country. (*David Nicholls, Mrs M Davies, Alison Pitman, and others*)

Bedrooms: 22. *Open*: all year. *Facilities*: ramp, 2 lounges (1 with TV), library, bar, restaurant, ballroom, business facilities, 2-acre garden (croquet, boules), only public rooms suitable for &. *Background music*: blues in bar, jazz in restaurant. *Location*: halfway between Malvern and Ledbury on B4218, train Colwall. *Smoking*: not allowed. *Children*: all ages welcomed. *Dogs*: allowed in 1 bedroom, not in public rooms. *Credit cards*: MasterCard, Visa. *Prices*: b&b £60–£95 per person, full alc £43, Christmas/New Year packages, 1-night bookings refused weekends. ***V***

****

Traveller's tale *Hotel in Cornwall* The food was truly terrible: tough veal, over-cooked trout, over-boiled vegetables were our first taste of the ghastly fare served in this huge room with no atmosphere and staff keen to leave as soon as possible. The wine list was hopeless.

****

CONSTANTINE BAY Cornwall   Map 1:D2

Treglos Hotel   *Tel* 01841-520727
Constantine Bay   *Fax* 01841-521163
Padstow PL28 8JH   *Email* stay@tregloshotel.com
                         Website www.tregloshotel.com

In landscaped gardens overlooking Constantine Bay, this traditional hotel has been run by the Barlow family for over 40 years. Regular visitors like 'the quiet, professional atmosphere' and the old-fashioned extras: early morning tea brought to the room (at a charge), nocturnal shoe cleaning, log fires. 'Charming, beautifully trained staff, excellent food, very comfortable bedrooms.' The beach, with access to the coastal path, is five minutes' walk away. This year, treatment rooms have been added to the 'very nice' small indoor swimming pool and spa. The Barlows like men to wear jacket and tie in the evening, except during summer school holidays. Wally Vellacott, the 'much-loved' *maître d'*, has retired after 35 years. Chef Paul Becker serves a daily-changing five-course dinner menu with plenty of choice, eg, shellfish bisque with rouille and Parmesan; roast pork with honey-baked apples. Families are welcomed, but not children under seven in the restaurant in the evening (they have supper at 5.30 pm). Breakfasts are 'commendable': hot dishes cooked to order include haddock and kippers. Bedrooms have light colour schemes. The garden has secluded sitting places and a children's play area. The Barlows also own Merlin Golf and Country Club (ten minutes' drive). (*Ian and Barbara Dewey, Juliet Sebag-Montefiore*)

Bedrooms: 42, some on ground floor, 2 suitable for &. *Open*: 12 Feb–28 Nov. *Facilities*: 2 lounges (pianist twice weekly), bar, restaurant, children's den, snooker room, beauty treatments, indoor swimming pool (10 by 5 metres), whirlpool, treatment rooms, 5-acre grounds (croquet, badminton, children's play area), sandy beach 5 mins' walk. *Background music*: none. *Location*: 3 miles W of Padstow. *Smoking*: not allowed. *Children*: no under-7s in restaurant at night. *Dogs*: not allowed in public rooms. *Credit cards*: MasterCard, Visa. *Prices*: b&b £63.25–£92 per person, d,b&b £78.25–£110, full alc £40, 4 nights for the price of 3 Mar, Apr, Oct, Christmas/New Year packages. *V*

COOKHAM DEAN Berkshire   Map 2:D3
See SHORTLIST

Our new website works in tandem with the printed *Guide*.

CORSE LAWN Gloucestershire   Map 3:D5

Corse Lawn House

Corse Lawn GL19 4LZ

Tel 01452-780771
Fax 01452-780840
Email enquiries@corselawn.com
Website www.corselawn.com

♔ *César award in 2005*

'Hurrah for *Corse Lawn House*, so peaceful and pleasant,' write returning visitors. This red brick Queen Anne Grade II listed building, set back from the village green and a busy road near Tewkesbury, is fronted by a large pond. Owner Baba Hine and her 'very helpful' staff 'make everyone welcome, including children'. She 'has a flair for colour and decor': she tells us that redecoration is now complete. Traditionally furnished bedrooms, 'like a comfortable spare room in someone's country house', have 'fridge with fresh milk, teapot, biscuits and fruit'. 'Our ground-floor room was spacious.' Chef Andrew Poole's cooking is thought 'first class': 'Superb megrim, a white fish not from over-fished stocks; truffled guinea fowl breast.' Smart casual dress is 'preferred' in the restaurant; T-shirts and jeans may be worn in the bistro. Breakfast, often cooked by Mrs Hine, is the 'best': 'magical' freshly squeezed orange juice, 'delicious' marmalade, nothing packaged. 'The black Labradors, Sugar and Spice, were an added attraction for our 11-year-old son'; visiting dogs are welcome. The swimming pool, tennis court and croquet lawn are liked; plans for a small luxury spa were approved as the *Guide* went to press. (*Joanna and Paul Lindsell, Caroline and Richard Faircliff, Gordon Hands*)

Bedrooms: 19, 5 on ground floor. *Open*: all year except 24–26 Dec. *Facilities*: lounge, bar lounge, bistro/bar, restaurant, 2 conference/private dining rooms, civil wedding licence, 12-acre grounds (croquet, tennis, covered heated swimming pool, 13 by 7 metres). *Background music*: none. *Location*: 5 miles SW of Tewkesbury on B4211. *Smoking*: not allowed. *Children*: all ages welcomed. *Dogs*: allowed in bedrooms, drawing rooms. *Credit cards*: all major cards. *Prices*: b&b £75–£95 per person, d,b&b £100–£120, set dinner £31.50, full alc £40, New Year package, 1-night bookings sometimes refused. *V*

When you make a booking you enter into a contract with a hotel. Most hotels explain their cancellation policies, which vary widely, in a letter of confirmation. You may lose your deposit or be charged at the full rate for the room if you cancel at short notice. A travel insurance policy can provide protection.

COVERACK Cornwall   Map 1:E2

The Bay Hotel   NEW   *Tel* 01326-280464
North Corner, Coverack   *Email* enquiries@thebayhotel.co.uk
nr Helston TR12 6TF   *Website* www.thebayhotel.co.uk

In a 'gorgeous little fishing village' on the coastal path, this is the
Lizard peninsula's first boutique hotel, say its owners, the House
family. Since buying the white-painted building in 2006, they have
completely refurbished in 'mellow coastal tones'. From the
'exquisite' conservatory restaurant, there are 'spectacular, unres-
tricted views', write the nominators who spent 'two perfect nights' in
this 'very comfortable' place. 'They made us genuinely welcome
without going over the top.' Gina House is the 'tireless front-of-
house'; her husband Ric's cooking is 'delicious'. He promises 'simply
cooked food with locally sourced seasonal produce including fish and
lobster from the bay', eg, Helford moules marinière; hake in tempura
batter with chips. His *table d'hôte* menu (priced for two or three
courses) changes nightly. A Cornish cream tea can be taken on the
garden terrace. The bedrooms have full or partial views across
Coverack Bay; the beach is nearby. 'There is no through traffic in the
village, guaranteeing peace,' we are told. (*Marie and Kevin Halliwell*)

Bedrooms: 13, some on ground floor. *Open*: Mar–2 Jan. *Facilities*: reception
lounge, lounge, bar lounge, restaurant, 1-acre garden. *Background music*: none.
Location: village centre, 10 miles SE of Helston. *Smoking*: not allowed. *Children*:
not under 8. *Dogs*: not allowed in public rooms. *Credit cards*: MasterCard, Visa.
Prices: b&b £57–£133 per person, d,b&b £67–£143, set dinner £20.95–£26.50,
website offers, Christmas/New Year house parties.

COWAN BRIDGE Lancashire   Map 4: inset D2

Hipping Hall   *Tel* 015242-71187
Cowan Bridge,   *Email* info@hippinghall.com
nr Kirkby Lonsdale LA6 2JJ   *Website* www.hippinghall.com

❦ *César award in 2008*

'Great comfort, good welcome, cheery service.' 'What a lovely place.'
Much praise this year for this small hotel/restaurant managed by its
'ever-present' owner, Andrew Wildsmith. The 17th-century house
and other stone buildings stand amid mature trees, lawns and shrub-
bery in a village near Kirkby Lonsdale. Their conversion 'blends
traditional and modern to create seamless perfection'. The sitting

room, with 'large, comfortable sofas', paintings, patterned wallpaper, has a traditional feel. 'Superb pre-starters, including frogs' legs' are served in the bar. The restaurant, a 'spectacular' double-height 15th-century Great Hall, with tapestries and minstrels' gallery, is 'a fitting setting' for the 'impressive' cooking of the 'talented' young chef, Jason 'Bruno' Birkbeck, 'served with pomp and ceremony'. 'Seared foie gras with quail's breast and a sauterne jelly was a conversation-stopper.' Main courses might include sea bass, saffron potatoes, aubergine caviar. 'Background music was turned down when we asked.' The bedrooms 'all highly individual, light, beautifully done out' have a contemporary decor. 'Our large room had white walls, a clean, neutral feel: no pictures, simple wooden bedside tables, big bed with duvet and quality bedlinen.' One couple would have liked a curtain in their suite's sitting room. Breakfast, 'another triumph, with Andrew Wildsmith in charge', has 'fine choice of cooked dishes, leaf tea, fresh juices, good toast'. Communicating with the hotel can be a problem. (*Tessa Mack, Gill Holden, Anne Thornthwaite, David and Kate Wooff, and others*)

Bedrooms: 9, 3 in cottage, 8 on ground floor. *Open*: all year except first 3 weeks Jan, restaurant closed Sun evening. *Facilities*: lounge, bar, restaurant, civil wedding licence. *Background music*: classical in restaurant, jazz in lounge and bar. *Location*: 2 miles SE of Kirkby Lonsdale, on A65. *Smoking*: not allowed. *Children*: no under-12s in restaurant. *Dogs*: allowed in Room 7 only. *Credit cards*: all major cards. *Prices*: b&b £77.50–£155.50 per person, d,b&b £102.50–£205, set dinner £49.50, Christmas/New Year packages, 1-night bookings refused Sat.

> Don't trust out-of-date editions of the *Guide*. Hotels change hands, deteriorate or go out of business. Every year, there are many new hotels and many are dropped.

CRANBROOK Kent   Map 2:E4

Cloth Hall Oast
Coursehorn Lane
Cranbrook TN17 3NR

Tel/Fax 01580-712220
Email clothhalloast@aol.com

Katherine Morgan's 'decidedly upmarket' guest house is a conversion of an oast house, barn and stables, set amid fields in the Kentish Weald. It drew praise from *Guide* readers again this year. Visitors are greeted with 'a pot of tea, warm scones, coffee cake and what Alan Bennett would call "fancies". Delightfully civilised.' 'The excellent hospitality provided by Mrs Morgan made our stay memorable.' She is 'informative about local attractions' (Sissinghurst, Chartwell, Bodiam Castle, etc). A Cordon Bleu cook, she presides at the communal dinner. Dinners might include home-made pâté or soup; stuffed leg of lamb with apricots. 'Lovely meals in a wonderful setting.' 'Relaxed evenings with imaginative home cooking.' No licence: bring your own wine. 'Fine china, home-made jams and good coffee made breakfast a pleasure.' The building is filled with Persian rugs, 'beautiful porcelain and silverware and delicate paintings'. Sofas and armchairs face a deep carved stone fireplace in the elegant lounge where 'expanses of glass look over the garden'. Two bedrooms are in the oast house, the third is off a galleried landing; one room is triple-bedded; bathrooms are 'state-of-the-art'. In the grounds are heated swimming pool, pergola and lily pond. (*Roger and Lesley Everett, G and AE Crossley, and others*)

Bedrooms: 3. *Open*: all year except Christmas. *Facilities*: sitting room, dining room, 5-acre garden (croquet, fishpond, heated swimming pool, 5 by 10 metres), unsuitable for &. *Background music*: none. *Location*: 1 mile SE of Cranbrook. *Smoking*: not allowed. *Children*: by arrangement. *Dogs*: not allowed. *Credit cards*: none. *Prices*: b&b £45–£75 per person, evening meal £25, 1-night bookings sometimes refused Sat and bank holidays.

****

Traveller's tale *Hotel in Edinburgh* The bedroom was large and had a comfortable bed, but the furniture looked as if it had been bought as a job lot at an auction. Very little of it matched. The TV could not be watched from the bed as the wooden bed-end was just high enough to obscure it. The sash window catch had only one part screwed into the frame, the other half rested loose and unfixed on the other frame. The wardrobe was only five feet tall.

****

CROFT-ON-TEES Co. Durham   Map 4:C4

Clow Beck House

Monk End Farm
Croft-on-Tees
nr Darlington DL2 2SW

Tel 01325-721075
Fax 01325-720419
Email david@clowbeckhouse.co.uk
Website www.clowbeckhouse.co.uk

❧ *César award in 2007*

In open countryside on the outskirts of Croft-on-Tees, David and
Heather Armstrong run their small, popular hotel 'decorated with
some flamboyance and individuality'. 'A fascinating and usual place,'
said inspectors. Returning visitors write: 'As good as ever, it stands out
for the wonderful service and all the extras provided.' The large, comfortable bedrooms are in stone-built outbuildings around a landscaped garden. Some have their own small garden. Decor is varied,
sometimes with a dash of theatricality. One room is 'cream, light and
airy with a touch of gold lustre and a king-size bed'. 'Ours had sparkly
chandeliers, carved wooden ceiling roses and bay window area like a
proscenium arch.' Wi-Fi is free. The 'most attractive' large restaurant,
on two levels, with beams, arched windows and tiled floor, leads to a
terrace. David Armstrong serves 'good, large rustic portions' of food,
perhaps oven-roasted chicken in a wholegrain mustard sauce; rack of
Yorkshire lamb with an apricot glaze. Puddings and cheeses are
'delicious'. 'Those with moderate appetite would do well to go for a
starter and dessert, which will keep you going until it's time to tackle
the huge breakfast.' Vegetarians are catered for. Children have their
own menu. (*CLH*)

Bedrooms: 13, 12 in garden buildings, 1 suitable for ♿. *Open*: all year except
Christmas, New Year, restaurant closed midday. *Facilities*: ramps, lounge,
restaurant, small conference facilities, 2-acre grounds in 100-acre farm.
Background music: in restaurant. *Location*: 3 miles SE of Darlington, via unmade
road (follow brown signs). *Smoking*: not allowed. *Children*: all ages welcomed.
Dogs: not allowed. *Credit cards*: Amex, MasterCard, Visa. *Prices*: b&b £67.50–
£85 per person, full alc £32–£38.

Readers' contributions, written on the forms at the back of the
book or sent by email, are the lifeblood of the *Good Hotel Guide*.
Our readers play a crucial role by reporting on existing entries
as well as recommending new discoveries. Everyone who
writes to the *Guide* is a potential winner of the Report of the
Year competition (page 63), in which a dozen correspondents
each year win a copy of the *Guide* and an invitation to our
annual launch party in October.

CROOKHAM Northumberland   Map 4:A3

The Coach House at Crookham   *Tel* 01890-820293
Crookham   *Fax* 01890-820284
Cornhill-on-Tweed   *Email* stay@coachhousecrookham.com
TD12 4TD   *Website* www.coachhousecrookham.com

Set back from the road near Flodden Field, close to the Scottish
border, this extended Grade II listed 17th-century dower house is run
by Toby and Leona Rutter, the 'very friendly' owners, who are proud
of their facilities for disabled visitors. Most of the bedrooms are in a
single-storey building linked by paved paths around a courtyard; three
rooms have a private bathroom adjacent; the bigger rooms have a large-
screen TV and DVD/CD-player. 'My spacious room had fresh flowers,
candles, views of fields and the Cheviot hills.' Children are welcome
(there are adjoining rooms, good for families); so are dogs, in the
courtyard rooms. Afternoon teas (free for arriving guests) and drinks
(from an honesty bar) are taken in the vaulted residents' lounge which
faces an orchard where Shetland ponies graze under damson trees.
Generous portions of traditional, 'wholesome' dishes are served at 7.30
pm. Eight choices of starter, eg, tuna fish cake with chilli dip; one main
course, perhaps lamb with redcurrant jelly and mint sauce; pudding or
cheese. Vegetarians are catered for. Breakfast 'is another happy
experience' (a large selection of fruits, yogurt and cereals, home-made
preserves; various egg dishes; smoked salmon, kippers and kedgeree
if ordered the night before). More reports, please.

Bedrooms: 11, 7 round courtyard, 3 suitable for &. *Open*: all year except
Christmas/New Year. *Facilities*: lounge, 2 dining rooms, terrace, orchard.
Background music: none. *Location*: On A697, 3 miles N of Milfield. *Smoking*: not
allowed. *Children*: all ages welcomed. *Dogs*: allowed in courtyard rooms only.
Credit cards: MasterCard, Visa. *Prices*: b&b £26–£48 per person, set dinner
£21.95, 1-night bookings refused weekends July/Aug.

CROSBY-ON-EDEN Cumbria   Map 4:B2

Crosby Lodge   *Tel* 01228-573618
High Crosby, Crosby-on-Eden   *Fax* 01228-573428
CA6 4QZ   *Email* enquiries@crosbylodge.co.uk
          Website www.crosbylodge.co.uk

Five minutes' drive from the M6, this traditional hotel is a 'great
place to break a journey'. 'The building is lovely,' says a visitor this
year, 'a bit old-fashioned but well cared for. The owners [Michael

and Patricia Sedgwick] were welcoming but not fussy.' The 'relaxed feel' is liked. In partly wooded grounds overlooking parkland and the River Eden (fishing available), the castellated, creeper-covered Grade II listed building (1805) has a chintzy decor. 'Atmosphere of a country house hotel of 30 years ago, in the best way. Not for those seeking a boutique hotel.' All the bedrooms are different; some face the park. 'Ours was comfortable, with stunning views.' In the 'particularly attractive' dining room ('old furniture, tasteful antiques, knick-knacks on shelves, family photos'), dinner comes in 'generous portions'. The set menu has a choice of six dishes for each of the first two courses, then dessert from a trolley, or cheese. Or you could go for the 'classic *à la carte*' (steak and chips; sole meunière, etc). 'Great breakfasts' have home-made yogurt, fresh berries, kippers, home-baked bread, silver teapot ('plentiful tea') and bone china. For lunch you could order haddock in beer batter. (*Ann Morrison, and others*)

Bedrooms: 11, 2 in converted stables (ramp), 1 on ground floor. *Open*: mid-Jan–24 Dec. *Facilities*: lounge/bar, restaurant, function facilities, 4½-acre grounds (walled garden with gazebo). *Background music*: in restaurant. *Location*: 4½ miles NE of Carlisle, off A689. *Smoking*: not allowed. *Children*: all ages welcomed. *Dogs*: allowed in stables rooms only. *Credit cards*: Amex, MasterCard, Visa. *Prices*: [2008] b&b £80–£105 per person, d,b&b £117.50–£142.50, full alc £65, special breaks.

CROSBY RAVENSWORTH   Map 4: inset C2
Cumbria

Crake Trees Manor   NEW   *Tel* 01931-715205
Crosby Ravensworth   *Email* ruth@craketreesmanor.co.uk
nr Penrith CA10 3JG   *Website* www.craketreesmanor.co.uk

In Eden valley, between villages of Crosby Ravensworth and Maulds Meaburn: Ruth Tuer's guest house (converted 18th-century barn) on traditional mixed farm with sheep, Jack Russells, meadows and pastures. Large galleried hall with wood fire and library; English farmhouse supper; generous Aga-cooked breakfast in Glass House (background radio). Large garden (pond, ha-ha). 'Warm welcome with tea and cakes; heavenly bedroom with green slate, oak and flagstones. Family atmosphere. Good value.' Open Mar–Dec; no dinner Sat/Sun except for house parties. No smoking. 4 bedrooms (2, with cooking facilities, in courtyard), 1 on ground floor. Dogs by arrangement. MasterCard, Visa accepted. Prices: b&b £45–£60 per person, set dinner £25.

CROSTHWAITE Cumbria   Map 4: inset C2

The Punch Bowl Inn	*Tel* 01539-568237
Crosthwaite, Lyth Valley	*Fax* 01539-568875
LA8 8HR	*Email* info@the-punchbowl.co.uk
	Website www.the-punchbowl.co.uk

'Smartly informal', this 300-year-old inn stands opposite St Mary's church in a village in the peaceful Lyth valley. Owned by a local consortium, including Paul Spencer and Stephanie Barton, which also runs *The Drunken Duck Inn*, Barngates, it is managed by Jenny Sisson. There are smartly set tables, leather dining chairs and polished floorboards in the low-ceilinged restaurant where chef Jonny Watson serves a *carte* of modern dishes, eg, confit duck and foie gras roulade; seared sea bass with parsnip and vanilla purée. Brasserie-style meals are served in the bar (12–6 pm). The bedrooms, named after former vicars of the church, have original beams, large bed, flat-screen TV. 'Our spacious, superior double room had a high ceiling, oversized sofa, subdued lighting from table lamps, adequate when supplemented by overhead spots; big bathroom with under-floor heating and claw-footed bath.' One room occupies the inn's whole third floor. One bathroom has two baths side-by-side. There are two terraces for alfresco eating and drinking. Breakfast has 'juice freshly squeezed; leaf tea'. The small lounge has deep leather sofas. The village post office is operated from Reception. More reports, please.

Bedrooms: 9. *Open*: all year. *Facilities*: lounge, 2 bar rooms, restaurant, 2 terraces, civil wedding licence, only restaurant suitable for &. *Background music*: none. *Location*: 5 miles W of Kendal, via A591. *Smoking*: not allowed. *Children*: all ages welcomed. *Dogs*: not allowed in bedrooms. *Credit cards*: Amex, MasterCard, Visa. *Prices*: b&b £62.50–£155 per person, full alc £40, Christmas/New Year packages.

CRUDWELL Wiltshire   Map 3:E5

The Rectory Hotel	*Tel* 01666-577194
Crudwell, nr Malmesbury	*Fax* 01666-577853
SN16 9EP	*Email* info@therectoryhotel.com
	Website www.therectoryhotel.com

In a walled garden by a church, this 16th-century former rectory has been given a 'contemporary feel' by owners Julian Muggridge (antique dealer) and Jonathan Barry (ex-Hotel du Vin group). 'A pleasant place to stay,' say visitors in 2008. The large hall/sitting room has soft chairs and magazines. 'A collection of ornamental glass is well displayed in the high-ceilinged bar lounge, with its plastic side tables and glass-shelved alcoves.' But this was 'not a cosy room when the young staff didn't light a fire during a winter storm and we had to spend most of the day indoors'. Bedrooms, named after hills on the Cotswold Way, are all different. 'Our spacious room had a miscellany of furniture but a brand-new king-size bed; sisal carpeting; a magnificent new bathroom.' The dining room, with original 'lovely' wooden panelling, faces a fish pond. Chef Peter Fairclough serves classic British dishes on a seasonal menu ('it didn't change in six days,' one couple wrote). 'Interesting, perfectly cooked,' said inspectors. Guests can also eat at *The Potting Shed*, a pub opposite, under the same ownership. At breakfast, the English platter was thought 'copious and tasty', but the orange juice was not liked. (*Noel Brooke, and others*)

Bedrooms: 12. *Open*: all year. *Facilities*: lounge, bar, dining room, civil wedding licence, 3-acre garden (heated 20-metre swimming pool), unsuitable for &. *Background music*: 'soft' in bar. *Location*: 4 miles N of Malmesbury. *Smoking*: not allowed. *Children*: all ages welcomed. *Dogs*: not allowed in dining room. *Credit cards*: Diners, MasterCard, Visa. *Prices*: b&b £52.50–£107.50 per person, full alc £32.50, midweek breaks, Christmas/New Year packages, 1-night bookings refused bank holidays.

DARLINGTON Co. Durham   Map 4:C4
See SHORTLIST

DARTMOUTH Devon   Map 1:D4

Knocklayd
Redoubt Hill, Kingswear
Dartmouth TQ6 0DA

Tel/Fax 01803-752873
Email stay@knocklayd.com
Website www.knocklayd.com

'Very much a home', this small guest house is run by its 'extremely hospitable' owner/managers, Susan and Jonathan Cardale. It stands at the highest point in Kingswear village, and has panoramic views over the estuary to Dartmouth. The owners, whose dog Molly, a bichon frise, is a retired hearing dog for the deaf (Jessie, their Labrador, has died), welcome visiting canines. They can sleep in the 'doggie dormitory' (the utility room) or by the Aga in the kitchen. On cold days, guests can sit by an Edwardian fireplace in the sitting room. The Garden Room (with TV/DVD) has French windows on to the lawn, and a huge picture window facing the river. All the bedrooms have the views: 'Everything was stylish and of quality in our pretty and thoughtfully appointed room. Fluffy towels and hot water were abundant.' Wi-Fi is available. Breakfast, taken at a table with white linen and silverware, has 'delicious fruit, excellent coffee, full English, smoked haddock or French toast with maple syrup. Mrs Cardale, a Cordon Bleu cook, will provide an evening meal by arrangement, perhaps seared scallops with orange and thyme; sea bass with puy lentils, Mediterranean vegetables and new potatoes. *Knocklayd* is on the market: prospective visitors should check the position before booking.

Bedrooms: 3. *Open*: all year, except Christmas/New Year. *Facilities*: lounge, garden room, dining room, garden, rock beach 300 yds, sailing nearby, unsuitable for &. *Background music*: none. *Location*: 5 mins' walk from ferry to Dartmouth. *Smoking*: not allowed. *Children*: all ages welcomed (under-12s in room with parents). *Dogs*: not allowed in bedrooms (they sleep in the doggie dormitory). *Credit cards*: MasterCard, Visa. *Prices*: b&b £45–£55 per person, set dinner £25–£30, reductions for 3 nights out of season.

Nonsuch House   *Tel* 01803-752829
Church Hill, Kingswear   *Fax* 01803-752357
Dartmouth TQ6 0BX   *Email* enquiries@nonsuch-house.co.uk
                           Website www.nonsuch-house.co.uk

❦ *César award in 2000*

Kit and Penny Noble, owners of this upmarket guest house, high on the south-facing Kingswear side of the Dart estuary, 'strive to please, and succeed', writes a visitor in 2008. Another reader found 'everything lovely about this place'. The public rooms of the Edwardian villa have canary-yellow walls, royal-blue carpets, 'interesting ornaments and books'. In good weather afternoon tea, with home-made cakes, is served under a parasol on the terrace, as boats go by. Digital TV and CD-players have been installed in the bedrooms, and there is free Wi-Fi access for guests. Meals, served in a 'beautiful conservatory', were 'nearly perfect'. Breakfast has 'proper bread', fresh orange juice, home-made muesli. Dinner is available four nights a week; the blackboard menu depends on local produce, eg, roasted red pepper soup; fillet of pollack with fine herbs and capers. Special needs are taken into account. No liquor licence – bring your own wine. When the dining room is closed, guests can take a ferry across the estuary to Dartmouth with its range of eating places. 'The only problem with *Nonsuch House* is that it is always fully booked.' (*Dr and Mrs Codd, Jo Woodcock*)

Bedrooms: 4. *Open*: all year, dining room closed midday, evening Tues/Wed/Sat. *Facilities*: ramps, lounge, dining room/conservatory, ¼-acre garden (sun terrace), rock beach 300 yds (sailing nearby), membership of local gym and spa. *Background music*: none. *Location*: 5 mins' walk from ferry to Dartmouth. *Smoking*: not allowed. *Children*: not under 10. *Dogs*: not allowed. *Credit cards*: MasterCard, Visa. *Prices*: b&b £52.50–£110 per person, d,b&b £70–£145, Christmas/New Year packages, 1-night bookings sometimes refused weekends.

See also SHORTLIST

DEDHAM Essex   Map 2:C5

The Sun Inn   NEW   *Tel* 01206-323351
High Street, Dedham   *Email* office@thesuninndedham.com
nr Colchester CO7 6DF   *Website* www.thesuninndedham.com

Opposite Dedham's church, this 15th-century building is owned by Piers Baker, who 'has dedicated much thought to his guests' comfort'. Ollie Banks is the 'helpful young manager'. Painted yellow outside and in the bar, it has old oak floorboards and beams, window seats, sofas, club chairs, board games, books, lots of local information. Praise this year: 'Such a warm welcome; young staff insisted on carrying upstairs our numerous pieces of luggage. We were given the choice of two beautifully furnished rooms. We felt totally relaxed in the warm atmosphere.' There are large beds, 'divinely comfortable mattresses', neutral fabrics, 'great showers', and 'quirky touches', eg, old packing cases for bedside tables. 'Three log fires in comfortable seating areas. Drawing room in country house style, much preferable to the minimalist style much favoured these days.' The 'more contemporary' restaurant has 'chairs that are actually comfortable' and 'a nice buzz'. Chef Ugo Simonelli's cooking is 'truly delicious, inventive, Italian style'. Breakfast, 'a treat', has 'big jug of fresh orange juice, melon, delicious raspberry jam, marmalade and honey, basket of rolls, toast, etc'. Children are welcomed (menus adapted; games, books; slide, swing, etc, in the large walled garden). There is a covered terrace with heaters. Background music plays all day, but at night 'only church bells might disturb the peace'. (*Kathy Armes*)

Bedrooms: 5. *Open*: all year except 25/26 Dec. *Facilities*: lounge, bar, dining room, ½-acre garden (covered terrace, children's play area), unsuitable for &. *Background music*: jazz/Latin/blues throughout. *Location*: central, 5 miles NE of

Colchester. *Smoking*: not allowed. *Children*: all ages welcomed. *Dogs*: not allowed in bedrooms. *Credit cards*: MasterCard, Visa. *Prices*: b&b £42.50–£65 per person, set menus £12.50–£13.50, full alc £25, midweek breaks.

See also SHORTLIST

DODDISCOMBSLEIGH Devon   Map 1:C4

The Nobody Inn	*Tel* 01647-252394
Doddiscombsleigh	*Fax* 01647-252978
nr Exeter EX6 7PS	*Email* info@nobodyinn.co.uk
	Website www.nobodyinn.co.uk

In January 2008, Andy and Rowena Whiteman bought this 'storybook' 16th-century inn which lies hidden among hills and fields of rural Devon. They describe it as a 'gastropub with modern European influences'. Visitors in the spring found them 'very welcoming' and had a 'really enjoyable stay, good dinner'. The bar and restaurant have been redecorated, retaining the original features (inglenook fireplaces, blackened beams, antique settles, etc; 'no piped music or fruit machines'). There are new outside dining areas. Work was in progress on the four bedrooms in the pub as the *Guide* went to press; three will have facilities *en suite* while a smaller, single room will have a shower opposite. The annexe rooms were not part of the sale. The flask of complimentary sherry will still be provided in the bedrooms; the lengthy wine and whisky lists (250 of each) remain, and cheeses are still a speciality. Simeon Baber is the new chef. Bar menus include fish pie; pork and leek sausages. In the restaurant you could dine on slow-cooked oxtail with red wine jus; asparagus ravioli, Parmesan and rocket leaves. (*David Crowe*)

Bedrooms: 4. *Open*: all year except 25/26 Dec, 1 Jan. *Facilities*: 2 bars, restaurant, 2½-acre grounds (small garden, patio, paddock), unsuitable for &. *Background music*: none. *Location*: 6 miles SW of Exeter. *Smoking*: not allowed. *Children*: by arrangement. *Dogs*: allowed in part of bar only. *Credit cards*: MasterCard, Visa. *Prices*: b&b £30–£55 per person, full alc £26, 1-night bookings sometimes refused bank holidays. *V*

New reports help us keep the *Guide* up to date.

DONCASTER South Yorkshire   Map 4:E4
See SHORTLIST

DOVER Kent *See SHORTLIST*   Map 2:D5

DURHAM Co. Durham *See SHORTLIST* Map 4:B4

DUXFORD Cambridgeshire   Map 2:C4
See SHORTLIST

EAST GRINSTEAD West Sussex   Map 2:D4

Gravetye Manor   *Tel* 01342-810567
Vowels Lane   *Fax* 01342-810080
East Grinstead RH19 4LJ   *Email* info@gravetyemanor.co.uk
                  Website www.gravetyemanor.co.uk

For one loyal follower this is the 'template for country house hotels'. It celebrates its 50th anniversary in 2008. The current owners, Andrew Russell (manager) and Mark Raffan (the *Michelin*-starred head chef), worked for many years with the founders, Peter and Sue Herbert. They have kept their pledge to make no major changes, just gradual renovation; no spa. But free Wi-Fi has been installed. The creeper-clad Elizabethan manor house (Relais & Châteaux) stands amid woodland in grounds (open only to hotel guests) designed by William Robinson, pioneer of the English natural garden. It has leaded windows, much polished wood, moulded plaster ceilings, log fires and antique furniture. Bedrooms (the best are large) have fruit, magazines and books; their decor may seem 'a bit dated'. In the oak-panelled restaurant (with open fire and patterned carpet), typical dishes include rich langoustine bisque; baby sea bass with saffron risotto, confit tomatoes. The kitchen garden has been restored ('50 chickens are laying well'). 'A good, if expensive, overnight stop before a flight from Gatwick.' (*DG*)

Bedrooms: 18. *Open*: all year, restaurant closed Christmas night to non-residents. *Facilities*: 3 lounges, bar, restaurant, private dining room, civil wedding licence, 30-acre grounds (gardens, croquet, trout lake, fishing), only restaurant suitable for ♿. *Background music*: none. *Location*: 5 miles SW of East Grinstead. *Smoking*: not allowed. *Children*: not under 7. *Dogs*: not allowed. *Credit cards*: Amex, MasterCard, Visa. *Prices*: [2008] room £110–£340, breakfast £13–£18, set dinner £35, full alc £61 (*12½ per cent discretionary service charge on food and drink*), off-season rates, New Year package, 1-night bookings refused Sat.

EAST LAVANT West Sussex   Map 2:E3

The Royal Oak   *Tel* 01243-527434
Pook Lane   *Email* rooms@royaloakeastlavant.co.uk
East Lavant PO18 0AX   *Website* www.royaloakeastlavant.co.uk

Charles Ullmann now owns this listed Georgian flint-stone inn in an attractive village near the South Downs (Hayley Edgar is his manager). He tells us that he is making no changes in style, personnel and ambience. 'What you see is what you get.' An inspector confirms: 'Same standards, same good food, same winning formula.' 'Good value,' is another comment. The bedrooms, in a converted barn and cottage, combine old features (inglenook fireplaces, beams, flagstones) with contemporary furniture, modern comforts ('excellent bathroom with under-floor heating and strong shower') and 'nice touches': flowers; flat-screen TV, CD/DVD-player, discs and films. 'Comfortable bed with big, soft pillows.' In the restaurant (popular with locals and Chichester theatre-goers), chef Sam Baker's modern *à la carte* menu includes beer-battered fish with pea purée; baked halibut on a crayfish cake with lime and coconut cream and pak choi; also daily blackboard specials. Breakfast has 'plenty of fresh fruit'; 'cooked dishes well up to standard'. 'Staff both efficient and friendly.' Children are warmly welcomed (cots, high chairs provided). Alfresco meals are served on the front terrace, which has country views; a small garden is at the side. There is a sister inn, *The Halfway Bridge*, at Petworth.

Bedrooms: 6, 3 in adjacent barn and cottage, 2 self-catering cottages nearby. *Open*: all year except 25/26 Dec. *Facilities*: bar/restaurant, terrace (outside meals), small garden, unsuitable for ♿. *Background music*: jazz/soul/ fantasy. *Location*: 2 miles N of Chichester. *Smoking*: not allowed. *Children*: all ages welcomed. *Dogs*: allowed in bar area only. *Credit cards*: Amex, MasterCard, Visa. *Prices*: b&b £42.50–£95, full alc £33, winter breaks, New Year package.

EASTBOURNE East Sussex   Map 2:E4
See SHORTLIST

EMSWORTH Hampshire   Map 2:E3

Restaurant 36 on the Quay   *Tel* 01243-375592
47 South Street   *Email* 36@onthequay.plus.com
Emsworth PO10 7EG   *Website* www.36onthequay.co.uk

On the picturesque quay of a fishing village on the Hampshire/Sussex border, this quayside restaurant-with-rooms is run by owners Ramon (the chef) and Karen (front-of-house) Farthing. The attractive 17th-century building has a smart interior, done in pastel shades. The cooking (modern British with French influence) holds a *Michelin* star for dishes like scallops with a peashoot, apple and Serrano ham dust; breasts of squab pigeon on a beetroot risotto. 'Our excellent meal included a little appetiser and fresh bread with seeds.' Four bedrooms are above the restaurant. Vanilla, the best, has low central beams, a sitting area with a large sofa, a 'comfortable, if narrow' bed and a harbour view. Cinnamon has a sitting area overlooking South Street's old fishermen's cottages. Nutmeg, though small, 'is tastefully decorated'; it overlooks the quay and harbour. Clove faces a boatyard. There is also a cottage with lounge (with sofa bed) and kitchen, across the road. A 'superb' continental breakfast included 'segments of pink grapefruit, peeled and sliced peaches; good coffee; hot brioche toast and croissants'. It is served in the rooms or the lounge area on the landing. Drinks are served here, too, and, on fine days, on the adjoining terrace. (*CJ, and others*)

Bedrooms: 5, 1 in cottage (with lounge) across road (can be let weekly). *Open*: all year except 25/26 Dec, 3 weeks Jan, 1 week May, 1 week Oct, restaurant closed Sun/Mon. *Facilities*: lounge area, bar area, restaurant, terrace, only restaurant suitable for &. *Background music*: none. *Location*: on harbour. *Smoking*: not allowed. *Children*: all ages welcomed. *Dogs*: only allowed in cottage, by arrangement. *Credit cards*: Diners, MasterCard, Visa. *Prices*: b&b £47.50–£90 per person, full alc £55.

ERMINGTON Devon   Map 1:D4

Plantation House   NEW   *Tel* 01548-831100
Totnes Road   *Email* info@plantationhousehotel.co.uk
Ermington, nr Plymouth   *Website* www.plantationhousehotel.co.uk
PL21 9NS

Twenty minutes' drive from Plymouth, on the sunny side of the
River Erme valley, this cream-painted former rectory (Grade II
listed) stands up a short drive off a 'main, but not too busy' road. Since
arriving in 2006, the 'hands-on' owners, Richard and Magdalena
Hendey, have extensively renovated, creating 'an idiosyncratic, very
pleasing ensemble'. 'A delightful hotel, beautifully decorated.
Charming, talented owners,' one visitor wrote. 'Our comfortable room
lacked for nothing,' said another. Inspectors added: 'The welcome
was warm, the decor light and modern: Matisse prints on pale pastel
walls, beautiful fresh flowers, striking chandeliers and artefacts. Our
spacious bedroom overlooked the walled garden. Furnished with
flair, it had TV, plants, fresh fruit, chocolates, a well-appointed, if
slightly dark bathroom.' Adjacent to the bar/lounge are two dining
rooms with wooden tables, cane armchairs, multicoloured glass
chandelier, bright modern paintings. 'The personable host is a
talented chef. Perfectly spiced cauliflower soup; delicious scallops
with Jerusalem artichoke purée; well-flavoured venison stew; desserts
as good as the rest. Service attentive and effective, though they had a
full house. An extensive wine list.' Breakfast has a buffet with
squeezed juices, 'excellent fruit salad; delicious smoked haddock;
well-judged scrambled eggs with smoked salmon'. 'Everything
showed meticulous attention to detail and seemed to be delivered
with effortless panache.' (*Christopher Hughes, Jenny Dawe, and others*)

Bedrooms: 9. *Open*: all year, restaurant closed midday, generally closed Sun.
Facilities: lounge/bar, 2 dining rooms, terrace, garden, unsuitable for &.
Background music: if required. *Location*: 10 miles E of Plymouth. *Smoking*: not
allowed. *Children*: 'well-behaved' children welcomed. *Dogs*: allowed in 1 bedroom, not in public rooms. *Credit cards*: Amex, MasterCard, Visa. *Prices*: b&b
£50–£60 per person, set dinner £36, New Year package, 1-night bookings
occasionally refused.

'Set menu' indicates a fixed-price meal, with ample, limited or
no choice. 'Full alc' is the hotel's estimated price per person of
a three-course *à la carte* meal, with a half bottle of house wine.
'Alc' is the price of an *à la carte* meal excluding the cost of wine.

EVERSHOT Dorset   Map 1:C6

Summer Lodge   *Tel* 01935-482000
9 Fore Street   *Fax* 01935-482040
Evershot DT2 0JR   *Email* summer@relaischateaux.com
                             Website www.summerlodgehotel.com

'A relaxing country house atmosphere. It stands out because of the
friendly, professional staff, who greet guests by name, are always on
hand but never overbearing.' This year's praise for this luxury hotel
(Relais & Châteaux), owned by the Red Carnation group; Charles
Lötter is the manager. Designed in part by Thomas Hardy for the
earls of Ilchester, the former dower house stands in large grounds in
an attractive Dorset village. The pretty bedrooms are traditionally
furnished (fine fabrics, heavy drapes, patterns, etc); some are thought
'small for the price'. In the 'elegant dining room', which faces a walled
garden, the 'excellent' chef, Steven Titman, serves modern British
dishes, perhaps baby spinach and coconut soup; crispy confit duck leg
with wild mushroom risotto. The spa has a 'very good' swimming
pool, aromatherapy and reflexology. Red Carnation also owns the less
expensive *Acorn Inn* in the village, and the little local shop. A large
deer park is nearby. (*Barbara Wood, and others*)

Bedrooms: 24, 9 in coach house and courtyard house, 4 in lane, 1 on ground floor
suitable for &. *Open*: all year. *Facilities*: ramps, drawing room, lounge/bar,
restaurant, indoor swimming pool (12 by 7 metres), civil wedding licence,
4-acre grounds (garden, croquet, tennis). *Background music*: 'mixed' in bar/
lounge. *Location*: 10 miles NW of Dorchester, train Yeovil/Dorchester (they will
fetch). *Smoking*: allowed in 1 bedroom. *Children*: all ages welcomed. *Dogs*:
allowed in some bedrooms, some public rooms. *Credit cards*: all major cards.
Prices: b&b £120–£340 per person, d,b&b £180–£400, set dinner £70, full alc £85,
Christmas/New Year packages, 1-night bookings sometimes refused weekends.

EVESHAM Worcestershire   Map 3:D6

The Evesham Hotel   *Tel* 01386-765566
Cooper's Lane, off Waterside   *Fax* 01386-765443
Evesham   *Freephone* 0800-716969 (reservations only)
WR11 1DA   *Email* reception@eveshamhotel.com
                          Website www.eveshamhotel.com

❦ *César award in 1990*

Families are welcomed at this quirky, informal hotel which John and
Sue Jenkinson have run since 1975. He is a 'dominant presence',

proud of being idiosyncratic, 'a caring owner who wears amazing ties'. 'If you can cope with the eccentricity, your children will love it,' said one visitor. 'Ours had a good time in the swimming pool and play area.' Children are charged according to age and amount eaten; they have a jokey high tea menu. Mrs Jenkinson designs the themed bedrooms, eg, Alice in Wonderland, a family suite among the beams; Apologies to Gaudí, dedicated to the equally quirky architect. Attention to detail is admired: all rooms have a silent fridge with soft drinks, milk and a half bottle of wine; bathroom fans are quiet; rooms in the extension have double doors to reduce corridor noise. The dining room will close for six weeks in January 2009 for refurbishment: air conditioning will be added, but the room will retain its Regency character. Staff are long-serving; three more complete 25 years' service during 2008. But the chef, Adam Talbot, is new. 'His style is more modern.' Plenty of choice on the menus, and a wine list almost devoid of French bottles. (*MM, and others*)

Bedrooms: 40, 11 on ground floor, 2 suitable for &. *Open*: all year except 25/26 Dec. *Facilities*: 2 lounges, bar, restaurant, private dining room, indoor swimming pool (5 by 12 metres), 2½-acre grounds (croquet, putting, swings, trampoline). *Background music*: none. *Location*: 5 mins' walk from centre, across river. *Smoking*: allowed in 2 bedrooms. *Children*: all ages welcomed. *Dogs*: not allowed in public rooms. *Credit cards*: all major cards. *Prices*: b&b £60.50–£86 per person, full alc £37, New Year package, 1-night bookings refused Sat.

EXETER Devon   Map 1:C5

Hotel Barcelona   NEW   *Tel* 01392-281000
Magdalen Street   *Fax* 01392-281001
Exeter EX2 4HY   *Email* barcelona@aliashotels.com
                                        Website www.aliashotels.com

'We have never before stayed in a hotel where staff wore jeans and T-shirt,' writes a correspondent this year, 'but their clothing didn't affect their cheeriness or efficiency.' Near the cathedral, this former Victorian eye infirmary, managed by Fiona Moores, has been cleverly converted (huge marble fireplace, 'big old radiators, fat old pipes'; one bedroom still bears the word 'Theatre'). Sound insulation can be poor. 'The furniture is quirky, the rooms are quirky, the feel is quirky and the spirit is fun.' *Kino*, the basement nightclub, is busy at weekends, but 'sound did not permeate to the rest of the hotel'. Some bedrooms have huge windows and 'marvellous views'; all have CD-player, etc. Front rooms face a main road. 'Our room was cold when we arrived and amenities were basic (no flannels, old-style TV).' 'My spacious room had comfy bed; smart bathroom.' The large, conservatory-style *Café Paradiso* faces a walled garden with a huge red bird sculpture. It serves 'excellent' pizzas, locally caught fish and West Country meat. Breakfast ('exceptional') has thick slices of brown toast; good choice of cereals and cooked dishes. 'Take the *Barcelona* in the spirit in which it is run, and you are assured of a relaxing stay bang in the middle of Exeter.' (*Louise Medcalf, and others*)

Bedrooms: 46, 2 on ground floor. *Open*: all year. *Facilities*: lift, ramps, lounge, cocktail bar, restaurant, private dining room, nightclub, 3 conference rooms, 1-acre garden. *Background music*: jazz, blues, Latin. *Location*: 5 mins' walk from centre (front rooms hear traffic), parking. *Smoking*: not allowed. *Children*: all ages welcomed (under-12s stay free in parents' room). *Dogs*: allowed, £15 (no charge for guide dogs), but not in restaurant, bar. *Credit cards*: all major cards. *Prices*: room £105–£125, breakfast £12.95, full alc £35, weekend rates, Christmas/New Year packages, 1-night bookings sometimes refused.

See also SHORTLIST

EXFORD Somerset   Map 1:B4

The Crown	*Tel* 01643-831554
Exford	*Fax* 01643-831665
Exmoor National Park	*Email* info@crownhotelexmoor.co.uk
TA24 7PP	*Website* www.crownhotelexmoor.co.uk

17th-century coaching inn, owned by Chris Kirkbride, Sara and Dan Whittaker, on green of picturesque village in Exmoor national park. 'Warm feel; traditional atmosphere.' 'Welcoming' public rooms have pictures of country pursuits. Large rustic bar, popular with locals; cosy residents' bar. New chef, Darren Edwards, with extensive menu this year. Candlelit restaurant. Tables and parasols in grounds; water garden; summer dining. 17 bedrooms: 'impressive, traditionally furnished'. Modern bathrooms. Background music: bar and restaurant. Unsuitable for ♿. No smoking. No dogs in restaurant. MasterCard, Visa accepted. Room: b&b £41.25–£70 per person, d,b&b £60–£95, full alc £45, Christmas/New Year packages, 1-night bookings sometimes refused holiday weekends. More reports, please.

We say 'Unsuitable for ♿' when a hotel tells us that it cannot accommodate wheelchair-users.

FALMOUTH Cornwall   Map 1:E2

The Rosemary   *Tel* 01326-314669
22 Gyllyngvase Terrace   *Email* therosemary@tiscali.co.uk
Falmouth TR11 4DL   *Website* www.therosemary.co.uk

On a quiet residential road, a short walk from the centre and from a Blue Flag beach, Suzanne and Geoff Warring run their B&B in a white-walled, grey-roofed Victorian house. It contains a collection of paintings by contemporary Cornish artists. There is Wi-Fi access throughout, a small bar, and a pretty south-facing garden with a sun deck. The 'very comfortable lounge' looks over the garden to the sea. There are good sea views too from the dining room, where the Warrings serve 'wonderful breakfasts using local produce'. Both Cornish, they 'have extensive local knowledge' (excursions, eateries, etc) and 'offer excellent value for money'. 'My request for blankets and sheets rather than duvet was immediately dealt with.' More bedrooms have been refurbished this year and all now have flat-screen TV. For families there are adjoining rooms. 'My Labrador was welcomed too.' (*Ann Mallinson, PL, and others*)

Bedrooms: 10 (two 2-bedroom suites). *Open*: Feb–Oct. *Facilities*: lounge, bar, dining room, small garden (sun deck), unsuitable for &. *Background music*: none. *Location*: 10 mins' walk from centre. *Smoking*: not allowed. *Children*: all ages welcomed. *Dogs*: not in dining room. *Credit cards*: MasterCard, Visa. *Prices*: [2008] b&b £32–£68.25 per person, 1-night bookings sometimes refused.

See also SHORTLIST

FAVERSHAM Kent   Map 2:D5

Read's   *Tel* 01795-535344
Macknade Manor   *Fax* 01795-591200
Canterbury Road   *Email* rona@reads.com
Faversham ME13 8XE   *Website* www.reads.com

♔ *César award in 2005*

'Drive up to the manor house from a busy road and you are suddenly in a different world.' This *Michelin*-starred restaurant-with-rooms continues to win plaudits. 'A professional enterprise with well-trained staff, yet a personal approach and an unfussy manner.' 'Superb food.'

The handsome Georgian building stands in immaculate gardens (lawns shaded by cedar, weeping willow and chestnut trees) near this old market town. Rona Pitchford is front-of-house, her husband, David, the chef. The walled kitchen garden provides herbs and vegetables for 'classic' seasonal dishes on a 'flexible menu', eg, crispy pork belly on black cabbage with honey-roasted turnips. At least four vegetarian options are offered verbally each day. The 'fantastic' wine list includes some 'very expensive' bottles, but a 'Best Buys' section has many reasonably priced wines. There are 'marvellous, soft-upholstered chairs' in the candlelit restaurant. 'The cooked breakfast was excellent, and croissants and delicious home-made jams were served by the friendly owner.' The bedrooms, 'old-fashioned by design rather than default', have 'rich, thick fabrics'. 'Ours was sizeable and had a complimentary sherry decanter.' Guests have access, on an honesty basis, to the Pantry, which has a fridge 'full of decent half bottles of wine', and tea/coffee-making kit. Behind the hotel is 'an Aladdin's cave of a farm shop'. (*Wolfgang Stroebe, Paul and Rosalind Bench, Elisabeth Biggs*)

Bedrooms: 6. *Open*: all year except 25/26 Dec, 1 Jan, restaurant closed Sun/Mon. *Facilities*: sitting room/bar, restaurant, private dining room, civil wedding licence, 3-acre garden (terrace, outdoor dining), unsuitable for &. *Location*: ½ mile SE of Faversham. *Smoking*: not allowed. *Children*: all ages welcomed. *Dogs*: not allowed. *Credit cards*: all major cards. *Rates*: b&b £82.50–£185 per person, d,b&b £130–£230, set lunch £24, dinner £52.

FLEET Dorset   Map 1:D6

Moonfleet Manor   *Tel* 01305-786948
Fleet Road, Fleet   *Fax* 01305-774395
nr Weymouth DT3 4ED   *Email* info@moonfleetmanorhotel.co.uk
                       Website www.moonfleetmanorhotel.co.uk

In large grounds 'in the middle of nowhere', above the Fleet lagoon and Chesil Beach, this rambling Georgian manor house is part of von Essen's Luxury Family Hotels group. The manager, Neil Carter, and chef, Tony Smith, have stayed on from the previous regime. The large public rooms have a colonial feel. Bedrooms vary in size. Children sharing their parents' room stay free of charge; cots and Z-beds are available. 'Our five-year-old daughter made loads of friends and enjoyed every minute,' said one returning visitor. The 'cheerful staff' are also mentioned. The 'excellent' facilities for children include two indoor swimming pools, a supervised nursery, the Four Bears' Den (where small children can be left); there are computer games, ping-pong, indoor tennis; swings, slide, sandpit, etc, in the grounds (see below). Special lunches are provided for the young, and high tea at 5 pm. Spicer, the hotel's dog, is in attendance. Sea bathing is not possible because of the strong currents, but there are good walks in either direction along the coast path, and the lagoon is home to a 'fantastic variety of birdlife'. More reports, please.

Bedrooms: 36, 6 in 2 annexes, 3 on ground floor. *Open*: all year. *Facilities*: lift, 2 lounges with dispense bar, restaurant, meeting room, games room/nursery, disco, indoor 10-metre swimming pool, sauna, solarium, sunbed, aromatherapy, snooker, 5-acre grounds (children's play areas, tennis, bowls, squash, badminton), riding, golf, sailing, windsurfing nearby. *Background music*: none. *Location*: 7 miles W of Weymouth. *Smoking*: not allowed. *Children*: all ages welcomed. *Dogs*: not allowed in restaurant. *Credit cards*: all major cards. *Prices*: [2008] b&b £85–£170 per person, d,b&b £102.50–£205, set dinner £38, Christmas/New Year packages, 1-night bookings refused weekends, bank holidays.

FLETCHING East Sussex   Map 2:E4

The Griffin Inn
Fletching, nr Uckfield
TN22 3SS

Tel 01825-722890
Fax 01825-722810
Email info@thegriffininn.co.uk
Website www.thegriffininn.co.uk

In a pretty village overlooking the Ouse valley, this 16th-century Grade II listed coaching inn is run by its owners, the Pullan family. Very popular, 'it combines the attributes of genuine village pub, first-class restaurant and excellent hotel', says a visitor this year. Four 'quirky' bedrooms are in the main building, others (with four-poster) in a renovated coach house, yet others in the recently opened *Griffin House* next door. Comments on the rooms range from 'charming', 'comfortable, with king-size bed', to 'poor lighting, cramped bathroom, awkward wardrobe'. Meals are served in the beamed and panelled bar (with open fires and hunting prints) and the 'pleasant' restaurant. 'Cooking of a high order. Staff consistently good and intelligent.' Andrew Billings and Nick Peterson serve modern British dishes with Mediterranean influences on a daily-changing menu, eg, salt-and-pepper-fried squid with sweet chilli dressing; fillet of sea bass with chorizo, spinach and tomato. 'On an unbelievably busy Saturday night, the staff couldn't have been more helpful.' Children are welcomed: there is a large garden (where Sunday lunch barbecues are held in summer) and a 'healthy' children's menu. Four golf courses are nearby. (*Charles Kingsley Evans, Peter and Kay Rogers, Zara Elliott*)

Bedrooms: 13, 4 in coach house, 5 in *Griffin House* next door, 4 on ground floor. *Open*: all year except 25 Dec, restaurant closed Sun evening, 1 Jan evening. *Facilities*: 2 lounge bars (1 with TV), restaurant, occasional live music Sun lunch, terrace (1-acre garden). *Background music*: none. *Location*: 3 miles NW of Uckfield. *Smoking*: not allowed. *Children*: all ages welcomed. *Dogs*: allowed in bar only. *Credit cards*: all major cards. *Prices*: [2008] b&b £42.50–£80 per person, Sun lunch £30, full alc £37–£39, 1-night bookings refused bank holidays. ***V***

FOLKESTONE Kent *See SHORTLIST*   Map 2:E5

FOWEY Cornwall   Map 1:D3

Old Quay House
28 Fore Street
Fowey PL23 1AQ

Tel 01726-833302
Fax 01726-833668
Email info@theoldquayhouse.com
Website www.theoldquayhouse.com

'A great place. So nice to be right on the water in this lovely town. Our delightful bedroom overlooked the estuary.' Praise this year for Jane and Roy Carson's modern hotel, a stylish conversion of a Victorian seamen's mission. Drinks, snacks and summer dinners are served on the rear terrace by the water; inside there is an 'eclectic collection of furnishings and ornaments' and 'lots of raffia'. Bedrooms are done in pale pastel shades. 'A DVD-player and waterproof coats were nice touches; excellent bathroom. The large bed had good linen but a standard mattress which made the sleeping experience utilitarian rather than sumptuous.' Soundproofing may not always be perfect. In *Q*, the large restaurant, chef Ben Bass serves a 'modern British menu with European influence' (eg, duck rillettes with grape chutney; rib-eye steak with lyonnaise potatoes). 'Excellent food, marred by weird music played too loud, turned down when we asked; attentive and pleasant service. A good breakfast, on the terrace, served by a delightful Polish couple.' Thanks to Fowey's narrow streets, the nearest car park is at Caffa Mill, a short (flat) walk away. (*David and Bridget Reed, and others*)

Bedrooms: 11. *Open*: all year. *Facilities*: open-plan lounge, bar, restaurant with seating area, civil wedding licence, waterside terrace, unsuitable for &. *Background music*: 'mellow' at meal times. *Location*: central, on waterfront, help given with parking. *Smoking*: not allowed. *Children*: not under 13. *Dogs*: not allowed. *Credit cards*: Amex, MasterCard, Visa. *Prices*: b&b £65–£300 per person, d,b&b £92.50–£335, set dinner £35, special breaks, Christmas/New Year packages, 1-night bookings refused weekends in high season. ***V***

See also SHORTLIST

FRITTON Norfolk   Map 2:B6

Fritton House   *Tel* 01493-484008
Church Lane   *Fax* 01493-488355
Fritton NR31 9HA   *Email* frittonhouse@somerleyton.co.uk
                          Website www.frittonhouse.co.uk

In open farmland near a lake (with rowing boats, pedalos, etc), this
'handsome, even imposing' 16th-century Grade II* listed inn has
been turned into a contemporary hotel/restaurant by the Hon. Hugh
Crossley. It is managed by the 'enthusiastic' Sarah Winterton. There
are 'fresh flowers everywhere, interesting artwork; in the lounge, a
large fireplace, comfy sofas, plentiful magazines and newspapers'. The
bedrooms, 'full of character', have broadband access, flat-screen
plasma TV, DVD-player. 'Ours, at £135, was probably the biggest and
best we have experienced at the price: double aspect, beautifully
furnished; modern, well-equipped bathroom.' In the cream-and-olive
restaurant ('like a gastropub'), 'food is decent, service more willing
than professional'. One couple was surprised to find 'a huge TV
showing a football match with associated noises throughout our meal'.
Another disliked the 'insidious' muzak and the breakfasts. Other
visitors thought that 'they haven't quite decided who they are trying
to appeal to'. Weddings are often held. The Somerleyton estate is
open to visitors during the day in summer; hotel guests have sole
access in the evenings and in winter. Norfolk has two Frittons: this one
is on the Suffolk border. (*Margaret and David Nicholls, CLH, and others*)

Bedrooms: 9. *Open*: all year. *Facilities*: lounge, bar, restaurant, private dining
room, civil wedding licence, 150-acre estate (formal gardens, lake, golf, walks),
unsuitable for &. *Background music*: in bar, restaurant. *Location*: 7 miles SW of
Great Yarmouth, off A143. *Smoking*: not allowed. *Children*: all ages welcomed.
Dogs: not allowed in restaurant, must be on lead. *Credit cards*: MasterCard, Visa.
Prices: [2008] b&b £68.50–£145 per person, full alc £35, Christmas/New Year
packages, 1-night bookings refused weekends. *V*

The *V* sign at the end of an entry indicates a hotel that has
agreed to take part in our Voucher scheme and to give *Guide*
readers a 25% discount on their room rates for a one-night stay,
subject to the conditions on the back of the vouchers and page 62.

FROGGATT EDGE Derbyshire   Map 3:A6

The Chequers Inn
Froggatt Edge
Hope Valley S32 3ZJ

Tel 01433-630231
Fax 01433-631072
Email info@chequers-froggatt.com
Website www.chequers-froggatt.com

'The staff, smartly turned out in long pinnies, are always friendly and helpful, no matter how busy they are,' say visitors returning to this 'well-cared-for' 16th-century inn. Set below rugged Froggatt Edge in some of the Peak District's best scenery, it has 'smart hanging flower baskets and troughs by the entrance'. A small back garden has panoramic views. In the 'very attractive' bar/restaurant (original heavy lintels, dark beams, library chairs, high-backed settees, countless knick-knacks), chef Phil Ball blends traditional with modern, providing food 'a cut above normal pub fare', eg, swordfish with wild mushroom, artichoke and port reduction; seafood risotto with saffron. Wines and dishes of the day are listed on blackboards. The bedrooms are simple, but thoughtfully furnished (pine furniture, country-style decor; bathroom with roll-top bath). A front room had 'all we could want', including double-glazed windows (the adjacent road is busy); a rear room was 'quiet, well kept and cosy'. At breakfast ('very good') a buffet is followed by cooked dishes (including vegetarian sausages). The owners, Jonathan and Joanne Tindall, 'are always around'. 'An excellent place provided you don't expect hotel facilities such as a lounge.' (*Padi and John Howard, GM*)

Bedrooms: 5. *Open*: all year except 25 Dec. *Facilities*: bar, 2 eating areas, terrace with seating, large garden, unsuitable for &. *Background music*: 'easy listening' all the time, radio at breakfast. *Location*: On A625, near Calver village. *Smoking*: not allowed. *Children*: all ages welcomed. *Dogs*: not allowed. *Credit cards*: Amex, MasterCard, Visa. *Prices*: b&b £37.50–£50 per person, full alc £35, 1-night bookings refused weekends.

****

Traveller's tale *Hotel in Cumbria* The food was institutional and uninspiring. Every evening we asked for a jug of water. It would turn up unwashed and smeared with finger marks. When we pointed this out and a new jug was brought, it was exactly the same. A sideboard in the dining room was spread with a white cloth which had not been changed, even though someone had spilled jam on it.

****

GATESHEAD Tyne and Wear   Map 4:B4

Eslington Villa   *Tel* 0191-487 6017
8 Station Road, Low Fell   *Fax* 0191-420 0667
Gateshead NE9 6DR   *Email* home@eslingtonvilla.co.uk
                             Website www.eslingtonvilla.co.uk

In 'beautiful grounds' in a residential area, Nick and Melanie Tulip's
Victorian villa is 'excellent all round', says a visitor this year. 'Nice
lounge and eating area.' 'Good value with friendly staff,' is another
comment. The attractive restaurant, with its conservatory extension,
is a 'buzzy place', popular with local diners (the lounge can be
crowded). Chef Andy Moore serves modern dishes, eg, peppered
pork with bubble and squeak, honey-roasted roots. Bedrooms in the
extension have a contemporary feel, those in the main house are more
traditional, perhaps 'sombre' ('reading was difficult'); three rooms
have a separate entrance from the car park. Breakfast has a wide
choice including smoked haddock risotto and 'tasty' kippers. The
only drawback is the 'intrusive' background music. Seminars, private
meetings and functions are often held. 'Within easy distance of the
many attractions of the Gateshead area.' (*Jerry Coleman, DB*)

Bedrooms: 18, 3 with separate entrance on ground floor. *Open*: all year except
Christmas, restaurant closed Sat lunch, Sun night. *Facilities*: ramp, lounge/bar,
conservatory, restaurant, conference/function facilities, 2-acre garden (patio).
Background music: jazz throughout. *Location*: 2 miles from centre, off A1.
Smoking: not allowed. *Children*: all ages welcomed. *Dogs*: not allowed. *Credit
cards*: Amex, MasterCard, Visa. *Prices*: b&b £44–£79 per person, set dinner £22,
full alc £34, New Year package. *V*

GATWICK West Sussex   Map 2:D4
See SHORTLIST

GILLINGHAM Dorset   Map 2:D1

Stock Hill House   *Tel* 01747-823626
Stock Hill   *Fax* 01747-825628
Gillingham SP8 5NR   *Email* reception@stockhillhouse.co.uk
                             Website www.stockhillhouse.co.uk

In wooded grounds (with terraced lawns, herbaceous borders, a small
lake with wildlife) on the Somerset/Dorset border, this small luxury

hotel in a late Victorian mansion is owned by Peter and Nita Hauser. It 'sets a standard right up there with the very best', says a report this year. 'We were welcomed like family friends.' Other comments: 'A pampering experience.' 'Luxurious comfort, very good food.' There are two guest lounges, one 'splendid and formal', the other 'cosy' with log fire. 'It is easy here for guests to get to know each other (if they want to).' The bedrooms, with a mix of antiques and curios, 'differ tremendously in size and facilities; the rates reflect this'. 'Our delight-ful bedroom had a sitting room overlooking the garden. Every detail had been thought of.' In the restaurant, Peter Hauser's cooking reflects his Austrian origins, eg, Viennese paprika beef goulash, with fried egg, pickled gherkin and spaetzle. 'Delicious' desserts include black cherry, kirsch and chocolate gateau. 'Good service from charm-ing Eastern European girls.' 'Nita is very much the hostess, chatting to the guests.' One visitor did not enjoy the formality of the 'synchronised restaurant service'. 'A fine breakfast' (with freshly squeezed juices, home-made jam and marmalade). 'Well-behaved' children are welcomed. (*Richard and Sheila Owen, Diane Moss, David Ward, and others*)

Bedrooms: 9, 3 in coach house. *Open*: all year. *Facilities*: ramp, 2 lounges, restaurant, breakfast room, private dining room, 11-acre grounds (tennis, croquet, small lake), unsuitable for &. *Background music*: none. *Location*: On B3081, 1½ miles W of Gillingham. *Smoking*: not allowed. *Children*: not under 7. *Dogs*: not allowed. *Credit cards*: MasterCard, Visa. *Prices*: d,b&b £120–£160 per person, set lunch £28, dinner £40, Christmas/New Year packages, 1-night bookings refused bank holidays.

GITTISHAM Devon   Map 1:C5

Combe House
Gittisham
nr Honiton EX14 3AD

Tel 01404-540400
Fax 01404-46004
Email stay@thishotel.com
Website www.thishotel.com

❦ *César award in 2007*

Approached by a mile-long drive, this extended Grade I listed Elizabethan manor house stands in a vast estate of woodland, meadows and pastures. Most visitors this year enjoyed their stay: 'A lovely place,' one wrote, 'staff are friendly, attentive, knowledgeable.' But another thought the garden 'needed attention'. The owners, Ken and Ruth Hunt, 'preside in an informal way', creating the 'feel of a true country house'. 'We were welcomed by the sight of a roaring fire

rather than a reception desk.' Public rooms have carved oak panelling, antiques, fresh flowers, 18th-century portraits. The bedrooms
vary: best ones have antiques and rich fabrics. The linen suite (former
laundry room) has a huge lounge and a six-foot circular copper bath in
its bathroom. One couple was unhappy with a smaller, 'draughty'
room. In the restaurant, redecorated this year, chef Hadleigh Barratt,
a *Michelin* 'rising star', serves modern cooking on a locally sourced
seasonal menu, eg, ham hock tortellini; brill, lobster ravioli, spinach
and leeks. Breakfast, served until 10 am, has 'the best toast, from
three types of home-baked bread, thickly cut and served hot when
required'. Children are welcomed. There is an 'African writers' camp'
in an arboretum. (*PE Carter, WW, and others*)

Bedrooms: 16, 1 in cottage. *Open*: all year except last 2 weeks Jan. *Facilities*:
ramp, sitting room, Great Hall, bar, restaurant, private dining rooms, civil
wedding licence, 10-acre garden in 3,500-acre estate (helipad), coast 9 miles,
only public rooms suitable for &. *Background music*: in hall 'when requested'.
Location: 2 miles SW of Honiton. *Smoking*: not allowed. *Children*: all ages
welcomed. *Dogs*: allowed in public rooms, some bedrooms. *Credit cards*:
MasterCard, Visa. *Prices*: b&b £85–£170 per person, d,b&b £122–£213, set
dinner £28–£42, full alc £57, Christmas/New Year packages, 1-night bookings
refused Fri/Sat most weekends.

GLASTONBURY Somerset   Map 1:B6
See SHORTLIST

GOLANT-BY-FOWEY Cornwall   Map 1:D3
See SHORTLIST

GOLCAR West Yorkshire   Map 4:E3

The Weavers Shed   *Tel* 01484-654284
Knowl Road, Golcar   *Fax* 01484-650980
Huddersfield HD7 4AN   *Email* info@weaversshed.co.uk
                              Website www.weaversshed.co.uk

A 'haven of peace', this converted 18th-century cloth-finishing mill,
in a village above the Colne valley, is run as a restaurant-with-rooms
by chef/*patron* Stephen Jackson with his wife, the 'warmly welcoming' Tracy. They 'take immense pride in their work', emphasising

sustainability and local produce. Fruit, vegetables and herbs ('as organic as possible') are grown in their kitchen garden in a neighbouring village; eggs are from their chickens and ducks. 'High-quality dinners', served in a stone-floored, beamed room, might include mushroom tarte Tatin; calf's liver, bacon mash, braised red cabbage, red onion. 'All perfectly (and promptly) served.' Home-made petits fours include fruit jellies and frozen lollipops. The Jacksons' policy of 'only one booking per table' means that 'diners can stay as long as they like'. The lounge and the bedrooms above it are in the former mill-owner's house next door (direct access from the main building). 'My large room was in the shadow of a tree, but imaginatively lit.' 'Free goodies' include a decanter of sherry. Each room has a well-stocked fridge; one has a four-poster, another a wrought-iron bed. The modern decor sets off original windows and high ceilings. Breakfast includes 'fresh juice, delicious scrambled egg and black pudding', 'preserves made by Tracy'. (*RG, CB*)

Bedrooms: 5, 2 on ground floor. *Open*: all year, except Christmas/New Year, restaurant closed Sun/Mon. *Facilities*: lounge/bar, restaurant, function/conference room, garden, unsuitable for &. *Background music*: classical/jazz at mealtimes. *Location*: 4 miles SW of Huddersfield. *Smoking*: not allowed. *Children*: all ages welcomed. *Dogs*: not allowed. *Credit cards*: all major cards. *Prices*: [2008] b&b £50–£80 per person, full alc £45.

GRANGE-OVER-SANDS   Map 4: inset C2
Cumbria *See SHORTLIST*

GRANTHAM Lincolnshire   Map 2:A3
See SHORTLIST

GRASMERE Cumbria   Map 4: inset C2

White Moss House   *Tel* 015394-35295
Rydal Water   *Fax* 015394-35516
Grasmere LA22 9SE   *Email* sue@whitemoss.com
        Website www.whitemoss.com

Dating from 1730, this grey stone creeper-covered house was bought by William Wordsworth in 1827 for his son, and it became the

Wordsworth family home for over a century. The home of Peter and Sue Dixon for nearly 30 years, it stands at the northern end of Rydal Water, between Grasmere and Windermere, a good location for exploring the Lakeland countryside. 'The pose factor was zero; refreshing these days,' was one comment. 'A very pleasant atmosphere.' There is a large lounge with wood-burning fire, flowers, books, games and sofas, and a terrace with seating for warm days. Room and breakfast only is offered, except for five 'dinner club' weekends and for house parties, but drinks and wines are available and there are plenty of eating places nearby. A busy road is close but windows are double glazed, and there is little traffic at night. Two peaceful bedrooms are in *Brockstone*, the cottage up the hill (equipped for self-catering for a minimum stay of three nights). In the main house, the small bedrooms have a tiny bathroom and many extras (herbal bathsalts, fresh flowers, books, etc). Breakfast includes Cumberland organic muesli, Cartmel Valley sausages, home-made marmalade. (*S and PG*)

Bedrooms: 7, 2 in cottage (10 mins' drive or footpath). *Open*: Feb–Nov. *Facilities*: lounge, restaurant, terrace, 1-acre garden/woodland, free use of indoor pool at local leisure club, unsuitable for &. *Background music*: none. *Location*: 1 mile S of Grasmere on A591. *Smoking*: not allowed. *Children*: all ages welcomed. *Dogs*: allowed in cottage only. *Credit cards*: MasterCard, Visa. *Prices*: [2008] b&b £39–£70 per person, special breaks, 1-night bookings refused weekends/bank holidays.

See also SHORTLIST

GREAT BIRCHAM Norfolk   Map 2:A5
See SHORTLIST

GREAT DUNMOW Essex   Map 2:C4

Starr Restaurant with Rooms   *Tel* 01371-874321
Market Place   *Fax* 01371-876337
Great Dunmow   *Email* starrrestaurant@btinternet.com
CM6 1AX   *Website* www.the-starr.co.uk

'My welcome was perfect,' reports an inspector visiting this restaurant-with-rooms on the market place of this little Essex town.

'A friendly lady carried my heavy bag to my room and later served me tea in the bar.' The timber-framed 15th-century former inn is run by owners Terence and Louise George with a 'helpful East European staff'. Inside 'all is smart and colourful'. The yellow-painted restaurant is in two parts, one with old beams stripped blond, the other a bright conservatory extension. Neat bedrooms are in a con-verted stable block in the rear courtyard. 'Mine had no great character but was immaculate. There was a green-patterned carpet, orangey checked bedspread (blankets not duvet), smart bathroom with large bath and separate shower cubicle.' The best room has a four-poster bed and a freestanding Victorian bath. The Pine Room has 'his and hers hand basins set in marble'. Dinner, prepared by chef Mark Pearson, 'was good, if pricey: wild mushroom soup, halibut, crème brûlée (delicious). Good choice of wines by the glass. Peaceful atmos-phere (no muzak).' Breakfast includes yogurt with fruit compote, freshly squeezed orange juice, a fry-up, 'good croissants', leaf tea. A busy road runs alongside, 'but it was quiet at night'. Stansted airport is 15 minutes' drive away.

Bedrooms: 8, in stable block in courtyard, 2 on ground floor. *Open*: all year except 26 Dec–5 Jan, restaurant closed Sun night. *Facilities*: bar/lounge, restaurant, 2 private dining rooms, unsuitable for &. *Background music*: none. *Location*: central. *Smoking*: not allowed. *Children*: all ages welcomed. *Dogs*: not allowed. *Credit cards*: all major cards. *Prices*: b&b £65–£90 per person, set dinner £48.75. *V*

GREAT LANGDALE Cumbria   Map 4: inset C2
See SHORTLIST

GREAT MILTON Oxfordshire   Map 2:C3

Le Manoir aux Quat'Saisons
Church Road
Great Milton OX44 7PD

Tel 01844-278881
Fax 01844-278847
Email lemanoir@blanc.co.uk
Website www.manoir.com

♛ *César award in 1985*

'Well worth while for the occasional treat', Raymond Blanc's famous *domaine* (Relais & Châteaux), co-owned with Orient Express Hotels, stands amid beautiful gardens with a 17th-century pond and an organic *potager*. The welcome is 'exemplary': a porter meets visitors in the car park; luggage is delivered to the bedrooms, which are supplied with fresh fruit and a decanter of Madeira. Many are in garden buildings; each has a theme: Opium has oriental influences; Botticelli has two freestanding baths (and a mural) in its bathroom; Citronnelle is done in vibrant yellow; Silk, traditionally decorated, has a four-poster bed, a small patio with table and chairs. There is a choice of menus in the famous conservatory restaurant (two *Michelin* stars for 23 years). A short *carte* (three choices for each course) might include fondant de saumon sauvage, copeaux de morue; filet de turbot braisé, crabe des Cornouailles. There is a 'most enjoyable' lunchtime *Menu du Jour*; a five-course *Les Classiques* ('best-loved' dishes) and a ten-course *Menu Découverte*. 'Superb freshly baked breads at dinner and breakfast.' Special events (eg, dinner with a distinguished guest speaker) are sometimes held. Manager Tom Lewis heads a 'discreet yet friendly' staff. Children are welcomed. (*J and JH, RC*)

Bedrooms: 32, 23 in garden buildings, some on ground floor. *Open*: all year. *Facilities*: ramps, 2 lounges, champagne bar, restaurant, private dining room, cookery school, civil wedding licence, 27-acre grounds (gardens, croquet, lake). *Background music*: 'relaxing' all day. *Location*: 8 miles SE of Oxford. *Smoking*: not allowed. *Children*: all ages welcomed. *Dogs*: not allowed in house (free kennels). *Credit cards*: all major cards. *Prices*: [2008] b&b (French breakfast) £190–£670 per person, cooked breakfast £25, set lunch £49, *Les Classiques* £95, *Menu Découverte* £116, full alc £116, special breaks, cookery courses, Christmas/New Year packages, 1-night bookings refused Sat May–Aug.

GREAT YARMOUTH Norfolk   Map 2:B6
See SHORTLIST

HALNAKER West Sussex   Map 2:E3

The Old Store   *Tel* 01243-531977
Stane Street, Halnaker, nr Chichester   *Email* theoldstore4@aol.com
PO18 0QL   *Website* www.theoldstoreguesthouse.com

Once the village store and bakery, this Grade II listed 18th-century red brick and flint house adjoining the Goodwood estate is an unpretentious guest house run by 'model hosts' Patrick and Heather Birchenough ('a delight to talk to'). 'Good to be back,' say returning visitors this year. There are beamed ceilings, and a small lounge (redecorated this year) and breakfast room downstairs. Some bedrooms look across fields to Chichester cathedral; some are suitable for a family. 'Mine, attractive, spotless, had mineral water, tea-maker, fresh milk in Thermos flask, biscuits and chocolate.' A 'perfect' breakfast had 'hot toast served in folded linen', free-range eggs, local sausages, etc. There is a pub for evening meals almost opposite and the Birchenoughs are 'helpful about other places to eat and details of walks'; they offer a laundry service and will make a packed lunch. A half-hourly bus service to Chichester passes the door ('traffic begins early on the busy road'). Plenty of interesting sightseeing: Arundel, Petworth, Uppark, Fishbourne Roman palace; a footpath leads to walks through woods to the South Downs. The village name is pronounced 'Hannaka'. (*Col AJW and Mrs HM Harvey, and others*)

Bedrooms: 7, 1 on ground floor. *Open*: all year except Christmas, Jan, Feb. *Facilities*: lounge, breakfast room, ¼-acre garden with seating, unsuitable for &. *Background music*: none. *Location*: 4 miles NE of Chichester. *Smoking*: not allowed. *Children*: all ages welcomed (under-5s free). *Dogs*: only guide dogs allowed. *Credit cards*: MasterCard, Visa. *Prices*: [2008] b&b £32.50–£45 per person (higher for Goodwood 'Festival of Speed' and 'Revival' meetings), 1-night bookings sometimes refused weekends.

HAMBLETON Rutland   Map 2:B3

Hambleton Hall
Hambleton
Oakham LE15 8TH

Tel 01572-756991
Fax 01572-724721
Email hotel@hambletonhall.com
Website www.hambletonhall.com

• *César award in 1985*

'Idyllically' set on a peninsula jutting into Rutland Water, Tim and Stefa Hart's 'splendid' country house hotel is much praised again this year. 'A rarity, a luxury hotel which does things well and is comfortable with itself.' 'Our favourite. Consistent standards. Small enough to be intimate. Excellent food. Good service.' 'Atmosphere formal but friendly, just right.' 'Expensive but worth it.' Stefa Hart designed the classic interiors (fine fabrics, antiques, good paintings, open fires, flowers) with Nina Campbell. Recently refurbished bedrooms, though more contemporary, retain 'an identifiable *Hambleton* look'. 'All are excellent, nice small touches like a Roberts radio.' The Croquet Pavilion suite is good for a family (children are welcomed; the very young get an early supper). In the dining room, which faces the water, Aaron Patterson has long held a *Michelin* star for his seasonal cooking ('exciting, it never disappoints'), eg, rabbit with carrot purée, pea and mint risotto. Continental breakfast, included in the price, is 'generous: a cornucopia of fruits and cereals; hot toast and croissants just when you want them'. 'Ospreys are nesting on the lake, and nightingales sing every evening.' Tim Hart also owns *Hart's Hotel*, Nottingham (*qv*). (*Roderic Rennison, David Grant, Michael Forrest, Humphrey and Frances Norrington*)

Bedrooms: 17, 2-bedroomed suite in pavilion. *Open*: all year. *Facilities*: lift, ramps, hall, drawing room, bar, restaurant, 2 private dining rooms, small conference facilities, civil wedding licence, 17-acre grounds (swimming pool, heated May–Sept, tennis, cycling, lake with fishing, windsurfing, sailing). *Background music*: none. *Location*: 3 miles SE of Oakham, train Peterborough/Kettering/Oakham (branch line), helipad. *Smoking*: not allowed. *Children*: only children 'of a grown-up age' in restaurant, except at breakfast. *Dogs*: not allowed in public rooms, unattended in bedrooms. *Credit cards*: all major cards. *Prices*: b&b £100–£300 per person, set dinner from £40, full alc £85, seasonal breaks, Christmas/New Year packages, 1-night bookings sometimes refused.

HARMONDSWORTH Middlesex   Map 2:D3
See SHORTLIST

HAROME North Yorkshire   Map 4:D4

The Pheasant
Harome, nr Helmsley
YO62 5JG

Tel 01439-771241
Fax 01439-771744
Email reservations@thepheasanthotel.com
Website www.thepheasanthotel.com

The 'unhurried' welcome from the Binks family was praised by the nominator of this old inn which provides 'peace and quiet' away from the village's better known but busy *Star Inn* close by (see next entry). Originally the village smithy, two cottages and a shop, it has a small oak-beamed bar with log fire. The large, 'chintzy' drawing room and dining room open on to a stone-flagged terrace. In the 'very attractive' conservatory dining room, traditional meals are served, eg, casserole of local game; hazelnut meringue with raspberry coulis. The bedrooms, 'spacious, if quite simple', face south or south-west; some overlook the village pond and millstream, others the courtyard and walled garden. The thatched *Holly Cottage*, down a lane, has two sitting rooms and two bedrooms, a large garden and a courtyard. Packed lunches can be provided. Reduced green fees are available at the 18-hole golf course at Kirkbymoorside. The *Pheasant* has a kidney-shaped indoor swimming pool and a deer park. (*JR*)

Bedrooms: 12, 2 in cottage nearby. *Open*: all year except Jan, restaurant closed Mon in winter. *Facilities*: sitting room, bar, dining room, conservatory, indoor swimming pool, courtyard, garden, 10-acre deer park. *Background music*: none. *Location*: in village. *Smoking*: not allowed. *Children*: not under 7. *Dogs*: allowed by prior arrangement. *Credit cards*: MasterCard, Visa. *Prices*: [2008] b&b £60–£70 per person, d,b&b £82–£85, set dinner £30, 1-night bookings refused Sat.

The Star Inn

Harome, nr Helmsley
YO62 5JE

Tel 01439-770397
Fax 01439-771833
Email jpern@thestarathrome.co.uk
Website www.thestarathrome.co.uk

❦ *César award in 2004*

In a village 'within easy range of beautiful country', this converted medieval cruck-framed longhouse is 'a watering hole for foodies', run by 'charming' owners, Jacquie and Andrew Pern. His Yorkshire-influenced modern cooking earns a *Michelin* star. Very popular, it generally 'buzzes with visitors'. A lunchtime visitor enjoyed 'courteous service, delicious liver with a splendid array of fresh vegetables in a shining pan', chosen from a menu with 'huge choice: local sourcing and fish to the fore'. In warm weather, meals are served in the garden, fragrant with herbs and lavender. Accommodation is in *Cross House Lodge*, opposite (groups can eat in its *Wheelhouse* restaurant), *Black Eagle Cottage*, close by, and a farmhouse five minutes' walk away. The last has four bedrooms, an honesty bar and a kitchen (a chef or a meal in a hamper can be provided). The decor is 'rustic/modern'; all rooms have TV, CD- and DVD-player, home-made biscuits, fruit and fudge; two have a private garden; several have a shower big enough for two. Continental breakfast is served in the bedroom or round a huge table in the *Wheelhouse*. There is an open-plan, split-level lounge. Paul Wanless is the manager. (*Robert Gower, and others*)

Bedrooms: 14, 8 in *Cross House Lodge* opposite, others in separate buildings. *Open*: all year except 24–26 Dec, 1 Jan. *Facilities*: 2 lounges, coffee loft, bar, breakfast room, restaurant, private dining room, civil wedding licence, 2-acre garden, unsuitable for ♿. *Background music*: varied CDs. *Location*: village centre. *Smoking*: not allowed. *Children*: all ages welcomed (children's menu). *Dogs*: not allowed. *Credit cards*: MasterCard, Visa. *Prices*: b&b £65–£115 per person, full alc £45.

Hotels do not pay to be included in the *Guide*.

HARROGATE North Yorkshire   Map 4:D4
See SHORTLIST

HARWICH Essex   Map 2:C5

The Pier at Harwich   *Tel* 01255-241212
The Quay   *Fax* 01255-551922
Harwich CO12 3HH   *Email* pier@milsomhotels.com
    Website www.milsomhotels.com

On the quay in old Harwich, with views of the Stour and Orwell estuaries, stand these two historic buildings, owned by Paul Milsom, managed by Nick Chambers. They are now accessible by water, following the opening of yacht berths at the adjacent Ha'Penny Pier marina. The two restaurants, and most bedrooms, are in the larger building. Other rooms, and the beamed lounge, are in a former pub. In the first-floor *Harbourside* restaurant, with its 'minimalist' decor, 'theatrical' lighting and polished pewter champagne bar, chef Chris Oakley specialises in seafood (fish comes daily from the harbour), eg, smoked haddock and pancetta chowder; seared peppered tuna loin steak on rhubarb pickle. 'Very fresh ingredients, well cooked.' Informal meals are served in the ground-floor *Ha'Penny Bistro*. Bedrooms have minibar, satellite TV and hospitality tray; many face the harbour, but some smaller rooms have a 'less than beautiful' outlook. All bathrooms have been upgraded. Breakfast includes freshly squeezed juice, 'thick slices of ham and cheese'. 'A good stay in every way,' one *Guide* correspondent wrote. Other praise: 'Management much in evidence. Service competent *and* friendly.' The Milsoms also own *Le Talbooth* restaurant in Dedham and two hotels: *milsoms*, a 'stylish gastropub with rooms', and *Maison Talbooth* (see Shortlist), which reopened in April 2008 after major alterations. More reports, please.

Bedrooms: 14, 7 in annexe, 1 on ground floor. *Open*: all year. *Facilities*: ramps, lounge (in annexe), restaurant, bistro, civil wedding licence, small front terrace. *Background music*: in bar. *Location*: on quay. *Smoking*: not allowed. *Children*: all ages welcomed. *Dogs*: only guide dogs allowed. *Credit cards*: all major cards. *Prices*: [2008] b&b £52.50–£95 per person, full alc £38.65, special breaks, Christmas package. *V*

HASTINGS Sussex *See SHORTLIST*   Map 2:E5

HATHERSAGE Derbyshire   Map 3:A6

The George Hotel
Main Road
Hathersage S32 1BB

Tel 01433-650436
Fax 01433-650099
Email info@george-hotel.net
Website www.george-hotel.net

'A happy place', this 600-year-old grey stone inn is owned by Eric Marsh, who also runs *The Cavendish* at nearby Baslow (*qv*). The manager, Philip Joseph, and some of the 'relaxed, friendly' staff work at both. An inspector received a 'warm welcome', help with luggage. The bedrooms, 'beautifully decorated in neutral colours', have high headboards, ceiling spotlights, comfortable chairs, plain white walls, 'attractive, unfussy' drapes. 'Our spacious back room, thoughtfully equipped, had decent sheets on bed, a small but well-thought-out bathroom.' Front rooms face a busy road and have double glazing. The lounge and bar were renovated in contemporary style in 2008: 'Rich brown carpet, dramatic fabrics, modern tables; seating in hospitable groups, we loved it.' Light lunches are taken here. The 'attractive' dining room has a beamed ceiling and stone walls. Executive chef Ben Handley has left, but head chef Helen Heywood remains: her modern English dishes include duck liver brulée with maple-roasted pears; pan-roasted venison with potato and black truffle terrine. 'The French restaurant manager uses Gallic charm to great effect. Excellent breakfast: a beautifully laid buffet with delicious muesli, fresh fruit, creamy yogurt but commercial juices; a perfect Full Monty, toast in relays.' 'Helen's home-made marmalade' is commended. (*H and HR, and others*)

Bedrooms: 22. *Open*: all year. *Facilities*: lounge/bar, restaurant, 2 function rooms, civil wedding licence, courtyard, only restaurant suitable for &. *Background music*: jazz in restaurant. *Location*: in village centre, parking. *Smoking*: not allowed. *Children*: all ages welcomed. *Dogs*: not allowed. *Credit cards*: all major cards. *Prices*: b&b £60.50–£132 per person, set dinner £35, special breaks, Christmas/New Year packages, 1-night bookings occasionally refused weekends. *V*

HAWORTH West Yorkshire   Map 4:D3
See SHORTLIST

HELMSLEY North Yorkshire   Map 4:C4

The Feversham Arms   *Tel* 01439-770766
1 High Street   *Fax* 01439-770346
Helmsley YO62 5AG   *Email* info@fevershamarmshotel.com
                        Website www.fevershamarmshotel.com

'A hotel of quality' (a comment this year), Simon and Jill Rhatigan's former coaching inn (Pride of Britain) stands on the main street of a 'delightful' town ('with some wonderful pastry shops') on the edge of the North Yorkshire moors. Extensive building work was continuing as the *Guide* went to press: a new poolside wing will have four new bedroom suites, and a new spa, due to open in autumn 2008, will contain eight treatment rooms, an underground car park and six poolside suites, each with private terrace. The bedrooms in the main house vary greatly; the larger ones are much liked: 'Ours was well equipped; enormous bed, divine bedlinen.' 'Suite the best we've seen in the UK; beautifully appointed, with flat-screen TV in both rooms, and log fire in the sitting room.' For families, some rooms have a sofa bed and some are interconnecting. There are 'relaxing' sitting areas and 'punctilious staff', though during a Christmas break service was 'a bit patchy'. In the high-roofed conservatory restaurant (extended this year) chef Simon Kelly uses local produce in his modern dishes, eg, tian of Whitby crab, ginger jelly; caramelised duck breast, crispy quail egg. Breakfast is 'exceptional'. (*Bianca Emberson, John and Annette Linton*)

Bedrooms: 27, 5 in garden, 6 by pool, 8 on ground floor. *Open*: all year. *Facilities*: 2 lounges, bar, conservatory restaurant, private dining room, terrace (outside dining), civil wedding licence, 1-acre garden (heated 13-metre swimming pool, spa). *Background music*: in restaurant, private dining room. *Location*:

central, safe parking. *Smoking*: not allowed. *Children*: all ages welcomed. *Dogs*: not allowed in public rooms. *Credit cards*: Amex, MasterCard, Visa. *Prices*: [2008] b&b £51–£97 per person, d,b&b £67.50–£285, set dinner £33–£45, full alc £55, special breaks, Christmas/New Year packages, 1-night bookings refused weekends.

See also SHORTLIST

HENLEY-ON-THAMES Oxfordshire   Map 2:D3
See SHORTLIST

HEREFORD Herefordshire   Map 3:D4
See SHORTLIST

HETTON North Yorkshire   Map 4:D3

The Angel Inn   *Tel* 01756-730263
Hetton, nr Skipton   *Fax* 01756-730363
BD23 6LT   *Email* info@angelhetton.co.uk
                         Website www.angelhetton.co.uk

Endorsed this year by an American visitor ('lovely suites and excellent food'), this old drovers' inn in the Yorkshire Dales was opened as a fine-dining pub in 1983 by Denis and Juliet Watkins. He died in 2004, but she continues to run it with Andrew Holmes as manager, retaining its *Michelin Bib Gourmand* for good cooking at moderate prices. Her son Pascal runs a wine 'cave' across the road in a converted barn which also has two studio bedrooms and three suites: they have brass bed fittings, bright fabrics, and are 'thoughtfully equipped' (tea-making equipment, an honesty bar, a well-lit, modern bathroom). A bar menu, with blackboard specials (eg, Swinton Park venison, apple polenta, beetroot fondant; Yorkshire pheasant two ways), is served in a series of panelled and beamed rooms (nooks and crannies, cosy alcoves). In the restaurant, chef director Bruce Elsworth and head chef Mark Taft use local produce for a *carte* of dishes like smoked salmon with lemon and caper dressing; duo of Bolton Abbey mutton, savoy cabbage, rosemary jus. Summer meals can be taken on a flagged forecourt overlooking

Cracoe Fell. Breakfast, served until 10 am, has 'very good' fresh juices, big bowls of cereals and fresh fruit, and an 'immense' Yorkshire platter. (*Richard Lamb*)

Bedrooms: 5 in barn across road, 1 on ground floor suitable for ♿. *Open*: all year except 25 Dec, 1 week Jan. *Facilities*: bar/brasserie, restaurant (2 rooms), terrace (outside dining), wine shop, civil wedding licence. *Background music*: none. *Location*: off B6265, 5 miles N of Skipton, car park. *Smoking*: not allowed. *Children*: all ages welcomed. *Dogs*: not allowed in public rooms. *Credit cards*: Amex, MasterCard, Visa. *Prices*: [2008] b&b £65–£165 per person, set Sat dinner £35, full alc £38, midweek breaks, New Year package.

HEXHAM Northumberland   Map 4:B3
See SHORTLIST

HINTON ST GEORGE Somerset   Map 1:C6

The Lord Poulett Arms   *Tel* 01460-73149
High Street   *Email* steveandmichelle@lordpoulettarms.com
Hinton St George   *Website* www.lordpoulettarms.com
TA17 8SE

♥ *César award in 2008*

'An enthusiastic couple', Steve Hill and Michelle Paynton have sensitively renovated this 17th-century pub in a pretty Somerset village. They serve 'superior gastropub cooking' while continuing to stock 'good honest barrels of local ale'. The busy bar is an informal place; 'dogs sleep on the hearth and interesting local conversations can be overheard'. The old building ('delightfully quirky,' said inspectors) has 'floors of bare flag or boards, tables of old oak or elm, antique chairs, open fires, numerous pictures'. Room 1, 'great fun', has 'big bed, massive carved headboard; huge old wooden wardrobe; old-fashioned bath (with optional screen) by the window; loo in what was probably once a large old cupboard'. No television (the information pack includes a section on how to spend your time without one). Gary Coughlan has been promoted to head chef; his short menu uses local, mainly organic produce, eg, smoked bacon and leek risotto; bangers and mash. 'Superb service; staff dressed in black; a good, buzzy atmosphere.' The 'excellent' breakfast, served until 9 am, has fresh juices, fruit compote, leaf tea, toasted home-made bread, local marmalade. Behind the building is a 'French-style' garden with a *boules* piste edged by lavender. (*EL, IM, and others*)

Bedrooms: 4. *Open*: all year except 26 Dec, 1 Jan, check-in 12 noon–3 pm, 6.30–11 pm. *Facilities*: bar, restaurant, private dining room, 1-acre grounds, unsuitable for &. *Background music*: none. *Location*: village centre. *Smoking*: not allowed. *Children*: all ages welcomed. *Dogs*: not allowed in bedrooms. *Credit cards*: MasterCard, Visa. *Prices*: b&b £44–£59 per person, full alc £30, 1-night bookings refused Sat.

HOARWITHY Herefordshire   Map 3:D4

Aspen House   NEW   *Tel* 01432-840353
Hoarwithy HR2 6QP   *Email* sallyandrob@aspenhouse.net
                                    Website www.aspenhouse.net

In a village (with a remarkable church) in the Wye valley, this pink 18th-century farmhouse is now a guest house run by its owners, Sally Dean and Rob Elliott. 'We liked their enthusiasm and dedication, their keenness for good food and local sources. Our room was comfortable and pretty, no frills,' wrote inspectors. 'Wow! If only all things could be this good,' another enthusiastic visitor wrote. 'Real rooms, real comfort.' There is some Polish influence in the no-choice (except for the first course) evening meal served at 7.15. The host, who is half Polish, promises that the cooking is not over-complicated: 'Ingredients are allowed to speak for themselves.' Everything comes from within a ten-mile radius. The main course might be slow-roasted pork belly and crackling on a dried mushroom buckwheat risotto. After-dinner entertainment consists of conversation with fellow guests, or watching TV in the bedroom. Breakfast can include grilled rare breed pork sausages, home-made baked beans, all varieties of cooked eggs, or a continental version with cold meats, local cheeses and Polish stuffed eggs. 'Excellent home-baked bread.' Local maps, magazines and large red sofas are in the lounge. Indian head massage can be arranged. (*Christine Farrell, and others*)

Bedrooms: 4. *Open*: all year except Christmas. *Facilities*: lounge, dining room, decked area, ¾-acre garden, unsuitable for &. *Background music*: light classical sometimes. *Location*: village centre, 4 miles NW of Ross-on-Wye. *Smoking*: not allowed. *Children*: not under 12. *Dogs*: not allowed. *Credit cards*: MasterCard, Visa. *Prices*: b&b £36–£43 per person, d,b&b £54.50–£65.50, set dinner £24.

HOLKHAM Norfolk *See SHORTLIST*   Map 2:A5

HOLMFIRTH West Yorkshire   Map 4:E3
See SHORTLIST

HOLT Norfolk   Map 2:A5

Byfords   *Tel* 01263-711400
1–3 Shirehall Plain   *Fax* 01263-714815
Holt NR25 6BG   *Email* queries@byfords.org.uk
          Website www.byfords.org.uk

On the main square of a charming little Norfolk town, this 'delightful' conversion of old houses (Grade II listed) is run by Iain and Clair Wilson as an unusual combination of 'posh B&B', café by day, bistro by night, and deli. Tables and chairs stand on the pavement outside; inside is a series of eating rooms, with old beams, exposed bricks, wooden tables. Inspectors, who 'would go back', received a 'warm welcome from a friendly manageress, but no help with luggage'. Their 'delightful' room, upstairs, was 'spacious, with rug on wooden floor, big bed with high wooden bedhead and half-tester canopy, *chaise longue*, two armchairs, flat-screen TV; lovely bathroom with double-ended bath, separate shower'. Free tea on arrival included 'delicious ginger cake'. Another visitor was pleased to be given a fan to cool his bedroom on a hot day. Meals are served all day in the café. In the evening 'the place was buzzing; cheerful bistro food included nice crab pasta; Eton mess. Very friendly service from a young Polish waiter.' At breakfast in a large, light room, there are juices, cereals, croissants, fruit compote, etc, on a central table; 'good scrambled eggs brought with a thick slice of toast. There was muzak, but not very loud.' Visitors are given a comprehensive handbook of information on the area. (*Brian A Jackson, and others*)

Bedrooms: 16, 1 on ground floor. *Open*: all year. *Facilities*: ramps, 5 internal eating areas, deli. *Background music*: jazz/'easy listening'. *Location*: Central, private secure parking. *Smoking*: not allowed. *Children*: all ages welcomed. *Dogs*: not allowed. *Credit cards*: MasterCard, Visa. *Prices*: b&b £70–£95 per person, d,b&b £92.50–£117.50, full alc £30, winter offers, Christmas/New Year packages, 1-night bookings refused Sat.

Inevitably, some hotels change hands or close after we have gone to press. You should always check the ownership when booking, particularly in the case of small establishments.

HOPE Derbyshire   Map 3:A6

Underleigh House   *Tel* 01433-621372
off Edale Road   *Fax* 01433-621324
Hope S33 6RF   *Email* info@underleighhouse.co.uk
                                     Website www.underleighhouse.co.uk

Reached down a narrow lane outside a village in the Hope valley
(within the Peak District national park), this extended barn and
cottage conversion, now a B&B, has good walking from the door. The
owners, Vivienne Taylor ('delightful, warm') and her husband,
Philip, will provide maps and packed lunches. They offer 'amazing
value'. 'Their generous hospitality never failed,' says a visitor in 2008.
Other praise: 'We were greeted by name and given tea with delicious
lemon cake.' All the bedrooms have tea/coffee-making equipment,
hairdryer, TV with DVD- and CD-player. 'Our small room had lots of
patterns, views on both sides of fields with sheep, everything one
could want, even bathrobes (nice lightweight ones); small bathroom
with a bath; a comprehensive information pack.' Breakfast is taken
around a large oak table in the flagstoned hall. Lots of choice: jugs of
orange juice, eight types of home-made jam, own-recipe muesli, fresh
and dried fruits from the buffet; porridge and croissants from the Aga;
sausages and black pudding from the Hope butcher. Drinks are
served in a large lounge with a log fire or on a terrace; recommendations are given on local eating places. (*Heather Parry, FR, and others*)

Bedrooms: 6, 2 on ground floor. *Open*: Feb–Dec, except Christmas/New Year.
Facilities: lounge, breakfast room, ⅓-acre garden, unsuitable for &. *Background
music*: none. *Location*: 1 mile N of Hope, train to Hope, bus from Sheffield.
Smoking: not allowed. *Children*: not under 12. *Dogs*: allowed by arrangement.
Credit cards: MasterCard, Visa (*both 3% surcharge*). *Prices*: [2008] b&b £37.50–
£60 per person, 3-night rates, 1-night bookings refused Fri/Sat.

See also SHORTLIST

How to contact the *Guide*
By mail: From anywhere in the UK, write to Freepost PAM
2931, London W11 4BR (no stamp is needed)
From outside the UK: *Good Hotel Guide*, 50 Addison Avenue,
London W11 4QP, England
By telephone or fax: 020-7602 4182
By email: editor@goodhotelguide.com
Via our website: www.goodhotelguide.com

HORDLE Hampshire   Map 2:E2

The Mill at Gordleton
Silver Street
Hordle, nr Lymington
SO41 6DJ

Tel 01590-682219
Fax 01590-683073
Email info@themillatgordleton.co.uk
Website www.themillatgordleton.co.uk

Owned by Elizabeth Cottingham and managed by Terri Seabright, this 'pleasant restaurant with rooms' is an ivy-covered converted 17th-century mill on the edge of the New Forest. The 'warm welcome' and 'uniformly friendly and efficient staff' are praised. 'Housekeeping of a high standard. The weekday calm impressed. Our room, furnished in artistic fawn and blue, had a large, comfortable bed and a nice terrace where we sat in the sun; a very modern bathroom with an intricate shower.' The decor is traditional. Outside are 'beautifully sculpted' gardens by a river with ducks and sometimes a heron. Meals can be served alfresco in fine weather. Service in the bustling restaurant, which faces the river, was 'friendly, measured and accurate'. The cooking of chefs Karl Wiggins and David Baker has 'a contemporary twist', perhaps twice-baked crab and Gruyère soufflé; breast of local wood pigeon. 'There was home-made bread; home-made ice creams, all magnificently served.' There is always a vegetarian dish of the day. The good wine list has a wide price range. A busy road is nearby, but 'our mini-suite was well positioned and insulated so there was no trace of noise'. A useful base for visiting Beaulieu, Buckler's Hard, the Isle of Wight, etc. (*WR*)

Bedrooms: 7. *Open*: open all year except 25 Dec, restaurant closed Sun night. *Facilities*: lounge, 2 bars, restaurant, private dining room, 3-acre grounds on river (fishing rights), only restaurant suitable for &. *Background music*: in public rooms. *Location*: 4 miles W of Lymington. *Smoking*: not allowed. *Children*: all ages welcomed. *Dogs*: allowed in front bar and gardens only. *Credit cards*: Amex, MasterCard, Visa. *Prices*: b&b £65–£97.50 per person, set lunch £12.50–£15.50, (Sun) £19.90, full alc £40–£45, 1-night bookings sometimes refused bank holidays.

****

Traveller's tale *Hotel in Somerset* The paintwork on the windows is revolting. The bathroom (torn carpet, peeling ceiling, disgusting surround around the bath, dressing gowns with enormous holes under the armpits) and the shabby staircase leading to the top floor all give an unloved feeling. We were stunned to be charged nigh on £200 for a room in such a state.

****

HORNINGSHAM Wiltshire   Map 2:D1

The Bath Arms   `NEW`   *Tel* 01985-844308
Longleat   *Fax* 01985-845187
Horningsham BA12 7LY   *Email* enquiries@batharms.co.uk
                                   Website www.batharms.co.uk

Inspectors in 2008 liked the 'informal, happy atmosphere' of this old inn: 'Our stay was fun.' Near the entrance to the Longleat estate, it is leased from the Marquis of Bath by the 'affable' Christoph Brooke and his wife, Sarah Montague (of the *Today* programme). Sara Elston is manageress. The 'handsome', square grey stone building, filled with Indian furniture and fabrics, some now 'a bit worn', 'plays an important part in village life'. It stands framed by lime trees, back from crossroads. The bedrooms, all different, also have an oriental theme (one, upstairs, is called Karma Sutra). There are exotic wallpapers, bright colours. 'Our garden room had quirky decor, carved Buddhas, delightful terrace, view of rolling fields, evening turn-down service. Poor lighting made it gloomy at night. In the bar (packed at night with locals), we had an excellent lunch.' The spacious restaurant has ancient oak floorboards, colourful rugs, Indian paintings, 'a splendid stone fireplace (alas no fire)', three massive gilded chandeliers. 'A charming, well-spoken young man served us dinner. Bread was excellent, monkfish was fresh and firm, steak was tough, vegetables were perfect. Brownie points for the carafe of tap water. At breakfast service was slow, the table was attractively laid, porridge was excellent.' Families are encouraged.

Bedrooms: 15, 6 in stables, 1 suitable for &. *Open*: all year. *Facilities*: ramp, lounge, bar, 2 dining rooms, Hip Bath (beauty treatments/therapies), 2 patios, lawn. *Background music*: bar and restaurant. *Location*: Longleat estate, 4 miles W of Warminster. *Smoking*: not allowed. *Children*: all ages welcomed. *Dogs*: allowed in bar and lounge only. *Credit cards*: MasterCard, Visa. *Prices*: [2008] b&b £40–£130 per person, d,b&b £69.50–£159.50, full alc £36.25, Christmas/New Year packages, 1-night bookings refused Fri.

HOVE East Sussex *See SHORTLIST*   Map 2:E4

HUDDERSFIELD West Yorkshire   Map 4:E3
See SHORTLIST

HULL East Yorkshire *See SHORTLIST* Map 4:D5

HUNGERFORD Berkshire   Map 2:D2

The Bear   *Tel* 01488-682512
41 Charnham Street   *Fax* 01488-684357
Hungerford RG17 0EL   *Email* info@thebearhotelhungerford.co.uk
                         Website www.thebearhotelhungerford.co.uk

*Refurbishment continues at historic inn once owned by Henry VIII, in town
centre; 33 (of 41) bedrooms given contemporary look ('stylishly comfortable';
custom-designed furniture, flat-screen TV with movies on demand, Wi-Fi).
Front rooms face busy A4; quietest ones, and restaurant, face River Dunn.
Manager Colin Heaney leads 'welcoming, efficient' staff. Chef Phillip Wild
serves much-admired modern European cooking; 'excellent' light meals
available. Weddings, functions, etc, held. Good advance-booked/weekend
rates. Small lounge, snug, bar area, restaurant (closed Sun night, bank holidays, except 25/26 Dec); background music; private dining room; courtyard
(meal/drinks service); meeting facilities; civil wedding licence. Riverside
terrace, small lawn area, island. Car park. Unsuitable for &. No smoking.
Amex, MasterCard, Visa accepted. Prices: [2008] room £85–£190, breakfast
£9.95–£12.95, full alc £39.50, weekend rates, Christmas/New Year package.*

HUNTINGDON Cambridgeshire   Map 2:B4

The Old Bridge   **NEW**   *Tel* 01480-424300
1 High Street   *Fax* 01480-411017
Huntingdon PE29 3TQ   *Email* oldbridge@huntsbridge.co.uk
                         Website www.huntsbridge.com

This handsome, creeper-clad 18th-century building, once a private
bank, stands by a medieval bridge over the River Ouse. It was
demoted to the Shortlist in 2008 following a critical inspection report,
but its owner, John Hoskins, tells us that now it 'is run more
personally than it has ever been. Much money has been spent on
improving bedrooms, gardens and car parking' (he has sold the rest of
his small Huntsbridge group of inns). Nina Beamond is manager.
This year's comments: 'Porterage much improved.' 'Wonderfully
comfortable, spacious, well-thought-out bedroom and bathroom.
Wine list outstanding, mark-ups reasonable or non-existent. Good

service.' In the 'lovely restaurant, with large oval cupola', new head chef Alex Tyndall serves traditional dishes like grilled lemon sole; slow-cooked belly of pork. The building is hedged in by a busy traffic system but has triple glazing and air conditioning, and the small riverside garden is relatively peaceful. The bedrooms are themed: there are mosaic tiles, *chaises longues*, up-to-date music systems, smart bathrooms (some with claw-footed bath). Early morning tea and a free newspaper are delivered to the room; shoes are cleaned. There is free Wi-Fi. Breakfast includes scrambled eggs with smoked salmon. Functions are held in a self-contained area. (*John Gibbon, Trevor Roberts, Jerry Coleman, and others*)

Bedrooms: 24, 2 on ground floor. *Open*: all year. *Facilities*: ramps, lounge, bar, restaurant, private dining room, wine shop, business centre, civil wedding licence, 1-acre grounds (terrace, garden), river (fishing, jetty, boat trips), unsuitable for &. *Background music*: none. *Location*: 500 yds from centre, parking, station 10 mins' walk. *Smoking*: not allowed. *Children*: all ages welcomed. *Dogs*: not allowed in public rooms. *Credit cards*: all major cards. *Prices*: b&b £65–£95 per person, full alc £30, Christmas/New Year packages.

HURSTBOURNE TARRANT   Map 2:D2
Hampshire

Esseborne Manor
Hurstbourne Tarrant, nr Andover
SP11 0ER

Tel 01264-736444
Fax 01264-736725
Email info@esseborne-manor.co.uk
Website www.esseborne-manor.co.uk

An 'unstuffy', traditional hotel with a 'family-run atmosphere' and 'most helpful staff'. This Victorian house has been sympathetically extended by its owners, Lucilla and Ian Hamilton; their son, Mark, is the manager. It is approached up a long drive, flanked by fields with sheep grazing, off a busy road (traffic noise audible in the garden). Some bedrooms in the main house have a spa bath, some a four-poster; six rooms around a courtyard are good for families (children are welcomed, though there are no special facilities for them); two small rooms are in cottages. Inspectors on a return visit were upgraded to a premier deluxe room with private patio overlooking the pretty herb garden. 'Very comfortable bed, huge open bathroom/dressing area with spa bath, separate multi-jet shower, loo in an enclosure with opaque glass (not keen on this), lots of storage, good lighting apart from bedside lights. In the dining room (red-patterned wallpaper, blue carpet, big windows), the Bosnian chef (since winter 2007), Anton

Babarovic, cooks modern English dishes with continental influences, eg, monkfish with Parmentier and a truffle sauce. At breakfast, 'buffet a little uninspiring: boring toast but good cooked dishes'. Weddings (marquee on the lawn) and meetings are catered for.

Bedrooms: 19, 6 in courtyard, 2 in cottages. *Open*: all year except 26 Dec–3 Jan. *Facilities*: 2 lounges, bar, restaurant, function room, civil wedding licence, 3-acre grounds (formal gardens, tennis, croquet), arrangements with nearby golf club and fitness centre. *Background music*: in bar. *Location*: on A343, midway between Andover and Newbury. *Smoking*: not allowed. *Children*: all ages welcomed. *Dogs*: not allowed in public rooms. *Credit cards*: all major cards. *Prices*: [2008] b&b £62.50–£130 per person, d,b&b £30 added, set menus £17–£34, full alc £42, special breaks. *V*

INKPEN Berkshire *See SHORTLIST*   Map 2:D2

IPSWICH Suffolk *See SHORTLIST*   Map 2:C5

IREBY Cumbria   Map 4: inset B2

Overwater Hall
Overwater, nr Ireby
CA7 1HH

Tel 017687-76566
Fax 017687-76921
Email welcome@overwaterhall.co.uk
Website www.overwaterhall.co.uk

Recommended to 'anyone who wants to relax away from the bustle of more touristy areas', this castellated Grade II listed Georgian mansion is owned and run by Stephen Bore and Adrian and Angela Hyde. Mr Bore is a 'gentle front-of-house', welcoming guests and carrying their luggage. Children are welcomed: high teas served for under-5s at 5.30 pm. Dogs may sit with their owners in one of the lounges (the other is designated dog free), and have the run of the large grounds. The public rooms have a bold decor: 'audacious' wallpaper, contrasting panelling and lights, a wood-panelled bar. 'Their opulence and individuality suit the house.' Redecoration of all the bedrooms was completed in 2008; all bathrooms have double-ended bath and a separate walk-in shower; extras include bathrobes, flowers, a fruit bowl and mineral water. 'Our bedroom had magnificent views and was extremely comfortable,' said a visitor who found *Overwater Hall* 'delightful'. Tables are 'elegantly laid' in the dining room where smart casual dress is expected. Adrian Hyde's four-course menus are thought 'well balanced, well proportioned', 'as considered as everything else. Very good service.' The cooking is modern, eg, sole mousse with saffron; saddle of venison with haggis and rabbit pie. Breakfast is served at table on linen cloths, 'a full Cumbrian affair'. Good walking from the door; red squirrels, deer and woodpeckers can be seen, and osprey nest nearby. (*Jane Corbett, SC, and others*)

Bedrooms: 11, 1 on ground floor. *Open*: all year. *Facilities*: drawing room, lounge, bar area, restaurant, civil wedding licence, 18-acre grounds, Overwater tarn 1 mile. *Background music*: classical in restaurant. *Location*: 2 miles NE of Bassenthwaite Lake. *Smoking*: not allowed. *Children*: not under 5 in restaurant (high tea at 5.30 pm). *Dogs*: allowed except in one lounge. *Credit cards*: MasterCard, Visa. *Prices*: [2008] b&b £60–£170 per person, d,b&b £40 added, set dinner £45, 4-night breaks all year, Christmas/New Year packages, 1-night bookings refused Sat.

KESWICK Cumbria   Map 4: inset C2
See SHORTLIST

KINGHAM Oxfordshire   Map 3:D6

The Kingham Plough   **NEW**   *Tel/Fax* 01608-658327
The Green   *Email* book@thekinghamplough.co.uk
Kingham, nr Chipping Norton   *Website*
www.thekinghamplough.co.uk
OX7 6YD

Emily Watkins (once *sous-chef* at the celebrated *Fat Duck* in Bray) and Adam Dorrien-Smith took over and renovated this old building in 2007. It quickly earned a reputation as a dining pub, serving 'outstanding food at keen prices' (say inspectors). Most of the modern bedrooms (with bath) are above the main house (first floor). 'Ours was spacious: white walls, pale blue curtains and bed canopy, old beams, wash basin in a cupboard, good storage.' The door of 'splendidly quirky' Room 2 'opens into a space with a claw-foot bath (loo behind a side door)'. The simpler annexe rooms (with shower) are 'good value'. No lounge: the bar (stone and wooden floors) and dining room (sisal matting, vaulted roof, original beams) have 'lots of stripped wood, wooden tables, non-matching chairs (a delightful mish-mash of styles)'. At dinner, with large candles and white linen, 'exceptional' dishes included 'wonderfully fresh crab; hot beetroot mousse; rabbit pie; sea trout with sea-shore vegetables; light rhubarb soufflé'. Staff are 'young, enthusiastic'. 'Breakfast passed the test with flying colours: simple, uncomplicated, with fresh ingredients. Jug of freshly squeezed orange juice; home-made muesli and preserves (delicious), two warm loaves of bread, no menu for cooked dishes, you ask for what you want.' Children and dogs are welcomed. Wi-Fi is available.

Bedrooms: 7, 3 in annexe. *Open*: all year except 25 Dec. *Facilities*: bar, restaurant, terrace, garden, only restaurant and bar suitable for &. *Background music*: 'varied' in bar. *Location*: 4 miles SW of Chipping Norton. *Smoking*: not allowed. *Children*: all ages welcomed. *Dogs*: allowed in annexe rooms only (£10). *Credit cards*: MasterCard, Visa accepted. *Prices*: b&b £42.50–£80 per person, full alc £35.

KING'S LYNN Norfolk   Map 2:A4
See SHORTLIST

KINGSBRIDGE Devon   Map 1:D4
See SHORTLIST

KIRKBY LONSDALE Cumbria   Map 4: inset C2
See SHORTLIST

KIRKBY STEPHEN Cumbria   Map 4:C3

Augill Castle   NEW   *Tel* 01768-341937
South Stainmore   *Email* enquiries@augillcastle.co.uk
nr Kirkby Stephen CA17 4DE   *Website* www.stayinacastle.com

In the peaceful upper Eden valley, Simon and Wendy Bennett run their Victorian Gothic folly in informal house-party style; it is their family home, shared with their children and Holly, a friendly Labrador. Lavishly restored, it has a panelled hall, vaulted ceilings, turrets, leaded or stained-glass windows, ticking clocks, historically authentic colours, an eclectic mix of antiques and old furniture. You might find a piano or a church pew in your bathroom. The informality doesn't suit everyone, some visitors found rooms cold, and the welcome offhand in the owners' absence. But there is enthusiasm too. 'A happy atmosphere.' 'We were invited to treat the place as our own. Our four-poster room, Pendragon, sumptuously decorated, had enough space to swing several tigers. Sherry and flapjacks replenished daily.' 'Our room was heavenly, though the mattress seemed saggy: beautiful white linen helped to make up for this.' 'Freshly ground coffee, deep bathtub, drenching waterfall shower, big, fluffy towels.' An evening meal, served communally, is available May to October, by arrangement. Children are welcomed (baby monitors, cots, toys, games, and a cookery school for over-sevens). The leisurely breakfast has freshly squeezed orange juice, home-made bread, real tea, cooked dishes like scrambled eggs with smoked salmon. 'Great walking' from the door. (*Mr and Mrs J Anderson, Patricia Higgins, and others*)

Bedrooms: 12, some on ground floor, 2 family in stable block (*Little Castle*). *Open*: all year except 22–28 Dec, dinner available daily May–Oct, by arrangement in winter, lunch for groups, by arrangement. *Facilities*: hall, drawing room (honesty bar), music (sitting) room, dining room, civil wedding licence, 15-acre grounds (landscaped garden, tennis). *Background music*: none. *Location*: 3 miles W of Kirkby Stephen, M6 exit 38, then A685. *Smoking*: not allowed. *Children*: all ages welcomed. *Dogs*: not allowed. *Credit cards*: MasterCard, Visa. *Prices*: b&b £80 per person, supper £20, dinner £40, New Year house party, 2-night bookings preferred weekends. ***V***

KIRTLINGTON Oxfordshire   Map 2:C2

The Dashwood
South Green, Heyford Road
Kirtlington OX5 3HJ

Tel 01869-352707
Fax 01869-351432
Email info@thedashwood.co.uk
Website www.thedashwood.co.uk

In an attractive Oxfordshire village with pretty mellow stone cottages, this Grade II listed old pub is run as a contemporary restaurant-with-rooms by owners Martin and Ros Lewis. Artwork by their daughter, Rebecca, hangs on walls. It is 'neat and well ordered both inside and out'. 'Splashes of colour from fabrics and paintings contrast well with the natural look of wood, leather, plain carpeting and stone,' said an inspector. In the informal bistro-style split-level restaurant (with bare brick, stone floors, and an open-style kitchen), chef Marcel Taylor's menus have a bias towards fish dishes, eg, squid ink pasta with lobster, prawn and crab; fish pie with saffron and

Parmesan mash. Bedrooms have a clean modern decor, hand-made oak furniture, free broadband Internet access, slimline TV; some are on a courtyard; one is in an attic. Rear ones are quietest. Breakfast is served until 10 am. The main drawback: no guests' sitting room, but there is a 'cosy' bar. 'We had a pleasant stay, smart and unpretentious, if not a spoiling experience.'

Bedrooms: 12, 7 in barn, 3 on ground floor, 1 suitable for &. *Open*: all year except New Year, restaurant closed to non-residents Sun evening. *Facilities*: small bar area, restaurant, small garden area. *Background music*: in bar and restaurant. *Location*: in village on A4095, 12 miles N of Oxford, car park. *Smoking*: not allowed. *Children*: all ages welcomed. *Dogs*: not allowed. *Credit cards*: Amex, MasterCard, Visa. *Prices*: b&b £55–£120 per person, set menu (2 courses) £13.50, full alc £32.

KNIGHTWICK Worcestershire   Map 3:D5

The Talbot
Knightwick
WR6 5PH

Tel 01886-821235
Fax 01886-821060
Email info@the-talbot.co.uk
Website www.the-talbot.co.uk

On the banks of the River Teme in lovely Herefordshire-Worcestershire border countryside, this 14th-century traditional coaching inn 'with a strong huntin', shootin' and fishin' theme', has long been owned by the Clift family. A visitor on a winter's evening found it 'heaving' with a large shooting party. 'No smart country house hotel pretensions here.' Following the floods in summer 2007, the ground floor has been refurbished. *The Talbot* is home to the Teme Valley Brewery, started 1997, using hops grown in the parish. The home-brewed ales ('This', 'That', 'T'other' and 'Wot') are served in a 'lively bar'. Its menu includes shepherd's pie; cold raised rabbit, gin and pork pie. In the oak-panelled dining room, cooking is also 'firmly rooted in local produce', eg, pot-roasted shoulder of mutton with white onion sauce, roast potatoes and parsnips. 'We make "in house" nearly everything we sell, including breads, preserves, black pudding, pâté, raised pies,' writes Annie Clift, 'but fish comes from Cornwall and Wales.' Most bedrooms have good views. 'Our large room's bathroom had an ultra-modern power shower.' Breakfast includes 'tasty black pudding and bacon'. 'Special mention for the fireplaces: one had almost half a tree blazing in the hearth.' Fishing can be arranged. More reports, please.

Bedrooms: 11. *Open*: all year except 25 Dec evening. *Facilities*: ramp, lounge bar, restaurant, patio, riverside picnic area, only restaurant suitable for &. *Background music*: none. *Location*: 7 miles W of Worcester, on to B4197. *Smoking*: allowed in 3 bedrooms. *Children*: all ages welcomed. *Dogs*: by arrangement, not allowed in restaurant. *Credit cards*: MasterCard, Visa. *Prices*: [2008] b&b £42–£50 per person, d,b&b £70, alc £30, New Year package.

KNUTSFORD Cheshire   Map 4:E3
See SHORTLIST

LACOCK Wiltshire   Map 2:D1

At the Sign of the Angel
6 Church Street
Lacock, nr Chippenham SN15 2LB

Tel 01249-730230
Fax 01249-730527
Email angel@lacock.co.uk
Website www.lacock.co.uk

❧ *César award in 1989*

'We felt we had come home,' writes a visitor who was welcomed at 11 pm one night to this 15th-century half-timbered inn in this ancient and picturesque National Trust village much used by film-makers (latterly *Cranford* and *Harry Potter*). 'Enchanting, great character,' was another comment. With oak panels, creaking doors, low ceilings, beams and ancient steps, it has long been run by owners Lorna and George Hardy. The bedrooms in the inn may be small, and the soundproofing 'not 21st century', but all have Wi-Fi. 'Our room had antiques, huge four-poster bed, quality linen sheets.' 'Ours was comfortable if cramped, which didn't matter as there is a spacious lounge and garden.' One bed formerly belonged to Isambard Kingdom Brunel. Four other bedrooms are in a cottage 'through the garden and over a brook': they were upgraded this year (under-floor heating, new bathroom, etc). In the medieval, candlelit dining rooms, guests enjoy 'exceptionally fresh, seasonal, high-quality English cooking', eg, steak and kidney pie; smoked haddock with Welsh rarebit topping. 'The best summer pudding we have ever tasted.' 'Wine list surprisingly good, reasonably priced.' 'Breakfast a delight; tasty local produce; home-made bread, home-laid eggs, etc.' (*Mrs PA Harper, Roland Cassam, SH*)

Bedrooms: 10, 3 on ground floor, 4 in cottage. *Open*: all year except 23–31 Dec (open for dinner 31 Dec), restaurant closed Mon except bank holidays. *Facilities*: ramps, lounge, bar, restaurant, civil wedding licence, unsuitable for &. *Background music*: none. *Location*: village centre. *Smoking*: not allowed. *Children*: all ages welcomed. *Dogs*: not allowed in public rooms. *Credit cards*: all major cards. *Prices*: [2008] b&b £60–£82 per person, set lunch £12.50, dinner £15.50, full alc £47.50.

LANGAR Nottinghamshire   Map 2:A3

Langar Hall
Langar NG13 9HG

Tel 01949-860559
Fax 01949-861045
Email info@langarhall.co.uk
Website www.langarhall.co.uk

&? *César award in 2000*

Imogen Skirving, whose family have owned this honey-stone house in the Vale of Belvoir since the mid-19th century, turned it into a hotel to meet mounting overheads. Long liked by readers for its informal style, it won its *César* for 'utterly enjoyable mild eccentricity'. 'Delightful staff, lovely room, very good food (particularly the desserts),' one guest wrote. Marcus Wellford has now been appointed manager. 'He takes dinner orders and is tidying up menus, service, kitchen,' Ms Skirving tells us. 'I may be retiring, but I am still keeping an eye on things, enjoying the guests, sorting out the decor.' The drawing room has a club fender, photographs of the Bloomsbury group; the small bar has cartoons, and prints associated with designer Paul Smith, a regular visitor. Frequent guests include barristers attending Nottingham Crown Court and cricket commentators broadcasting at Trent Bridge. Family portraits line the stairs that lead from the flagstoned hall to themed bedrooms, all different in size and style, eg, Cartland, dedicated to the romantic novelist (another visitor); Barristers, 'masculine, with painted panelling'. The daily-changing menu uses local ingredients and fish from Scotland. There is an 'excellent' wine list. Light meals are served all day in a conservatory. (*SP, and others*)

Bedrooms: 12, 1 on ground floor, 1 garden chalet. *Open*: all year. *Facilities*: ramps, sitting room, study, library, bar, garden room, restaurant, private dining room, small conference/function facilities, civil wedding licence, 20-acre grounds (gardens, children's play area, croquet, ponds, fishing), unsuitable for &. *Background music*: none. *Location*: 12 miles SE of Nottingham. *Smoking*: not allowed. *Children*: all ages welcomed. *Dogs*: small dogs on a lead allowed, in chalet only. *Credit cards*: MasterCard, Visa. *Prices*: b&b £47.50–£115 per person, d,b&b (Sun/Mon) from £75, set dinner £25, full alc £40, special offers. *V*

LANGFORD BUDVILLE Somerset   Map 1:C5

Bindon Country House
Langford Budville
nr Wellington TA21 0RU

Tel 01823-400070
Fax 01823-400071
Email stay@bindon.com
Website www.bindon.com

By a nature reserve on the Somerset-Devon border, this old building with a baroque Bavarian look is owned by Lynne Jaffa. It is liked for its 'feel of a hunting lodge rather than a grand country house'. The staff are 'courteous'; the welcome is 'warm': bags carried. The hall has 'stunning' floor tiles, a panelled staircase under a stained-glass cupola. The two best bedrooms, at the front, face the lovely gardens. They are 'light, with large sash windows; big bathroom; slightly dated fabrics; big, comfortable bed'. Another room (a late booking) was 'adequate, not luxurious'. Oil candles burn in the wood-panelled library, where 'interesting canapés' are served before dinner. Tables are well spaced in the attractive candlelit dining room. Mike Davies's cooking is admired: 'Portions well judged; tasty little extra courses, eg, velouté of celery to start, a light strawberry mousse as pre-desert; delicious starters, perfectly pink rump of lamb; attentive service.' The pace is relaxed at breakfast which has a buffet of fruits, freshly squeezed orange juice, cheeses, meats, cereals; cooked dishes include: kipper; smoked halibut; smoked salmon and scrambled eggs. There is Wellington memorabilia in the public rooms (the Iron Duke took his name from the nearby town). (*JR, and others*)

Bedrooms: 12, 1 on ground floor. *Open*: all year, only party bookings at Christmas/New Year. *Facilities*: hall, lounge, study, bar, restaurant, 2 conference rooms, civil wedding licence, 7-acre grounds (kitchen garden, rose garden, heated 10-metre swimming pool, tennis, croquet, boules, chapel). *Background music*: Classic FM in public rooms. *Location*: 4 miles NW of Wellington. *Smoking*: not allowed. *Children*: not under 7 in restaurant. *Dogs*: allowed. *Credit cards*: Amex, MasterCard, Visa. *Prices*: [2008] b&b £72.50–£112.50 per person, set dinner £35, Christmas/New Year packages.

The *Guide* welcomes recommendations from readers for new entries. Please write or send us an email about any hotel, inn or B&B that you feel should be included.

LANGHO Lancashire   Map 4:D3

Northcote Manor   *Tel* 01254-240555
Northcote Road, Langho   *Fax* 01254-246568
nr Blackburn BB6 8BE   *Email* sales@northcotemanor.com
                              Website www.northcotemanor.com

In a 'bucolic landscape of rolling farmland' this late Victorian/
Edwardian residence is run as an informal restaurant-with-rooms
(*Michelin* star) by chef/*patron* Nigel Haworth and his business partner,
Craig Bancroft. They have recently renovated while keeping the
original Edwardian features (beautiful wooden doors and windows,
the brown leather armchairs and sofas in the sitting rooms). Inspectors
said: 'Our "superior" bedroom, comfortable rather than stylish, had a
magnificent Victorian wardrobe, large bed, *chaise longue*, games, magazines, CD-player, flat-screen TV, fridge; well-equipped, efficient
bathroom. Gold wallpaper added to the sombre ambience, but the
huge bay window, with view of fields, brought light and colour.' The
window tables are the best in the restaurant where service was 'good-
humoured, attentive'. A five-course tasting menu was 'impressive,
well balanced': it included carpaccio of lamb; an organic porridge of
shrimps with a 'refreshing sharpness'; unpasteurised British cheese
'in perfect condition'. 'Generous breakfast: the usual cereals; traditional cooked dishes; cheerful waitresses.' The red brick building
stands in wooded grounds with views of the Ribble valley, near the
busy A59 (windows are double glazed).

Bedrooms: 14, 4 on ground floor, 1 suitable for &. *Open*: all year except 25 Dec.
Facilities: ramp, lounge, drawing room, cocktail bar, restaurant, private
dining/meeting room, civil wedding licence, 2-acre garden. *Background music*:
jazz in restaurant. *Location*: 4½ miles N of Blackburn, on A59. *Smoking*: not
allowed. *Children*: all ages welcomed. *Dogs*: not allowed. *Credit cards*: Amex,
MasterCard, Visa. *Prices*: b&b £90–£195 per person, set dinner £55–£85, full
alc £65, gourmet breaks.

LANGTHWAITE North Yorkshire   Map 4:C3

The Charles Bathurst Inn   *Tel* 01748-884567
Langthwaite, Arkengarthdale   *Fax* 01748-884599
DL11 6EN   *Email* info@cbinn.co.uk
                                      Website www.cbinn.co.uk

Once the home of Charles Bathurst, a local land and mine owner, this
'convivial' 18th-century inn is familiarly known to Arkengarthdale

residents as the *CB*. It stands high up in a remote dale in wonderful walking country, on the edge of the Pennine Way and close to Wainwright's Coast to Coast route. The owners, Charles and Stacy Cody, used local craftsmen in their renovation; the Terrace room is furnished with tables and chairs by Robert Thomson, the 'Mouse-man', renowned for including a carved mouse in his furniture pieces. There are open fires and antique pine furniture. Recent visitors 'loved this lively place, warts and all; our pleasant room had good views. The cooking was excellent at breakfast and dinner.' The menu is written on a large mirror (it might include home-made hare sausage with Yorkshire pudding; breast of duck with beetroot purée). Orders are taken at the bar. On busy days some meals are served in an annexe. Breakfast is 'hearty'. Packed lunches can be provided. Water comes from the inn's own spring. Eleven bedrooms are in a new wing: many have an open truss ceiling. For children there are special menus and a toy box. The Codys also own the *Punch Bowl Inn* at Low Row, Swaledale. More reports, please.

Bedrooms: 19, 11 in annexe. *Open*: all year except 25 Dec. *Facilities*: ramps, lounge, 2 bars, restaurant, pool room, small garden (children's play area). *Background music*: public rooms, all day. *Location*: 5 miles NW of Reeth. *Smoking*: not allowed. *Children*: all ages welcomed. *Dogs*: only guide dogs allowed. *Credit cards*: MasterCard, Visa. *Prices*: b&b £40–£90 per person, d,b&b £52.50–£102.50, full alc £31, New Year package, 1-night bookings refused weekends.

LASTINGHAM North Yorkshire   Map 4:C4

Lastingham Grange   *Tel* 01751-417345
Lastingham YO62 6TH   *Fax* 01751-417358
                    Email reservations@lastinghamgrange.com
                       Website www.lastinghamgrange.com

❦ *César award in 1991*

'Truly a family-run hotel', this converted 17th-century farmhouse has been a favourite of readers since the first edition of the *Guide*. 'Bertie Wood, the eldest son, is clearly in charge, from the initial welcome to dispensing wine,' says one visitor. 'His mother, Jayne, often appears, and brother Tom is also on deck.' Other praise this year: 'So restful, it is like another home.' 'One of the friendliest places on earth.' 'Outstanding service.' On the edge of the North Yorkshire Moors national park ('good walking and picturesque drives'), the house stands in extensive gardens. The decor is traditional: 'Floral carpet, floral tiles, floral shower curtain, floral wallpaper.' 'Very comfortably furnished' bedrooms have 'real cotton sheets and blankets rather than the dreaded duvet, and excellent lighting; sheer bliss'. The 'good, plain English cooking' of Paul Cattaneo and Sandra Thurlow 'has improved a notch to include more creative dishes'. 'We enjoyed grouse, and game; and there is still the ragout of kidneys in red wine.' 'Good breakfasts' have 'excellent kippers'. Rates include newspaper, morning coffee and afternoon tea ('good as ever, with hot scones, jam and cream'). There is an adventure playground for children. (*Elizabeth and Roger Smith, Peter Buckley, Anne and Denis Tate, Richard Lamb, Harry and Annette Medcalf*)

Bedrooms: 12, also cottage in village. *Open*: all year except Christmas, Jan, Feb. *Facilities*: ramps, hall, lounge, dining room, laundry facilities, 10-acre grounds (terrace, garden, adventure playground, croquet, boules), limited assistance for &. *Background music*: none. *Location*: 5 miles NE of Kirkbymoorside. *Smoking*: not allowed. *Children*: all ages welcomed. *Dogs*: not allowed in public rooms. *Credit cards*: MasterCard, Visa. *Prices*: [2008] b&b £75–£120 per person, d,b&b £95–£150, set dinner £37.50. *V*

LAVENHAM Suffolk   Map 2:C5

The Great House
Market Place
Lavenham CO10 9QZ

Tel 01787-247431
Fax 01787-248007
Email info@greathouse.co.uk
Website www.greathouse.co.uk

César award: Restaurant-with-rooms of the year

'A classic French establishment within the walls of a historic English building', this restaurant-with-rooms stands by the market cross of the medieval wool town. It has been run for many years in true Gallic style by its 'amiable' owners, Régis and Martine Crépy. Recent enlargement and redecoration, and variations in the menu, have made the restaurant 'an even more agreeable place to visit', say regular diners. The candlelit dining room has a 'more modern decor, in harmony with the very English surroundings'. 'Superb food, very good value,' say other visitors. The chef, Enrique Bilbault, combines modern dishes (eg, curry-marinated carpaccio of seared Sri Lanka tuna) with French classics (eg, breast of Les Landes corn-fed chicken), 'always to the highest standards'. Service has 'winning warmth', and children are welcomed. Four of the five bedrooms are a suite, with king-size bed (one is a Jacobean four-poster), antiques, old beams, a marble bathroom; also sherry and fresh flowers. All have been redecorated in sophisticated style: 'Ours had olive-green walls, large windows, smart bathroom with window and underfloor heating. Very good information pack,' said inspectors. Light lunches are available from Wednesday to Saturday. (*David Nicholls, Pat and Bruce Orman, and others*)

Bedrooms: 5. *Open*: Feb–Dec, restaurant closed Sun night, Mon, Tues midday. *Facilities*: lounge/bar, restaurant, ½-acre garden (patio, swings), unsuitable for &. *Background music*: French. *Location*: by Market Cross, near Guildhall, public car park. *Smoking*: not allowed. *Children*: all ages welcomed. *Dogs*: not allowed in public rooms. *Credit cards*: MasterCard, Visa. *Prices*: [2008] room: single £85–£180, double £95–£180, suite £99–£180, breakfast continental £8.50, English £12.50, set lunch £18.95, dinner £27.95, full alc £38–£45, midweek breaks, 1-night bookings refused Sat.

Lavenham Priory

Water Street
Lavenham CO10 9RW

Tel 01787-247404
Fax 01787-248472
Email mail@lavenhampriory.co.uk
Website www.lavenhampriory.co.uk

Once a Benedictine priory, later an Elizabethan merchant's house, this half-timbered, Grade I listed medieval house has been sympathetically restored by Tim and Gilli Pitt. They are 'very welcoming hosts', says a visitor in 2008. 'We arrived on a wet and windy evening. It was like stepping into another world. Earlier guests liked the combination of 'old-fashioned charm and modern comfort'. The approach is through a garden with herbs and old roses. There are comfortable sofas and chairs in the 13th-century Great Hall, which has a beamed ceiling, huge inglenook fireplace and antique furniture; the 'snug' has TV, books, etc. The spacious bedrooms, reached up an oak Jacobean staircase, have sloping beamed ceilings, mullioned windows, old oak floorboards and unusual beds (four-poster, sleigh or polonaise). The suite has a sitting room. The 'excellent' breakfast is served around a large table in the Merchants Room or sometimes, in summer, in the herb garden. 'You squeeze your own orange juice, and make your own toast', and there are kippers, smoked haddock, scrambled eggs, three types of bread. The Pitts have a licence to sell alcohol, and help is given with booking in local restaurants. (*Joyce Neville*)

Bedrooms: 6. *Open*: all year except Christmas/New Year. *Facilities*: Great Hall/sitting room, snug, breakfast room, 3-acre garden (medieval courtyard, herb garden), unsuitable for &. *Background music*: none. *Location*: central. *Smoking*: not allowed. *Children*: not under 10. *Dogs*: not allowed. *Credit cards*: MasterCard, Visa. *Prices*: [2008] b&b £50–£85 per person, winter midweek discount for 2 nights or more, 1-night bookings refused Sat, some holidays.

LEDBURY Herefordshire   Map 3:D5

The Feathers **NEW**	*Tel* 01531-635266
High Street	*Fax* 01531-638955
Ledbury HR8 1DS	*Email* mary@feathers-ledbury.co.uk
	Website www.feathers-ledbury.co.uk

'A fascinating place,' says a visitor in 2008 to this 16th-century half-timbered inn which 'looks as if it could have been visited by Mr Pickwick'. 'Brought up to date in a tasteful way', and run by Mary Diggins with a 'cheerful staff', it is 'part of the social scene' of this 'genuine old market town'. The 'air of quiet bustle' is liked. The welcome is warm: 'Bags carried up a characterful old staircase (no lift), off which were bedroom doors of various heights. Our second-floor room had beamed walls washed in yellow, nice lounge area. Period charm meant uneven floors and one step up to and then down into a large bathroom whose floor had clearly never seen a spirit level. Everything was well kept. Double glazing made outside noise minimal.' Another visitor found his room 'a bit dark'. There is a 'nice, old-fashioned' reception area and an 'inviting' beamed lounge. In *Fuggles Brasserie*, a 'varied and well-executed menu' included 'tasty tomato and sweet potato soup; enjoyable baked halibut'. 'Excellent, not over-priced wines.' 'Service extremely friendly. Breakfasts well presented; good full English.' Summer meals can be served in the garden. Also liked: the absence of muzak, and the leisure centre. (*Roland Cassam, WG Watkins, and others*)

Bedrooms: 22, 1 suite in cottage. *Open*: all year. *Facilities*: lounge, bar, brasserie, function/conference facilities, spa (swimming pool, whirlpool, gym), civil wedding licence, courtyard garden (fountain, alfresco eating), unsuitable for &. *Background music*: none. *Location*: town centre, parking. *Smoking*: not allowed. *Children*: all ages welcomed. *Dogs*: allowed, except in brasserie. *Credit cards*: all major cards. *Prices*: b&b £62.50–£125 per person, full alc £45, New Year package, 1-night bookings refused weekends in season.

LEEDS West Yorkshire   Map 4:D4

42 The Calls	*Tel* 0113-244 0099
42 The Calls	*Fax* 0113-234 4100
Leeds LS2 7EW	*Email* hotel@42thecalls.co.uk
	Website www.42thecalls.co.uk

'A must-stay if you are in Leeds on business or pleasure', this 'fabulous' conversion of a grain mill in the city centre (one of the first designer hotels) is now part of the Eton Collection (see also *The Scotsman*, Edinburgh). Its long-serving manager is Belinda Dawson. Designed 'with flair', it has 'hundreds of original paintings and drawings', bold fabrics, stylish public rooms. Many bedrooms are spacious; all have trouser press, iron and ironing board. The river-facing rooms (the quietest) are supplied with a fishing rod. A wheelchair-user praised the accessibility of his room. Another reporter was pleased with the 'huge desk by the bedroom window, wireless and hub access', but not the 'very expensive Internet connection'. Also liked: 'The white-painted original brick walls; fresh milk in the fridge, cafetière for coffee, yummy shortbread biscuits, well-presented bathroom with soft robe, fluffy towels' and the 'attractive weekend rates'. The handmade beds are 'supremely comfortable'; duvets have a 'high-quality cotton cover'. A continental breakfast can be delivered to the room (via a 'secret hatch'); an 'excellent cold buffet' and 'delicious' cooked breakfasts (including organic sausages) are served in the River Room. The independently run restaurant next door, *Brasserie 44*, has a *Michelin Bib Gourmand*. (*Sue Davies, and others*)

Bedrooms: 41, 1 suitable for &. *Open*: all year except 3 days at Christmas, restaurant closed Sun. *Facilities*: lift, lounge/bar, breakfast room, adjacent restaurant (independently run), conference facilities. *Background music*: radio in River Room. *Location*: central, nr Corn Exchange. *Smoking*: not allowed. *Children*: all ages welcomed. *Dogs*: not allowed in public rooms. *Credit cards*: all major cards. *Prices*: [2008] room £105–£395, breakfast £14.75, early bird dinner £19.95, full alc £35.80, 1-night bookings sometimes refused. *V*

See also SHORTLIST

LEONARD STANLEY Gloucestershire Map 3:E5

The Grey Cottage
Bath Road, Leonard Stanley
Stonehouse GL10 3LU

Tel/Fax 01453-822515
Website www.greycottage.ik.com

❧ *César award in 1999*

At her much-loved little stone Cotswolds guest house, Rosemary Reeves 'continues to amaze with her attention to detail', says a returning visitor. Others wrote of 'another pampering stay', 'wonderful meals'. Appreciated 'extra touches' include help with luggage and leaf tea and biscuits on arrival. The 'immaculate' bedrooms have fruit, bottled water, fresh milk in a flask for the tea tray, clothes brush, torch and 'a hand bell to summon Rosie in an emergency'. 'Our superb room had a massive double bed.' One room has its bathroom down a short hall. There is an honesty bar, and guests can bring their own wine (no corkage charge). Dinner is by arrangement; no choice: preferences discussed at the time of booking. 'Beautifully laid tables' have 'proper linen napkins'. 'We feasted on osso bucco with tagliatelle, organic green pesto and a selection of vegetables.' 'Portions were huge.' Breakfast includes freshly squeezed orange juice, smoked salmon with scrambled eggs, home-made jams, loaves of home-made bread for DIY toasting, 'butter balls, loads of cereals'. In the garden is a yew hedge planted in 1840. Traffic noise and farm machinery might just be audible in summer when windows are open. (*Gordon Franklin, Sue and Colin Raymond, and others*)

Bedrooms: 3. *Open*: all year except Christmas/New Year, occasional holidays. *Facilities*: sitting room with TV, conservatory, dining room, ¼-acre garden, unsuitable for &. *Background music*: none. *Location*: 3 miles SW of Stroud. *Smoking*: not allowed. *Children*: not under 10. *Dogs*: not allowed. *Credit cards*: none. *Prices*: b&b £32.50–£60 per person, set dinner £24–£27, 1-night bookings refused bank holidays.

LEWDOWN Devon   Map 1:C3

Lewtrenchard Manor	*Tel* 01566-783222
Lewdown	*Fax* 01566-783332
nr Okehampton EX20 4PN	*Email* info@lewtrenchard.co.uk
	Website www.lewtrenchard.co.uk

In a wooded hollow below Dartmoor, this 'wonderfully romantic' 17th-century stone manor house is managed by chef/*patron* Jason Hornbuckle for the von Essen group. Once the home of the Revd Sabine Baring Gould who wrote 'Onward, Christian Soldiers' and whose desk still stands in the front hall, it is a 'Victorian/Elizabethan fantasy'. It has ornate plaster ceilings, oak panelling, a profusion of ornaments and carvings, stained glass, huge fireplaces, family portraits and antiques. The bedrooms are off a 'delightful' music gallery, reached by a fine wooden staircase: 'Our comfortable, well-furnished suite had king-size bed, and small sitting room. The bathroom, recently refurbished, was well laid out and equipped.' Other beds include four-posters, sleigh beds and deep divans. Typical dishes on the three-course dinner menu: pressed lamb, cumin and apricot terrine; pan-fried seabass with lobster ravioli. 'A good range of options including fresh orange juice was on offer at breakfast.' The 'idyllic' grounds have an avenue of copper beech and elm trees, a dovecote, sunken garden and lake with swans. Vegetables, salads and soft fruits are grown in a renovated walled garden. (*AJW, and others*)

Bedrooms: 14, 1 suitable for &. *Open*: all year, restaurant closed Mon lunch. *Facilities*: 2 lounges, bar, restaurant, 2 dining rooms, beauty treatments, function facilities, civil wedding licence, 12-acre garden. *Background music*: classical/jazz in restaurant. *Location*: 10 miles N of Tavistock town centre. *Smoking*: not allowed. *Children*: not under 8 at dinner. *Dogs*: allowed in bedrooms, lounge areas. *Credit cards*: Amex, MasterCard, Visa. *Prices*: [2008] b&b £97.50–£245 per person, set menu £47.50, Christmas/New Year packages. *V*

LEWES East Sussex   Map 2:E4

Berkeley House
2 Albion Street
Lewes BN7 2ND

Tel/Fax 01273-476057
Email enquiries@berkeleyhouselewes.co.uk
Website www.berkeleyhouselewes.co.uk

'Good value for money in this affluent town', this late Georgian house (circa 1820) has 'an interesting history, nicely presented in pictures and prose', says a visitor this year. It has been run since 1966 as a small B&B by Roy Patten and Steve Johnson. 'On a wild, wet, windy night, it was a pleasure to be given a cordial welcome and shown to our cosy bedrooms.' The 'bright, airy' rooms, 'filled with *objets d'art*', are on the second and third floors (no lift). 'Ours were spotless, very quiet.' 'Mine looked over roofs to the South Downs; traditional bedding, bottled water, alarm clock, etc.' A roof terrace shares the views. The residents' lounge has lots of material relating to nearby Glyndebourne. 'We enjoyed a glass or two of wine here, with local friends.' Drinks, tea and coffee are available 'at all reasonable times'. The 'comfortably furnished' breakfast room overlooks a small courtyard garden, and has a vast mirror, large oak dresser and flowers. The copious breakfast 'was excellent: fresh fruit, good cereals, delicious cooked dishes, plenty of tea and coffee. For dinner, they gave suggestions and made a booking for us.' Wi-Fi is available free of charge. (*TL, and others*)

Bedrooms: 3. *Open*: all year. *Facilities*: lounge, breakfast room, roof terrace, unsuitable for &. *Background music*: none. *Location*: town centre, restricted street parking 8 am to 6 pm Mon–Sat (1-day vouchers for guests), also 1 parking space, public car park nearby. *Smoking*: not allowed. *Children*: not under 8. *Dogs*: not allowed. *Credit cards*: all major cards. *Prices*: b&b £35–£65 per person, 1-night bookings refused Sat in summer. *V*

The Shelleys   `NEW`
135 High Street
Lewes BN7 1XS

Tel 01273-472361
Fax 01273-483152
Email reservations@the-shelleys.co.uk
Website www.the-shelleys.co.uk

Once owned by the poet's family, this 16th-century yellow manor house stands in the centre of town. It was taken over by the Fernando family in 2007. They 'are committed to a serious upgrade while retaining many of the excellent staff', notably the 'hands-on' manager Graeme Coles. 'He is enthusiastic and knowledgeable about opera, and has taken the staff to dress rehearsals,' writes a visitor who was 'very impressed' during a four-night stay in 2008. 'Good food, service efficient as well as pleasant, a large, sensibly planned bedroom with large, spotless bathroom, excellent, unobtrusive housekeeping, all amounting to a 'good hotel'. Some other rooms are smaller. Other comments: 'Tasteful decoration. Interesting menus, good wine, delightful ambience.' 'Good breakfast.' 'Pleasant not to have to face the nightmare of a buffet.' 'An item from the lunch menu was cheerfully offered for dinner when we wanted something light.' 'Lovely alfresco lunch.' Inside is a 'rabbit warren of corridors, steps and doors'. 'Best ask for a bedroom facing the charming garden, some other rooms might hear traffic.' (*Gwyneth Brock, Michael Lewis, Mary Wilmer*)

Bedrooms: 19. *Open*: all year. *Facilities*: lounge, bar, restaurant, function facilities, civil wedding licence, terrace, 1-acre garden, unsuitable for &. *Background music*: none. *Location*: central, free parking adjacent. *Smoking*: not allowed. *Children*: all ages welcomed. *Dogs*: allowed (must be on a lead in public rooms). *Credit cards*: Amex, MasterCard, Visa accepted. *Prices*: [2008] b&b £82.50–£130 per person, set dinner £38, Christmas/New Year packages.

LICHFIELD Staffordshire   Map 2:A2
See SHORTLIST

Readers' contributions, written on the forms at the back of the book or sent by email, are the lifeblood of the *Good Hotel Guide*. Our readers play a crucial role by reporting on existing entries as well as recommending new discoveries. Everyone who writes to the *Guide* is a potential winner of the Report of the Year competition (page 63), in which a dozen correspondents each year win a copy of the *Guide* and an invitation to our annual launch party in October.

LIFTON Devon

Map 1:C3

The Arundell Arms
Lifton PL16 0AA

Tel 01566-784666
Fax 01566-784494
Email reservations@arundellarms.com
Website www.arundellarms.com

🏆 *César award in 2006*

'Lovely atmosphere, friendly staff, brilliant food.' A returning visitor praises this creeper-covered sporting hotel which Anne Voss-Bark has run for over 40 years. Others wrote of 'unpretentiousness', 'charming welcome', 'attentive staff'. Many visitors come for the fishing: an experienced fly-fisher herself, Mrs Voss-Bark has 20 miles of fishing on the Tamar and its four tributaries, and a three-acre stocked lake. Fishing courses offer instruction at all levels. Non-sporting visitors and children ('we like them') are just as welcome. The traditional lounge has slate floors, rugs, comfortable sofas and chairs in front of a log fire. The bedrooms have antiques, flat-screen TV, modern bathroom: the best are in an extension at the rear. 'Ours, quiet and comfortable, had peaceful views of the garden.' The chef, Steven Pidgeon, has won an award for his promotion of local food suppliers, who are listed on the menu. Dishes might include grilled Cornish mackerel on iced tomato soup; mignon of wild venison with glazed salsify, garlic and shallot confit. 'Service was exemplary, timing just right.' The bar meals are 'very good' too. The terraced rear garden has seating for alfresco meals, and a circular rod room (once the cockpit). (*Margaret Wilson, J and DA*)

Bedrooms: 21, 4 on ground floor. *Open*: all year except Christmas. *Facilities*: ramp, lounge, cocktail bar, public bar, 2 dining rooms, conference/meeting rooms, games room, skittle alley, civil wedding licence, ½-acre garden, 20 miles fishing rights on River Tamar and tributaries (3-acre stocked lake, fishing school). *Background music*: 'gentle' classical. *Location*: ½ mile off A30, 3 miles E of Launceston (road-facing rooms double glazed). *Smoking*: not allowed. *Children*: all ages welcomed. *Dogs*: not allowed in restaurant, or on river bank. *Credit cards*: all major cards. *Prices*: [2008] b&b £85–£120 per person, d,b&b £120, set dinner £40, full alc £52, off-season breaks, sporting, gourmet, etc, New Year package. *V*

LINCOLN Lincolnshire
See SHORTLIST

Map 4:E5

LITTLE EASTON Essex   Map 2:C4

Roslyns   NEW   *Tel* 01371-852177
Duck Street   *Fax* 08715-036786
Little Easton, nr Great Dunmow   *Email* clare@roslynsbandb.co.uk
CM6 2JF   *Website* www.roslynsbandb.co.uk

'A warm welcome' from Clare Taege was received by a fellow *Guide* hotelier on arrival at this former Victorian village school house in a village near Great Dunmow. She has run it as a B&B since June 2006; her New Zealander husband, Peter, pursues his own career. 'They radiate a friendly "home from home" atmosphere. She was head housekeeper at *The Lygon Arms* in Broadway and *The Savoy* in London, and her experiences are reflected in the cleanliness and attention to detail. Our family room, with queen-size bed and sofa, was quiet, simply furnished, and had shortbread, flowers, fluffy bath towels, constant hot water.' No residents' lounge, but guests are given 'excellent information on where to dine and local attractions'. Breakfast (continental or full English) is taken around a large table in a 'modern, airy' kitchen/dining area, or on fine days by a fishpond overlooking farmland, in the 'well-maintained' garden. Hot dishes, cooked to order, include local sausages, 'sumptuous' scrambled eggs, and 'excellent toast'. 'A comfortable, congenial overnight stop, handy for Stansted airport (limited parking is available and transfers can be arranged). (*Rosemary Reeves*)

Bedrooms: 3. *Open*: all year. *Facilities*: breakfast room, small garden, unsuitable for &. *Background music*: 'easy listening' at breakfast. *Location*: 2 miles N of Great Dunmow. *Smoking*: not allowed. *Children*: all ages welcomed. *Dogs*: not allowed. *Credit cards*: MasterCard, Visa. *Prices*: [2008] b&b £35–£60 per person.

LITTLE PETHERICK Cornwall   Map 1:D2

Molesworth Manor   NEW   *Tel* 01841-540292
Little Petherick   *Email* molesworthmanor@aol.com
nr Wadebridge PL27 7QT   *Website* www.molesworthmanor.co.uk

'Very comfortable accommodation, plenty of sitting room and bedroom space. Breakfasts superb: imaginative options, home-made muffins and marmalades.' This 17th-century former rectory, run as a B&B by its owners, Jessica Clarke and Geoff French, stands in an attractive garden in a tiny village near Padstow. 'Beautiful features' include an elaborately carved staircase, stained glass, 'nice art work'.

Guests can listen to music and have a drink in the lounges (the manor is licensed to serve wines, spirits and beer). 'The atmosphere is friendly; they welcome you with complimentary tea but are not intrusive,' one couple wrote. Bedrooms, named according to their earlier use or their position, vary in size and grandeur: Her Ladyship's (large double, 'tasteful, traditional, furnishings'), Butler's, etc. 'My top-floor room had far-reaching views, attractive period furniture.' Afternoon tea can be taken on a terrace. The continental breakfast, based on organic ingredients, has fresh fruit salads and compotes, freshly baked muffins and a 'daily special'. Many pubs, bistros and restaurants are near: a list is provided. A footpath leads along the river to Padstow. The whole house can be booked for a conference, wedding, etc. (*RJW, and others*)

Bedrooms: 12, 3 on ground floor in cottage. *Open*: Feb–Oct. *Facilities*: 3 lounges, 1 with home cinema, breakfast conservatory, terrace, garden (children's play area). *Background music*: none. *Location*: 1½ miles SE of Padstow off A389 to Wadebridge. *Smoking*: not allowed. *Children*: all ages welcomed. *Dogs*: not allowed. *Credit cards*: none. *Prices*: b&b £40–£75 per person. *V*

LITTLE SHELFORD Cambridgeshire   Map 2:C4
See SHORTLIST

LITTLEBURY GREEN Essex   Map 2:C4

The Chaff House
Ash Grove Barns
Littlebury Green
nr Saffron Walden CB11 4XB

Tel/Fax 01763-836278
Email thechaffhouse@googlemail.com

Owned by the 'kind and thoughtful' Diana Duke ('a fascinating person with many interests'), this picturesque barn conversion is on a large estate in a quiet rural village. 'We loved our short stay,' say American visitors this year. 'When we arrived after a long journey, we found that Mrs Duke had printed a picture of our newborn grandchild with an email from our son. She produced champagne and joined us in a toast.' One bedroom is in the *Chaff House*, where Mrs Duke lives; the other two are in the *Dairy* and the *Log Shed* ('king-size bed, limited storage; small but adequate bathroom'). On weekdays Mrs Duke, 'an accomplished cook', serves farmhouse meals using local produce. 'Delicious dinners included smoked venison with mango slices; fish pie; fruit compote with ginger.' Some good local pubs are nearby, including *Cricketers* at Clavering, run by Jamie Oliver's parents. Stansted airport and Cambridge are about 30 minutes' drive. (*Tara and Rick Varco*)

Bedrooms: 3, 2 in annexe on ground floor. *Open*: all year except Christmas/New Year, dining room closed midday and Sat/Sun. *Facilities*: lounge, dining room, kitchen for guests' use in annexe, small courtyard garden, in 900-acre estate, unsuitable for &. *Background music*: none. *Location*: 4 miles W of Saffron Walden. *Smoking*: not allowed. *Children*: not under 10. *Dogs*: not allowed. *Credit cards*: Diners, MasterCard, Visa. *Prices*: b&b £32.50–£45 per person, set dinner £25 (*not VAT-rated*).

LIVERPOOL Merseyside   Map 4:E2

Hope Street Hotel
40 Hope Street
Liverpool L1 9DA

Tel 0151-709 3000
Fax 0151-709 2454
Email sleep@hopestreethotel.co.uk
Website www.hopestreethotel.co.uk

Visitors this year enjoyed the 'modern style and enthusiastic staff' of this conversion, by a local consortium, of 19th-century carriage works built in the style of a Venetian *palazzo*. 'Very well run', it is managed by Jane Farrelly. Original iron columns, beams and exposed brick-work have been retained. Following comments about corridor noise, the sea-grass matting has been given a new underlay. 'Our suite had a small bedroom and an equally small sitting room on a mezzanine floor; a very good bathroom. Next time we would choose a studio with more space (and room for a wardrobe).' The trendy bar, *The Residents' Lounge*, has leather sofas and pop music. There are dramatic floor-to-ceiling glass sculptures, bare oak and yellow brickwork in the restaurant, *The London Carriage Works*. Chef/*patron* Paul Askew provides 'very good food': 'beautifully cooked fish, extra helpings (by request) of good vegetables'. The wine list is 'wide ranging in type, price and quality'. Breakfast can be *à la carte*, continental or a 'super' cooked affair. The area is the city's cultural centre (the Philharmonic Hall is opposite). Thirty-nine more bedrooms, a gym and more con-ference facilities are due to open in November 2008. (*Peter Buckley, Meriel Packman*)

Bedrooms: 48. *Open*: all year. *Facilities*: lift, ramps, lobby, reading room, bar, restaurant, conference facilities. *Background music*: jazz/soul/pop in bar and restaurant. *Location*: opposite Philharmonic Hall. *Smoking*: not allowed. *Children*: all ages welcomed. *Dogs*: small dogs allowed in bedrooms only. *Credit cards*: all major cards. *Prices*: room £140–£350, breakfast £15 (full English), set dinner £20–£25, full alc £38.

See also SHORTLIST

LODDISWELL Devon   Map 1:D4

Hazelwood House   *Tel* 01548-821232
Loddiswell   *Fax* 01548-821318
nr Kingsbridge TQ7 4EB   *Email* info@hazelwoodhouse.com
                           Website www.hazelwoodhouse.com

In a designated area of outstanding natural beauty, this early Victorian house stands above the River Avon in unspoilt woodland, rich in wildlife. It offers accommodation ranging from 'rustic to more salubrious', say the 'charming' owners Jane Bowman, Gillian Kean and Anabel Farnell-Watson. It is 'wonderfully friendly' (guests on their own feel at ease). It won't suit everyone, but devotees love the 'spiritual quality', the 'informal but professional' hospitality, the 'very good' meals, the 'comfort without frills'. 'Slow food' is the theme in the dining room: chef Christopher Scantlebury might offer local quail wrapped in bacon, roasted with a redcurrant jus. The house is filled with simple furniture, antiques and paintings; log fires burn in the public rooms. The bedrooms on the first floor have *en suite* facilities and central heating, the second-floor rooms were due to be upgraded in 2008. The best bedroom is spacious, but some rooms are small. Cultural courses, concerts and weekends with entertainments (painting, story-telling, etc) are held. Weddings take place in a former chapel, now a studio and gallery. Children are welcomed. A non-refundable deposit of the cost of a night's stay is requested on booking. The sea is six miles away. (*SR, and others*)

Bedrooms: 14, 7 with facilities *en suite*. *Open*: all year. *Facilities*: hall with piano, drawing room, study/TV room, dining room, function/conference facilities, civil wedding licence, 67-acre grounds (river, boathouse, chapel), only restaurant suitable for &. *Background music*: on request. *Location*: 2 miles N of Loddiswell. *Smoking*: not allowed. *Children*: all ages welcomed. *Dogs*: not in dining room, on leads elsewhere. *Credit cards*: MasterCard, Visa. *Prices*: b&b £40–£90 per person, d,b&b £55–£115, full alc £45, Christmas/New Year packages. ***V***

Every year we give a free copy of the *Guide* to each of the 12 readers who send us the best reports. Every report received is considered in this competition.

LONGHORSLEY Northumberland   Map 4:B3

Thistleyhaugh Farm
Longhorsley, nr Morpeth
NE65 8RG

Tel 01665-570629
Email thistleyhaugh@hotmail.com
Website www.thistleyhaugh.co.uk

In an 'utterly remote corner of rural Northumberland', this Georgian house by the River Coquet is run by Enid Nelless with daughters-in-law Zoe and Janice. It is on a large organic cattle and sheep farm worked by her husband, Henry, with their two sons. 'This rich, productive land encompasses you from the moment of arrival. Soon, due to the warmth of Mrs Nelless, you're assimilated into it,' says a visitor this year. 'Much of the space of this gracious old farmhouse is yours, with three splendid rooms (dining and sitting rooms, and the garden room extension) crammed with antique furniture, but never feeling overcrowded.' The five bedrooms, priced according to size, are 'spotless', and 'decorated to a high standard'; choice between duvet and blankets; small refrigerator with milk and bottled water. Complimentary pre-dinner sherry is served in the garden room; the meal is taken communally around a huge oak table at 7.30 pm. Four courses, no choice, 'all superbly cooked from prime ingredients': home-made soups; roast local organic meat. Vegetarians are catered for, given notice. Wine is available at £8 per bottle. Breakfast, 'a sumptuous meal', has porridge, cereals, sausages, eggs, bacon from the farm or locally cured. (*Canon Michael Bourdeaux*)

Bedrooms: 5. *Open*: all year except Christmas, Jan. *Facilities*: 2 lounges, dining room, 720-acre farm, ¾-acre garden (summer house), fishing, shooting, golf, riding nearby, unsuitable for &. *Background music*: during evening meals. *Location*: 10 miles N of Morpeth, E of A697. *Smoking*: not allowed. *Children*: all ages welcomed. *Dogs*: not allowed (kennels nearby). *Credit cards*: MasterCard, Visa. *Prices*: b&b £37.50–£50 per person, d,b&b £20 added, 1-night bookings refused May–Oct.

LONGSTOCK Hampshire   Map 2:D2

The Peat Spade Inn
Village Street
Longstock SO20 6DR

Tel 01264-810612
Fax 01264-811078
Email info@peatspadeinn.co.uk
Website www.peatspadeinn.co.uk

In a village in the Test valley ('fly-fishing capital of the world'), this old inn and 'rooming house', 'full of character', is owned by Lucy Townsend (front-of-house) and Andy Clark (chef). Popular with locals, it gets very busy at the weekend. Last year's comment: 'Excellent in every way. Well decorated. Food and atmosphere very good – unpretentious.' Inspectors add: 'All you could wish for in a country pub: hands-on management, cheerful and efficient service (cases carried), straightforward food, reasonable prices'. Our charming room, up a flight of steps, was in the *Peat House*. It had steeply sloping ceiling, olive-green walls, pale carpet, fridge with fresh milk, modem point. Beautiful shower room (skylight, large cabinet, huge shower head).' In the three dining rooms (with wooden tables and pictures of fishermen, fish, horses, etc, on walls), 'simple, fresh, classic' dishes include potted shrimp with toasted sourdough; rib-eye steak with chips and Béarnaise sauce. 'Wines chosen with care; real ales stocked. Lucy came to chat as we ate.' Breakfast (no menu) includes eggs as you like, 'delicious fresh fruit salad, chunky toast'. There is a residents' lounge with fire, books and games, and a 'delightful rear patio'. (*BR, and others*)

Bedrooms: 6, 4 in the *Peat House* at rear. *Open*: all year except 25/26 Dec, restaurant closed Sun night. *Facilities*: ramps, lounge, bar, restaurant, private dining room, patio. *Background music*: in bar. *Location*: centre of village, 1 mile N of Stockbridge. *Smoking*: not allowed. *Children*: not under 10 in bedrooms. *Dogs*: not in bedrooms. *Credit cards*: Amex, MasterCard, Visa. *Prices*: b&b £60–£120 per person, set meal £30, full alc £37.50.

LOOE Cornwall   Map 1:D3

The Beach House   *Tel* 01503-262598
Marine Drive, Hannafore   *Fax* 01503-262298
Looe PL13 2DH   *Email* enquiries@thebeachhouselooe.co.uk
                                  Website www.thebeachhouselooe.co.uk

'A perfect place to stay,' says a visitor returning to this B&B in this popular resort. White-walled and gabled, it stands in a row of houses across a road from the sea. Near the centre, it has direct access to the beach, and panoramic views of the coastline; the South West Coastal Path runs past. 'Dedicated' owners, Rosie and David Reeve, provide 'a warm welcome with tea and a chat'. Four bedrooms face the sea. 'Ours, Fistral, the most expensive, was worth it for the view: huge patio windows opened on to a balcony. The decor was subtle, cream and gold; extras made it more like a five-star hotel than a B&B.' Rear rooms are 'decent sized' too: from Mullion, the cheapest, 'you have only to cross a corridor to sit in the tiny garden room and enjoy the view'. Breakfasts, 'the highlight', are taken in a sea-facing room. You order the evening before, to coordinate at 15-minute intervals with other guests. Cooked dishes included 'cheese omelette one day, pancakes the next: we couldn't eat lunch after such a feast'. The afternoon cream teas are 'highly recommended'. A non-refundable deposit of one night's tariff is required to confirm a booking. (*Pam Adams, Michael Bourdeaux, and others*)

Bedrooms: 5. *Open*: all year except Christmas. *Facilities*: garden room, breakfast room, terrace, small garden, beach opposite, unsuitable for &. *Background music*: in breakfast room. *Location*: ½ mile from centre. *Smoking*: not allowed. *Children*: not under 16. *Dogs*: only guide dogs allowed. *Credit cards*: MasterCard, Visa. *Prices*: [2008] b&b £40–£60 per person, New Year package, 1-night bookings refused high season.

See also SHORTLIST

LORTON Cumbria   Map 4: inset C2

New House Farm
Lorton
nr Cockermouth CA13 9UU

Tel 01900-85404
Fax 01900-85478
Email hazel@newhouse-farm.co.uk
Website www.newhouse-farm.com

'The welcome is warm, and the countryside is beautiful' at Hazel Thompson's Grade II listed 17th-century, whitewashed farmhouse in the Lorton/Buttermere valley. It has 'marvellous views' in all directions. There are oak beams and rafters, flagged floors and stone open fireplaces in the house; comfortable seating in the small lounges which have bright colours, silver and antiques; also Wi-Fi. Two of the bedrooms (each has a four-poster bed) are in converted outbuildings (the old dairy and stable); they are both on the ground floor. Low Fell, in the oldest part of the old house, has a Victorian bath with a large slipper bath. Dinners are perhaps the weak point: large portions of traditional dishes for simple no-choice meals; eg, cream of tomato soup; pheasant cooked in cider. Breakfast has fresh grapefruit, prunes, eggs and bacon, home-made marmalade. Lunches and teas are served in the café in a converted barn. Pets are allowed the run of the grounds but not the public rooms; riders can bring their own horses. Traffic passes on the country road in front of the house, but the two rear bedrooms are 'perfectly quiet'. (*Sally Weatherill*)

Bedrooms: 5, 1 in stable, 1 in old dairy. *Open*: all year. *Facilities*: 3 lounges, dining room, 17-acre grounds (garden, hot tub, streams, woods, field, lake and river (safe bathing) 2 miles), unsuitable for &. *Background music*: none. *Location*: on B5289, 2 miles S of Lorton. *Smoking*: not allowed. *Children*: not under 6. *Dogs*: not allowed in public rooms. *Credit cards*: MasterCard, Visa. *Prices*: b&b £80–£120 per person, d,b&b £25 added, 1-night bookings sometimes refused.

See also SHORTLIST

LOWESTOFT Suffolk *See SHORTLIST* Map 2:B6

LUDLOW Shropshire   Map 3:C4

Mr Underhill's   *Tel* 01584-874431
Dinham Weir   *Website* www.mr-underhills.co.uk
Ludlow SY8 1EH

❦ *César award in 2000*

'Wonderful. I have never eaten a dinner of such amazing quality and subtlety.' Praise for this restaurant-with-rooms by the River Teme below Ludlow Castle. A returning visitor agrees: 'The cooking goes from strength to strength.' Since suffering flooding twice in summer 2007, the owners, Christopher and Judy Bradley, have built a new defence system and redecorated the dining room in autumnal colours. He holds a *Michelin* star; she runs front-of-house, with 'approachable formality'. Guests are told the proposed set menu (alternatives can be offered). 'Dinner kicks off with three Hobbit-sized dishes (eg, marinated salmon, pea velouté, duck liver custard). Pavé of halibut with crunchy vegetables was one of the most enjoyable fish dishes I have eaten. Rhubarb crumble with clove ice cream followed, worth every calorie. Wine list a winner; bottles to suit all tastes and pockets.' 'Superbly trained staff.' Breakfast has fresh fruit, 'excellent brioche', yogurt or a cooked dish. Guests are asked not to arrive before 3.30 pm. The four suites are spacious; the four other rooms 'are too small to sit in for long'. The *Shed* suite, in the garden, is particularly liked; the lower suite in *Miller's House* opposite, by the road, can be noisy. (*Richard Creed, Padi Howard*)

Bedrooms: 8, 3 in annexes. *Open*: all year except Christmas, 10 days June, 10 days Nov, restaurant closed Mon/Tues. *Facilities*: small lounge, restaurant, function facilities, ⅓-acre courtyard, riverside garden (fishing, swimming), unsuitable for &. *Background music*: none. *Location*: below castle, on River Teme, station ½ mile, parking. *Smoking*: not allowed. *Children*: not 2–8. *Dogs*: not allowed. *Credit cards*: MasterCard, Visa. *Prices*: b&b £82.50–£132.50 per person, set dinner £48–£53, New Year packages, 1-night bookings often refused Sat.

See also SHORTLIST

LYDFORD Devon   Map 1:C4

The Dartmoor Inn   *Tel* 01822-820221
Moorside   *Fax* 01822-820494
Lydford, nr Okehampton   *Email* info@dartmoorinn.co.uk
EX20 4AY   *Website* www.dartmoorinn.com

♕ *César award in 2007*

'A restaurant-with-rooms that does not disappoint', Karen and Philip Burgess's small inn stands on a busy road west of Dartmoor. One visitor wrote of its 'charm without chintz'. In two ground-floor rooms Mrs Burgess runs a 'rather fabulous' boutique selling Swedish linen and glassware, French quilts and locally designed jewellery. The other ground-floor rooms form a series of dining areas, some formal, with wood-burning stove, others more casual. The modern cooking of Philip Burgess and Andrew Honey is 'exquisite: roasted pumpkin soup was a highlight; then traditional oxtail with proper mashed potatoes and hot vegetables; finally a light custard tart with delicious pastry'. The 'beautifully furnished' bedrooms are 'large, warm, with really comfortable bed'. A Roberts radio is provided; TV is available on request. Dissenters, who arrived when the bar was closed, were disappointed that a tea tray is not provided, and at the response when they asked for one. 'Breakfast was interesting, eg, good muesli, lovely fresh fruit, a pot of chocolate to finish.' (*Dr D Tumath, and others*)

Bedrooms: 3. *Open*: all year, restaurant closed Sun evening, Mon lunch. *Facilities*: 2 bars, restaurant, small sunken garden, unsuitable for &. *Background music*: none. *Location*: 6 miles E of Tavistock on A386 to Okehampton, train Exeter/Plymouth, parking. *Smoking*: not allowed. *Children*: not really suitable for small children. *Dogs*: not allowed in bedrooms. *Credit cards*: Amex, MasterCard, Visa. *Prices*: [2008] b&b £55–£95 per person, full alc £35, Christmas/New Year packages, 1-night bookings refused bank holiday weekends.

LYME REGIS Dorset *See SHORTLIST*   Map 1:C6

LYMINGTON Hampshire   Map 2:E2

Britannia House   *Tel* 01590-672091
Station Street   *Email* enquiries@britannia-house.com
Lymington SO41 3BA   *Website* www.britannia-house.com

In an 'excellent location for those wanting to enjoy Lymington's lovely marina, cobbled streets and smart shops', this small B&B is run in two houses opposite each other by Tobias Feilke, 'a perfectionist'. In the older building, the large upstairs sitting room has wide views (harbour and marina) and 'a lovely ambience: decorated in dramatic blue and yellow, large, enveloping sofas, good lighting, plenty of books (lots in German), and magazines'. Bedrooms here have plain walls, Berber carpets, patterned curtains, bedcovers and cushions. 'Our top-floor room was decent sized, very pleasant, with adjacent romantic, spacious bathroom. Downstairs rooms are smaller, darker.' Three bedrooms in the more modern quayside building have a plainer style with check fabrics, pine and painted furniture. Mr Feilke cooks a good breakfast, served at a 'convivial' communal table in the large pine kitchen: 'delicious mushrooms, non-meat sausages for vegetarians'. 'Noise from trains does not affect, but crack-of-dawn Monday rubbish collection might.' (*MT, and others*)

Bedrooms: 6. *Open*: all year. *Facilities*: lounge, kitchen/breakfast room, courtyard garden, unsuitable for &. *Background music*: none. *Location*: 5 mins' walk from High Street/quayside, parking. *Smoking*: not allowed. *Children*: not under 12. *Dogs*: not allowed. *Credit cards*: Diners, MasterCard, Visa. *Prices*: b&b £37.50–£90 per person, midweek discount, 1-night bookings refused weekends.

LYNMOUTH Devon *See SHORTLIST*   Map 1:B4

When you make a booking you enter into a contract with a hotel. Most hotels explain their cancellation policies, which vary widely, in a letter of confirmation. You may lose your deposit or be charged at the full rate for the room if you cancel at short notice. A travel insurance policy can provide protection.

LYNTON Devon   Map 1:B4

Lynton Cottage	*Tel* 01598-752342
North Walk, Lynton	*Fax* 01598-754016
EX35 6ED	*Email* enquiries@lynton-cottage.co.uk
	Website www.lynton-cottage.co.uk

The cliff-top location of this north Devon hotel commands 'stunning views' of Lynmouth Bay, Countisbury Hill, Watersmeet and even, on a clear day, Wales. The owners, Heather Biancardi, Allan Earl (the chef), Davie Mowlem and Bettina Earl, say they 'try to offer the ultimate escape in a relaxed and informal hideaway'. The 'friendly atmosphere' was praised by a reader who added: 'If you are looking for culture, CS Lewis mentions *Lynton Cottage* in his 1923 diary.' All bedrooms face the sea, some have a four-poster, some a small balcony, some a beamed ceiling. 'Ours, the Bay Room, was worth every penny for the amazing circular vista of the bay, let alone the furnishings.' The restaurant has paintings by a Cornish artist, David Hosking, and 'spectacular' views. Food is praised, particularly desserts; 'first class, the pear tart melted in the mouth'. Main courses might include organic salmon, rösti, local spinach. At breakfast, 'the American-style pancakes are delicious, but pride of place must go to the home-made bread'. Light lunches and cream teas are served (on the terrace in fine weather). You can walk down through the garden to the village, 600 feet below. (*JW*)

Bedrooms: 16, 1 on ground floor. *Open*: all year except 3 Dec–11 Jan. *Facilities*: lounge, bar, restaurant, terrace, 2½-acre garden, unsuitable for &. *Background music*: in bar. *Location*: 5 mins from town centre. *Smoking*: not allowed. *Children*: all ages welcomed. *Dogs*: allowed in some bedrooms, not restaurant. *Credit cards*: Amex, MasterCard, Visa. *Prices*: b&b £45–£54 per person, d,b&b £70–£86, set dinner £32. *V*

LYTHAM Lancashire *See SHORTLIST* Map 4:D2

How to contact the *Guide*
By mail: From anywhere in the UK, write to Freepost PAM 2931, London W11 4BR (no stamp is needed)
From outside the UK: *Good Hotel Guide*, 50 Addison Avenue, London W11 4QP, England
By telephone or fax: 020-7602 4182
By email: editor@goodhotelguide.com
Via our website: www.goodhotelguide.com

MALVERN WELLS Worcestershire   Map 3:D5

The Cottage in the Wood

Holywell Road	*Tel* 01684-575859
Malvern Wells	*Fax* 01684-560662
WR14 4LG	*Email* reception@cottageinthewood.co.uk
	Website www.cottageinthewood.co.uk

High on the wooded eastern slopes of the Malvern hills, this traditional hotel has 'stunning views' over the Severn vale to the Cotswolds. 'You can walk from the door to the top of the hills: the 360-degree views make the stay worthwhile,' say visitors this year. Others liked the 'cheerful atmosphere'. Owners John and Sue Pattin run it with son Dominic (chef) and son-in-law Nick Webb (manager). Seven bedrooms 'with a country feel' are in the main house; four are in *Beech Cottage*. The best, newer rooms are in the purpose-built *Pinnacles* 100 yards away; most have the views (binoculars provided), though in a ground-floor room this 'was obscured by scrub and trees'. The rooms contain free Wi-Fi, tea-making kit, home-made short-bread, a 'comprehensive information guide'. 'Ours had French doors and a terrace.' In the panoramic restaurant, most visitors enjoyed their dinner, though one couple experienced long waits. The menus have been restructured 'to give greater flexibility and wider choice'. They might include whisky-marinated salmon with grain mustard blinis; pot-roasted pheasant with a parcel of confit leg and chestnuts. 'A wonderful selection of wines.' 'Service good, if sometimes rushed.' Comments on the breakfast vary from 'ordinary' to 'generally good'. Mr Pattin has lowered his rates this year. As to muzak, he writes: 'Over my dead body.' (*SAM, and others*)

Bedrooms: 30, 4 in *Beech Cottage*, 70 yds, 19 (1 suitable for &) in *The Pinnacles*, 100 yds. *Open*: all year. *Facilities*: lounge, bar, restaurant, function facilities, 7-acre grounds (terrace), golf, squash nearby. *Background music*: none. *Location*: 3 miles S of Great Malvern. *Smoking*: not allowed. *Children*: all ages welcomed. *Dogs*: guide dogs welcomed, other dogs in *The Pinnacles* only. *Credit cards*: Amex, MasterCard, Visa. *Prices*: [2008] b&b £49.50–£109 per person, d,b&b £62–£114, full alc £45.50, Christmas/New Year packages, 1-night bookings sometimes refused. *V*

MANCHESTER *See SHORTLIST*   Map 4:E3

Report forms (Freepost in UK) are at the end of the *Guide*.

MARAZION Cornwall   Map 1:E1

Mount Haven Hotel & Restaurant
Turnpike Road
Marazion TR17 0DQ

Tel 01736-710249
Fax 01736-711658
Email reception@mounthaven.co.uk
Website www.mounthaven.co.uk

'Very relaxing'; 'Good value. A well-oiled machine, it hums with activity.' Praise this year for this contemporary hotel owned by Mike and Orange Trevillion and Tom Johnstone, in a village overlooking St Michael's Mount. 'The modern square shapes and white-painted walls may look unpromising, but inside all is done in good taste.' Originally a coach house, much altered in 1970, it has been given an Asian look: a Buddha over the entrance; silks from Mumbai, tapestries from Jaipur, modern paintings and pastel shades. The large lounge/bar has a picture window leading to a terrace with smart steel and slatted furniture and views of Mount's Bay. The young staff 'are genuinely interested in visitors but not over-familiar'. Many of the bedrooms have a balcony. 'My room was small but the shower room was immaculate; the view was stunning.' A larger room with a bath and shower was 'modern and meticulously done'. The cooking of chef Julie Manley has a 'good choice of locally landed fish'; there is a 'small but adequate' wine list. A team of holistic therapists comes to give treatment to guests (Indian head massage, etc). (*T Harley-Hale, Bill Watkins*)

Bedrooms: 18, some on ground floor. *Open*: Feb–Dec. *Facilities*: lounge/bar, restaurant, healing room (holistic treatments), sun terrace, ½-acre grounds (rock/sand beaches 100 yds), unsuitable for &. *Background music*: 'chill-out' music all day, bar, lounge. *Location*: 4 miles E of Penzance, car park. *Smoking*: not allowed. *Children*: all ages welcomed. *Dogs*: allowed in public rooms. *Credit cards*: MasterCard, Visa. *Prices*: b&b £45–£160 per person, d,b&b £27 added, full alc £39, 3-night breaks spring/autumn, min. 2 nights on bank holidays.

MARKINGTON North Yorkshire   Map 4:D4

Hob Green
Markington
nr Harrogate HG3 3PJ

Tel 01423-770031
Fax 01423-771589
Email info@hobgreen.com
Website www.hobgreen.com

In extensive farmland with 'views to die for' across a valley, this 18th-century house with award-winning gardens 'is ideal for a country break'. It is run in traditional style by the Hutchinson family, its owners for many years. Christopher Ashby is manager. 'A delightful hotel in glorious grounds, the staff were most helpful,' says one visitor this year. Outside is a panoramic terrace; inside, original panelling and moulding, antiques and curios; 'plenty of choice of sitting rooms with comfortable chairs'; 'lovely displays of fine china'. The bedrooms, all different, have flowery fabrics and patterned wallpaper; also tea-making kit, fresh milk in a fridge, 'very good' biscuits, chocolates, books, a pincushion and an evening turn-down service. 'Our room was pleasantly furnished and decorated, exceptionally well equipped; good lighting; wonderful views.' Chris Taylor's cooking, 'professionally presented, very fresh', is praised: 'The fish menu on Friday is particularly good; delicious halibut.' The 'excellent' breakfast has wide choice, including kipper and smoked haddock; 'proper pieces of butter (no wrapping to fight), good marmalade and jam'. Light lunches and teas are served. 'Enjoyable walks in the grounds and the village.' Conferences and functions are catered for. Fountains Abbey is three miles away. (*PJK, and others*)

Bedrooms: 11. *Open*: all year. *Facilities*: hall, drawing room, sun lounge, restaurant, civil wedding licence, 2½-acre garden (children's play area), 800-acre grounds, unsuitable for &. *Background music*: classical in public rooms. *Location*: 1 mile SW of Markington, 5 miles SW of Ripon. *Smoking*: not allowed. *Children*: all ages welcomed. *Dogs*: not allowed in public rooms. *Credit cards*: all major cards. *Prices*: [2008] b&b £57.50–£95 per person, d,b&b (min. 2 nights) £77.50–£118, set Sun lunch from £18.95, dinner from £26.50, full alc £39.50, 1-night bookings refused weekends.

MARTINHOE Devon   Map 1:B4

Heddon's Gate Hotel   *Tel* 01598-763481
Martinhoe, Parracombe   *Email* hotel@heddonsgate.co.uk
EX31 4PZ   *Website* www.heddonsgate.co.uk

Formerly a Victorian hunting lodge, this small hotel, reached up a long private drive, stands on the steep slopes of the 'magnificently wooded' Heddon valley. The owners, Anne and Eddie Eyles, have changed little since buying it in 2005: 'The decor is unsophisticated, but any misgivings were soon dispelled by the welcome,' say visitors this year. There are stags' antlers and black leather furniture in the bar; tapestries on green walls; cases of china ornaments in the lounge. Other comments: 'Don't go if you require modern style; *Heddon's Gate* has old-fashioned comfort, immaculate housekeeping, obliging hosts.' 'Perfect quietness. No music to spoil it.' The complimentary cream tea on arrival is appreciated. Dinner (at 7.30–8 pm) is generally enjoyed. The daily-changing five-course menu (with limited choice) has 'mostly traditional' dishes using local produce. 'They varied between good and extremely good; roast duck, venison Wellington and grilled lemon sole remain in my memory.' The bedrooms vary greatly (some are large). Some are named after their original use: Grandma's ('nicely furnished', Victorian-style); Nanny's (antique stained-glass windows); Servants' Quarters (private sitting room). Beds are turned down at night. Good walks start from the door. (*M and J Awty, Dr and Mrs RJF Walsh, Ken and Mildred Edwards, Charles Grant, Richard Creed, PE Carter*)

Bedrooms: 10. *Open*: 1 Mar–1 Nov, occasionally during winter, dining room closed midday. *Facilities*: 2 reception halls, 2 lounges, library, bar, dining room, 2½-acre grounds, river, fishing, riding, pony trekking nearby, sea ¾ mile, unsuitable for &. *Background music*: none. *Location*: 6 miles W of Lynton. *Smoking*: not allowed. *Children*: not under 12 (except in parties taking exclusive use). *Dogs*: not allowed in dining room, not unattended in bedrooms. *Credit cards*: MasterCard, Visa. *Prices*: [2008] b&b £48–£74 per person, d,b&b £75–£101, set dinner £31.50, special breaks, 1-night bookings occasionally refused. *V*

****

Traveller's tale *Hotel in Wales* At dinner there was only one French girl to serve, and she was stretched to the limit. Throughout the meal, wild guffaws and loud conversations between the cooking and waiting staff emanated from the adjoining kitchen. The latter kept bringing out dishes and taking them back, either because they did not know which table they were for, or because the previous course's plates had not been taken away. In the lounge next door, the lady of the house was in loud conversation with a customer, braying with mirth at his jokes, while her staff struggled to get the meals out of the kitchen.

****

MASHAM North Yorkshire   Map 4:D4

Swinton Park   *Tel* 01765-680900
Masham, nr Ripon   *Fax* 01765-680901
HG4 4JH   *Email* enquiries@swintonpark.com
                                     Website www.swintonpark.com

In huge, 'fantastic' landscaped grounds, this creeper-clad, castellated
17th-century castle (Grade II* listed) has been the Cunliffe-Lister
family home since the early 19th century. Today, Mark and Felicity
Cunliffe-Lister run it as a luxury hotel with a wide range of activities
in the grounds (see below), a cookery school and a spa. It hosts many
events, including weddings. The 'superb facilities and helpful staff'
were praised by readers this year. 'A friendly porter welcomed us at
the door; the manager, Andrew McPherson, left a greeting in our
room.' The large reception rooms have antique furniture, family portraits, mirrors, rugs on polished floors. The restaurant, *Samuel's*, has a
gold-leaf ceiling, sumptuous decor, mahogany panelling, open fire.
'The food is outstanding.' The chef, Simon Crannage, serves a
seasonal market menu, eg, velouté of fennel, oyster tempura; breast
of duck, samosa of the leg and ginger; 'signature' dishes available for
a supplement. 'English breakfast cooked to perfection.' There are
'stunning views' from many of the spacious bedrooms, and from the
shower room in the circular three-floor Turret suite. All rooms have
Wi-Fi access; four have 'disabled-friendly fittings'. For children there
are cots, high chairs, a special menu. An eco-friendly laundry has been
installed to complement the 'carbon neutral' wood-chip boiler.
(*Deana and Ian Leeman, Anthony Bradbury*)

Bedrooms: 30, 4 suitable for &. *Open*: all year. *Facilities*: lift, ramps, 3 lounges,
library, bar, restaurant, banqueting hall, private dining room, spa, games room,
snooker room, cinema, conference facilities, civil wedding licence, 200-acre
grounds (grotto, orangery, deer park, 5 lakes, fishing, falconry centre, model
boat racing, swings, play castle, bowls, croquet, cricket, 9-hole golf course,
clay-pigeon shooting, riding, falconry, kite flying, etc). *Background music*: jazz/
classical in bar and dining rooms. *Location*: 1 mile SW of Masham. *Smoking*: not
allowed. *Children*: no under-8s in restaurant. *Dogs*: not allowed in public rooms,
or unattended in bedrooms. *Credit cards*: all major cards (*Amex 3% service
charge*). *Prices*: [2008] b&b £80–£270 per person, d,b&b £115–£340, set dinner
£42, special breaks, Christmas/New Year packages, 1-night bookings sometimes refused Sat. *V*

Smaller hotels, especially in remote areas, may close at short
notice off-season. Check before travelling that a hotel is open.

MATLOCK Derbyshire   Map 3:A6
See SHORTLIST

MATLOCK BATH Derbyshire   Map 3:B6

Hodgkinson's Hotel   NEW   *Tel* 01629-582170
150 South Parade   *Fax* 01629-584891
Matlock Bath, Matlock   *Email* enquiries@hodgkinsons-hotel.co.uk
DE4 3NR   *Website* www.hodgkinsons-hotel.co.uk

In a wooded ravine, this old spa town is a tourist centre for the
Derbyshire dales and the Peak District. Though it now has amuse-
ment arcades and take-away food outlets, it retains some charm, and
its oldest hotel, 'stuck in a Victorian time warp', 'suits it well', says
a correspondent this year. The 'rather severe-looking' stone
building, cut into the cliff face, stands on the Matlock–Derby road
(rear rooms are quietest). The 'quirky ambience' is liked: original
fittings (stained glass, etc) remain with antiques plus 'esoteric
items' (old books and prints, fox furs, hats, Staffordshire china). The
owner, Dianne Carrieri, 'is pleasant and chatty'. The award-winning
breakfast has porridge, freshly squeezed orange juice, non-
packaged butter and conserves. 'Dinner very good too.' Chef
Krisztian Hadszala serves Mediterranean-style dishes, eg, red
mullet with a citrus and basil sauce. Bedrooms, priced according to
size (the single is tiny), are on four floors, no lift. 'Our spotless first-
floor room was stuffed with Victoriana: beautiful bed with heavy,
curved footboard and headboard, marble-topped dresser, fitted
wardrobe with lovely panelling. Quality bedlinen, soaps, etc.' The
small rear garden has roses and a pergola built of brick, old chimney
pots and timber. (*Esler Crawford, and others*)

Bedrooms: 8. *Open*: all year except Christmas. *Facilities*: lounge, bar, restaurant,
private dining room, 1½-acre garden (opposite River Derwent, fishing, day
ticket), unsuitable for &. *Background music*: blues/jazz, classical. *Location*:
central (2 quiet rooms at rear), parking for 5 cars. *Smoking*: not allowed.
Children: all ages welcomed. *Dogs*: not allowed in restaurant. *Credit cards*:
Amex, MasterCard, Visa. *Prices*: b&b £39.50–£85, set dinner £26.50, 2-night
breaks, New Year package, 1-night bookings refused Sat Aug–Oct. *V*

The 'New' label indicates hotels which are appearing in the
Guide for the first time or have been readmitted after an absence.

MAWGAN PORTH Cornwall   Map 1:D2

Bedruthan Steps Hotel
Mawgan Porth
TR8 4BU

Tel 01637-860555
Fax 01637-860714
Email stay@bedruthan.com
Website www.bedruthan.com

'Highly recommended. A most enjoyable stay. Lovely staff, excellent food, attractive decor.' Praise this year for this large, purpose-built family hotel, 'spectacularly set' above a golden, sandy North Cornwall beach. Its owners, sisters Emma Stratton, Deborah Wakefield and Rebecca Whittington, follow a green ethos. They have appointed a sustainability manager; visitors can join a quarterly clean-up of the beach, and are invited to pay £10 towards the carbon offsetting of their journey to Cornwall. Children are welcomed, and there is much for them to do: an indoor adventure play area, an Ofsted-registered nursery, a soft play and ball pool for toddlers, a junior assault course and a teenagers' room. Babysitters and nannies are available. For adults, the Ocean Spa has an indoor pool, a hammam and treatments (eg, seaweed wraps). The main building has slate flooring, neutral browns and creams, lots of oak. Accommodation ranges from 'villa suites', ideal for a family, to 'value rooms' (no view, let at a discount). A wheelchair-bound visitor was impressed by the kind treatment he received. Adam Clark's *table d'hôte* menus are 'a mix of classic and contemporary', eg, potted Cornish crab; curried monkfish, Bombay new potatoes. (*Diana Morgan, PF*)

Bedrooms: 101, 1 suitable for &. *Open*: all year except 22–26 Dec. *Facilities*: lift, 2 lounges, 2 bars, 3 dining rooms, ballroom (live music 2/3 times a week), 4 children's clubs, spa (indoor swimming pool), civil wedding licence, 5-acre grounds (heated swimming pools, tennis, playing field). *Background music*: occasional. *Location*: 4 miles NE of Newquay. *Smoking*: not allowed. *Children*: all ages welcomed. *Dogs*: only guide dogs allowed. *Credit cards*: MasterCard, Visa. *Prices*: [2008] d,b&b £67–£142, 1-night bookings sometimes refused.

MAWNAN SMITH Cornwall   Map 1:E2

Budock Vean
Helford Passage, Mawnan Smith
nr Falmouth TR11 5LG

Tel 01326-252100
Fax 01326-250892
Email relax@budockvean.co.uk
Website www.budockvean.co.uk

Martin and Amanda Barlow, owners of this traditional hotel above the River Helford, 'greet old and new guests with friendliness, interest and concern', say returning visitors this year. A family party, aged from two to 70, enjoyed 'the huge swimming pool with plenty of loungers and hot tub'. A country club in the large grounds has a nine-hole golf course, tennis and croquet. The garden leads down past terraced ponds and waterfalls to a secluded creek. 'The staff are friendly, hugely efficient; someone always on hand to provide tea, coffee, drinks.' 'Superior' bedrooms are recommended as 'standard ones can be basic. Our large, comfortable room overlooked the valley.' 'Outstanding housekeeping; our room, prepared to per-fection, had bathrobes, slippers, and towels for swimming.' Men must wear jacket and tie after 7 pm in the bar and main restaurant. Chef Darren Kelly's traditional cooking is generally liked. 'We enjoyed tian of crab, smoked salmon and avocado; roast sirloin of beef melted in the mouth.' Breakfast has fresh fruit and good fish dishes but 'packaged orange juice; £2 supplement for freshly squeezed'. The Barlows have a Green Tourism Gold Award for their commitment to sustainable business practices. (*Mary Woods, Janet and Dennis Allom, Kathleen Craddock, David RW Jervois*)

Bedrooms: 57, 4 self-catering cottages. *Open*: all year except 2–23 Jan (for refur-bishment). *Facilities*: lift, ramps, 3 lounges, conservatory, 2 bars, restaurant, snooker room, civil wedding licence, 65-acre grounds (covered heated swim-ming pool, 15 by 8 metres, hot tub, health spa, country club with bar, restaur-ant, 9-hole golf course, tennis, croquet, archery), river frontage (water sports, boat trips), unsuitable for &. *Background music*: live in restaurant. *Location*: 6 miles SW of Falmouth. *Smoking*: not allowed. *Children*: no under-7s on ground floor after 7 pm. *Dogs*: allowed in some bedrooms, not in public rooms. *Credit cards*: Diners, MasterCard, Visa. *Prices*: [2008] b&b £63–£111 per person, d,b&b £75–£123, set dinner £32.50, full alc £50, themed breaks, Christmas/New Year/Easter packages, 1-night bookings refused weekends, except off-season.

Meudon

Mawnan Smith
nr Falmouth TR11 5HT

Tel 01326-250541
Fax 01326-250543
Email wecare@meudon.co.uk
Website www.meudon.co.uk

'The place to stay if you want a relaxed holiday in beautiful scenery, personal and attentive service, delightful places to visit nearby.' Praise for the Pilgrim family's red brick hotel: its subtropical 'hanging gardens' lead down a valley to a private beach. Harry Pilgrim is chairman; his son, Mark, is managing director. Though *Meudon* has a new website (with online booking), they promise that 'traditional standards are still our cornerstone': these include turn-down service at night and shoe cleaning. 'Staff, rooms and variety and quality of food all excellent,' says a visitor who also appreciated help given when he had difficulty starting his car. Others wrote: 'Our 31st visit in 25 years.' 'Bright, clean decor, thankfully no chintz.' All bedrooms have double-glazed windows. Suites have a patio or balcony; one has an adjoining room for children. The comfortable main lounge has open fire, flowers and 'lovely garden views'. A 'dress code of jacket and tie' is encouraged in the restaurant where chef Alan Webb uses local produce, including fresh fish from Newlyn, for his daily-changing menus, eg, terrine of seafood on endive with baby capers; roast loin of Cornish lamb. 'The cooking is inspirational, never repetitive.' (*Alan Langton, Ken and Mildred Edwards*)

Bedrooms: 29, 16 on ground floor, 2 suitable for &, self-catering cottage. *Open*: all year except Jan. *Facilities*: lift, ramps, 3 lounges, bar, restaurant, 8-acre grounds (gardens, private beach, yacht), golf, riding, windsurfing nearby. *Background music*: none. *Location*: 4 miles SW of Falmouth. *Smoking*: not allowed. *Children*: all ages welcomed. *Dogs*: not allowed in public rooms. *Credit cards*: all major cards. *Prices*: b&b £80–£145 per person, set dinner £35, full alc £50, special breaks, Christmas package.

MELTON MOWBRAY Leicestershire   Map 2:A3

Sysonby Knoll
Asfordby Road
Melton Mowbray LE13 0HP

Tel 01664-563563
Fax 01664-410364
Email reception@sysonby.com
Website www.sysonby.com

In a 'magical' garden that leads to the River Eye, this red brick Edwardian house (manicured lawn in front, trees on either side) is run as a traditional hotel by Jenny and Gavin Howling; Wayne Jenson is the manager. 'Good value; clean, well cared for', it has been extended as a quadrangle around a central courtyard, which most bedrooms face. They vary greatly in size and shape: two four-poster rooms look over the garden and river to cattle in fields. Rooms at the back are 'quiet, but slightly anonymous'. In the 'very comfortable' annexe rooms 'soundproofing can be poor'. 'Meals can be taken in the bar (eg, steak and kidney pie; grilled steak) or from a short *table d'hôte* menu: 'Interesting, with an emphasis on local produce; cooking of an excellent standard' (dishes like home-made mushroom soup with granary bread; orange, bacon and brie chicken). Susan Meakin is chef. 'Staff are very willing.' Children are not specifically catered for, but 'well-behaved ones are welcome' and there is a family room. Melton

Mowbray, known for pork pies and Stilton, is a market town that 'seems to have kept its identity intact'. (*J and JJ, MM-D*)

Bedrooms: 6 in annexe (30 yds), some on ground floor. *Open*: all year, except 26 Dec–2 Jan. *Facilities*: ramps, reception/lounge, upstairs lounge, coffee lounge, bar, restaurant, function room, 5-acre grounds on river (fishing), unsuitable for &. *Background music*: 'as appropriate'. *Location*: On A6006, ¾ mile from town centre. *Smoking*: not allowed. *Children*: all ages welcomed. *Dogs*: allowed in most bedrooms. *Credit cards*: all major cards. *Prices*: b&b £41–£89 per person, d,b&b £56–£104, set dinner £20, full alc £35. ***V***

MIDDLEHAM North Yorkshire   Map 4:C3

Waterford House
19 Kirkgate
Middleham DL8 4PG

Tel 01969-622090
Fax 01969-624020
Email info@waterfordhousehotel.co.uk
Website www.waterfordhousehotel.co.uk

Visitors in 2008 'were made to feel so welcome' at this 'truly amazing place'. Owned by Martin and Anne Cade, the Grade II listed Georgian stone house overlooks the main square of this unspoilt little town, noted for its racehorses. Inspectors also appreciated the personal touch: 'Martin came out to meet us and introduced us to his charming wife.' The house has an 'intensely Victorian feel, thick fringed curtains, tassels, dark William Morris wallpaper'. It is 'chock-full' of antiques, *objets d'art* and bric-a-brac 'on the theme of horses, hunting and country pursuits'. The residents' lounge has a baby grand piano, log fire and huge pine dresser. A 'lovely' first-floor bedroom had 'supremely comfortable bed, nice extras (sherry, home-made cakes and chocolates)'. A low-ceilinged room in the attic was less liked: 'gloomy, with exposed beams, minute window at floor level, sombre prints, tiny bathroom'. The 'striking' dining room has 'burgundy-coloured walls, well-spaced tables, red bows on chair backs, candles'. 'Anne is a wonderful cook, and modest with it; delicious home-made bread, melt-in-the-mouth slow-cooked casseroles; I was enchanted by my harissa-spiced lamb pie. Generous selection of vegetables; genial service by Martin. Breakfast was a fried feast.' (*Mary Sproxton, David and Joan Marston, and others*)

Bedrooms: 5. *Open*: all year except Christmas/New Year, restaurant closed Sun night. *Facilities*: drawing room, TV room, restaurant, walled garden, patio, unsuitable for &. *Background music*: none. *Location*: village centre. *Smoking*: not allowed. *Children*: not under 12. *Dogs*: not allowed. *Credit cards*: MasterCard, Visa. *Prices*: [2008] £45–£95 per person, set dinner £33, 1-night bookings occasionally refused at weekends.

MIDHURST Sussex *See SHORTLIST*   Map 2:E3

MIDSOMER NORTON Somerset   Map 2:D1

The Moody Goose at The Old Priory
Church Square
Midsomer Norton
nr Bath BA3 2HX

Tel 01761-416784
Fax 01761-417851
Email info@theoldpriory.co.uk
Website www.theoldpriory.co.uk

In a town that 'reflects its Victorian mining past', this handsome Grade II listed building, which dates in part to 1152, stands by the church in a peaceful walled garden. Run as a restaurant-with-rooms by proprietor/chef Stephen Shore, it has flagged floors, beams and old fireplaces, artefacts and antiques in the hall. Visitors this year who had flown in from Australia (and been 'defeated by poor signposting') were given a 'friendly and calming welcome'. The bedrooms vary in size and style: 'Ours was small but very comfortable, especially the bed.' Earlier visitors had a 'four-poster bed; towelling robes and decent soaps in the bathroom; only downside the view of a neighbouring house'. A dissenter this year found her room (the Chapel) 'small and sombre'. Mr Shore's modern cooking was thought 'exceptional; attention to detail and freshness lived up to expectations'. His three-course set menu (three choices for each course) might include terrine of red mullet and courgette; braised shin of beef, rösti, horseradish cream. Breakfast in the cheerful rear dining room has croissants, toasted brioche, freshly squeezed juice, full English, cheese, ham and smoked haddock. 'Superb: it made lunch redundant.' But one couple found all tables occupied, and the juice and haddock unavailable. (*John and Annette Linton, and others*)

Bedrooms: 7. *Open*: all year, except Christmas/New Year, restaurant closed Sun night, Mon. *Facilities*: 2 lounges, 2 dining rooms, private dining/function room, ¼-acre garden, unsuitable for ♿. *Background music*: classical in restaurants. *Location*: 9 miles SW of Bath. *Smoking*: not allowed. *Children*: all ages welcomed. *Dogs*: not allowed. *Credit cards*: Diners, MasterCard, Visa. *Prices*: [2008] b&b £55–£95 per person, set dinner £25, full alc £60.

The more reports we receive, the more accurate the *Guide* becomes. Please don't hesitate to write again about an old favourite, even if it is only to endorse the entry. New reports help us keep the *Guide* up to date.

MILDEN Suffolk   Map 2:C5

Milden Hall   *Tel/Fax* 01787-247235
Milden, nr Lavenham   *Email* hawkins@thehall-milden.co.uk
CO10 9NY   *Website* www.thehall-milden.co.uk

Near historic Lavenham this eco-friendly B&B is a listed, 'much-loved Georgianised 16th-century hall farmhouse', say its owners, Juliet and Christopher Hawkins. 'You can walk, run, hug trees, pond dip, sing, eat and be merry.' They hold a Gold Award for Green Tourism, and manage their farm on sustainable principles. It stands down a quiet farm drive, amid wildflower meadows, hedged countryside and a walled garden. 'What a place,' said a recent visitor. 'A warm welcome on a cold autumn night. Our huge bedroom had an amazing array of antique prints and maps of Suffolk.' Overlooking the garden and countryside, the three bedrooms share a spacious bathroom; and there is a second bathroom downstairs for busy times. The largest room is in Adam style; the Gallery room has armchairs and twin queen-size beds. The 'superb' breakfast, taken in the large, sunny hall/living room, has the farm's own free-range eggs, bacon and sausages, and compote of home-grown fruit. 'Well-behaved' children are welcomed (toys, cots, nature trails, etc). Their visit might coincide with a 'farm fungus foray, dragonfly dawdle, or another wildlife event'. Wedding receptions and humanist weddings are sometimes held. 'Group self-catering' is offered in a 'magnificent' Tudor barn. More reports, please.

Bedrooms: 3. *Open*: all year (sometimes closed Christmas/New Year). *Facilities*: hall/sitting/dining room, civil wedding licence, 3-acre garden (tennis), 500-acre farm, unsuitable for &. *Background music*: none. *Location*: 3 miles SE of Lavenham. *Smoking*: not allowed. *Children*: all ages welcomed. *Dogs*: not allowed. *Credit cards*: none. *Prices*: b&b £30–£40 per person, 1-night bookings sometimes refused.

MILTON ABBOT Devon   Map 1:D3

Hotel Endsleigh   *Tel* 01822-870000
Milton Abbot   *Fax* 01822-870578
nr Tavistock PL19 0PQ   *Email* mail@hotelendsleigh.com
                                        Website www.hotelendsleigh.com

'More than a hotel, it's a holiday experience,' writes a correspondent after a 'relaxed visit' in 2008. 'No noise from traffic or aeroplanes, but plentiful noise, in huge, wonderful grounds, from birds, and streams and waterfalls cascading down to the wide River Tamar [on which the *Endsleigh* owns seven rods]. The gardens [Grade I listed, designed by Humphry Repton] are well maintained, and there are many rare and grand trees.' This luxurious Regency shooting and fishing lodge is owned by Olga Polizzi of *Hotel Tresanton*, St Mawes (*qv*). Her daughter Alex, the new presenter of Channel 5's *Hotel Inspector*, has been appointed a director but is 'still very hands on'; Stuart MacLeod is manager. 'Front-of-house is well organised.' Many original features were retained in the restoration, 'a triumph of design, and an obvious labour of love', creating the atmosphere of 'a modern, comfortable country house'. 'Superb log fires.' At night, candles provide much of the lighting. 'Beautifully kept bedrooms; our suite had lovely views.' Head chef Nick Fisher's daily-changing menu (modern European) was thought 'more than adequate, if sometimes a bit complicated' (eg, fillet of beef, artichoke barigoule, celeriac purée). One visitor was not keen on the desserts. 'Excellent breakfasts, but service occasionally strained.' 'Wonderful walks (waterproofs and wellies provided).' (*Dr Alec Frank, and others*)

Bedrooms: 16, 1 on ground floor, 1 in lodge. *Open*: all year. *Facilities*: drawing room, library, card room, bar, 2 dining rooms, terraces, civil wedding licence, 108-acre estate (fishing, ghillie available). *Background music*: none. *Location*: 7 miles NW of Tavistock, train/plane Plymouth. *Smoking*: not allowed. *Children*: all ages welcomed. *Dogs*: not allowed in restaurant. *Credit cards*: Amex, MasterCard, Visa. *Prices*: b&b £100–£200 per person, set dinner £39, Christmas/New Year packages, 1-night bookings refused weekends.

MINCHINHAMPTON Gloucestershire Map 3:E5

Burleigh Court
Minchinhampton, nr Stroud
GL5 2PF

Tel 01453-883804
Fax 01453-886870
Email info@burleighcourthotel.co.uk
Website www.burleighcourthotel.co.uk

'Impressively' set on a steep hillside facing the westernmost ridge of the Cotswolds, this 'well-appointed' 18th-century Cotswold stone manor house is owned by Louise Noble; it is managed by Christine Read. Their staff are 'attentive but unobtrusive', say *Guide* readers. The 'superb, well-tended' landscaped grounds were designed by Clough Williams-Ellis; they have hidden pathways, terraces, ponds and a Victorian plunge pool. Bedrooms in the main house have garden or valley view; some of the 'versatile' coach house rooms have a private entrance and terrace. Drinks and light meals are served in the panelled *Oak Bar*, with open fire, oriental rugs, comfortable chairs and sofas. The formal dining room has chandeliers, flowers, white linen, good cutlery and glass. Adrian Jarrad, head chef, serves dishes like scallops on a pea purée; duo of free-range pork with black pudding, cider cream sauce. 'The cooking was excellent and well presented, but we would have liked more variety as the menu didn't change over three days.' Breakfast has fresh orange juice, fresh fruit and pastries, 'nicely cooked dishes'. Children sharing their parents' room are charged for meals only. (*Bryan and Mary Blaxall*)

Bedrooms: 18, 7 in coach house, some on ground floor. *Open*: all year except Christmas. *Facilities*: ramps, lounges, bar lounge, 2 dining rooms, civil wedding licence, 4½-acre grounds (heated plunge pool, croquet). *Background music*: classical in lounge and restaurants. *Location*: SE of Stroud, via A419 towards Cirencester. *Smoking*: not allowed. *Children*: all ages welcomed. *Dogs*: allowed in coach house only (£10). *Credit cards*: Diners, MasterCard, Visa. *Prices*: b&b £65–£95 per person, d,b&b £85–£120, full alc £40, New Year package, 1-night bookings sometimes refused. *V*

MISTLEY Essex   Map 2:C5

The Mistley Thorn
High Street
Mistley, nr Manningtree
CO11 1HE

Tel 01206-392821
Fax 01206-390122
Email info@mistleythorn.co.uk
Website www.mistleythorn.com

'Excellent; good food; good value,' says a regular *Guide* correspondent about this yellow-painted old inn on the Stour estuary. Run as a restaurant-with-rooms by Sherri Singleton from California, and her husband, David McKay, it has a 'seasidey freshness' with sage-green panelling. The 'uncluttered' bedrooms, recently upgraded (new TV, chairs and tables), have a decor of taupe and cream, large bed, two chairs, plenty of cupboard space, organic tea and coffee. All bathrooms have a double-ended bath and a shower. Wi-Fi Internet access is available throughout. In the restaurant (with wooden tables, basket-weave chairs and modern artwork), the menus of chef Chris Pritchard (*Michelin Bib Gourmand*) emphasise seafood and seasonal local produce, eg, wild brill with walnut and spinach pesto; fish and mussel stew with tomatoes, chilli, saffron. 'We enjoyed fish on three nights, an excellent steak on the fourth.' Families are welcomed: the children's menu has 'not a turkey twizzler in sight'. Breakfast includes eggs Benedict and Buck's Fizz. There only a small sitting area for residents, 'but there is plenty to do outdoors in this interesting and attractive area'. Sherri Singleton runs cookery workshops and has extended her 'little foodie empire' by opening an Italian restaurant, *Lucca Enoteca*, in nearby Manningtree. (*Gordon Murray*)

Bedrooms: 5. *Open*: all year, except 25 Dec. *Facilities*: ramp, small sitting area, bar, restaurant, bedrooms unsuitable for &. *Background music*: light jazz in restaurant. *Location*: village centre, 9 miles W of Harwich. *Smoking*: not allowed. *Children*: all ages welcomed. *Dogs*: allowed. *Credit cards*: MasterCard, Visa. *Prices*: b&b £40–£90 per person, d,b&b £52.50–£115, full alc £28, cookery courses, 1-night bookings refused bank holidays.

MOCCAS Hereford and Worcester   Map 3:D4

Moccas Court
Moccas, nr Hereford
HR2 9LH

Tel 01981-500019
Fax 01981-500095
Email info@moccas-court.co.uk
Website www.moccas-court.co.uk

❧ *César award in 2008*

In a park designed by Capability Brown and Humphry Repton, and with a 12th-century church, this is one of Herefordshire's great houses. Grade I listed and Georgian (original designs by the Adam brothers), it stands by the River Wye. It is the family home of Ben and Mimi Chester-Master who offer visitors 'the chance to live the landed lifestyle for a weekend'. Everything 'is in excellent shape: grounds in neat trim; house immaculate'; a stone-floored hall leads to a magnificent cantilevered staircase below a glass dome. The informal hosts ('we immediately went to first-name terms') join guests for pre-dinner drinks in the library hung with family portraits; their son, Jake, may come in his pyjamas to say goodnight. Dinner, by arrangement, is cooked by Ben, who is passionate about local ingredients, perhaps rack roast of lamb with redcurrant, rosemary and port wine reduction. Guests eat around a communal table in an 'exquisite circular room'. A spacious first-floor bedroom ('best ever') had 'fabulous fabrics and decor; big bathroom, piping hot water'. Upper rooms are smaller. Breakfast has hot croissants, good preserves and cooked dishes. Zulu, the black Labrador, will take guests for walks. (*A and CR, and others*)

Bedrooms: 5. *Open*: 1 Apr–31 Jan, closed Sun/Mon, Christmas. *Facilities*: 2 lounges, music room, TV room, dining room, civil wedding licence, 75-acre grounds (river, fishing), unsuitable for &. *Background music*: none. *Location*: 10 miles W of Hereford. *Smoking*: not allowed. *Children*: not under 16 except by arrangement. *Dogs*: not allowed in house. *Credit cards*: Amex, MasterCard, Visa. *Prices*: b&b £70–£202 per person, set dinner £40.

MORETON-IN-MARSH   Map 3:D6
Gloucestershire

The Redesdale Arms
High Street
Moreton-in-Marsh
GL56 0AW

Tel 01608-650308
Fax 01608-651843
Email info@redesdalearms.com
Website www.redesdalearms.com

'Very enjoyable,' says a visitor this year to this centuries-old coaching
inn. With its honey-coloured Georgian facade, it stands on the main
street of this attractive market town. Co-owner Robert Smith is the
'friendly manager'. Other praise: 'Extremely pleasant staff.' 'Good
value for the Cotswolds.' 'Bedrooms of a high standard.' Eight rooms
are in the main building, newer 'executive' ones are in a converted
stable yard and an annexe: one is equipped for disabled visitors
(most of the building is on ground level). A spacious first-floor suite
had 'high sloping ceiling, neutral colours, large sitting room which
opened on to a small roof terrace; real ground coffee with the
hospitality tray, complimentary sherry'. Two rooms have a whirlpool
bath. Front ones have double glazing, but when windows are open in
hot weather there can be noise from the street and from the oak-
panelled bar below (a popular local). Dinner (6.30 and 9.30 pm)
might include pressed Gloucestershire ham hock terrine; traditional
Redesdale beef Wellington. Chef Craig Malins also offers a short list
of daily specials. Breakfast is a buffet for both hot and cold dishes. A
supplement of £20 is charged for early or late check-in. (*Elizabeth
Radnedge, and others*)

Bedrooms: 23, 15 in stable yard and annexe, 11 on ground floor, 1 suitable for
&. *Open*: all year. *Facilities*: lounge bar/reading room, public bar, 2 restaurants,
heated open dining area. *Background music*: in all public areas. *Location*: town
centre. *Smoking*: not allowed. *Children*: all ages welcomed. *Dogs*: allowed in bar
only. *Credit cards*: MasterCard, Visa. *Prices*: b&b £35–£70 per person, d,b&b
£65–£95, full alc £30, 1-night Sat bookings refused 1 Apr–1 Nov. *V*

MORPETH Northumberland   Map 4:B4
See SHORTLIST

Always discuss accommodation in detail when making a
booking, and don't hesitate to ask for an upgrade on arrival if a
hotel is obviously not full.

MORSTON Norfolk   Map 2:A5

Morston Hall   *Tel* 01263-741041
Morston, Holt   *Fax* 01263-740419
NR25 7AA   *Email* reception@morstonhall.com
                                Website www.morstonhall.com

'As near perfection as it gets.' 'Food as good as ever.' 'This is how it
should be done.' Praise for this *Michelin*-starred hotel/restaurant in an
area of outstanding natural beauty on the north Norfolk coast. Tracy
Blackiston is front-of-house, her husband Galton, chef/*patron*, sometimes appears on TV; in his absence, Samantha Wegg and Richard
Bainbridge 'keep standards high' in the busy restaurant. 'Everyone
gathers at 7.30 pm for aperitifs and canapés; a great buzz of antici-
pation.' The four-course dinner menu changes daily; no choice until
pudding or cheese: menus discussed when you book. 'Interesting use
of herbs; a tiny serving of delicious garlic and parsley soup; wonderful
lamb with such variety of fresh flavours; my request for low-fat food
was taken seriously. We liked the recommended wine of the month.'
'Galton emerged from the kitchen each night to discuss the meal.
Charming, enthusiastic young staff.' Six 'excellent', spacious new
bedrooms are in a pavilion in the 'charming' garden. 'Impeccable
housekeeping: no dust but never the sound of a vacuum cleaner';
beds turned down during dinner. Only a small room in the eaves
disappointed. 'Excellent' breakfasts: 'local ingredients perfectly
cooked'. 'Expensive, but value for money.' (*Rodney Stone, Anne and
Denis Tate, Meriel Packman, Pat Harman, Roger Down*)

Bedrooms: 13, 6 in garden pavilion. *Open*: all year except Christmas, Jan, restaurant closed midday. *Facilities*: hall, lounge, conservatory, restaurant, 3½-acre
garden (pond, croquet). *Background music*: none. *Location*: 2 miles W of
Blakeney. *Smoking*: not allowed. *Children*: all ages welcomed. *Dogs*: not allowed
in public rooms. *Credit cards*: Diners, Visa. *Prices*: d,b&b £140–£240 per person,
set dinner £50, 1-night bookings refused Sat.

MORTEHOE Devon   Map 1:B4

The Cleeve House   *Tel* 01271-870719
North Morte Road   *Email* info@cleevehouse.co.uk
Mortehoe, nr Woolacombe   *Website* www.cleevehouse.co.uk
EX34 7ED

In a pretty village above Woolacombe, this small, unpretentious and
'welcoming' hotel is recommended for its 'good value'. 'Our fifth

visit, David and Anne Strobel are such helpful hosts,' says a visitor in 2008. In the restaurant, hung with local artwork, 'the cooking was even better, more imaginative; main courses by David [eg, baked breast of free-range chicken stuffed with herby mascarpone; cod with lemon and parsley butter], puddings by Anne'. They write: 'We make everything ourselves; bread, cakes, muesli, jam, sauces, chocolate truffles and fudge.' The dining room closes during the school summer holidays, when 'most guests prefer B&B'. Breakfast can be continental or full English. The bedrooms, with their pine furniture, 'are fairly small, but have everything you might need'. Rear rooms have country views. There is a 'comfortable lounge'. The South West Coastal Path is nearby. (*Mrs CM Moore*)

Bedrooms: 6, 1 on ground floor suitable for &. *Open*: Apr–Sept, restaurant closed Wed, and evenings 21 July–31 Aug. *Facilities*: ramp, lounge, bar area, dining room, ½-acre garden (patio), golf nearby, Woolacombe beach 1½ miles. *Background music*: none. *Location*: 4 miles W of Ilfracombe, train/coach Barnstaple. *Smoking*: not allowed. *Children*: not under 12. *Dogs*: not allowed. *Credit cards*: MasterCard, Visa (*both 1% charge*). *Prices*: b&b £37–£55 per person, d,b&b £20 added, 1-night bookings sometimes refused Sat.

MUCH WENLOCK Shropshire   Map 3:C5
See SHORTLIST

NAYLAND Suffolk *See SHORTLIST*   Map 2:C5

NEAR SAWREY Cumbria   Map 4: inset C2

Ees Wyke Country House   **NEW**   *Tel* 015394-36393
Near Sawrey   *Email* mail@eeswyke.co.uk
Ambleside LA22 0JZ   *Website* www.eeswyke.co.uk

Beatrix Potter once owned this 'most attractive' Georgian house with panoramic views of Esthwaite Water and the fells beyond. It is now owned by the 'most hospitable' Richard (the chef) and Margaret Lee. Its 'cosy English decor' and 'unpretentious atmosphere' are liked. The two 'nicely decorated, bright' lounges have 'comfortable sofas, good pictures and ornaments'. Inspectors were 'warmly greeted' by the owner (in his whites) and two friendly Old English sheepdogs, Harry and Teddy. 'Our room, not large, was comfortably furnished:

blue-striped wallpaper, large antique wardrobe (captive coat-hangers, alas), lovely views, small TV; shower slightly small and old-fashioned.' Two bedrooms have their bathroom across a landing (dressing gown provided): one has 'wonderful views from the bath'. The 'excellent' dinner is at 7.30, in a 'lovely room with super views, well-spaced tables, nicely laid'. Guests choose at 6.30 from a five-course menu (three choices for each course). 'Delicious salmon with garlic pea mash; perfect lemon sole. Beautifully cooked, well presented, portions not over large. Good local cheeses. Well-detailed wine list, reasonably priced. Excellent service.' Breakfast has a buffet (cereals, yogurts, freshly squeezed orange juice, etc); 'scrambled eggs the best of our trip; honey in the comb'. Mr Lee's hobby is building model helicopters. 'We don't know how he finds the time.' (*Mrs E Talbot, and others*)

Bedrooms: 7, 1 on ground floor. *Open*: all year except Christmas. *Facilities*: 2 lounges, restaurant, veranda, 1-acre garden, unsuitable for &. *Background music*: none. *Location*: edge of village 2½ miles SE of Hawkshead on B5286. *Smoking*: not allowed. *Children*: not under 12. *Dogs*: not allowed. *Credit cards*: Amex, MasterCard, Visa. *Prices*: [2008] b&b £49–£80 per person, d,b&b £85–£112, set dinner £34, New Year package, 1-night bookings refused for bank holidays if more than a week ahead.

NETLEY MARSH Hampshire   Map 2:E2

Hotel TerraVina   **NEW**   *Tel* 02380-293784
174 Woodlands Road   *Fax* 02380-293627
Netley Marsh   *Email* info@hotelterravina.co.uk
nr Southampton SO40 7GL *Website* www.hotelterravina.co.uk

César award: Newcomer of the year

Gérard Basset, 'probably the most knowledgeable *sommelier* in the UK', and his wife, Nina, were co-founders of the Hotel du Vin group, which has now been sold. In 2007, they opened this 'stylish contemporary hotel' in the New Forest. Suzi Glaus is manager. 'The hands-on owners,' say inspectors, 'made great efforts to give us a pleasant stay; staff are enthusiastic. No stuffiness.' The interior of this 'not particularly distinguished' building is 'open, modern; everything tastefully done: top-quality fittings, glass panels, natural wood or slate flooring'. 'Our spacious room had desk, free Wi-Fi, TV/DVD-player, minibar, etc, but could have benefited from a chest of drawers. Bathroom well equipped.' Most rooms have a patio or terrace. There is a 'lovely sitting room', a 'nicely lit bar area', and colonial-style roofed terrace overlooking the large garden. One side of the large dining room faces the open kitchen. 'The chefs [led by Rory Duncan] work hard behind their counter. Delicious, refined cooking, eg, duck with quince, kale and swede. Organically grown local produce preferred. Portions just right; imaginative combinations. Wine cellar eclectic, with huge choice and some surprisingly reasonable prices.' Breakfast has a buffet; smoked salmon and scrambled eggs, full English, etc, 'all excellent, though toast was ordinary. M. Basset came to shake hands on our departure.'

Bedrooms: 11, some on ground floor. *Open*: all year except 29/30 Dec. *Facilities*: ramp, lounge, bar, restaurant, private dining room, civil wedding licence, 1½-acre grounds (swimming pool, heated in summer). *Background music*: none. *Location*: NW of Southampton, 2 miles W of Totton. *Smoking*: not allowed. *Children*: all ages welcomed. *Dogs*: not allowed. *Credit cards*: Amex, MasterCard, Visa. *Prices*: room £140–£195, breakfast £9.50–£12.50, full alc £45.

NEW ROMNEY Kent   Map 2:E5

Romney Bay House
Coast Road, Littlestone
New Romney TN28 8QY

Tel 01797-364747
Fax 01797-367156

Reached by a private road along the sea wall, this red-roofed, white-fronted house was designed by Sir Clough Williams-Ellis of Portmeirion fame in the late 1920s, for the American actress/journalist Hedda Hopper. It is run 'professionally, in friendly, personal fashion' by owners Clinton and Lisa Lovell, say visitors on their fifth visit. 'High standards have been maintained.' Everyone is 'courteous, smiling and helpful', says another guest. The house is 'full of character', filled with antiques, pictures and knick-knacks; at night, candles burn, and there is a log fire. In the dining room, which has 'a lovely seaside atmosphere', a four-course no-choice dinner is cooked by Mr Lovell on four days of the week, eg, scallop and crab chowder; honey-glazed duck with spiced plum, port and lime jus. 'An excellent meal, portions not too large.' The bedrooms, 'colourful and airy', have nearly floor-length windows with views of sea or golf course, plain carpet, light colours, four-poster or half-tester bed, armchairs. Housekeeping is 'first class'. Breakfast is full English, or continental (cold meats, cheese, fruits, croissants, toast). Cream teas are served. (*B and P Orman, and others*)

Bedrooms: 10. *Open*: all year except 1 week Christmas, dining room closed midday, Sun/Mon/Thurs evenings. *Facilities*: 2 lounges, bar, conservatory, dining room, small function facilities, 1-acre garden (croquet, boules), opposite sea (sand/pebble beach, safe bathing, fishing), unsuitable for &. *Background music*: none. *Location*: 1½ miles from New Romney. *Smoking*: not allowed. *Children*: not under 15. *Dogs*: not allowed. *Credit cards*: Amex, MasterCard, Visa. *Prices*: b&b £65–£82.50 per person, set menu £42.50 (*'optional' 5% service charge added to bill*), New Year package, 1-night advance bookings refused weekends. *V*

NEWBURY Berkshire *See SHORTLIST* Map 2:D2

NEWCASTLE UPON TYNE   Map 4:B4
Tyne and Wear

Jesmond Dene House   *Tel* 0191-212 3000
Jesmond Dene Road   *Fax* 0191-212 3001
Newcastle upon Tyne   *Email* info@jesmonddenehouse.co.uk
NE2 2EY   *Website* www.jesmonddenehouse.co.uk

'A haven of calm and excellence', this luxury hotel, owned by Terry Laybourne (Newcastle restaurateur) and Peter Candler, is in a 'secluded, densely wooded park' in the suburbs of north Newcastle. 'Service, always by name, was friendly,' says a visitor this year. The house, built by a Victorian industrialist, has a wood-panelled Great Hall and two 'smart' lounges (one the former billiard room). Inspectors liked the 'charming location' and the combination of modern decor with retained Arts and Crafts interiors. 'Bedrooms are fitted to the highest quality, with flat-screen TV, digital radio and smartly designed furniture; a commodious bath and double basin.' Some rooms are high-ceilinged, others 'cosy'. The spacious suites in the recently built *New House* have a sitting room, big bed, bold wallpaper. There are two dining areas, one in the former music room (with delicate plasterwork), the other in the 'light and leafy' oak-floored garden room. A new chef, Pierre Rigothier, joined in January 2008. His modern dishes include smoked salmon risotto; roast rare breed collar of pork. 'My room-service supper of pea and watercress soup and fillet steak was excellent. Exquisite scrambled egg and bacon for breakfast.' Conferences, weddings and other celebrations are catered for. (*Robert Gower, and others*)

Bedrooms: 40, 8 in adjacent annexe, 2 suitable for ⅖. *Open*: all year. *Facilities*: lift, 2 lounges, cocktail bar, restaurant, conference/function facilities, civil wedding licence, 2-acre garden. *Background music*: in public areas. *Location*: 5 mins' drive from centre via A167. *Smoking*: not allowed. *Children*: all ages welcomed. *Dogs*: only guide dogs allowed. *Credit cards*: all major cards. *Prices*: [2008] room £165–£295, breakfast £16, full alc £65, Christmas/New Year packages.

See also SHORTLIST

NEWMARKET Suffolk   Map 2:B4
See SHORTLIST

NEWQUAY Cornwall *See SHORTLIST* Map 1:D2

NORTH MOLTON Devon   Map 1:B4

Heasley House	*Tel* 01598-740213
Heasley Mill	*Fax* 01598-740677
North Molton EX36 3LE	*Email* enquiries@heasley-house.co.uk
	Website www.heasley-house.co.uk

In a pretty hamlet on the southern edge of Exmoor national park, this Grade II listed Georgian dower house is owned by the 'hospitable' Jan and Paul Gambrill. All around are wooded slopes and water meadows running down to the tiny River Mole. The welcome is warm, with 'tea and excellent fruitcake'. Inspectors appreciated 'the things that cost nothing but make guests feel special'. In the restaurant, open to non-residents, Mr Gambrill, 'passionate about cooking' and with a keen interest in wine, serves a three-course menu of modern dishes, eg, king prawn linguine; best end of Exmoor lamb with flageolet purée and sauté potatoes. 'A first-class dinner.' The wine list is 'very good, with modest mark-up'. Breakfast has freshly squeezed orange juice, home-made bread, 'really good porridge, super scrambled eggs and decent coffee'. All the bedrooms have been redecorated in pastel colours; they have Egyptian cotton linen; some of the *en suite* bathrooms have a power shower. 'Our spacious room was wonderfully peaceful.' Downstairs are deep leather chairs, stripped wooden floors, original artwork. Dogs are 'positively welcomed'; a new lobby links to the garden; ground-floor rooms have direct access to the car park. (*DRW, and others*)

Bedrooms: 8, some on ground floor. *Open*: all year except Christmas, Feb (private parties only at New Year). *Facilities*: 2 lounges, bar, restaurant, ¼-acre garden, unsuitable for &. *Background music*: on request. *Location*: N of N Molton. *Smoking*: not allowed. *Children*: all ages welcomed. *Dogs*: not allowed in restaurant. *Credit cards*: MasterCard, Visa. *Prices*: [2008] b&b £60–£90 per person, full alc £30. ***V***

NORTH WALSHAM Norfolk   Map 2:A6

Beechwood   *Tel* 01692-403231
20 Cromer Road   *Fax* 01692-407284
North Walsham   *Email* enquiries@beechwood-hotel.co.uk
NR28 0HD   *Website* www.beechwood-hotel.co.uk

'Memorable; the welcome is warm; everything runs like clockwork.' Praise from a returning visitor for this creeper-clad Georgian house (with 'Victorian character') owned and managed by Lindsay Spalding and Don Birch. 'Don's ebullience and bonhomie is a perfect contrast with Lindsay's calm and unflappable management.' They and their staff are 'charming, attentive'. Arriving guests are given tea and coffee with home-baked biscuits and 'delicious ginger cake'. 'The rooms are well proportioned': those in the new extension are particularly liked: 'Ours had half-tester bed; fine, well-lit bathroom in black-and-white and chrome, with power shower and full-size slipper bath.' Wi-Fi and flat-screen TVs have been introduced this year. The food is generally thought 'consistently good, showing a real interest in local ingredients': Steven Norgate's *table d'hôte* menus (modern British with a Mediterranean influence) might include smoked mackerel mille-feuille; loin of lamb on caraway seed and pistachio spring cabbage. Portions may be over-large for some. 'Wine list magnificent, not overpriced.' The 'excellent' breakfast has freshly squeezed juice, cereals galore, an 'artistic' buffet of sliced fruits; a choice of fish. In the 'lovely' garden are shrubs, a long lawn and a sunken area. Dogs are welcomed (two resident Airedale terriers, Harry and Emily, appear at night). (*Roderic Rennison, John Albutt, and others*)

Bedrooms: 17, some on ground floor, 1 suitable for &. *Open*: all year, except Christmas, restaurant closed midday Mon–Sat. *Facilities*: 2 lounges, bar, restaurant, 1-acre garden (croquet). *Background music*: none. *Location*: near town centre. *Smoking*: not allowed. *Children*: not under 10. *Dogs*: allowed (3 'dog' bedrooms). *Credit cards*: MasterCard, Visa. *Prices*: b&b £45–£80 per person, d,b&b £55–£90, set dinner £36, Christmas/New Year packages, 1-night bookings sometimes refused Sat in season. *V*

NORTHAM Devon   Map 1:B4

Yeoldon House
Durrant Lane
Northam, nr Bideford
EX39 2RL

Tel 01237-474400
Fax 01237-476618
Email yeoldonhouse@aol.com
Website www.yeoldonhousehotel.co.uk

The Union flag flies from a staff on the roof of this 'gentleman's residence', a 19th-century gabled house with lawns sloping down towards the River Torridge. 'Pleasant and welcoming', it is 'very much a family concern', owned and managed by Jennifer and Brian Steele. There are suitcases and teddy bears on the stairs, old stained glass, a large lounge. 'Nice ambience and gardens.' Bedrooms 'each have their own charm': one has 'a cosy, country style', another, with its 'grand four-poster', has been refurbished this year. The popular Crow's Nest overlooks the estuary and has a battlemented balcony. The restaurant, also river-facing, is named after the famous chef, Alexis Soyer. Guests 'will feel comfortable in any attire', says Mr Steele, who 'takes pride in cooking and presenting good food in a relaxing atmosphere'. His 'chef's collection' dinner menu has a choice of five 'traditional' dishes for each course, eg, duck liver and orange parfait; roast loin of pork wrapped in bacon, creamy mustard sauce. Wines are 'fairly priced'. Lunch is now served on weekdays. Breakfast is traditional English or continental. Books and games are provided. Donkeys graze in a meadow up the drive. Nearby are Rosemoor Garden and the delightful fishing town of Appledore. (*TJBP*)

Bedrooms: 10. *Open*: all year except Christmas, restaurant closed midday Sat, all day Sun. *Facilities*: lounge/bar, restaurant, civil wedding licence, 2-acre grounds, beach 5 mins' drive, unsuitable for ♿. *Background music*: classical/ 'easy listening' lunchtime and evenings in public rooms. *Location*: ½ mile N of Bideford. *Smoking*: not allowed. *Children*: all ages welcomed. *Dogs*: allowed, but not left unattended. *Credit cards*: Amex, MasterCard, Visa. *Prices*: b&b £55–£80 per person, d,b&b £82.50–£110, set menu £30, New Year package. *V*

The *Guide* has hotels to meet most tastes and budgets. We are as pleased to hear about simple, cheaper hotels as we are about the better-known, expensive ones.

NORWICH Norfolk   Map 2:B5

By Appointment   *Tel/Fax* 01603-630730
25–29 St George's Street   *Email* puttii@tiscali.co.uk
Norwich NR3 1AB   *Website* www.byappointmentnorwich.co.uk

❦ *César award in 1999*

Housed in three 15th-century beamed merchants' dwellings, this
restaurant-with-rooms has long been liked for its theatrical style,
'warm welcome' and 'excellent food'. The owners, Timothy Brown
and Robert Culyer, have named the bedrooms after royalty; each has
a distinct character and is described in detail on the website. Queen
Alexandra, which looks over St George's Street, has a Victorian brass
bed; Queen Mary, approached through a maze of winding corridors
and steps, has a Victorian roll-top bath; Queen Consort has two crystal
chandeliers. The house is entered through a tiny courtyard with a
Della Robbia relief on the wall; inside are antiques and 'interesting/
unusual pieces' (Edwardian wardrobes, hat boxes, old suitcases, etc).
'Not for the disabled or the very tall.' In the four small dining rooms,
dotted around the building, the menu, by chef Edward Mulley, is
displayed on gilt-framed blackboards. Typical dishes: chowder of
smoked haddock with Italian herb bread; roast breast of guinea fowl
with caramelised apples and calvados. The admired breakfast has
freshly squeezed juice, croissants, scrambled eggs with smoked
salmon and wild mushrooms. More reports, please.

Bedrooms: 5. *Open*: all year except 25 Dec, restaurant closed midday, and Sun
and Mon evenings. *Facilities*: 2 lounges, restaurant, small courtyard, unsuitable
for ♿. *Background music*: in restaurant. *Location*: city centre. *Smoking*: not
allowed. *Children*: not under 12. *Dogs*: not allowed. *Credit cards*: MasterCard,
Visa. *Prices*: b&b £55–£70 per person, full alc £47.40.

See also SHORTLIST

How to contact the *Guide*
By mail: From anywhere in the UK, write to Freepost PAM
2931, London W11 4BR (no stamp is needed)
From outside the UK: *Good Hotel Guide*, 50 Addison Avenue,
London W11 4QP, England
By telephone or fax: 020-7602 4182
By email: editor@goodhotelguide.com
Via our website: www.goodhotelguide.com

NOTTINGHAM Nottinghamshire   Map 2:A3

Hart's Hotel	*Tel* 0115-988 1900

Hart's Hotel
Standard Hill, Park Row
Nottingham NG1 6GN

Tel 0115-988 1900
Fax 0115-947 7600
Email reception@hartshotel.co.uk
Website www.hartsnottingham.co.uk

❦ *César award in 2007*

'Every city should have one,' say visitors to this modern hotel a short walk from the centre. Built on the site of Nottingham's medieval castle by Tim Hart, owner of *Hambleton Hall*, Hambleton (*qv*), it is managed by Paul Fearon. His staff are 'young, bright, enthusiastic'. One couple wrote of a 'very pleasant' welcome. The 'well-thought-out' building has curved buttresses, lots of glass, limestone floors; wide views over ramparts to the university and the hills beyond. Many of the bedrooms have the view; they are 'well equipped, and naturally ventilated through louvred shutters, giving pleasant air quality without dryness or noise'. Each of the six garden rooms has a private terrace. Light meals are served all day in *Park's Bar*. Breakfast, criticised in the past, has a better report this year (it costs extra). 'Perfectly prepared coffee by the cup, freshly squeezed orange juice, the freshest fruit salad, fine local pork sausages and free-range eggs. It may not be huge, but what does one need?' Booking is required for *Hart's*, the adjacent restaurant in the former radiology department of Nottingham's general hospital. Mark Osborne is the chef; we would welcome reports on his modern cooking. (*Prof Richard Noss, and others*)

Bedrooms: 32, 2 suitable for &. *Open*: all year, restaurant closed 26 Dec and 1 Jan. *Facilities*: lift, ramps, reception/lobby, bar, restaurant (30 yds), conference/ banqueting facilities, small exercise room, civil wedding licence, small garden. *Background music*: 'easy listening' in bar. *Location*: city centre. *Smoking*: not allowed. *Children*: all ages welcomed. *Dogs*: not allowed in bar, or unattended in bedrooms. *Credit cards*: Amex, MasterCard, Visa. *Prices*: room £120–£260, breakfast £8.50–£13.50, set dinner £22.50, full alc £50. *V*

See also SHORTLIST

'Set menu' indicates a fixed-price meal, with ample, limited or no choice. 'Full alc' is the hotel's estimated price per person of a three-course *à la carte* meal, with a half bottle of house wine. 'Alc' is the price of an *à la carte* meal excluding the cost of wine.

OBORNE Dorset   Map 1:C6

The Grange at Oborne
Oborne, nr Sherborne
DT9 4LA

Tel 01935-813463
Fax 01935-817464
Email reception@thegrange.co.uk
Website www.thegrangeatoborne.co.uk

Near the historic city of Sherborne, this 'very trim', 200-year-old stone-built house, in attractive gardens, is reached by a quiet country lane with a notice warning of 'ducks crossing'. Managed by Jennifer and Jon Fletcher (they married in 2007), and owned by her parents, Ken and Karenza Mathews, it has been undergoing refurbishment. The lounge furniture, criticised by a *Guide* reader last year, has been replaced, and there are plans to improve the lighting. Bedrooms are a mix of modern and traditional; some have a patio and direct garden access; two have a balcony. 'Ours, large and nicely furnished, faced the garden. Traditional bedding, which we prefer, and there is a choice of pillows.' In the 'most attractive', candlelit dining room, Martin Barrett's cooking (rustic English) might include warm Portland crab and spinach tart; confit of lamb rump with broad beans and a mint pesto. 'To end, a dessert trolley, very popular with the guests. Wine list excellent, and fairly priced. Breakfast was fine, including a generous plateful of scrambled eggs and bacon.' The staff, mainly female, young and local, are 'exceptionally well trained'. The treatment of visitors in a wheelchair has been praised. There is a large room for functions, weddings, etc. (*PE Carter, BB, and others*)

Bedrooms: 18, 1 suitable for &. *Open*: all year, only light suppers on Sun evenings. *Facilities*: lounge, bar, restaurant, 2 function rooms, civil wedding licence, ¾-acre garden. *Background music*: all day, in public rooms. *Location*: 2 miles NE of Sherborne by A30. *Smoking*: not allowed. *Children*: all ages welcomed. *Dogs*: not allowed. *Credit cards*: all major cards. *Prices*: b&b £52.50–£100 per person, d,b&b £68.50–£108, set dinner £26–£32, hibernation breaks Oct–Mar, Christmas/New Year packages, 1-night bookings sometimes refused Sat in summer. *V*

OLD HUNSTANTON Norfolk   Map 2:A5

The Neptune Inn & Restaurant   NEW   *Tel* 01485-532122
85 Old Hunstanton Road
Old Hunstanton PE36 6HZ

Email reservations@theneptune.co.uk
Website www.theneptune.co.uk

Kevin and Jacki Mangeolles formerly worked at *The George*, Yarmouth, Isle of Wight (she was general manager, he the *Michelin-*

starred chef). In 2007, they bought this 18th-century coaching inn near the north Norfolk coast. Refurbishment is in progress: digital radio, TV and Wi-Fi have been installed in all bedrooms. 'An excellent restaurant-with-rooms,' said inspectors. 'Our room (No. 7), up steep steps, though small, was thoughtfully equipped and comfortable. It had a sitting area with Lloyd Loom-style sofa, white walls and furniture, nice pale blue carpet, magazines, decent toiletries, excellent bed, very small shower room, like a ship's galley.' The residents' lounge and the bar (with a nautical feel) are also small. The 'centre of the action' is the 'smart, attractive' restaurant (well-spaced, smartly laid tables, parquet floor, high-backed Lloyd Loom chairs). 'Interesting dishes included a crab mousse appetiser; starter of beetroot risotto with salmon, walnuts and black pepper cream; excellent main course of monkfish, asparagus and morels. Presentation was careful. Wine list fairly short, but generously priced. The very friendly waitress was efficient. Good breakfast: freshly squeezed orange juice, nice fruit yogurt, two types of toast, home-made croissants, delicious scrambled eggs. The half-board price (£80) was extremely good value.' The sea is a short walk away.

Bedrooms: 6, all with shower. *Open*: all year, closed Christmas night/Boxing Day, Mon in low season. *Facilities*: residents' lounge, bar, restaurant, unsuitable for &. *Background music*: jazz in bar and restaurant. *Location*: village centre, on A149. *Smoking*: not allowed. *Children*: not under 10. *Dogs*: not allowed. *Credit cards*: MasterCard, Visa. *Prices*: [2008] b&b £45–£65, full alc £40, New Year package, 1-night bookings refused some weekends.

ORFORD Suffolk   Map 2:C6

The Crown and Castle   *Tel* 01394-450205
Orford, nr Woodbridge   *Email* info@crownandcastle.co.uk
IP12 2LJ   *Website* www.crownandcastle.co.uk

'Everything about it leaves you feeling good,' say visitors returning in 2008 to this red brick inn, 16th-century in origin, much altered in 1896, in a peaceful coastal village. Owners cookery writer Ruth Watson and her husband, David, run it with manager Tim Sunderland and an 'obliging, cheerful' young staff. A gallery selling photographs has now opened, the office/reception wing has been renovated, and there is a new suite above it. The bedrooms range from 'good' and 'better' (house doubles) to 'best' (house doubles and garden rooms, the latter recently refurbished). A best house double, 'chosen for the sea view', was 'not huge, but homely, with large, comfortable bed, big modern bathroom; fresh milk for tea/coffee'. One visitor found 'rather a lot of notes and notices about the place'. The large bar lounge has a big chrome bar and designer tables and chairs. In the bistro-style *Trinity* restaurant (*Michelin Bib Gourmand*), Ruth Watson and Max Dougal serve seasonal dishes like deep-fried spiced quail; hake with chorizo-stuffed squid. The cooking was, with one exception, admired by readers this year. Children are welcomed, 'but in limited numbers, and not in *Trinity* at dinner'. Snack lunches are served at the *King's Head*, opposite, also run by the Watsons. (*CLH, Judith and John Albutt, and others*)

Bedrooms: 18, 10 (all on ground floor) in garden, 2 in courtyard. *Open*: all year except 5–8 Jan, *Trinity* open only to residents evenings of 25/26 Dec. *Facilities*: lounge/bar, restaurant, private dining room, gallery (with Wi-Fi), 1-acre garden. *Background music*: none. *Location*: Market square. *Smoking*: not allowed. *Children*: not under 8, except babes-in-arms. *Dogs*: allowed in bar, 4 garden rooms (£10). *Credit cards*: MasterCard, Visa. *Prices*: [2008] b&b (Sun to Thurs) £57.50–£77.50 per person, d,b&b £77.50–£230, set dinner £50, special breaks, 1-night bookings refused Sat.

OSWESTRY Shropshire   Map 3:B4

Pen-y-Dyffryn
Rhydycroesau
Oswestry SY10 7JD

Tel 01691-653700
Fax 01978-211004
Email stay@peny.co.uk
Website www.peny.co.uk

♧ *César award in 2003*

The 'excellent service' by 'cheerful', 'well-trained' young staff is praised again by visitors this year to this 'attractive' country hotel. A listed Georgian rectory, it stands peacefully on the last hill in Shropshire, 100 yards from the Welsh border: 'a delightful, almost isolated setting'. Miles and Audrey Hunter are the 'marvellous, caring' owner/managers, who 'work hard at keeping guests comfortable and happy'. Bedrooms in the main house vary in size: the double-aspect Rector's Room is liked; Rose Room, next door, 'beautifully decorated in blue and cream', has 'just enough space'. Each of the four 'airy, well-lit' rooms in the coach house has a patio leading to the garden with its 'lovely views'; these rooms are popular with visitors with dogs. The chef, David Morris, uses local ingredients for his 'excellent' daily-changing menu, eg, Wynnstay estate wild duck, steamed pak choi. The large dining room has a 'happy buzz of conversation', though some find it crowded when the hotel is full. Breakfast has DIY fresh orange juice, organic porridge, 'excellent full English'. Good walking from the door, including the Offa's Dyke circular path. (*John and Jackie Tyzack, Brian and Gwen Thomas, and others*)

Bedrooms: 12, 4, each with patio, in coach house, 1 on ground floor. *Open*: 16 Jan–20 Dec, New Year. *Facilities*: 2 lounges, bar, restaurant, 5-acre grounds (dog-walking area), unsuitable for &. *Background music*: classical/light in evening. *Location*: 3 miles W of Oswestry off B4580, train Oswestry. *Smoking*: not allowed. *Children*: not under 3. *Dogs*: not allowed in public rooms after 6 pm. *Credit cards*: MasterCard, Visa. *Prices*: b&b £58–£87 per person, d,b&b £85–£115, set dinner £36, New Year package, 1-night bookings refused Sat. *V*

OTTERBURN Northumberland   Map 4:B3
See SHORTLIST

OXFORD Oxfordshire   Map 2:C2

Malmaison   NEW

3 Oxford Castle
New Road
Oxford OX1 1AY

Tel 01865-268400
Email oxford@malmaison.com
Website www.malmaison.com

For a correspondent who came in 2008 for a romantic Valentine's Day stay, this unusual hotel 'exceeded expectations in every way, especially sheer drama'. A pathway, dramatically lit at night, leads to the towering stone walls of Oxford's Victorian castle gaol (Grade I listed). 'Walk through the modern reception (over-sized furniture, staff in black designer wear), go up in the lift, you come out in prison.' The imaginative conversion retains original features: metal walkways, cell doors, keys, spyholes (reversed). 'We stayed in the Governor's Suite, a spacious open-plan room with fabulous bathroom. With dark brown walls, furniture and floors, the effect was a little stygian, if deeply trendy. In the brasserie (booking necessary) the food was fine, if not memorable. The cocktail (a mojito) was fabulous, as was the wine by the glass. Breakfast came in a large hamper, a bit gimmicky, too much food for one, too little for two. The staff were all young, very professional, but welcoming too – not a bit stuffy.' Some rooms (each comprising three cells) are on the A Wing atrium, around a huge oblong space. The jokes about incarceration, 'doing time', gym called The Exercise Yard, etc, may seem a bit laboured to some, but there is no denying the 'Wow' factor. Stephen Woodhouse is manager. (*Avril Campbell*)

Bedrooms: 94, 16 in *House of Correction*, some in *Governor's House*, 3 suitable for &. *Open*: all year. *Facilities*: ramps, *Visitors' Room* lounge, 2 bars, brasserie, 2 private dining rooms, gym, free Wi-Fi, outside seating. *Background music*: yes. *Location*: central, pre-booked parking (£20 a night). *Smoking*: not allowed. *Children*: all ages welcomed. *Dogs*: allowed. *Credit cards*: all major cards. *Prices*: [2008] room £160–£465, breakfast from £11.95.

Old Bank

92–94 High Street
Oxford OX1 4BJ

Tel 01865-799599
Fax 01865-799598
Email info@oldbank-hotel.co.uk
Website www.oldbank-hotel.co.uk

Its 'fantastic location' makes this contemporary hotel 'an excellent base': the elegant conversion of three buildings, one a former bank, is opposite All Souls. 'Check-in and restaurant service are efficient,' says a visitor in 2008. The decor is 'stylish without being too cutting-edge; mushroom cream and muted red, modern but relaxing'. Most of the 'nicely finished' bedrooms face the 'dreaming spires'. 'Our comfortable attic room had armchairs, desk, a pleasingly spacious bathroom with powerful shower, dressing gown, slippers.' An earlier comment: 'Thought has been applied to "what guests want": firm, large bed, good bath products, Wi-Fi and, bliss, a quiet room when asked for.' Owner Jeremy Mogford's collection of modern art ('a delight') is displayed in the old banking hall which houses *Quod*, the lively bar/restaurant. This 'has a great youthful buzz, but is popular with all ages. Good choice of pizzas, pastas, bistro favourites (eg, braised lamb shanks) and robust daily specials (fish and chips with mushy peas on Friday).' One visitor found service 'impersonal'; others thought it 'superb, by a bright, young team'. The 'excellent' breakfast is served from 7 to 10.30 am ('my small daughter loved the egg soldiers with a pot of Marmite'). (*Michael and Eithne Dandy, Sara Hollowell, Carin Burton*)

Bedrooms: 42, 1 suitable for &. *Open*: all year. *Facilities*: lift, residents' lounge/bar, bar/grill, dining terrace, 2 meeting/private dining rooms, small garden. *Background music*: jazz/'easy listening'. *Location*: central (windows facing High St double glazed), access to rear car park. *Smoking*: not allowed. *Children*: all ages welcomed. *Dogs*: only guide dogs allowed. *Credit cards*: Amex, MasterCard, Visa. *Prices*: [2008] room £185–£325, breakfast £10.95–£12.95, set menu £28.50, full alc £35, Christmas package.

Make sure the hotel has included VAT in the prices it quotes.

Old Parsonage
1 Banbury Road
Oxford OX2 6NN

Tel 01865-310210
Fax 01865-311262
Email reception@oldparsonage-hotel.co.uk
Website www.oldparsonage-hotel.co.uk

By St Giles Church on the busy Banbury Road, this wisteria-covered 17th-century building, 'full of history', has the 'ambience of a small country house' with 'the smell of wood smoke in the lobby'. Its owner, Jeremy Mogford, also owns the *Old Bank* (see above); Marie Jackson is the manageress. A massive oak door opens into the bar/restaurant (a popular meeting place for town and gown) with its year-round log fire ('such a nice room; busy but not overcrowded'). 'All very congenial, and diners seemed not to notice guests tramping through to get to their rooms.' Some bedrooms are small: a visitor this year disliked a 'poky room' overlooking the road. A ground-floor bedroom was 'characterful and comfortable, more spacious than some of the first-floor rooms'. 'Our small room faced the car park. Reading lights abysmal (25 watts).' Nick Seckington was appointed chef in January 2008. His all-day menu has 'classic British dishes with a modern interpretation', eg, sea trout ballottine, pickled girolles; stuffed saddle of rabbit, crushed potato. A 'very high tea' (wide range of sandwiches) is also available. 'Cooked breakfast full and satisfying.' In fine weather, the 'pretty walled front terrace' is 'a chic spot for tea or a meal'. One visitor in 2008 encountered some linguistic problems. (*AW, AR, and others*)

Bedrooms: 30, 10 on ground floor, 1 suitable for &. *Open*: all year. *Facilities*: lounge, bar/restaurant, civil wedding licence, terrace, roof garden, small walled garden. *Background music*: jazz in bar/restaurant area. *Location*: NE end of St Giles, some traffic noise, windows double glazed, small car park. *Smoking*: not allowed. *Children*: all ages welcomed. *Dogs*: not allowed in restaurant. *Credit cards*: Amex, MasterCard, Visa. *Prices*: room £150–£250, breakfast £12–£14, set dinner £37.50 (*plus 12½ per cent service charge*), full alc £85, special breaks, Christmas package, 1-night bookings sometimes refused Sat.

See also SHORTLIST

****

Traveller's tale *Hotel in Ireland* A notice in the bathroom asked me not to remove the toiletries. I had no intention of doing so, and I felt a little offended. I don't think it would have deterred a thief.

****

PADSTOW Cornwall   Map 1:D2

The Seafood Restaurant   **NEW**   *Tel* 01841-532700
Riverside   *Fax* 01841-532942
Padstow PL28 8BY   *Email* reservations@rickstein.com
                                         Website www.rickstein.com

Celebrity chef Rick Stein offers four places to eat and five places to
stay in this north Cornish port (such is his dominance, it is sometimes
called 'Padstein'). David Sharland is chef in the waterfront flagship
Seafood Restaurant, recently totally refurbished (main courses like
monkfish vindaloo; lemon sole with wild garlic, sorrel and asparagus).
St Petroc's Bistro (one of Padstow's oldest buildings, with 'pleasant sitting room and library', courtyard and garden and ten bedrooms)
serves 'unfussy cooking with the freshest of ingredients: perfect skate
wing, simply presented with aioli and watercress'. There is also
Middle Street Café (the three cheapest bedrooms and an 'interesting'
lunch menu) and a fish-and-chip shop (communal wooden tables).
The bedrooms vary greatly: one family was sharply critical of the
accommodation. Inspectors fared better: 'St Neot, at the rear of the
restaurant, was lovely: large sleeping area, smaller sitting area,
excellent bathroom with window. Decor modern but not aggressively
so. First-class breakfast: wonderful buffet table; crisp toast; four types
of cooked fish, excellent sausages, eggs and bacon.' A front room,
'light and airy, had wide-screen TV, well-designed bathroom,
magnificent view if you ignored the municipal car park'. The priciest
('minimalist') accommodation is in *St Edmund's House* (with private
garden) and the one-bedroom *Bryn Cottage*. Rick Stein may not be
around all the time, but manager Rupert Wilson leads a 'friendly,
efficient' staff. (*JH, CP, and others*)

Bedrooms: 40, in 5 buildings, some on ground floor, 2 suitable for &. *Open*: all
year except 24–26 Dec, restaurants also closed 1 May. *Facilities*: ramps,
Seafood: conservatory bar, restaurant, *St Petroc's*: lounge, reading room, bar,
bistro, courtyard, *Café* unsuitable for &. *Background music*: St Petroc's and Café.
Location: *Seafood Restaurant* on harbour; other buildings nearby. *Smoking*: not
allowed. *Children*: all ages welcomed, but not under 4 in restaurant. *Dogs*:
allowed in public rooms except restaurants, some bedrooms. *Credit cards*:
MasterCard, Visa. *Prices*: b&b £45–£147.50 per person, *Restaurant* tasting
menu £65, full alc £60, *St Petroc's Bistro* winter set menu £15, full alc £40, *Café*
full alc £30, 1-night bookings refused Sat.

Prices may change – always check them when booking.

PENRITH Cumbria Map 4: inset C2
See SHORTLIST

PENZANCE Cornwall   Map 1:E1

The Abbey Hotel   *Tel* 01736-366906
Abbey Street   *Fax* 01736-351163
Penzance TR18 4AR   *Email* hotel@theabbeyonline.co.uk
                           Website www.theabbeyonline.co.uk

High above the harbour, overlooking Mount's Bay, this small blue-painted B&B hotel is owned by Michael and Jean Cox; their son, Thaddeus, is the manager. A listed building (dating from 1660), it has a pretty Victorian garden, a courtyard and period features. The 'fascinating' contents include Greek statues, antiques, curios, fresh flower arrangements, lots of books; 'gorgeous fabrics and colour schemes, chintz sofas and chairs'. The lounge faces the garden, as do some bedrooms; the best bedrooms, 'full of character', face the sea. Room 1 has 'almost floor-to-ceiling windows'. Room 7 has a private bathroom across the corridor. One couple was disappointed to be given a 'cramped' attic room instead of the ground-floor one they had requested. 'All very low-key,' is another comment. Breakfast is served in an oak-panelled room. There are plenty of places to eat in town, including Ben Tunnicliffe's *Michelin*-starred *Abbey Restaurant* next door (not connected with the hotel). More reports, please.

Bedrooms: 6, also 2 apartments in adjoining building. *Open*: Feb–Dec. *Facilities*: drawing room, dining room, small garden, unsuitable for &. *Background music*: none. *Location*: 300 yds from centre, parking. *Smoking*: not allowed. *Children*: all ages welcomed (no facilities). *Dogs*: not allowed in public rooms. *Credit cards*: Amex, MasterCard, Visa. *Prices*: [2008] b&b £60–£170 per person.

See also SHORTLIST

PETERSFIELD Hampshire   Map 2:E3
See SHORTLIST

PETWORTH West Sussex   Map 2:E3

The Old Railway Station
Petworth GU28 0JF

Tel 01798-342346
Fax 01798-343066
Email info@old-station.co.uk
Website www.old-station.co.uk

Most of the bedrooms of this unusual B&B are in restored Pullman
carriages beside a Grade II* listed Victorian station on a disused
railway line. 'We love it. A unique and nostalgic experience,' says a
returning visitor this year. Restored 'with flair', it is owned by
Gudmund Olafsson (Icelandic) and Catherine Stormont. They have
redecorated throughout and added another Pullman carriage to give
two new bedrooms. Mr Olafsson is 'always on hand to talk about the
refurbishment, and clearly has a great relationship with his staff'. The
biggest bedrooms (one up a spiral staircase and through a library) are
in the station building. Those in the Pullman cars (of the type used for
the original Orient Express) are, inevitably, narrow but are 'beautifully
restored, well designed, with comfortable bed and a surprising amount
of furniture'. A 'first-class' breakfast is taken in the waiting room (with
vaulted ceiling and original ticket office windows), on the platform or
in the carriages. 'Served in a leisurely fashion, it uses the best local
ingredients.' Menus of local eating places are in the information
folders. The pretty garden has ancient trees, a sunken lawn, and steep
banks covered with shrubs. (*Sally Matson*)

Bedrooms: 10 bedrooms, 8 in Pullman carriages, 1 suitable for &. *Open*: all year
except Christmas/New Year. *Facilities*: lounge/bar/breakfast room, platform/
terrace, 2-acre garden. *Background music*: soft classical/1940s in waiting room.
Location: 1½ miles S of Petworth, car park, train to Pulborough. *Smoking*: not
allowed. *Children*: not under 10. *Dogs*: not allowed. *Credit cards*: Amex,
MasterCard, Visa. *Prices*: b&b £37.50–£107 per person, 3-night winter midweek breaks, 1-night bookings refused weekends.

PICKERING North Yorkshire   Map 4:D4

The White Swan Inn
Market Place
Pickering YO18 7AA

Tel 01751-472288
Fax 01751-475554
Email welcome@white-swan.co.uk
Website www.white-swan.co.uk

In a 'charming' market town, this old coaching inn has been updated
by Victor and Marion Buchanan, the second generation of the family
who have owned it for more than 20 years. Alison Dunning is the

manageress; the staff are 'welcoming, efficient'. The residents' lounge has an open fire, complimentary tea and coffee, an honesty bar, pool table, newspapers and magazines. The absence of muzak is appreciated. The newer, contemporary bedrooms, in an annexe, are 'exceptionally good, and free of traffic noise'. The rooms in the main house have been refurbished. 'It gets better and better,' says a returning visitor in 2008. 'Our redecorated suite had a huge plasma TV and DVD-player in the room where our small children slept and another in our bedroom.' In the restaurant ('candlelit, comfortable, relaxed') are flagstones, open fire, low ceiling and Gothic screens. Darren Clemmit's 'country cooking' uses meat from the 'unique' local Ginger Pig food producer. 'Excellent meals, with high-quality ingredients, large portions, and good daily specials.' Children have their own menu; games and baby-listening. 'Excellent breakfast: home-made breads and jams, first-rate Whitby kippers and haddock.' The produce is sold in the Buchanans' shop in Market Place. (*John and Margaret Walker, Chris Godsmark, Malcolm and Jane Levitt*)

Bedrooms: 21, 9 in annexe. *Open*: all year. *Facilities*: ramps to ground-floor facilities, lounge, bar, Club Room, restaurant, private dining room, conference/meeting facilities, civil wedding licence, small terrace (alfresco meals), 1½-acre grounds. *Background music*: none. *Location*: central. *Smoking*: not allowed. *Children*: all ages welcomed. *Dogs*: not allowed in restaurant. *Credit cards*: Amex, MasterCard, Visa. *Prices*: b&b £72.50–£130 per person, d,b&b £30 added, full alc £30, Christmas/New Year packages, 1-night bookings sometimes refused weekends. *V*

PICKHILL North Yorkshire   Map 4:C4

The Nag's Head
Pickhill, nr Thirsk
YO7 4JG

Tel 01845-567391
Fax 01845-567212
Email enquiries@nagsheadpickhill.co.uk
Website www.nagsheadpickhill.co.uk

In a Domesday-old village in Herriot country, this 18th-century coaching inn continues to be liked for its 'welcoming ambience'. Visitors this year write: 'It is a simple place; bedrooms while clean and adequate are basic and somewhat noisy (thin walls). Corridors are spartan. But the cooking is excellent, the service pleasant and prompt, the breakfast satisfying. It is impeccably run.' Another reader commended the location ('peaceful yet handy for the A1'). Edward and Janet Boynton are in charge (their family have owned the inn for 30 years). 'The place is teeming of an evening' and booking is essential for the dining room. An extensive menu ('three boards of starters and two of main courses') is served in both bar and restaurant: dishes enjoyed this year include potted shrimps; slow-roasted lamb with roasted roots ('really tasty'); 'a great plate of English sheep, goat and cow cheeses'. In the large, pleasant breakfast room, 'with oak bookshelves, plants and traditional ornaments galore', there was 'an adequate buffet, and my fresh, plump, kipper was especially good'. Children 'with one or two careful owners' are welcomed, and pets 'must be properly controlled'. (*Francine and Ian Walsh, Sir John B Hall; also Martin Wyatt*)

Bedrooms: 14, 6 in annexe, 2 in cottage, 3 on ground floor. *Open*: all year except 25 Dec. *Facilities*: ramps, 2 bars, restaurant, meeting facilities, lawn (croquet, putting). *Background music*: in bars and restaurant. *Location*: 5 miles SE of Leeming. *Smoking*: not allowed. *Children*: all ages welcomed. *Dogs*: allowed by prior arrangement, not in public rooms. *Credit cards*: MasterCard, Visa. *Prices*: b&b £40–£65 per person, full alc £30, themed breaks.

PLYMOUTH Devon *See SHORTLIST*   Map 1:D4

POOLE Dorset *See SHORTLIST*   Map 2:E1

PORLOCK Somerset   Map 1:B5

The Oaks
Porlock TA24 8ES

Tel 01643-862265
Fax 01643-863131
Email info@oakshotel.co.uk
Website www.oakshotel.co.uk

Run 'virtually single-handed', with 'quiet efficiency', by Tim and Anne Riley ('a charming couple'), this gabled Edwardian country house has an elevated position beside a village on the northern edge of Exmoor. Standing in pretty gardens with wide lawns and oak trees, it is liked for the 'peace and quiet', and the fine views of Porlock and the Bristol Channel. 'The welcome was as warm as ever,' say visitors on their fifth visit. 'Cases carried, coffee and shortbread served. Our first-class room was beautifully kept and had comfortable easy chairs and important little extras like flowers, fresh milk and fruit.' The main lounge has an open fire, chintzes, oil paintings and prints. In the restaurant, tables are arranged around the panoramic windows so everyone can enjoy the view. Anne Riley 'has the lightest touch with sauces and changes the menu daily, such a rarity'. Her four-course menus have three choices for both starters and the main course. Typical dishes: grilled fresh sardine fillets in herb butter; sautéed tenderloin of Somerset pork. 'Superb service by Tim Riley.' A warning: 'The hotel's entrance is at a sharp angle of the main road.' (*DRM Stewart, Ken and Mildred Edwards, Michael and Jenifer Price*)

Bedrooms: 8. *Open*: Apr–Nov, Christmas/New Year. *Facilities*: 2 lounges, bar, restaurant, 1-acre garden, pebble beach 1 mile, unsuitable for &. *Background music*: classical during dinner. *Location*: edge of village. *Smoking*: not allowed. *Children*: not under 8. *Dogs*: not allowed. *Credit cards*: MasterCard, Visa. *Prices*: b&b £72.50–£102.50 per person, d,b&b £89–£135, special breaks, Christmas/New Year packages.

PORT ISAAC Cornwall   Map 1:D2

Port Gaverne Hotel
Port Gaverne
nr Port Isaac
PL29 3SQ

Tel 01208-880244
Freephone 0500 657867
Fax 01208-880151
Email graham@port-gaverne-hotel.co.uk
Website www.port-gaverne-hotel.co.uk

In the 'lovely' setting of a quiet cove outside busy Port Isaac, this unpretentious inn, owned and run by Graham and Annabelle Sylvester, is recommended again this year: 'A simple, friendly place.' 'A most enjoyable visit.' It is 'very dog friendly' (the Sylvesters' dogs often sit under tables in the bar). 'I could walk my dog straight out of the door on to the coastal path and other doggy walks.' The simple bedrooms are up steep steps; sound insulation may not be perfect. 'A bit faded, but no complaints,' one visitor wrote. A large room with a balcony 'was comfortable, well equipped; powerful shower over the bath'. The bar, with its slate floors, wooden beams, local artwork (for sale) and log fire, is often busy with locals. It provides good meals (specials on a blackboard). In the restaurant, Ian Brodey's cooking was thought 'excellent'. Main courses include pheasant casserole; baked sea bass with garlic, ginger, lemon grass. Breakfast has a buffet for cereals, packaged juices, good cooked dishes brought to the table; good marmalade, pats of butter, 'but not much choice of fruit'. '*The* place to stay when visiting Port Isaac, no parking problem.' (*Zara Elliott, Mrs EM Sullivan*)

Bedrooms: 14. *Open*: all year except Christmas, restaurant closed 1–13 Feb. *Facilities*: lounge, 2 bars, restaurant, beer garden, rock cove 60 yds, golf, fishing, surfing, sailing, riding nearby, unsuitable for &. *Background music*: none. *Location*: ½ mile N of Port Isaac. *Smoking*: not allowed. *Children*: all ages welcomed. *Dogs*: allowed throughout. *Credit cards*: Diners, MasterCard, Visa. *Prices*: £42.50–£62.50 per person, set dinner £27, New Year package.

PORTSCATHO Cornwall   Map 1:E2

driftwood hotel
Rosevine
nr Portscatho TR2 5EW

Tel 01872-580644
Fax 01872-580801
Email info@driftwoodhotel.co.uk
Website www.driftwoodhotel.co.uk

'As near a perfect place to stay as I have yet found in the UK: situation, comfort, welcome, service and value for money.' A warm endorsement this year for this small Cornish hotel. 'A tranquil haven,' was another comment. It stands above a quiet cove on the Roseland peninsula; steep steps through woodland lead down to the beach. The owners, Paul and Fiona Robinson, are 'so nice; we were relaxed, happy and very well cared for'. The interiors are contemporary, with simple white background and various shades of blue, rugs on bare floorboards, driftwood table lamps and mirrors. A large decked terrace (where summer lunches can be served) faces the sea. Almost all the bedrooms have the views. The two-roomed Cabin (with sitting room and kitchenette), on the hillside, is 'tremendous fun'. In the candlelit dining room, which looks across the garden to the sea, the chef, Chris Eden, serves modern European dishes, perhaps celeriac and chanterelle lasagne, wild garlic, Madeira and thyme; sea bass, mushroom duxelle, squid and kohlrabi carpaccio. Breakfast is 'lavish and of high quality'. The Eden Project and the Heligan Gardens are within a half-hour drive. (*Michael Mackenzie, John and Sara Leathes*)

Bedrooms: 15, 4 in courtyard, also 2 in Cabin (2 mins' walk). *Open*: 5 Feb–8 Dec. *Facilities*: 2 lounges, bar, restaurant, children's games room, 7-acre grounds (terraced gardens, private beach, safe bathing), unsuitable for &. *Background music*: jazz in restaurant and bar. *Location*: N side of Portscatho. *Smoking*: not allowed. *Children*: all ages welcomed. *Dogs*: not allowed. *Credit cards*: Amex, MasterCard, Visa. *Prices*: b&b £115–£172.50 per person, d,b&b (Nov–Mar) £100, set dinner £40, tasting menu £56, 1-night bookings sometimes refused weekends.

Hotels do not pay to be included in the *Guide*.

PRESTBURY Cheshire   Map 3:A5

White House Manor   *Tel* 01625-829376
New Road   *Fax* 01625-828627
Prestbury SK10 4HP   *Email* info@thewhitehouse.uk.com
                             Website www.thewhitehouse.uk.com

Noted for its unusual themed bedrooms, Ryland and Judith
Wakeham's renovated manor house (built of red brick despite its
name) has a rural setting on the edge of an affluent commuter village
near Manchester. Bedrooms have home-made chocolates, fruit, a
hidden TV and CD-player, lots of CDs. Aphrodite, 'the most romantic room', has a Turkish steam bath; Earl Grey, in Wedgwood blue
and sunshine yellow, has a display of English china, teas and tisanes;
Trafalgar has rich burgundy drapes with gold braid and naval
artefacts. A ground-floor bedroom, Chantilly, has a 'shabby chic' look,
with French château-style furniture, 'a fabulous bathroom with walk-
in wet room and invigorating body jets'. All rooms have free Wi-Fi.
Breakfast may be taken in the bedroom, the *Orangerie* (a lounge/bar
conservatory), or on a patio; it can be continental, healthy or full
English. 'Continental, served in the room, was good – croissants and
muffins wrapped in a napkin.' Details are provided of the eating
places in the village, including the affiliated *White House Restaurant*, a
short walk away, where guests can charge meals to their room. More
reports, please.

Bedrooms: 12, 1 in coach house annexe, 2 on ground floor. *Open*: all year except
25/26 Dec. *Facilities*: lounge, conservatory with honesty bar, breakfast room,
½-acre garden (patio), unsuitable for &. *Background music*: none. *Location*: edge
of village on A538. *Smoking*: not allowed. *Children*: not under 10. *Dogs*: not
allowed. *Credit cards*: Amex, MasterCard, Visa. *Prices*: [2008] room £50–£150,
breakfast £7.50–£11.50.

PURTON Wiltshire   Map 3:E5

The Pear Tree at Purton   *Tel* 01793-772100
Church End   *Fax* 01793-772369
Purton, nr Swindon SN5 4ED   *Email* stay@peartreepurton.co.uk
                             Website www.peartreepurton.co.uk

'Probably the best-managed hotel of its kind that we have visited.'
'House, furnishings and garden all lovely. Charming, chatty owners.'
Praise this year for Francis and Anne Young's Cotswold old stone
former vicarage (Pride of Britain). It stands in extensive grounds on

the edge of a Saxon village in the Vale of the White Horse. It has 'attractive landscaped gardens, a comfortable bar and a cosy library with a log fire'. 'The feeling of confidence developed from the moment that Anne Young took our telephone booking.' In the bedrooms (each named after a village character), fresh flowers match the colour scheme. 'Our large first-floor room, Sir Charles Brooke, opened on to a small terrace leading to the garden. It had a comfortable bed and a spacious bathroom with whirlpool bath.' Dinners, in the candlelit green-and-white restaurant, 'are the work of a highly competent chef. Excellent lamb and venison, good beef and duck. The impressive wine list has house wines under £20.' At breakfast 'cooked dishes could show more imagination'. The Youngs' 'attention to detail extended beyond our visit. We added a gratuity to our payment because the service was good. A receptionist wrote to thank us and explain that gratuities are shared among all the staff.' (*Ann Walden, Ian Malone*)

Bedrooms: 17, some on ground floor. *Open*: all year except 26–30 Dec, restaurant closed Sat midday. *Facilities*: ramps, lounge/bar, library, restaurant, function/conference facilities, civil wedding licence, 7½-acre grounds (vineyard, croquet, pond, jogging route). *Background music*: none. *Location*: 5 miles NW of Swindon. *Smoking*: not allowed. *Children*: all ages welcomed. *Dogs*: not unattended in bedrooms, not in public rooms. *Credit cards*: all major cards. *Prices*: b&b £57.50–£135 per person, set dinner £34.50, special breaks. *V*

RAMSGILL-IN-NIDDERDALE   Map 4:D3
North Yorkshire

The Yorke Arms
Ramsgill-in-Nidderdale
nr Harrogate HG3 5RL

Tel 01423-755243
Fax 01423-755330
Email enquiries@yorke-arms.co.uk
Website www.yorke-arms.co.uk

❦ *César award in 2000*

By the green of a village in Nidderdale (an area of outstanding natural beauty), this old inn is popular with visitors drawn by the 'memorable' cooking of Frances Atkins; her husband, Bill, is thought an 'ideal host'. For six years she has held a 'well-deserved' *Michelin* star for her classically based seasonal menu which might include Wensleydale soufflé, sea scallops; stuffed veal kidney, osso bucco, truffled pomme purée. Comments on the bedrooms vary from 'bang-up-to-date; rarely have I seen such high-tech fittings and ultra-modern bathrooms, all within a traditional stone, ivy-clad building' to 'comfortable but small and expensive'. Breakfast, between 8 and 9 am, includes strong-cured bacon and home-made marmalade. The sitting areas have flagged floors, settles and wooden tables where walkers take a drink or a snack. Bar lunches (which can be alfresco in summer) include home-made soup; gratin of scallops, spinach and bacon). 'Staff are well trained and friendly.' (*Miranda Mackintosh, and others*)

Bedrooms: 12. *Open*: all year, Sun dinner for residents only. *Facilities*: ramp, lounge, bar, 2 dining rooms, function facilities, 2-acre grounds, unsuitable for &. *Background music*: classical in dining rooms. *Location*: centre of village, train from Harrogate. *Smoking*: not allowed. *Children*: not under 12. *Dogs*: allowed by arrangement. *Credit cards*: all major cards. *Prices*: [2008] b&b £75–£120 per person, d,b&b £150–£190, tasting menu £65, full alc £70, Christmas/New Year packages.

READING Berkshire *See SHORTLIST*   Map 2:D3

REETH North Yorkshire   Map 4:C3

The Burgoyne Hotel
On the Green
Reeth, nr Richmond
DL11 6SN

Tel/Fax 01748-884292
Email enquiries@theburgoyne.co.uk
Website www.theburgoyne.co.uk

❧ *César award in 2002*

Inspectors had 'a most enjoyable stay' in 2008 at this handsome Grade II listed Regency house. In a commanding position above the green of an attractive village in the Yorkshire Dales national park, it is 'well run' by Derek Hickson, 'a hands-on host', and his 'smiling, well-trained staff'. The front bedrooms have 'lovely views over Swallowdale'. A 'comfortable' rear room had antique pine furniture which matched the panelling around the large sash windows; 'masses of storage space, numerous little extras; a small pile of novels; a spotless, well-fitted bathroom; nice views. Though it partly over-looked the car park, it was peaceful.' Downstairs, the traditional sitting rooms have 'squashy sofas and armchairs, lots of magazines'. In the green-walled, 'long, thinnish' restaurant, chefs Paul Salonga and Chris Harker's daily-changing four-course dinner menu (six choices for each course) is served at 8 pm. 'Very good, traditional dishes; top ingredients from local suppliers; large portions. A huge hot smoked haddock flan on dressed leaves; excellent fish pie; tasty salmon and sea bass in a crisp filo pastry; refreshing pineapple and strawberries.' For breakfast, 'a good fresh fruit salad, but packaged orange juice; eggs Benedict (a nice change); fresh kippers and smoked haddock also on the menu'.

Bedrooms: 8, 1 suitable for &. *Open*: 8 Feb–2 Jan, restaurant closed midday. *Facilities*: 2 lounges, dining room, ⅓-acre garden. *Background music*: jazz/ classical 'when required'. *Location*: village centre. *Smoking*: not allowed. *Children*: not under 10. *Dogs*: not allowed in 1 lounge, dining room, or unattended in bedrooms. *Credit cards*: MasterCard, Visa. *Prices*: [2008] b&b £64–£170 per person, set dinner £32.50, midweek/Christmas/New Year packages, 1-night bookings sometimes refused Sat, Christmas/ New Year.

RICHMOND North Yorkshire   Map 4:C3

Millgate House
Richmond DL10 4JN

Tel 01748-823571
Fax 01748-850701
Email oztim@millgatehouse.demon.co.uk
Website www.millgatehouse.com

'Beautifully and imaginatively' furnished by its owners, Austin Lynch and Tim Culkin, this 'spectacular' town house, dating from the 1720s, has 'charming public rooms filled with delightful objects', says a visitor in 2008, 'but the fabric of the building may need attention'. Set off the market place of this attractive north Yorkshire town, it has an award-winning walled garden (open to the public from April to October). 'The views are wonderful.' Each of the spacious bedrooms (two face the garden and the River Swale beyond) has a large bathroom. These may be 'not luxurious' and 'let down by scratchy towels'. One double bed is 'so high you wonder how to get into it'. 'A vast range of choices' for breakfast (8–9 am) is served in the elegant green-walled dining room. 'Perfect croissants, top-notch cooked English.' The owners, who write, 'We are not a restaurant/hotel, this is our home', are 'hospitable in every way'. An evening meal, served in the Georgian dining room, is available for groups of 16 or more, and an 'outstanding magician' can be arranged to perform for the guests. (*Wendy Ashcroft, and others*)

Bedrooms: 3, also self-catering facilities for 12. *Open*: all year. *Facilities*: hall, drawing room, dining room, unsuitable for &. *Background music*: sometimes, in dining room. *Location*: town centre. *Smoking*: not allowed. *Children*: not under 7. *Dogs*: allowed throughout. *Credit cards*: none. *Prices*: b&b £42.50–£65 per person, Christmas/New Year packages.

RIPLEY North Yorkshire   Map 4:D4

The Boar's Head

Ripley Castle Estate, Ripley
nr Harrogate HG3 3AY

Tel 01423-771888
Fax 01423-771509
Email reservations@boarsheadripley.co.uk
Website www.boarsheadripley.co.uk

🏵 *César award in 1999*

Visitors in 2008 had a 'very enjoyable stay' at this old inn (near the castle) which has been renovated by Sir Thomas and Lady Ingilby (his family has lived on the estate for 700 years). Managed by Steve Chesnutt, it is an agreeable 'combination of pub and country hotel, elegant but not stuffy'. The young European staff are praised: 'Very good service under the watchful eye of the jovial, professional head waiter.' The 'superior' bedrooms in *Birchwood House*, across a court-yard, have flowers, fresh fruit, bottled water, sherry, big bed. 'We booked a superior and a standard double room. Both had good quality co-ordinated fabrics, a pleasant mix of old and modern furniture. Spotlessly clean. Only letdowns: the small bath without a shower in the standard; lack of storage space in the superior.' Lounges have antique and period furniture, portraits and pictures from the castle's attics. 'Three good dinners: the menu didn't change, but provided plenty of choice. We particularly liked the fish dishes, red mullet, sea bass and turbot, and the excellent puddings' (Andy Flockhart is the chef). Simpler meals and snacks are available in the bistro. Children and 'well-behaved dogs' are welcomed. Hotel guests have access to the castle grounds. (*Jenny Buckley, SH*)

Bedrooms: 25, 10 in courtyard, 6 in *Birchwood House* adjacent, some on ground floor. *Open*: all year. *Facilities*: ramps, 2 lounges, bar/bistro, restaurant, civil wedding licence (in castle), 150-acre estate (deer park, lake, fishing, 20-acre garden). *Background music*: none. *Location*: 3 miles N of Harrogate. *Smoking*: not allowed. *Children*: all ages welcomed. *Dogs*: allowed in 2 bedrooms, not in public rooms. *Credit cards*: Amex, MasterCard, Visa. *Prices*: [2008] b&b £62.50–£125 per person, full alc from £30, Christmas/New Year packages.

****

Traveller's tale *Hotel in Cornwall* The owner is very pleased with himself. He tells you about his numerous awards and prodigious achievements. The former are hung in frames all over the walls of the house. But our bedroom was poky and filled with car boot sale tat. The bathroom was minute, the lighting dismal, and water was never more than lukewarm.

****

RIPON North Yorkshire   Map 4:D4

The Old Deanery
Minster Road
Ripon HG4 1QS

Tel 01765-600003
Fax 01765-600027
Email reception@theolddeanery.co.uk
Website www.theolddeanery.co.uk

Linda Whitehouse is owner/manager of this stylishly modernised
hotel opposite the 'awe-inspiring' cathedral, the oldest in England.
The building, which dates back to 1625, is on the site of a former
monastery. Visitors who look for 'peaceful surroundings, good food,
comfortable rooms with modern bathroom' found 'all of these qualities; we were impressed'. 'Much more room to eat and drink' has been
created by the relocation of the bar/lounge to the front of the house;
it has leather sofas and a log fire on cold days. No lift: an oak staircase
leads up to the bedrooms. The six first-floor rooms have original pine
shutters and panelling; two have a Victorian-style slipper bath, two a
four-poster. The 'characterful' second-floor rooms have a 'splendid'
shower, old beams and sloping ceilings. All rooms have broadband
Internet access, fresh fruit and bottled water. In the candlelit dining
room, with 'striking' contemporary decor (bare dark floorboards,
leather seats and crystal chandeliers), chef Barrie Higginbotham uses
local ingredients in his modern dishes, eg, slow-roast pig's cheeks;
spatchcock poussin grilled with 'loads of garlic and herb butter'. In
summer, teas, drinks and meals are served in the garden. (*MB*)

Bedrooms: 11. *Open*: all year except Christmas, restaurant closed Sun evening.
Facilities: lounge, bar, restaurant, conference facilities, civil wedding licence,
1-acre garden, only restaurant suitable for &. *Background music*: jazz/classical in
bar, restaurant rooms. *Location*: town centre. *Smoking*: not allowed. *Children*: all
ages welcomed. *Dogs*: not allowed in public rooms. *Credit cards*: Amex,
MasterCard, Visa. *Prices*: b&b £62.50–£95 per person, d,b&b £92.50–£125, set
dinner £30, full alc £42, special breaks, New Year package, 1-night bookings
sometimes refused Sat in season. *V*

ROCK Cornwall *See SHORTLIST*   Map 1:D2

If you dislike piped music, why not join Pipedown, the
campaign for freedom from piped music? It is at 1 The Row,
Berwick St James, Salisbury SP3 4TP. *Tel* 01722-690622,
www.pipedown.info.

ROMALDKIRK Co. Durham   Map 4:C3

The Rose and Crown   *Tel* 01833-650213
Romaldkirk   *Fax* 01833-650828
nr Barnard Castle   *Email* hotel@rose-and-crown.co.uk
DL12 9EB   *Website* www.rose-and-crown.co.uk

♻ *César award in 2003*

'Excellent in every way; good food, kind service, pretty and comfort-able rooms.' Praise comes this year from a renowned Irish hotelier for this popular 18th-century creeper-clad coaching inn which stands opposite the green in a Durham village. It is owned and run by Alison and Christopher Davy (he is joint chef with Andrew Lee); Jenny Ranner is their manager. In the public rooms there are log fires, panelling, old farming implements, gleaming brasses and fresh flowers. The bedrooms vary in size; all but two have now been refurbished (remaining work will be completed over the winter of 2008). Room 10, which has 'lovely gold-coloured fabrics, bedspread and curtains, comfortable bed, good lighting', has been given bedside tables after a comment in the *Guide*. Some courtyard bedrooms, good for dog-owners and walkers, open on to the car park. In the restaurant, the cooking is modern English with a regional influence, eg, Cumberland farmhouse ham, honey roast figs; roast fillet of British pork, black pudding, apple and prune compote. 'Does anywhere serve better breakfasts?' asks one reader. Bread, marmalade, jams and chutneys are home made. The Davys have written a 'very useful' guidebook to local attractions. (*Myrtle Allen, and others*)

Bedrooms: 12, 5 in rear courtyard, some ground floor. *Open*: all year except 24–26 Dec. *Facilities*: residents' lounge, lounge bar, Crown Room (bar meals), restaurant, fishing (grouse shooting, birdwatching) nearby. *Background music*: none. *Location*: village centre. *Smoking*: not allowed. *Children*: all ages wel-comed. *Dogs*: allowed in bar, not unattended in bedrooms. *Credit cards*: MasterCard, Visa. *Prices*: [2008] b&b £67.50–£117.50 per person, d,b&b £97.50–£145, set dinner £30, New Year package, winter discounts, 1-night bookings refused Sat 'except quiet periods'. *V* (Nov–Mar)

The *V* sign at the end of an entry indicates a hotel that has agreed to take part in our Voucher scheme and to give *Guide* readers a 25% discount on their room rates for a one-night stay, subject to the conditions on the back of the vouchers and explained in 'How to use the *Good Hotel Guide*' (page 62).

ROSS-ON-WYE Herefordshire   Map 3:D5

The Bridge at Wilton

Wilton Road
Ross-on-Wye HR9 6AA

Tel 01989-562655
Fax 01989-567652
Email info@thebridgeatwilton.com
Website www.thebridgeatwilton.com

Run by owners Michael and Jane Pritchard, this restaurant-with-rooms has a 'lovely position' by the River Wye: its partially walled gardens run down to the water's edge. 'The welcome was most warm,' says a visitor who arrived in 2008 in heavy rain. 'Dinner was excellent; breakfast of the same high standard' (it can be full English or continental). Other visitors were equally enthusiastic about the 'imaginative, well-prepared dinners' ('especially fine desserts'), but less sure about the breakfasts. An earlier report told of 'good value; friendly service'. Local ingredients are used in dishes like twice-baked Hereford hop cheese soufflé; breast of duck with crushed celeriac. 'The wine list, starting at £16 per bottle, represents good value for money.' The bedrooms vary: many have 'inspirational' views across the gardens and river to Ross-on-Wye. 'My room, generously sized, with a capacious four-poster, had a balcony ideal for sitting, glass in hand, taking in the view to the opposite bank. It had a spacious shower room with good toiletries.' But one room was 'a bit poky, with inadequate shower', and another was 'poorly maintained'. The bar has artwork by local artists. (*Gwyn Morgan, RG, and others*)

Bedrooms: 9. *Open*: all year. *Facilities*: lounge, bar, restaurant, conservatory, 2-acre garden, unsuitable for &. *Background music*: in public areas. *Location*: village centre. *Smoking*: not allowed. *Children*: not under 12. *Dogs*: not allowed. *Credit cards*: Amex, MasterCard, Visa. *Prices*: b&b £49–£90 per person, full alc £40, 3-night d,b&b rates, Christmas/New Year packages, 1-night bookings occasionally refused.

Wilton Court

Wilton Lane, Ross-on-Wye
HR9 6AQ

Tel 01989-562569
Fax 01989-768460
Email info@wiltoncourthotel.com
Website www.wiltoncourthotel.com

'In a beautiful position on the banks of the River Wye', this hotel in a part-Elizabethan building is 'warm, welcoming, stylish'. 'We could not fault it,' says a returning visitor this year. The 'pleasant, hands-on' owners are Helen and Roger Wynn; their manager, Jason Davies, leads a 'helpful' staff. There are ancient beams, leaded windows, uneven floors, a huge fireplace with its original iron grate; the 'restful' sitting room has furniture and ornaments from the Far East. 'Our bedroom, enchantingly pretty in blue, had a river view and very comfortable beds with crisp cotton sheets and striped duvet. Kimonos in the wardrobe, big bath sheets in the sparklingly clean bathroom.' The conservatory-style *Mulberry* restaurant (named after the 300-year-old tree in the garden, which it faces) has blue/green Lloyd Loom tables and chairs. Chef Hans Peter Hulsmann's food was thought 'excellent, particularly the slow-roasted Gressingham duck with plum and port sauce; a proper side dish of vegetables'. Breakfast, 'another luxurious feast', had 'exceptional fruit salad and generous cooked dishes'. The garden is in 'country' style, with 'interesting trees' and mature shrubs: 'Well tended, even in October.' (*Mary Woods, JB*)

Bedrooms: 10. *Open*: all year, restaurant closed Sun night and weekdays off-season (full menu served in bar). *Facilities*: sitting room, bar, restaurant, private dining room, conference facilities, civil wedding licence, 2-acre grounds (riverside garden, fishing), unsuitable for &. *Background music*: at mealtimes in restaurant. *Location*: ¼ mile from centre. *Smoking*: not allowed. *Children*: all ages welcomed. *Dogs*: allowed in bedrooms, bar, lounge. *Credit cards*: Amex, MasterCard, Visa. *Prices*: b&b £47.50–£105 per person, d,b&b £72.50–£145, full alc £37.50, special breaks, Christmas/New Year packages, 1-night bookings sometimes refused Sat in season. *V*

See also SHORTLIST

ROSTHWAITE Cumbria   Map 4: inset C2

Hazel Bank NEW	*Tel* 017687-77248
Rosthwaite	*Fax* 017687-77373
nr Keswick CA12 5XB	*Email* enquiries@hazelbankhotel.co.uk
	Website www.hazelbankhotel.co.uk

In a 'stunning' Borrowdale location, with views of surrounding fells, this 'intimate' hotel is 'very personally run' by its owners, Glen and Brenda Davies. They 'treat guests generously and attentively seven days a week', says one visitor. The Victorian building (with neo-Gothic influences) so impressed Hugh Walpole that he used it in two of his novels. 'Spotless and quiet', it has a devoted following, though some 'might prefer a leaner style of decoration' and mealtimes are 'tightly fixed'. 'Not for those who want choice when to eat, or who spend a lot of time in their bedroom.' The 'convivial routine' and 'reassuring integrity' are liked, so is the hostess's 'superb traditional cooking'. 'First courses are works of art. Fine ingredients excellently balanced.' No choice until dessert ('Mrs Davies emerges from the kitchen with her husband to wheel a trolley bearing the day's two puddings.') The 'interesting wine list' has 'reasonable mark-ups'. Bedrooms vary from 'good-sized' to 'compact'. 'Sitting room cramped at busy times.' 'Breakfasts exactly what is needed for the day; choice sandwiches for a packed lunch.' The village is largely owned by the National Trust, and the area is 'hard to beat for a walker'. (*Tom and Sarah Mann, and others*)

Bedrooms: 8, 2 on ground floor, also self-catering cottage. *Open*: all year except Christmas. *Facilities*: ramp, lounge, honesty bar, dining room, drying room, 4½-acre grounds (croquet, woods, becks). *Background music*: none. *Location*: 6 miles S of Keswick on B5289 to Borrowdale. *Smoking*: not allowed (house and garden). *Children*: not under 12. *Dogs*: not allowed. *Credit cards*: MasterCard, Visa. *Prices*: d,b&b £65–£95 per person, set dinner £32.50, New Year package, 1-night bookings sometimes refused.

ROWSLEY Derbyshire   Map 3:A6

The Peacock at Rowsley
Bakewell Road
Rowsley DE4 2EB

Tel 01629-733518
Fax 01629-732671
Email reception@thepeacockatrowsley.com
Website www.thepeacockatrowsley.com

Visitors from the United States 'loved the *Peacock*', enjoying 'peace and relaxation' at the 'attractive' building with its Derbyshire stone exterior. The former dower house for Haddon Hall, it stands in grounds that run down to the River Derwent. Owned by Lord Edward Manners, it is managed by Ian and Jenni MacKenzie. The interior combines 'modern simplicity' with 'country antiques and original features such as beams and stone fireplaces'. Service in the 'dark and minimalist' dining room is 'friendly, polished'. The chef, Daniel Smith, serves modern dishes, eg, lemon sole, braised snails, garlic, parsley gnocchi; we would welcome reports on his cooking. Lunches and suppers are served in the bar. Bedrooms are around a series of corridors, with short flights of steps between different levels. 'Our beautiful room overlooking the garden had a king-size bed'; rooms at the front hear traffic from the busy A6. Breakfast is a buffet (cooked costs extra). Guests can walk on the peaks, shoot on the estate, and visit Haddon Hall (50% discount). A fisherman's log book in the front hall records catches on the Derwent and the Wye. (*Tara and Rick Varco, MW*)

Bedrooms: 16. *Open*: all year except 24/25 Dec. *Facilities*: lounge, bar, dining room, live classical guitar Fri, conference rooms, civil wedding licence, garden on river, fishing Apr–Oct, unsuitable for &. *Background music*: no. *Location*: village centre. *Smoking*: not allowed. *Children*: 'no children at weekends.' *Dogs*: not allowed in public rooms. *Credit cards*: Amex, MasterCard, Visa. *Prices*: b&b £72.50–£110 per person, d,b&b £102.50–£140, cooked breakfast £6.95, full alc £62, 1-night bookings refused Sat.

RUSHLAKE GREEN East Sussex   Map 2:E4

Stone House
Rushlake Green
Heathfield TN21 9QJ

Tel 01435-830553
Fax 01435-830726
Website www.stonehousesussex.co.uk

'A quintessential English country home', this 15th-century manor house, with 18th-century modifications, has been owned by one family for over 500 years. Peter and Jane Dunn, who run it 'with great charm', 'have a gift for hospitality', says a report in 2008. 'Well-trained staff, welcoming and helpful at every turn.' A grand double staircase rises from the black-and-white marble floor of the entrance hall. The largest bedrooms are in the Georgian section: two have a four-poster. Rooms in the Tudor wing are smaller but 'characterful' (beams, sloping ceilings, antiques). Winter visitors found theirs an 'adequate size, with effective radiator (no central heating). Shower arrangements reminiscent of French hotels of yester year. Jane Dunn's enthusiasm for things culinary was evident in the three dinners that we enjoyed' (*Michelin Bib Gourmand* for French- and Thai-influenced cooking, eg, roasted trompolino soup with chilli oil; duck with orange, ginger, brown sugar and honey on puy lentils). Continental breakfast can be taken in the bedroom; a traditional one has a 'superb buffet'. There are many sporting activities in the huge grounds; the walled garden has ornamental lake, gazebos, a 100-foot herbaceous border. A picnic can be provided for Glyndebourne, 20 minutes' drive away. (*Elisabeth Biggs, Catrin Treadwell, and others*)

Bedrooms: 6. *Open*: all year except 21 Dec–1 Jan. *Facilities*: hall, drawing room, library, dining room, billiard room, 1,000-acre estate (5½-acre garden, farm, woodland, croquet, shooting, pheasant/clay-pigeon shooting, 2 lakes, rowing, fishing), unsuitable for &. *Background music*: none. *Location*: 4 miles SE of Heathfield, by village green. *Smoking*: not allowed. *Children*: not under 9. *Dogs*: not allowed in public rooms. *Credit cards*: MasterCard, Visa. *Prices*: [2008] b&b

£62.50–£135 per person, d,b&b £51–£97, set dinner £28, set meals (advance booking for lunch necessary) £28, Glyndebourne hamper (*no VAT*) £32, weekend house parties, winter breaks, cookery courses, 1-night bookings sometimes refused Sat. *V* (1 Nov–31 Mar; not Fri/Sat)

RYE East Sussex   Map 2:E5

The George in Rye
98 High Street
Rye TN31 7JT

Tel 01797-222114
Fax 01797-224065
Email stay@thegeorgeinrye.com
Website www.thegeorgeinrye.com

In the centre of the old cinque port, this 16th-century inn has been given 'quirky' modern touches by Alex and Katie Clarke. A film set designer, she has styled the bedrooms: there are tapestries, corduroy sofas, *chaises longues*, antique mirrors, roll-top baths, psychedelic prints and 'funky lighting'. Some bedrooms are in the main building, others across a courtyard. 'Superb bed, very nice sheets; cashmere-covered hot-water bottle.' Inspectors observed 'lapses of attention to detail' but nevertheless found the inn 'charming, an enjoyable place to stay'. A visitor this year wrote: 'Staff were helpful with our young daughter, but there was a lack of overall management.' In the rambling old building 'little sunlit courtyards are hidden behind unfrequented stairs; rooms tucked in behind gables'. There is a 'pleasant open terrace'. The large, lively bar (which serves Sussex wines) is frequented by locals (noise from this could be a problem for residents). In the bistro-style restaurant (brown walls, plain wooden tables), the cooking of chef Rod Grossman is modern British with Mediterranean influence, eg, char-grilled sardine with harissa; roasted guinea fowl with puy lentils. Functions are held in the 'magnificent' ballroom with its minstrels' gallery.

Bedrooms: 24, 6 in annexe. *Open*: all year. *Facilities*: sitting room, lounge/bar, restaurant, ballroom, civil wedding licence, terrace, courtyard garden, unsuitable for &. *Background music*: in bar. *Location*: town centre, pay-and-display car park nearby. *Smoking*: not allowed. *Children*: all ages welcomed. *Dogs*: 'well-behaved' dogs allowed in bar/courtyard. *Credit cards*: MasterCard, Visa. *Prices*: b&b £62.50–£175 per person, full alc £40, special breaks, Christmas/New Year packages.

Please always send a report if you stay at a *Guide* hotel, even if it's only to endorse the existing entry.

Jeake's House
Mermaid Street
Rye TN31 7ET

Tel 01797-222828
Fax 01797-222623
Email stay@jeakeshouse.com
Website www.jeakeshouse.com

❦ *César award in 1992*

In a converted wool store and the adjoining Quaker meeting house, this much-liked B&B stands on a quiet cobbled street, perhaps 'the most beautiful in Rye'. The owners, Jenny Hadfield and Richard Martin, are 'most helpful', say visitors this year. 'Jenny went to some trouble to obtain special items for breakfast.' The American novelist Conrad Aiken lived here and entertained other writers and artists, after whom the bedrooms are named. 'Our quiet room, the Malcolm Lowry suite, was comfortable, with a four-poster bed and a large bathroom with a walk-in shower and roll-top bath; housekeeping was of a high standard.' The Conrad Aiken suite is 'an enormous top-floor room, with a big window seat looking over the garden to fields of sheep and the salt marsh'. The building is filled with antiques, pictures and samplers. There is a 'nice lounge', with a book-lined honesty bar and a folder with sample menus from nearby restaurants. The 'excellent' breakfast is served in the red-walled old Quaker meeting house, with high windows, good china, and plants. The private car park (£3 a day) is 'a real bonus'. (*John and Margaret Speake; also David Reed, Florence and Russell Birch*)

Bedrooms: 11. *Open*: all year. *Facilities*: parlour, bar/library, breakfast room, unsuitable for &. *Background music*: classical in breakfast room. *Location*: central, car park (£3 per 24 hours, advance booking needed). *Smoking*: not allowed. *Children*: not under 8. *Dogs*: not allowed in breakfast room. *Credit cards*: MasterCard, Visa. *Prices*: b&b £45–£79 per person, 2-night midweek breaks Nov–Mar, 1-night bookings sometimes refused.

See also SHORTLIST

How to contact the *Guide*
By mail: From anywhere in the UK, write to Freepost PAM 2931, London W11 4BR (no stamp is needed)
From outside the UK: *Good Hotel Guide*, 50 Addison Avenue, London W11 4QP, England
By telephone or fax: 020-7602 4182
By email: editor@goodhotelguide.com
Via our website: www.goodhotelguide.com

ST ALBANS Hertfordshire   Map 2:C3

St Michael's Manor
Fishpool Street
St Albans AL3 4RY

Tel 01727-864444
Fax 01727-848909
Email reservations@stmichaelsmanor.com
Website www.stmichaelsmanor.com

In 'pretty gardens with a lake', this manor house stands in the oldest part of the city beneath the cathedral. It has been owned and run by the Newling Ward family for more than 40 years; Paul Crossey is the manager, the staff are 'very friendly'. In the conservatory restaurant overlooking the garden, the chef, Haydn Laidlow, serves a modern menu, eg, warm goat's cheese mousse; fillet of gilthead bream with tarragon crushed potato. 'Good food and service; excellent wine list.' Bedroom styles vary. The rooms in the main house, named after trees in the grounds, have a period decor; Japanese is the theme in the modern wing ('comfy bed; stylish, "wet" bathroom; spotlessly clean'). Children are welcomed: they have a special menu, snacks all day, cots and babysitting (but there are no interconnecting or family rooms). Weddings, conferences and functions are often held. To avoid them you could visit one of the 'five attractive pubs down the road at Verulamium', or the family's restaurant, *Darcy's*, 15 minutes' walk away. (*PSD*, *WB*)

Bedrooms: 30, 8 in garden wing, some on ground floor, 1 suitable for &. *Open*: all year. *Facilities*: ramps, 2 lounges, bar, restaurant, conservatory, private dining room, civil wedding licence, 5-acre gardens (croquet, lake). *Background music*: relaxing, in lounge and restaurant. *Location*: old St Albans, near cathedral. *Smoking*: allowed in 6 bedrooms. *Children*: all ages welcomed. *Dogs*: only guide dogs allowed. *Credit cards*: all major cards. *Prices*: [2008] b&b £90–£230 per person, set dinner £30, full alc £50, weekend breaks, Christmas/New Year packages. *V*

ST HILARY Cornwall   Map 1:E1

Ennys
Trewhella Lane, St Hilary
nr Penzance TR20 9BZ

Tel 01736-740262
Fax 01736-740055
Email ennys@ennys.co.uk
Website www.ennys.co.uk

'A lovely ambience, such a tranquil place.' Reached up a long, narrow drive, this creeper-covered Grade II listed 17th-century manor house is an 'elegant, stylish' B&B, run by travel writer Gill Charlton. 'You can tell she is well travelled,' says an inspector, 'by the little comforts in the bedrooms: big waffle bathrobes, a good selection of books and magazines, nice smellies. Our classically fitted room, in pale turquoise, had wood and cane furniture, interesting fabrics, beautiful cushions. The bed was super-comfortable; fine linen and pillows conducive to a good night's sleep.' All bedrooms have flat-screen TV and free Wi-Fi. 'Breakfast fuelled us for the day: freshly squeezed orange juice, stewed prunes, mini-croissants, lovely marmalade, jam and lemon curd; good toast (butter in little packs), generous coffee in a vacuum jar, scrumptious cooked dishes.' There is a 'delightful', big sitting room, with interesting artwork and souvenirs of the owner's travels. 'We were given a door key and encouraged to feel at home, though you clearly aren't expected to be around during the day.' *Ennys*, surrounded by fields that lead to the River Hayle, has a pretty garden with exotic planting and a swimming pool (available to visitors in the morning and late afternoon).

Bedrooms: 5, 2 in barns, 3 self-catering apartments (can be B&B off-season). *Open*: 20 Mar–1 Nov. *Facilities*: sitting room, breakfast room, 3-acre grounds (tennis, 13-metre heated swimming pool, not available to residents 1–4 pm), unsuitable for &. *Background music*: none. *Location*: 5 miles E of Penzance. *Smoking*: not allowed. *Children*: not under 5. *Dogs*: not allowed. *Credit cards*: MasterCard, Visa. *Prices*: [2008] b&b £45–£90 per person, 1-night bookings refused high season, bank holidays.

ST IVES Cornwall   Map 1:D1

Boskerris Hotel   NEW   *Tel* 01736-795295
Boskerris Road   *Email* reservations@boskerrishotel.co.uk
Carbis Bay   *Website* www.boskerrishotel.co.uk
St Ives TR26 2NQ

Owners since 2004, Jonathan and Marianne Bassett and his parents have refurbished this 1930s hotel in contemporary style. Inspectors found it 'an exceptionally friendly, low-key little place'. High above sandy Carbis Bay, a 30-minute coastal walk to town (five minutes by local train), it has panoramic ocean views and a bright white interior. Bedrooms include 'standard', 'celebration' and a family suite. 'We had one of five uniform rooms along a tiled corridor, on the floor below the lounge. Small, black wooden furnishings, TV/DVD-player, impractical glass bowl basin (water went everywhere) in a bathroom with louvre doors.' There are 'splendid views over the bay' from the big lounge with its white-painted wooden floors, 'plenty of interesting books'. At breakfast 'the buffet had freshly squeezed juice, fabulous home-made muesli, a big bowl of cut fresh fruit, newspapers on a side table. A good atmosphere, friendly service, guests talking to each other.' A new chef, Jane Collins (New Zealander), who has worked with Marco Pierre White and Michel Roux, arrived with her team as we went to press. She promises 'elegant, unfussy cooking with a hint of the Med' and much use of fresh fish. We'd like reports on the meals.

Bedrooms: 15, 1 on ground floor. *Open*: Feb–end Nov. *Facilities*: lounges, bar, restaurant, private dining/meeting room, decked terrace, 1½-acre garden. *Background music*: jazz/Latin. *Location*: 1½ miles from centre (5 mins by local train), car park. *Smoking*: not allowed. *Children*: not under 7. *Dogs*: not allowed. *Credit cards*: MasterCard, Visa. *Prices*: b&b £47.50–£112.50 per person, d,b&b £75–£130, set dinner £21–£27.50, full alc £33.50, 1-night bookings generally refused bank holidays.

Primrose Valley Hotel

Primrose Valley
Porthminster Beach
St Ives TR26 2ED

Tel/Fax 01736-794939
Email info@primroseonline.co.uk
Website www.primroseonline.co.uk

Above the Blue Flag Porthminster Beach with its popular café, this Edwardian villa has been given a striking modern interior with polished wooden floors, leather sofas, bright staircase carpets. The owners, Andrew and Sue Biss and Rose Clegg, place 'huge emphasis on sustainability': an optional £1 charge is added to the bill to go towards marine conservation initiatives; local and Fairtrade food is used; waste is recycled where possible. The bedrooms are on the first and second floors: two have a balcony. Inspectors loved their sea view, 'though our room, smartly decorated in white, was very small'. A suite has a 'ridiculously comfortable, beautiful' freestanding bath. The 'excellent' breakfast, taken at specially made walnut and oak tables, has a buffet with fresh fruit salad, fresh juices, yogurts, leaf teas, a range of cooked dishes, and it can be accompanied by champagne. All the producers are named on the menu. A range of Cornish platters and snacks is served throughout the day and evening. A therapy room (massages, facials, etc) was due to open in July 2008. The little coastal railway that links St Ives with the main line runs by the beach, 'but the single-carriage train trundles in and out with very little noise'. An easy walk to the station and the centre. More reports, please.

Bedrooms: 9. *Open*: Feb–Dec except 25/26 Dec. *Facilities*: lounge, bar, dining room, patio, Porthminster Beach 4 mins' walk, unsuitable for ♿. *Background music*: at breakfast in dining room, in bar at night. *Location*: private road, 2 mins from station, free parking (£2.50 discount if not required). *Smoking*: not allowed. *Children*: all ages welcomed in specified rooms. *Dogs*: not allowed. *Credit cards*: MasterCard, Visa. *Prices*: b&b £50–£117.50 per person, special breaks, New Year package, 1-night bookings sometimes refused.

See also SHORTLIST

ST LEONARDS-ON-SEA East Sussex   Map 2:E4

Zanzibar International Hotel
9 Eversfield Place
St Leonards-on-Sea
TN37 6BY

Tel/Fax 01424-460109
Email max@zanzibarhotel.co.uk
Website www.zanzibarhotel.co.uk

On the seafront of this South Coast seaside resort, Max O'Rourke has transformed this Victorian white-fronted town house into an exotic small B&B hotel. Bedrooms are themed, reflecting his travels and interests (hence the 'International'). South America has a Brazilian hand-carved bed and a whirlpool bath for two; Bali is small, with an in-room massage shower and steam cabin. Antarctica, on the second floor ('very relaxing'), has floor-to-ceiling bay windows facing the sea, varnished wooden floors; in its bathroom 'a sauna and shower unit with every combination of jets and sprinklers imaginable; good lighting'. Visitors are asked to phone 15 minutes before arriving: 'If I'm upstairs, I may not hear the bell,' explains Mr O'Rourke. There is an honesty bar and a conservatory. Breakfast, ordered by 9 pm the night before, is served in the bedroom or at a large table in the Grand Salon, which has sofas, newspapers and 'extravagant flowers'. It includes Buck's Fizz, freshly squeezed juices, fruit, cereals, full English and vegetarian. 'Butter and jams in pots. Excellent coffee and tea.' Help is given with reservations at local restaurants.

Bedrooms: 8, 1 on ground floor. *Open*: all year. *Facilities*: lounge, bar, breakfast room, conservatory, small garden, beach across road. *Background music*: none. *Location*: seafront, 650 yds W of Hastings pier, free parking vouchers issued. *Smoking*: not allowed. *Children*: all ages welcomed (not under 8 in 'Morocco'). *Dogs*: allowed in Bali only, not Fri–Sun, not in public rooms. *Credit cards*: MasterCard, Visa. *Prices*: [2008] b&b £49.50–£220 per person, midweek winter discounts, 1-night bookings refused weekends (£50 supplement in 'exceptional circumstances').

ST MARTIN'S Isles of Scilly   Map 1: inset C1

St Martin's on the Isle
Lower Town, St Martin's
Isles of Scilly, Cornwall
TR25 0QW

Tel 01720-422092
Fax 01720-422298
Email stay@stmartinshotel.co.uk
Website www.stmartinshotel.co.uk

By a white sandy beach on the western shore, the only hotel on this charming island was built in the style of a row of fisherman's cottages. Owned by Peter and Penny Sykes, it is managed by Keith Bradford. Inspectors in 2008 found much to praise, but had some reservations: 'Staff, without exception friendly, addressed us by name. We were greeted at the pier, luggage taken to our room.' Most of the bedrooms have sea views. 'Our large superior room had big, comfortable bed, blankets and sheets (preference asked when booking). As in most public areas, the decor was locked in 1980s style: multi-coloured curtains, toning fabrics on bedspread and chairs; bland furnishings. TV on a table, you couldn't watch it from bed or chairs. Poor soundproofing.' In the upstairs *Teän* restaurant ('lots of local paintings'), chef Kenny Atkinson gained a *Michelin* star in 2008. 'A memorable dinner. Superb cannelloni of carrot and local crab with tender scallops; splendid Scillonian pollock with lobster risotto; delicious lemon and rhubarb panna cotta with plums.' Simpler meals are served in the bar and the 'jolly' bistro (where children have high tea). Breakfast has a big buffet; 'excellent fruit salad but packaged juices; delicious hot dishes cooked to order'.

Bedrooms: 30, some on ground floor. *Open*: Apr–Oct, bistro closed Mon night. *Facilities*: ramps, lounge, lounge bar, restaurant, 11-metre indoor swimming pool, civil wedding licence, 2½-acre grounds (garden on beach, jetty, boating, diving, water sports). *Background music*: 'not normally played, it annoys our older clientele.' *Location*: N end of island, boat/helicopter to St Mary's from Penzance, or fixed-wing aircraft from several local airports in SW England, then boat to St Martin's. *Smoking*: not allowed. *Children*: no under-10s in restaurant. *Dogs*: not allowed in public rooms. *Credit cards*: all major cards. *Prices*: b&b £125–£255 per person, d,b&b £150–£280, set dinner £47.50, 10% discount for pre-paid 5-night or longer bookings.

We update the *Guide* every year. Hotels are dropped if there has been a change of owner (unless reports after the change are positive), if this year's reports are negative, or in rare cases where there has been no feedback. A lot of hotels fall by the wayside every year, and many new ones are added.

ST MARY'S Isles of Scilly   Map 1: inset C1

 Star Castle
The Garrison, St Mary's
Isles of Scilly
Cornwall TR21 0JA

Tel 01720-422317
Fax 01720-422343
Email info@star-castle.co.uk
Website www.star-castle.co.uk

César award: Island hotel of the year

In a commanding position above Hugh Town and with 'magnificent views across all the islands', this star-shaped Tudor fortress, with additional buildings in gardens, has a 'real family-run feel'. Owner Robert Francis co-manages with his son, James; their staff are 'that rare combination, professional yet friendly'. Visitors in 2008 had a 'very warm welcome'. The castle's decor is 'in keeping with the building: antique furniture, tapestries and pictures relating to its history'. The bar is the former dungeon. In the 'welcoming' dining room (white tablecloths, silver napkin rings, candles), inspectors enjoyed chef Gareth Stafford's cooking: 'An excellent five-course meal with well-paced service: carpaccio of beef; refreshing citrus granita; perfect pink rump of lamb; melting custard tart with baked figs.' Alternative dining is in a conservatory restaurant which specialises in fish. All bedrooms have been refurbished. Those in the castle are 'most attractive': interesting shapes fitted into the star-shaped walls. Rooms in the two single-storey garden wings have 'thoughtfully designed interior, crisp and modern'; many have sea views. Breakfast has a 'well-stocked buffet table with big jugs of freshly squeezed fruit juices'; fish options include 'especially good smoked haddock'. Following storm damage, the swimming pool has been upgraded. (*Sue Davies, T and M Schofield, and others*)

Bedrooms: 38, 27 in 2 garden wings. *Open*: all year except Jan. *Facilities*: lounge, bar, 2 restaurants, 3-acre grounds (covered swimming pool, 12 by 3 metres, tennis), beach nearby, golf, bicycle hire, riding, sailing, diving, fishing available, unsuitable for &. *Background music*: none. *Location*: ¼ mile from town centre, boat (2¾ hours)/helicopter (20 mins) from Penzance, air links from Newquay, Exeter, Bristol. *Smoking*: not allowed. *Children*: all ages welcomed. *Dogs*: not allowed in restaurants. *Credit cards*: Amex, MasterCard, Visa. *Prices*: [2008] d,b&b £65–£164 per person, Christmas/New Year packages.

We asked hotels to quote their 2009 tariffs. Many had yet to fix these rates as we went to press. Prices should always be checked on booking.

ST MAWES Cornwall   Map 1:E2

Tresanton
27 Lower Castle Road
St Mawes TR2 5DR

Tel 01326-270055
Fax 01326-270053
Email info@tresanton.com
Website www.tresanton.com

César award: Luxury hotel of the year

'Self-assured, elegant; super food; well managed.' Praise in 2008 for
Olga Polizzi's 'stunning', luxurious yet informal hotel (managed by
Federica Bertolini) on the edge of this seaside village. Other comments: 'She shows how to combine the best of the old and new,
blowing away tired, stuffy ideas while retaining the elements that
make a guest feel special. Her smiling staff are cheerful and bright.'
'Without going over the top, they made us feel at home.' Set
'incomparably' amid terraced subtropical gardens, the cluster of old
houses looks across a narrow promenade to the Fal estuary. Inside are
'subtle marine shades'. Most bedrooms have sea views; the best are
big. Meals can be taken alfresco on the terrace ('like being on a ship's
deck') or in the restaurant with its 'wonderful' white mosaic floor and
white-topped tables close together: at busy times guests may be
'cheek by jowl when rain forces them inside'. Paul Wadham's short
daily-changing menu is 'simply delicious, avoiding richness –
important if you dine several consecutive nights'. The informal dress
code is appreciated. Children have a games room, special menus, etc.
'Good breakfast: fruit, croissants, cooked dishes.' 'Expensive, but
so carefully run I didn't begrudge a penny.' Mrs Polizzi also owns
Hotel Endsleigh, Milton Abbot (*qv*). (*Cynthia Oakes, Alastair Kameen,
JR Bright, and others*)

Bedrooms: 29, some in 3 annexes. *Open*: all year, except 4–15 Jan. *Facilities*:
2 lounges, bar, restaurant, cinema, playroom, conference facilities, civil
wedding licence, terrace, ¼-acre garden, by sea (shingle beach, safe bathing,
15-metre yacht), unsuitable for &. *Background music*: none. *Location*: on seafront, valet parking (car park up hill). *Smoking*: not allowed. *Children*: all ages
welcomed. *Dogs*: allowed in 2 bedrooms, not in public rooms. *Credit cards*:
Amex, MasterCard, Visa. *Prices*: b&b £92.50–£230 per person, set dinner
£42, special breaks, Christmas/New Year packages, 1-night bookings
refused weekends.

We say 'Unsuitable for &' when a hotel tells us that it cannot
accommodate wheelchair-users.

SALCOMBE Devon   Map 1:E4

The Tides Reach   *Tel* 01548-843466
South Sands   *Fax* 01548-843954
Salcombe TQ8 8LJ   *Email* enquire@tidesreach.com
                                       Website www.tidesreach.com

'I was impressed that the *maître d'* remembered my name within hours of my arrival,' says a visitor who enjoyed her stay at the Edwards family's traditional seaside hotel on the south Devon coast. Well situated for safe bathing and water sports, the 'functional' 1960s building, which faces south across Salcombe estuary, has angular balconies, and bright blue awnings against white-painted walls. 'My nice dual-aspect room had good views.' Most bedrooms have big windows that face the sheltered garden where summer visitors take snack lunches (soups, sandwiches, kedgeree, etc) by a large duck pond. Colours are bright. There is a small sea-water aquarium in the bar. In the dining room (sea views from some tables) the chef, Finn Ibsen, serves modern and traditional dishes, eg, chargrilled yellow-fin tuna steak; roast rack of Dartmoor lamb. 'Meals were good, starters and puddings were slightly better than main courses where plates tended to be hotter than the food.' Dress required for dinner is 'smart casual'. The swimming pool is in an 'exotic conservatory' which opens to the outside on fine days. There is easy access to the Coast Path. (*Andrea Newman, and others*)

Bedrooms: 32. *Open*: Feb–Nov. *Facilities*: lift, ramps, 3 lounges, 2 bars, restaurant, leisure centre (indoor swimming pool (13 by 6 metres), gym, games room, beauty treatments), ½-acre grounds (pond), sandy beach 10 yds, unsuitable for ♿. *Background music*: none. *Location*: on Salcombe estuary, 1 mile from town. *Smoking*: not allowed. *Children*: not under 8. *Dogs*: allowed in bedrooms, 1 lounge. *Credit cards*: all major cards. *Prices*: [2008] b&b £52–£123 per person, d,b&b £62–£143, set dinner £35, 1-night bookings sometimes refused. *V*

SALISBURY Wiltshire   Map 2:D2
See SHORTLIST

SCARBOROUGH North Yorkshire   Map 4:C5
See SHORTLIST

SCOTBY Cumbria   Map 4:B2

Willowbeck Lodge   *Tel* 01228-513607
Lambley Bank   *Fax* 01228-501053
Scotby, nr Carlisle CA4 8BX   *Email* info@willowbeck-lodge.com
                                     Website www.willowbeck-lodge.com

'A B&B of outstanding class in a delightful situation.' John and Liz
McGrillis's architect-designed house stands by a large pond amid
peaceful woodland with birdlife, in a village near Carlisle. Built in
bright, modern Scandinavian style, it has a large lounge with soaring
ceiling, huge window, gallery and wood-burning stove. 'Everything is
new and fully functioning,' says a 'smitten' visitor this year. 'Liz is an
excellent chef; he is the genial general factotum.' Bedrooms have
'plenty of hanging space, comfortable easy chairs', flat-screen
television set, 'good-quality bedlinen, efficient shower'. Bathrooms
are 'superbly fitted': 'Separate shower, not a shower curtain in sight.'
There are 'high-speed Internet connections throughout'. The three-
course dinner is served by arrangement, menu agreed in consultation,
perhaps roasted butternut squash soup with honey; fresh salmon
marinated in lime juice with Cajun spices. Breakfast, ordered the
night before, has home-made bread and Greek yogurt, free-range
scrambled eggs, Craster kippers. 'If the juice you want isn't out, just
ask,' says the menu. (*Peter and Kay Rogers, N and RW*)

Bedrooms: 6, 2 in annexe. *Open*: all year. *Facilities*: lounge, lounge/dining room,
conference/function facilities, 1½-acre garden (stream, pond), unsuitable for
&. *Background music*: 'when guests choose'. *Location*: 2½ miles E of Carlisle.
Smoking: not allowed. *Children*: not under 12. *Dogs*: not allowed. *Credit cards*:
Amex, MasterCard. *Prices*: [2008] b&b £50–£110 per person, set dinner £30.

SEAVIEW Isle of Wight   Map 2:E3

The Seaview   *Tel* 01983-612711
High Street   *Fax* 01983-613729
Seaview PO34 5EX   *Email* reception@seaviewhotel.co.uk
                                     Website www.seaviewhotel.co.uk

Near the sea, in a 'delightful little village', this 'well-run' hotel/
restaurant was recently renovated by owner Brian Gardener; the
manager is the 'courteous' Andrew Morgan. Inspectors found much
to praise: 'We liked the flexible eating arrangements and the friendly
local waitresses. When there were problems, they took immediate

action.' 'Charming' public rooms are filled with nautical memorabilia, and there is free Wi-Fi. Meals are served in two restaurant rooms (one intimate, the other larger, with a conservatory) or informally in the bars. Chef Graham Walker's modern cooking is enjoyed, eg, grilled pollock, crab risotto, black olive and tomato dressing, herb foam. 'Service by delightful local girls. Very busy with locals and yachties.' In the bedrooms are seagrass carpets, luxurious fabrics. A large ground-floor room was 'spruce, quiet, light; sheets and blankets on bed; flat-screen TV/DVD-player; table and chairs on a terrace by the pretty garden'. Some new rooms are in the adjacent *Seaview Modern*. At breakfast, 'a helpful lady presided, pouring lashings of fresh orange juice. Good buffet (cereals, fruit, etc). Porridge and succulent kippers on the menu. Nothing packaged.' Children are welcomed. 'You can walk for miles by the seashore: the path starts at the bottom of the road.' (*Fredina Minshall, and others*)

Bedrooms: 27, 7 in annexe, 4 on ground floor, 1 suitable for &. *Open*: all year. *Facilities*: lift, ramps, lounge, 2 bars, 2 dining rooms, function room, patio, access to local sports club (swimming pool, gym, tennis, etc). *Background music*: none. *Location*: village centre. *Smoking*: not allowed. *Children*: all ages welcomed. *Dogs*: not allowed in bedrooms. *Credit cards*: all major cards. *Prices*: b&b £60–£199 per person, d,b&b £90–£230, full alc £35, Christmas/New Year packages, 1-night bookings refused weekends.

SHAFTESBURY Dorset   Map 2:D1

La Fleur de Lys   NEW

Bleke Street
Shaftesbury SP7 8AW

Tel 01747-853717
Fax 01747-853130
Email info@lafleurdelys.co.uk
Website www.lafleurdelys.co.uk

'Wholeheartedly recommended' this year, this restaurant-with-rooms in this charming old town is run with 'dedicated staff' by owners David Shepherd, Mary Griffin and Marc Preston (they moved it here in 2003 after 13 years in other premises). 'It offers excellent food by David, who loves to chat, and a warm welcome from Mary, who seems to run everything.' She is a cat enthusiast, and cat ornaments are everywhere. There is a comfortable lounge with sofas and armchairs. In the 'immaculate' bedrooms (each named after a wine grape, chardonnay, merlot, etc) are a fridge, Internet access and 'delicious home-baked biscuits'. One room is suitable for a family (a cot can be provided). In the smart dining room, modern English dishes include breast of guinea fowl with bacon and wild mushrooms and a tarragon sauce; apricot crème brûlée with ginger biscuits. The 'excellent' breakfast has fresh orange juice, porridge, butter and marmalade in pots. Afternoon tea and pre-dinner drinks can be served in the courtyard. The entrance to the car park is narrow. (*Kay and Peter Rogers*)

Bedrooms: 7, some on ground floor. *Open*: all year, restaurant closed Sun night, midday Mon and Tues. *Facilities*: lounge, bar, dining room, conference room, small courtyard. *Background music*: none. *Location*: edge of centre, car park. *Smoking*: not allowed. *Children*: all ages welcomed. *Dogs*: not allowed. *Credit cards*: Amex, MasterCard, Visa. *Prices*: b&b £50–£95 per person, set menus £25–£30, full alc £45, Christmas/New Year packages.

SHANKLIN Isle of Wight   Map 2:E2

Rylstone Manor   *Tel/Fax* 01983-862806
Rylstone Gardens   *Email* rylstone.manor@btinternet.com
Popham Road, Shanklin   *Website* www.rylstone-manor.co.uk
PO37 6RG

In 'glorious' parkland gardens, this Victorian country house is done in a blend of Gothic, Tudor and Georgian styles. The 'charming' owners, Mike and Carole Hailston, who took over in 2006, have revamped two bedrooms and redecorated the dining room. 'We inherited a loyal clientele, so have made only subtle changes,' they say. 'All needs are catered for,' writes one satisfied fan. The bedrooms, named after English trees (Beech, Oak, Yew, Maple, etc), vary in size; all mattresses are new this year. A four-poster bed has 'beautiful lacy linen and attractive bedding'. The green-walled lounge has books and ornaments; there is a 'nice Victorian-style covered patio', with basket chairs and magazines. The food has been upgraded. Mr Hailston is the chef; he serves traditional meals on a daily-changing menu in the candlelit dining room, perhaps seafood platter with a balsamic dressing; roast sirloin of beef with a Stilton and Madeira jus. The simple wine list is 'fairly priced'. From the garden, guests have direct access to beaches via steep cliff steps. (*LB*)

Bedrooms: 9. *Open*: all year except early Jan. *Facilities*: drawing room, bar lounge, dining room, terrace, 1-acre garden in 4-acre public gardens, direct access to sand/shingle beach, unsuitable for &. *Background music*: classical, 'easy listening', in bar, restaurant. *Location*: Shanklin old village. *Smoking*: not allowed. *Children*: not allowed. *Dogs*: not allowed. *Credit cards*: Amex, MasterCard, Visa. *Prices*: [2008] b&b £55–£62.50 per person, d,b&b £75–£82.50, set dinner £23. 1-night bookings refused 'when busy', 3-night min. June–Sept. *V*

SHEFFIELD South Yorkshire   Map 4:E4
See SHORTLIST

SHIPSTON-ON-STOUR Warwickshire Map 3:D6
See SHORTLIST

SHIPTON GORGE Dorset   Map 1:C6

Innsacre Farmhouse   *Tel* 07506-728198
Shipton Gorge   *Email* innsacre.farmhouse@btinternet.com
Bridport DT6 4LJ   *Website* www.innsacre.com

'Idyllically' set in a small valley of fields, orchard and woodland, this
17th-century farmhouse is run in 'highly individual' style by Sydney
and Jayne Davies. 'Charming and welcoming' owners, they have
long been committed to green policies. They have their own water
supply, and they recycle and compost as much as possible. 'He is an
interesting host with a wry sense of humour. She is welcoming, not
intrusive, and a sound cook.' One couple this year found the decor
'depressing, with its dark colours; our small bedroom and bathroom,
dark blue, had dark brown towels'. Earlier visitors enjoyed 'lots of
hot water and bath luxuries including a head rest; blissful after a day
tramping the hills'. All the bedrooms are on the first floor (no lift).
The downstairs area has now been made more spacious, and given
new lighting and soft furnishings. 'Congenial pre-dinner drinks' are
taken in comfortable chairs around a large fireplace. A three-course
no-choice dinner is served, by arrangement, at 8 pm. Modern dishes
include rice cake with sun-dried tomato dressing; roast pork with
rosemary mashed potato. 'Sydney takes his wines seriously.
Helpings are generous. Thankfully no muzak.' The 'brilliant'
breakfast has a 'daily goody', and 'superb fruit compote'. Visitors
should not check in before 4.30 pm.

Bedrooms: 4. *Open*: all year except Christmas/New Year, 5 weeks mid-Sept–mid-
Oct, dining room closed midday, and Sat. *Facilities*: lounge/bar, dining area, 22-
acre grounds (nature trail), shingle/sand beach nearby, unsuitable for &.
Background music: none. *Location*: 1½ miles SE of Bridport. *Smoking*: not allowed.
Children: not under 10. *Dogs*: not allowed unattended in bedrooms. *Credit cards*:
MasterCard, Visa. *Prices*: [2008] b&b £45–£57.50 per person, d,b&b £22.50
added, 1-night bookings refused weekends/bank holidays.

THE GOOD HOTEL GUIDE 2009

Use this voucher to claim a 25% discount off the normal price for bed and breakfast at hotels with a ***V*** sign at the end of their entry. **You must request a voucher discount at the time of booking and present this voucher on arrival. Further details and conditions overleaf.** Valid to 6th October 2009.

THE GOOD HOTEL GUIDE 2009

Use this voucher to claim a 25% discount off the normal price for bed and breakfast at hotels with a ***V*** sign at the end of their entry. **You must request a voucher discount at the time of booking and present this voucher on arrival. Further details and conditions overleaf.** Valid to 6th October 2009.

THE GOOD HOTEL GUIDE 2009

Use this voucher to claim a 25% discount off the normal price for bed and breakfast at hotels with a ***V*** sign at the end of their entry. **You must request a voucher discount at the time of booking and present this voucher on arrival. Further details and conditions overleaf.** Valid to 6th October 2009.

THE GOOD HOTEL GUIDE 2009

Use this voucher to claim a 25% discount off the normal price for bed and breakfast at hotels with a ***V*** sign at the end of their entry. **You must request a voucher discount at the time of booking and present this voucher on arrival. Further details and conditions overleaf.** Valid to 6th October 2009.

THE GOOD HOTEL GUIDE 2009

Use this voucher to claim a 25% discount off the normal price for bed and breakfast at hotels with a ***V*** sign at the end of their entry. **You must request a voucher discount at the time of booking and present this voucher on arrival. Further details and conditions overleaf.** Valid to 6th October 2009.

THE GOOD HOTEL GUIDE 2009

Use this voucher to claim a 25% discount off the normal price for bed and breakfast at hotels with a ***V*** sign at the end of their entry. **You must request a voucher discount at the time of booking and present this voucher on arrival. Further details and conditions overleaf.** Valid to 6th October 2009.

1. Hotels with a *V* have agreed to give readers a discount of 25% off their normal bed-and-breakfast rate.
2. One voucher is good for a single-night stay only, at the discounted rate for yourself alone or for you and a partner sharing a double room.
3. Hotels may decline to accept a voucher reservation if they expect to be fully booked at the full room price.

CONDITIONS

- -

1. Hotels with a *V* have agreed to give readers a discount of 25% off their normal bed-and-breakfast rate.
2. One voucher is good for a single-night stay only, at the discounted rate for yourself alone or for you and a partner sharing a double room.
3. Hotels may decline to accept a voucher reservation if they expect to be fully booked at the full room price.

CONDITIONS

- -

1. Hotels with a *V* have agreed to give readers a discount of 25% off their normal bed-and-breakfast rate.
2. One voucher is good for a single-night stay only, at the discounted rate for yourself alone or for you and a partner sharing a double room.
3. Hotels may decline to accept a voucher reservation if they expect to be fully booked at the full room price.

CONDITIONS

- -

1. Hotels with a *V* have agreed to give readers a discount of 25% off their normal bed-and-breakfast rate.
2. One voucher is good for a single-night stay only, at the discounted rate for yourself alone or for you and a partner sharing a double room.
3. Hotels may decline to accept a voucher reservation if they expect to be fully booked at the full room price.

CONDITIONS

- -

1. Hotels with a *V* have agreed to give readers a discount of 25% off their normal bed-and-breakfast rate.
2. One voucher is good for a single-night stay only, at the discounted rate for yourself alone or for you and a partner sharing a double room.
3. Hotels may decline to accept a voucher reservation if they expect to be fully booked at the full room price.

CONDITIONS

- -

1. Hotels with a *V* have agreed to give readers a discount of 25% off their normal bed-and-breakfast rate.
2. One voucher is good for a single-night stay only, at the discounted rate for yourself alone or for you and a partner sharing a double room.
3. Hotels may decline to accept a voucher reservation if they expect to be fully booked at the full room price.

CONDITIONS

SHREWSBURY Shropshire   Map 3:B4
See SHORTLIST

SIDMOUTH Devon *See SHORTLIST*   Map 1:C5

SNETTISHAM Norfolk   Map 2:A4

The Rose & Crown   *Tel* 01485-541382
Old Church Road, Snettisham   *Fax* 01485-543172
nr King's Lynn   *Email* info@roseandcrownsnettisham.co.uk
PE31 7LX   *Website* www.roseandcrownsnettisham.co.uk

'A lovely old country pub in a pleasant Norfolk village': Jeannette and Anthony Goodrich's 'superbly located' 14th-century inn has twisting passages, hidden corners, low ceilings and old beams. Kim Tinkler is the 'excellent, hands-on' manageress. Residents have their own lounge 'with log fire, comfortable seating'; there are three bars and three dining areas, 'elegant' and contemporary. Chef Keith McDowell's cooking was praised by visitors in 2008: 'Delicious baked Portobello mushroom rarebit on toasted brioche; main course of seafood chowder and julienne of vegetables. The staff were delightful.' Older bedrooms have been upgraded in the contemporary style of the five newer rooms. 'Our stylish room had white with touches of bright blue, good lighting and excellent furnishings; a good-sized bath and efficient power shower. Information folder the best I've seen.' A smaller room was 'fine and well equipped'. A room above the kitchen has been given air conditioning and improved soundproofing. 'Breakfast was first-rate, plenty of fresh fruit, particularly good scrambled eggs and smoked salmon.' There is free wireless broadband access throughout. The walled garden, once the village bowling green, has herbaceous borders and two large willow trees. (*Michael and Eithne Dandy, Louisa Davies, Mary Hewson*)

Bedrooms: 16, 2 suitable for ♿. *Open*: all year. *Facilities*: ramp, garden room with guests' seating area, lounge, 3 bars, 3 dining areas, large walled garden (play fort, barbecue, heat lamps), beaches 5 and 10 mins' drive, golf, birdwatching nearby. *Background music*: none. *Location*: 4 miles S of Hunstanton. *Smoking*: not allowed. *Children*: all ages welcomed. *Dogs*: allowed. *Credit cards*: MasterCard, Visa. *Prices*: [2008] b&b £45–£90 per person, full alc £35, Christmas/New Year packages. *V*

SOAR MILL COVE Devon   Map 1:E4

Soar Mill Cove Hotel   *Tel* 01548-561566
Soar Mill Cove   *Fax* 01548-561223
nr Salcombe TQ7 3DS   *Email* info@soarmillcove.co.uk
                                Website www.soarmillcove.co.uk

'Spectacularly set' on National Trust land leading to an isolated cove,
this purpose-built stone and slate single-storey hotel is popular with
families in summer, and older visitors off-season. 'Guests of all ages
(one to 80) are equally well catered for,' says a fan (one of many regu-
lars). The owner, Keith Makepeace, leads an 'exceedingly helpful'
staff. The building is 'no beauty', but recent refurbishment has made
the lounge 'light and bright: though it has more seating, it seems
larger'. The decor of the champagne bar (black velvet, gold walls,
black and red leather seats) evokes 'mixed feelings'. The formal
Serendipity restaurant has 'wonderful views' through a picture window. Chef Ian MacDonald's cooking is generally enjoyed (portions
are large): 'First courses light and well flavoured; lamb always
excellent; really fresh fish.' *Castaways*, a coffee bar, is 'for muddy paws
and boots and younger guests'. Breakfast has good choice, including
fruit salad and 'beautiful' marmalade. Soundproofing may not be
perfect in the bedrooms, which vary in size; all open on to a terrace.
For children there are small swimming pools, play areas, activity
packs. 'Colourful garden. Deer and pheasants came to the field.'
'Glorious coastal walks' from the door. (*Margaret Box, and others*)

Bedrooms: 22, all on ground floor. *Open*: Dec–Oct. *Facilities*: lounge, 2 bars,
restaurant (pianist), coffee shop, indoor swimming pool (10 by 6 metres),
treatment room (hairdressing, reflexology, aromatherapy, etc), free Internet
access, 10-acre grounds (swimming pool, 10 by 7 metres, tennis, putting, children's play area, jogging trail), sea, sandy beach, 600 yds. *Background music*:
occasional. *Location*: 3 miles SW of Salcombe. *Smoking*: not allowed. *Children*:
all ages welcomed. *Dogs*: well-behaved small dogs allowed, but not in public
rooms. *Credit cards*: MasterCard, Visa. *Prices*: [2008] b&b £39.50–£193 per
person, d,b&b £74.50–£233, set dinner £50, Christmas/New Year packages,
1-night bookings sometimes refused high season. *V*

****

   Traveller's tale *Hotel in Scotland* We arrived on a cold
   afternoon to find that our room was cold and the heating was
   not due to come on for some time. We sat and shivered until,
   after two phone calls, an electric heater was brought.

****

SOMERTON Somerset   Map 1:C6

The Lynch Country House
4 Behind Berry
Somerton TA11 7PD

Tel 01458-272316
Fax 01458-272590
Email the_lynch@talk21.com
Website www.thelynchcountryhouse.co.uk

In a small town above the Cary valley, this Grade II listed Regency house is a 'superior, stylish B&B' run by its owner, the 'interesting' Roy Copeland, a former jazz musician. In his absence, guests are welcomed with 'quiet, unassuming friendliness' by his manager, Dave Williamson. In the main house, one couple had a 'good-sized room with high ceilings, practical but pleasant furniture, restful colour scheme, beautiful views'. Some rooms have a four-poster. Smaller bedrooms are under the eaves. Four other rooms are in a single-storey coach house. At the top of the house, a little observatory (with telescope) gives wide views. Breakfast is served in the 'attractive, bright' orangery with tall windows overlooking a lake with fish, black swans and exotic ducks. 'A delight: no struggles with butter papers, no fingernails broken when opening foil covers; toast of the right thickness. We were encouraged to explore, and could have picnicked in the garden had we wished.' 'Our small dog was made most welcome.' Advice is given, with menus, on where to dine. 2,800 trees have been planted around the house to create a wildlife sanctuary. Somerton's church is worth visiting. (*PK, and others*)

Bedrooms: 9, 4 in coach house, 4 on ground floor. *Open*: all year except 31 Dec. *Facilities*: breakfast room, small sitting area, 2½-acre grounds (lake), unsuitable for &. *Background music*: none. *Location*: N edge of village. *Smoking*: not allowed. *Children*: all ages welcomed. *Dogs*: allowed. *Credit cards*: all major cards. *Prices*: b&b £35–£65 per person.

SOUTH ZEAL Devon   Map 1:C4

The Oxenham Arms   **NEW**
South Zeal
EX20 2JT

Tel 01837-840244
Fax 01837-840791
Email theoxenhamarms@aol.com
Website www.theoxenhamarms.co.uk

In April 2007, Mark Payne, who previously worked for four years at the *Royal Crescent Hotel* in Bath, took over this historic ivy-clad inn (first licensed in 1477), a scheduled ancient monument in a hamlet near Okehampton. He arrived with manager Richard Huxtable and chef Carol Eagles. Her 'excellent' rustic British contemporary cook-ing has rapidly established a good name in the area, says the nominator. 'They were very busy over Easter.' The building has been completely refurbished (new carpets, curtains, etc) by its 'enthusi-astic owner', with 'remarkable attention to detail'. In the 'very well-appointed' bedrooms, new beds include three four-posters; up-to-date touches include a modem connection. There are mullioned windows, a beamed and panelled bar, a small lounge with a monolith set in its wall, and a main lounge with a large granite fireplace. In the restaurant, the menus have plenty of choice including, perhaps, chicken liver parfait with gooseberry chutney; Mediterranean fish stew. The garden has 'lovely views'. (*Jane Evans*)

Bedrooms: 7. *Open*: all year. *Facilities*: Sitting area, bar, 2 dining rooms, terrace, large garden, unsuitable for &. *Background music*: classical/soul/blues. *Location*: village centre, off A30 Exeter–Okehampton. *Smoking*: not allowed. *Children*: all ages welcomed. *Dogs*: not allowed in restaurant, some bedrooms. *Credit cards*: Amex, MasterCard, Visa. *Prices*: b&b £52.50–£100 per person, full alc £28, Christmas/New Year packages.

SOUTHWOLD Suffolk   Map 2:B6
See SHORTLIST

STADDLEBRIDGE North Yorkshire   Map 4:C4

McCoy's at the Tontine   NEW   *Tel* 01609-882671
The Cleveland Tontine   *Fax* 01609-882660
Staddlebridge   *Email* enquiries@mccoystontine.co.uk
Northallerton DL6 3JB   *Website* www.mccoystontine.co.uk

César award in 1989

Following warm commendations, this 'shamelessly eccentric' restaurant-with-rooms, a northern institution long owned by the McCoy brothers, Tom and Eugene, returns to the *Guide* after a time with no reports. 'Dark panelled corridors, a giant fireplace by Vanbrugh in his grimmest mood, all offset by smiling staff (young and old) and the best côte de boeuf I've had this side of the Channel.' An earlier comment: 'Good fun; comfortable rather than smart.' The candlelit bistro ('slightly subterranean'), made lighter by huge mirrors, has a blackboard menu and closely packed tables. Head chef Stuart Hawkins's eclectic menu includes 'luscious fresh foie gras and brioche; syrupy ginger pudding, served with obvious good will'. Bedrooms have vibrant colours, bright soft furnishings. 'Mine had dark blue William Morris-type wallpaper with iridescent pink flowers and columns of pink and green leaves; a deep raspberry ceiling. Nothing so mundane as tea-making facilities and Internet connection.' 'A fabulous, cavernous bath.' 'Delicious breakfast in a lovely room with huge windows facing the garden.' 'Asked if I could breakfast at 10 am; they gave me the kitchen's number and said: "Ring when you're ready." Heaven!' The stone Victorian house occupies a triangular site between the A19 and a slip road on the edge of the North Yorkshire moors (windows are double glazed). (*Freddie Stockdale, Sue Davies*)

Bedrooms: 6. *Open*: all year except 25/26 Dec, 1/2 Jan. *Facilities*: 2 lounges (residents only), breakfast room, bar, bistro, function rooms, unsuitable for &. *Background music*: 'eclectic'. *Location*: 6 miles NE of Northallerton, at junction of A19/A172. *Smoking*: not allowed. *Children*: all ages welcomed. *Dogs*: not allowed in public rooms. *Credit cards*: all major cards. *Prices*: b&b B £60–£95 per person, set lunch from £14.95, full alc £45, 3-night d,b&b package.

STAMFORD Lincolnshire   Map 2:B3

The George   *Tel* 01780-750750
71 St Martins   *Fax* 01780-750701
Stamford   *Email* reservations@georgehotelofstamford.com
PE9 2LB   *Website* www.georgehotelofstamford.com

♥ *César award in 1986*

'One of my favourites for 40 years; standards are always consistent.' An endorsement this year for Lawrence Hoskins's 16th-century coaching inn in the centre of this unspoiled market town. Another visitor wrote of its 'sterling qualities and excellent staff'. An inspector agreed: 'Well run. It takes trouble with its guests. Good value.' The public rooms ('always busy') have log fires, mullioned windows, antique panelling, creaking floorboards, good flower arrangements. There is a 'nice courtyard with plants', where meals are served on warm days, and a pretty walled garden. 'In the bar I lunched on a good range of sandwiches, promptly served, with excellent coffee.' In the formal, oak-panelled restaurant, where men are asked to wear a jacket or a tie at night, the 'essentially traditional' menu might include terrine of ham hock, black pudding; sirloin of beef roasted rare to medium, carved at the table. The *Garden Lounge* serves less formal meals and breakfast ('good service and choice; good cooked dishes'). A courtyard bedroom 'nicely furnished, modern, clean, comfortable, had space for everything; well-equipped bathroom with power shower *and* bath. Morning tea came on time, with freshly squeezed orange juice.' The car park has been extended this year. (*Dr Margaret West, and others*)

Bedrooms: 47. *Open*: all year. *Facilities*: ramps, 2 lounges, 2 bars, 2 restaurants, 4 private dining rooms, business centre, 2-acre grounds (courtyard, herb garden, monastery garden, croquet), unsuitable for &. *Background music*: none. *Location*: ½ mile from centre (front windows double glazed). *Smoking*: not allowed. *Children*: all ages welcomed. *Dogs*: allowed, but not unattended in bedrooms, only guide dogs in restaurant. *Credit cards*: all major cards. *Prices*: [2008] b&b £65–£135 per person, full alc £50, Christmas/New Year packages, 1-night bookings refused Sat.

STANSTED Essex *See SHORTLIST*   Map 2:C4

STANTON WICK Somerset   Map 1:B6

The Carpenters Arms
Stanton Wick, nr Pensford
BS39 4BX

Tel 01761-490202
Fax 01761-490763
Email carpenters@buccaneer.co.uk
Website www.the-carpenters-arms.co.uk

Converted from a row of miners' cottages in a hamlet near Bristol and Bath, this small hotel/pub is recommended for its 'friendly' public bar and busy restaurant. The manager, Simon Pledge, is 'most attentive', said visitors who had 'an excellent night's stay'. The modern bedrooms have lights with dimmer, a large TV, Wi-Fi and a 'well-equipped bathroom'. Food was 'good and plentiful', on a traditional menu, eg, chicken Caesar salad followed by steak, kidney and ale pie. 'Wines were reasonably priced and very acceptable.' Real ales are available. Generous breakfasts include fresh orange juice, fruit, full English. Meals are served on the large landscaped patio in fine weather. Guests' cars are locked in a yard at night, 'though it hardly seems necessary on such a quiet country road'. Children under 12 stay free in their parents' room. (*JW*)

Bedrooms: 12. *Open*: all year except Dec 25/26 at night. *Facilities*: bar, 2 restaurants, function room, patio, unsuitable for &. *Background music*: none. *Location*: 7 miles S of Bristol, 8 W of Bath. *Smoking*: not allowed. *Children*: all ages welcomed. *Dogs*: allowed in bar and on patio only. *Credit cards*: all major cards. *Prices*: [2008] b&b £52.50–£72.50 per person, d,b&b (min. 2 nights) £22.50 added, alc £30.

STOKE CANON Devon
See SHORTLIST

Map 1:C5

STOKE FLEMING Devon

Map 1:D4

Stoke Lodge
Cinders Lane
Stoke Fleming
TQ6 0RA

Tel 01803-770523
Fax 01803-770851
Email mail@stokelodge.co.uk
Website www.stokelodge.co.uk

'Good value in a relatively expensive area', this white, south-facing traditional hotel stands on the south Devon coast near Dartmouth. The Mayer family owners, says a recent visitor, 'are all pleasant, kindly and helpful. Everywhere is warm, clean and cosy. Our good-sized bedroom with lovely sea view (extra charge) had ample storage space, good lighting, wide, comfortable beds (one made with duvet, the other with blankets, as we had requested).' The lounges have 'plenty of squashy sofas and chairs, plus tables for bridge, etc'. The bar is 'very elegant', in dark green. In the 'very pleasant' grounds are gardens, lawns, wooded areas, a pond with ducks, a swimming pool surrounded by loungers, a giant chess set and a tennis court. The chef, Paul Howard, serves a four-course *table d'hôte*, daily-changing dinner menu (sample dishes: Stilton field mushrooms; Blackawton sirloin beef with Yorkshire pudding). We would welcome reports on his cooking. Breakfasts have a good buffet of fruits, cereals, etc. Cream teas are served, on the lawn in fine weather. 'Staff are cheerful and anxious to please. High standards.' (*MW*)

Bedrooms: 26. *Open*: all year. *Facilities*: 2 lounges, bar, restaurant, games room, snooker room, indoor swimming pool (sauna, whirlpool), 3-acre garden (heated swimming pool, 5 by 10 metres, tennis), unsuitable for &. *Background music*: in restaurant. *Location*: 2 miles E of Stoke Fleming, on coast, 2 miles S of Dartmouth. *Smoking*: not allowed. *Children*: all ages welcomed. *Dogs*: not allowed in public rooms. *Credit cards*: MasterCard, Visa. *Prices*: b&b £46–£71 per person, d,b&b £68–£94, set dinner £27.50, full alc £35. ***V***

We say 'Unsuitable for &' when a hotel tells us that it cannot accommodate wheelchair-users. We do not have the resources to inspect such facilities or to assess the even more complicated matter of facilities for the partially disabled. We suggest that you discuss such details with the hotel.

STUCKTON Hampshire   Map 2:E2

The Three Lions Inn
Stuckton, nr Fordingbridge
SP6 2HF

Tel 01425-652489
Fax 01425-656144
Email the3lions@btinternet.com
Website www.thethreelionsrestaurant.co.uk

Mike Womersley, the chef, and his wife, Jayne, 'charming, very
switched on', are the 'very friendly' owners of this restaurant-with-
rooms in a quiet setting on the edge of the New Forest national
park. 'A most pleasant place,' say visitors this year. Earlier,
inspectors were greeted in the car park by Mr Womersley: 'Clad in
his whites, he carried our bags to our chalet-style "superior" annexe
room, high-ceilinged, light, fresh, with creamy yellow walls, sand-
coloured carpet, shot silk patterned curtains in orange and gold. A
French door opened on to the attractive garden (with hot tub and
sauna). Everything looked loved and cared for.' Some ground-floor
rooms 'provide easy access for the less mobile'. Free Wi-Fi is
available. The main building has a bar, small lounge area and
conservatory. No printed menus; you order from a portable
blackboard. 'Tables gleamed with good glassware and cutlery. The
food was exceptional, we could not fault the quality of any dish.'
(They include sautéed scallops and shrimps; roast quail and
chanterelle mushrooms.) The 'first-class' continental breakfast,
included in the price, has fruit, cereals, 'good croissants, delicious
coffee'; full English ('one of the best ever') costs £7.50. Children are
welcomed. (*John and Penny Wheeler, and others*)

Bedrooms: 7, 4 in courtyard block on ground floor. *Open*: all year except last
2 weeks Feb, restaurant closed Sun night/Mon. *Facilities*: ramps, conservatory,
meeting/sitting room, public bar, restaurant, 2½-acre garden (sauna, whirlpool). *Background music*: in bar. *Location*: 1 mile E of Fordingbridge. *Smoking*:
not allowed. *Children*: all ages welcomed. *Dogs*: not allowed in bar, restaurant.
Credit cards: MasterCard, Visa. *Prices*: b&b £40–£79 per person, cooked
breakfast £7.50, set lunch £19.75, full alc £43, special breaks. *V*

Readers' contributions, written on the forms at the back of the
book or sent by email, are the lifeblood of the *Good Hotel Guide*.
Our readers play a crucial role by reporting on existing entries
as well as recommending new discoveries. Everyone who
writes to the *Guide* is a potential winner of the Report of the
Year competition (page 63), in which a dozen correspondents
each year win a copy of the *Guide* and an invitation to our
annual launch party in October.

STURMINSTER NEWTON Dorset   Map 2:E1

Plumber Manor   *Tel* 01258-472507
Sturminster Newton DT10 2AF   *Fax* 01258-473370
                            Email book@plumbermanor.com
                            Website www.plumbermanor.com

César award in 1987

'The building and setting are really lovely,' writes a visitor to this
early 17th-century manor house (Pride of Britain), which Richard
Prideaux-Brune, his wife, Alison, and brother, Brian (the chef), have
run for many years as a restaurant-with-rooms (the family have owned
it since it was built). Set in parkland with a small river running
through, it is surrounded by manicured lawns and herbaceous borders. Inside are antiques, contemporary art, open fires in bar and
dining rooms in winter. Bedrooms in the main house lead off a gallery
hung with family portraits. The best rooms are in a converted barn:
'Large and pretty in a chintzy sort of way if a little dated; an avocado
suite in the bathroom.' Dinner, served in three rooms, was 'excellent:
plenty of choice, good ingredients nicely cooked'. Cooking is on the
traditional side, eg, lemon sole with grapes and white wine. At breakfast (no menu) 'nice strawberries and grapes, small boxes of cereal,
good marmalade, well-cooked English breakfast, but the only juice
was orange'. Complimentary tea with home-made fruitcake is served
in the lounge or alfresco, and there is tea-making equipment in the
bedrooms. 'Service and hospitality faultless; they made us most
welcome.' (*CLH*)

Bedrooms: 16, 10 on ground floor in courtyard. *Open*: all year except Feb,
restaurant closed midday except Sun. *Facilities*: lounge, bar, 3 dining rooms,
gallery, 3-acre grounds (garden, tennis, croquet, stream). *Background music*: none.
Location: 3 miles SW of Sturminster Newton. *Smoking*: not allowed. *Children*: all
ages welcomed. *Dogs*: allowed in some bedrooms, not in public rooms. *Credit
cards*: all major cards. *Prices*: b&b £60–£95 per person, set dinner £28.50.

SUTTON COLDFIELD Warwickshire   Map 3:C6
See SHORTLIST

Many hotels increase their prices in the spring. The tariffs we
quote are subject to change, especially from April/May 2009.
You should always check when booking.

SWAFFHAM Norfolk   Map 2:B5

Strattons   *Tel* 01760-723845
4 Ash Close   *Fax* 01760-720458
Swaffham PE37 7NH   *Email* enquiries@strattonshotel.com
                                     Website www.strattonshotel.com

❦ *César award in 2003*

A comprehensive environmental policy is followed at Vanessa and
Les Scott's Grade II listed Palladian-style villa: waste management,
recycling, fresh local ingredients in the kitchen; in the bathroom,
refillable pump dispensers. 'It may be a green hotel, but *Strattons* is at
the opposite end of the scale to Spartan,' said one visitor. Another
wrote of the 'very friendly welcome'. Filled with original paintings,
sculptures and ornaments, it 'should appeal to the most hedonistic
person'. 'For the environmentally aware lover of luxury,' was another
comment. Though near the centre of the old town, it has a rural feel
(bantams and ducks peck under trees in the garden). The themed
bedrooms include Opium (bed flanked with Doric columns and a
freestanding bath big enough for two); the Red Room (rich fabrics);
Boudoir ('sensual, with a Parisian feel'); Stalls ('captures the feeling
of the old horse block'). In the restaurant (refurbished this year),
Vanessa Scott and Maggie Cooper serve 'interesting and tasty' modern dishes on a monthly-changing menu, eg, roasted organic chicken
with bubble and squeak and roasted chestnuts. The 'excellent'
breakfast has freshly squeezed juices, free-range eggs, home-made
breads. The Scotts' daughter, Hannah, and Dominic Hughes are the
managers. An old print workshop in the grounds is to be turned into a
café/bistro. (*Michael Mayer-Jones, JR, and others*)

Bedrooms: 10, 2 in annexe, 2 on ground floor. *Open*: all year except 1 week at
Christmas. *Facilities*: drawing room, reading room, restaurant, terrace, 1-acre
garden, unsuitable for &. *Background music*: in bar. *Location*: central, parking.
Smoking: not allowed. *Children*: all ages welcomed. *Dogs*: not allowed in public
rooms, or unaccompanied in bedrooms. *Credit cards*: MasterCard, Visa. *Prices*:
b&b £75–£175 per person, set dinner £40, special breaks, New Year package,
1-night bookings refused weekends/holidays.

SWAY Hampshire *See SHORTLIST*   Map 2:E2

New reports help us keep the *Guide* up to date.

SWINDON Wiltshire *See SHORTLIST*   Map 2:C2

TALLAND-BY-LOOE Cornwall   Map 1:D3

Talland Bay Hotel
Talland-by-Looe
PL13 2JB

Tel 01503-272667
Email info@tallandbayhotel.co.uk
Website www.tallandbayhotel.co.uk

In a 'special setting', amid subtropical gardens 150 feet above a quiet bay, this old manor house is sheltered by ancient pines. It is a 'very fine family-run hotel', say fans. The owner/managers, George and Mary Granville, and their staff are 'courteous, obliging and efficient'. 'Lovely, well-furnished rooms, charming owners,' writes a visitor in 2008. The decor is 'pleasingly country house; some rooms a little faded, we like this'. Bedrooms vary greatly; the best have 'smart draperies and great views'. 'Our delightfully chic ground-floor room had a classic iron bedhead, good lighting, modern shower room. French windows opened on to a south-facing private garden.' Five rooms are in cottages: one, near car park and kitchen, can be noisy. In the wood-panelled dining room, with small-paned windows, antique china in alcoves, flowers and log fire, the best tables have good views. Steven Buick's modern cooking is praised: 'An *amuse-bouche* each night, perfect soups, wonderful home-baked breads.' 'Beautifully cooked and presented duck breast; lovely fillets of bream.' Breakfasts, accompanied by the weather forecast, have toasted home-made bread, freshly squeezed juices, good, cooked dishes. Light lunches are served in the bar or on the terrace. Children are welcomed (child-listening, high teas for under-fives). (*Dr D Tumath, Peter Jacobsen*)

Bedrooms: 23, some on ground floor. *Open*: Feb–Dec. *Facilities*: lounge, library, bar, restaurant, patio, 2-acre garden (heated swimming pool (7 by 13 metres) May–Sept, badminton, putting, croquet), beach 5 mins' walk, golf nearby. *Background music*: none. *Location*: 2½ miles SW of Looe, off Looe–Polperro road. *Smoking*: not allowed. *Children*: all ages welcomed. *Dogs*: not allowed in public rooms. *Credit cards*: MasterCard, Visa. *Prices*: b&b £47.50–£117.50 per person, d,b&b £77.50–£147.50, set dinner £32.50, seasonal breaks, Christmas/New Year packages, 1-night bookings refused Sat. *V*

When we quote the range of prices per person, the lowest is for one person sharing a double room out of season, the highest for a single room in high season.

TAUNTON Somerset   Map 1:C5

The Castle at Taunton
Castle Green
Taunton TA1 1NF

Tel 01823-272671
Fax 01823-336066
Email reception@the-castle-hotel.com
Website www.the-castle-hotel.com

♾ *César award in 1987*

'The kindness, skill and care shown by all the staff' impressed recent
visitors to this wisteria-covered castellated hotel owned by Kit
Chapman, who grew up here. His wife, Louise, has decorated the
bedrooms, concentrating on 'a sense of welcome rather than anonymous designer chic'. Kevin McCarthy is the 'delightful' long-serving
manager. An inn since the 12th century, the former Norman fortress
has elegant public rooms with old oak furniture, tapestries, paintings,
elaborate flower arrangements. A fine wrought iron staircase leads to
bedrooms of varying size and style. All contain flat-screen TV, free
Wi-Fi, tea/coffee-making kit. 'Ours had large, firm bed, settee, plenty
of cupboard space.' Front rooms are triple-glazed against local noise;
quietest ones face the garden. The penthouse suite, with its roof
garden, has wide views. In the L-shaped restaurant, chef Richard
Guest serves modern British dishes using fish and seafood from
Brixham, game from Exmoor and the Quantocks. Sample dishes: ham
hock in cider jelly; roast leg of duck with Anna potatoes. 'Excellent
wines.' Salads, grills, omelettes, etc, are served in *Brazz*, the lively
café/bistro adjacent. 'Breakfast was fine: dishes under domes good
and freshly cooked; home-made jams and marmalade.' Musical
weekends of quality are held. (*CE, CJ*)

Bedrooms: 44. *Open*: all year, restaurant closed Sun night. *Facilities*: lift, ramps,
lounge, bar, restaurant, brasserie, private dining/meeting rooms, civil wedding
licence, 1-acre garden, shop. *Background music*: in brasserie. *Location*: central.
Smoking: not allowed. *Children*: all ages welcomed. *Dogs*: small 'well-behaved'
dogs allowed, not in public rooms. *Credit cards*: all major cards. *Prices*: [2008]
b&b £115–£162.50 per person, d,b&b £125–£177.50, set lunch/dinner
£22.50–£27.50, special breaks, Christmas/New Year packages. *V*

The *V* sign at the end of an entry indicates a hotel that has
agreed to take part in our Voucher scheme and to give *Guide*
readers a 25% discount on their room rates for a one-night stay,
subject to the conditions on the back of the vouchers and
explained in 'How to use the *Good Hotel Guide*' (page 62).

TEFFONT EVIAS Wiltshire   Map 2:D1

Howard's House   *Tel* 01722-716392
Teffont Evias   *Fax* 01722-716820
nr Salisbury SP3 5RJ   *Email* enq@howardshousehotel.co.uk
                                Website www.howardshousehotel.co.uk

In a 'delightful, unspoilt hamlet' on the little River Teff, this mellow
stone dower house (1632) stands in a garden with ancient box hedges,
lawns and pond with fountain. 'Our weekend was real value for
money,' said one *Guide* reader. Other comments: 'As good as ever.'
'Lovely, relaxing; a personal air; excellent food.' 'In the absence of
the manageress, Noële Thompson, we were looked after by a welcoming young major-domo who carried our bags. Courteous, welcoming staff.' 'Once checked in, we never had to identify ourselves.' The
'charming' lounge has a stone fireplace, yellow walls, bright fabrics,
exposed beams. Tea and home-made biscuits are served here and on
the terrace. Bedrooms have pastel colours, floral prints, bathrobes.
'Our spacious room had idyllic views of the hillside garden and
church.' But most rooms are smallish, and beds may be on the small
side too. In the dining room, which opens on to the garden, chef Nick
Wentworth serves modern dishes, eg, loin of Wiltshire pork, black
pudding Pithiviers. 'Good wine by the glass.' At breakfast, served at
table, 'toast and croissants wrapped in a serviette are brought with the
cooked course, so are warm when you eat them'. Children and dogs
are welcomed. (*MB, Joanna Russell*)

Bedrooms: 9. *Open*: all year except Christmas. *Facilities*: lounge, restaurant,
2-acre grounds (croquet), river, fishing nearby, unsuitable for &. *Background
music*: classical/jazz in restaurant. *Location*: off B3089, 10 miles W of Salisbury.
Smoking: not allowed. *Children*: all ages welcomed. *Dogs*: not allowed in public
rooms. *Credit cards*: Amex, MasterCard, Visa. *Prices*: [2008] b&b £82.50–£105
per person, set dinner £28.95, full alc £55, winter breaks, New Year
package. *V*

TEIGNMOUTH Devon   Map 1:D5

Thomas Luny House   *Tel* 01626-772976
Teign Street   *Email* alisonandjohn@thomas-luny-house.co.uk
Teignmouth TQ14 8EG   *Website* www.thomas-luny-house.co.uk

'A tremendously good-value B&B', this early 19th-century house was
built by the marine artist Thomas Luny when the town was favoured
by Nelson's admirals and captains. Reached via an archway in a high

whitewashed wall ('a bit of thought needed before you drive through'), it is 'attractive, fresh and clean'. John and Alison Allan are 'charming, welcoming hosts who maintain very high standards', says a fan who has stayed many times. The spacious double drawing room and breakfast room, each with an open fire and furnished with antiques, lead through French windows on to the 'pretty suntrap garden'. 'It is very pleasant to sit outside in summer and drink John's excellent tea and eat Alison's delicious cake.' Upstairs, three of the bedrooms are spacious, the fourth is small. One has a Chinese decor, another is Edwardian in feel, another nautical. All have flowers, Malvern water, books and magazines, tea-making facilities and bathrobes. 'Excellent' breakfasts have 'lovely fruit compote, home-made bread, good leaf tea'. (*Marilyn Frampton*)

Bedrooms: 4. *Open*: all year. *Facilities*: 2 lounges, breakfast room, small walled garden, sea (sandy beach 5 mins' walk), unsuitable for &. *Background music*: none. *Location*: town centre. *Smoking*: not allowed. *Children*: not under 12. *Dogs*: not allowed. *Credit cards*: MasterCard, Visa. *Prices*: [2008] b&b £40–£68 per person, 1-night bookings sometimes refused.

See also SHORTLIST

TEMPLE SOWERBY Cumbria   Map 4: inset C3

Temple Sowerby House
Temple Sowerby
nr Penrith CA10 1RZ

Tel 017683-61578
Fax 017683-61958
Email stay@templesowerby.com
Website www.templesowerby.com

Thanks to the opening of the long-awaited Temple Sowerby bypass, this Grade II listed house in a conservation village in the Eden valley is now 'truly peaceful', write the owners, Paul and Julie Evans. Returning visitors in 2008 found it 'still comforting and welcoming'. Part 17th-century, brick-fronted with thick walls and a Georgian wing, it faces Cross Fell, the highest peak in the Pennines. Recent comments: 'Hotel, rooms and food all excellent.' 'The owners seem always to be on hand to meet visitors' needs.' The bedrooms range from 'superior' (with views) to 'classic' (smaller, many with old beams). An extensive redecoration programme has been completed: several of the newly fitted bathrooms have aqua-spa bath and hydrotherapy shower. Changes have been made to reduce the environmental impact (energy-efficient boilers, new recycling measures). The conservatory-style restaurant, which faces the walled garden with its terrace, is 'perfect for a glass of local beer in late afternoon sun'. Chef Ashley Whittaker's menus 'based on the best traditions of British and classic French cooking' using much local produce include, eg, risotto of wild mushrooms with a poached free-range egg; grilled trout with dill gnocchi. Breakfast has 'delicious bread and rolls', 'nice jam, unwrapped butter'. Meetings, seminars and 'discreet gatherings' are catered for. Ullswater is 15 minutes' drive away. More reports, please. (*Sarah and Tony Thomas*)

Bedrooms: 12, 2 on ground floor, 4 in coach house (20 yds). *Open*: all year except Christmas. *Facilities*: 2 lounges, bar, restaurant, conference/function facilities, civil wedding licence, 2-acre garden (croquet). *Background music*: in restaurant at night. *Location*: village centre. *Smoking*: not allowed. *Children*: not under 12. *Dogs*: by prior arrangement, not allowed in public rooms. *Credit cards*: MasterCard, Visa. *Prices*: b&b £60–£90 per person, full alc £40, special breaks, New Year package, 1-night bookings occasionally refused.

TETBURY Gloucestershire   Map 3:E5

Calcot Manor	*Tel* 01666-890391
nr Tetbury GL8 8YJ	*Fax* 01666-890394
	Email reception@calcotmanor.co.uk
	Website www.calcotmanor.co.uk

❦ *César award in 2001*

'We don't just accept children, we love having them,' says Richard Ball. He is the managing director of this Cotswold hotel with extensive facilities for adults and their offspring; his wife, Cathy, runs its spa. 'If you have children in the family but also want a civilised hotel for adults, this is it,' says a 'whole-hearted' endorsement in 2008. The converted 14th-century farmhouse, cottages and outbuildings are 'unusually well appointed: communal areas, our suite, the crèche [Ofsted-registered] and the swimming pool were all in tremendously good nick'. *The Mez* is an unsupervised area for older children. The staff 'though formally attired were friendly, helpful'. The suites, in the courtyard, have a double bedroom and a sitting room with bunks or sofa bed; also video, TV, small fridge, baby-listening. 'Ours reminded us of home, high praise.' In the *Conservatory Restaurant*, Michael Croft's modern cooking was thought 'excellent' again this year. 'No fuss when we asked if our daughter could eat with us.' Families are more likely to gather in the informal

Gumstool pub: 'High chairs were much in use on a busy Saturday, but the staff coped well. Delicious starters, good selection of light main courses, a crab and leek tart, top-drawer fish and chips.' Breakfasts have fresh orange juice, 'a memorable berry compote'. (*Jane Bailey, Gilbert Hall, and others*)

Bedrooms: 35, 10 (family) in cottage, 11 around courtyard, on ground floor. *Open*: all year. *Facilities*: ramps, lounge, 2 restaurants, 2 bars, private dining room, cinema, conference facilities, crèche, civil wedding licence, 220-acre grounds (tennis, heated outdoor 8-metre swimming pool, children's play area, croquet, bicycles, spa with 15-metre swimming pool, sauna, treatments, etc). *Background music*: in restaurants. *Location*: 3 miles W of Tetbury. *Smoking*: not allowed. *Children*: all ages welcomed. *Dogs*: not allowed. *Credit cards*: all major cards. *Prices*: [2008] b&b £110–£198 per person, d,b&b (midweek) £140–£218, set dinner £50, 2-day breaks, Christmas/New Year packages, 1-night bookings refused Sat.

See also SHORTLIST

THIRSK North Yorkshire   Map 4:C4
See SHORTLIST

THORPE ST ANDREW Norfolk   Map 2:B5
See SHORTLIST

TISBURY Wiltshire *See SHORTLIST*   Map 2:D1

TITCHWELL Norfolk   Map 2:A5

Titchwell Manor
Titchwell, nr Brancaster
PE31 8BB

Tel 01485-210221
Fax 01485-210104
Email margaret@titchwellmanor.com
Website www.titchwellmanor.com

Built as a farmhouse in 1890, this small hotel/restaurant/bar is run by Margaret and Ian Snaith; their son Eric is the chef. 'Impressive and tastefully done', it is popular with walkers and birdwatchers. It stands on the busy main coastal road; the RSPB Titchwell nature reserve is close by, though not easily reached on foot. Public rooms have mosaic tiled floors, dark woodwork, Lloyd Loom furniture, potted plants. The walled garden 'is a pleasant place to take a drink or a light lunch'. The newest bedrooms ('generous, modern and well equipped') are around a 'pretty garden square with lavender and herbs'; two are suitable for disabled visitors. Inspectors felt that the prices charged should have included help with luggage, a turndown service and better local information. The bar, with its 'feel of a gastropub', serves light meals all day. Children under 12 have their own menu. In the conservatory dining room, the starters are enjoyed (eg, 'a little plate with aubergine crisps and vine tomatoes') more than some main courses and desserts. 'Breakfast had good thick toast (brought too early) and leaf tea'; 'kipper the finest I have tasted', but 'orange juice not freshly squeezed'. 'Staff are multinational, and we didn't get a very personal feel.'

Bedrooms: 26, 19 on ground floor, in herb garden, 2 suitable for &. *Open*: all year. *Facilities*: 2 lounges, bar, restaurant, ½-acre garden (beaches, golf nearby). *Background music*: in bar. *Location*: on coast road, 5 miles E of Hunstanton. *Smoking*: not allowed. *Children*: all ages welcomed except under-14s at Christmas. *Dogs*: allowed in bar, some bedrooms. *Credit cards*: all major cards. *Prices*: b&b £50–£125 per person, d,b&b £25 added, full alc £55, midweek breaks, Christmas/New Year packages, 1-night bookings sometimes refused Sat. *V*

How to contact the *Guide*
By mail: From anywhere in the UK, write to Freepost PAM 2931, London W11 4BR (no stamp is needed)
From outside the UK: *Good Hotel Guide*, 50 Addison Avenue, London W11 4QP, England
By telephone or fax: 020-7602 4182
By email: editor@goodhotelguide.com
Via our website: www.goodhotelguide.com

TITLEY Herefordshire   Map 3:C4

The Stagg Inn   *Tel* 01544-230221
Titley, nr Kington   *Fax* 01544-231390
HR5 3RL   *Email* reservations@thestagg.co.uk
                                     Website www.thestagg.co.uk

On the site of a medieval inn, Steve and Nicola Reynolds's
white-fronted old pub 'must be the most unpretentious and laid-
back *Michelin*-starred establishment in Europe' (said an
inspector). It stands by the road in a small, straggling village in
rolling Herefordshire countryside. The restaurant areas are
spread around inside, 'all higgledy-piggledy', some up a few
steps, some down. They have 'country-style plain wooden tables
and simple upholstered chairs'. The seasonally changing menus
use local produce (and the pub's own pigs and home-grown
vegetables) for dishes like mushroom, leek and Parmesan tart;
porchetta of sucking pig with mustard sauce. Three bedrooms
are above the pub. 'We were impressed by ours: bright, tastefully
decorated, reasonable sized, heavily beamed; a garden-facing
window. We weren't bothered by noise from passing traffic.'
Three other rooms are down the road in a listed Georgian ex-
vicarage, backed by a garden with stream, chickens, 'a friendly
Labrador, and cats'. 'A lovely place to stay; Steve's mother was
very helpful.' 'Our splendid room had two large beds, effective
heating, fresh milk in a refrigerator.' Breakfast includes fruit,
porridge with honey, 'excellent scrambled eggs, toast made from
lovely bread, a large chunk of butter'. 'All very good value.' (*FR,
GM, and others*)

Bedrooms: 6, 3 at *Old Vicarage* (300 yds). *Open*: all year except 25–27 Dec, Sun
night/Mon, 10 days early Nov. *Facilities*: (*Old Vicarage*) sitting room, 2-acre
garden, (*Stagg Inn*) bar, restaurant areas, small garden, unsuitable for &.
Background music: none. *Location*: on B4355 between Kington (3½ miles) and
Presteigne. *Smoking*: not allowed. *Children*: all ages welcomed. *Dogs*: allowed in
pub only. *Credit cards*: MasterCard, Visa. *Prices*: b&b £42.50–£100 per person,
full alc £36, 1-night bookings refused at peak times.

We update the *Guide* every year. Hotels are dropped if there
has been a change of owner (unless reports after the change
are positive), if this year's reports are negative, or in rare cases
where there has been no feedback. A lot of hotels fall by the
wayside every year, and many new ones are added.

TORVER Cumbria   Map 4: inset C2

The Old Rectory   *Tel* 015394-41353
Torver, nr Coniston   *Fax* 015394-41156
LA21 8AX   *Email* enquiries@theoldrectoryhotel.com
                   Website www.theoldrectoryhotel.com

In a 'beautiful position beneath the peaks of Coniston Old Man', this unpretentious 19th-century white-painted house stands amid gardens and woods. 'The welcome and hospitality were exceptional,' writes a visitor this year. 'A very relaxed feeling.' The bedrooms are 'comfortable, beautifully decorated and spotless'. 'Our bright superior room, with modern bathroom, was well furnished, very clean.' A four-course dinner (no choice until dessert) is served in the conservatory dining room. The owners, Paul and Elizabeth Mitchell, call the food 'adventurous traditional', eg, roast tomato soup with a purée of basil; poached breast of chicken with a caramelised shallot sauce. 'The dinners were beautifully cooked, and Elizabeth Mitchell went to a great deal of trouble to prepare an interesting vegetarian dish for us each evening. The staff were attentive, friendly. Even the breakfast boiled eggs were cooked to perfection, a rarity.' For children there are high teas, cots and baby monitors. Dogs are 'warmly welcomed', too. Coniston Water is reached by a 20-minute stroll along a tarmac lane; there is good walking and climbing nearby. (*Simon Rodway, PK*)

Bedrooms: 9, 1 in annexe, 10 yds, 1 on ground floor. *Open*: all year except Dec/Jan, dining room closed to non-residents. *Facilities*: lounge, dining room, ½-acre garden plus 2-acre woodland. *Background music*: none. *Location*: 2½ miles SW of Coniston on A593. *Smoking*: not allowed. *Children*: all ages welcomed. *Dogs*: not allowed in public rooms. *Credit cards*: MasterCard, Visa. *Prices*: b&b £33–£43 per person, d,b&b £58–£68, set dinner £25, 1-night bookings refused bank holidays, Sat.

TOTNES Devon *See SHORTLIST*   Map 1:D4

When you make a booking you enter into a contract with a hotel. Most hotels explain their cancellation policies, which vary widely, in a letter of confirmation. You may lose your deposit or be charged at the full rate for the room if you cancel at short notice. A travel insurance policy can provide protection.

TRESCO Isles of Scilly

Map 1: inset C1

The Island Hotel

Old Grimsby, Tresco
Isles of Scilly
Cornwall TR24 0PU

Tel 01720-422883
Fax 01720-423008
Email islandhotel@tresco.co.uk
Website www.tresco.co.uk

In a 'magnificent' position, on a promontory by a large sandy beach on this tiny private island, this sprawling one-storey hotel is managed by Euan Rodger. It is popular with families in summer (buckets, spades, pushchairs, high teas provided). In spring and autumn, older visitors are attracted by the cheaper rates (many come to see Tresco's famed subtropical Abbey Gardens). Guests are met at the pier or heliport and ferried to the hotel by tractor and trailer. 'There is nothing stuffy; staff are friendly and efficient,' one wrote. Another said: 'Our room was spotless, well planned and spacious; everything worked.' A dissenter complained of poor communication and some housekeeping problems. Most bedrooms have a sea view; some have a balcony. Pictures from the modern art collection of the island's owner, Robert Dorrien-Smith, hang in the bedrooms and public areas. The decor reflects the colours of sea and beach. 'No music of any kind, a profound relief.' Tables are rotated in the dining room so that everyone gets the view. The chef, Peter Marshall, serves traditional/modern dishes, eg, salmon in green tea marinade, soy noodle; Cornish venison, roasted parsnip purée. Breakfast is 'excellent'; 'lunch menu just right'. There are bar meals and cream teas. (*MTS, RL*)

Bedrooms: 48, 8 in 2 annexes, 3 on ground floor. *Open*: Mar–Oct. *Facilities*: lounge, TV room, games room, bar, 2 dining rooms, 2-acre grounds (terrace, tennis, croquet, bowls, heated 25-metre swimming pool May–30 Sept), nearby beach (safe bathing, diving, snorkelling), bicycle hire (book in advance), golf buggies and wheelchairs for &. *Background music*: none. *Location*: NE side of island, boat/helicopter from Penzance (hotel will make travel arrangements). *Smoking*: not allowed. *Children*: all ages welcomed. *Dogs*: not allowed. *Credit cards*: MasterCard, Visa. *Prices*: d,b&b £130–£360, set dinner £42, special breaks.

****

Traveller's tale *Hotel in the Midlands* The bathroom had been designed with no thought of the user. There was just one tiny towel rail, and clean towels were stacked on a strange tall wooden stand next to the loo, as far as possible from the shower. There was nowhere to put toiletries except the floor, and in the shower nowhere to place shampoo or soap.

****

TRURO Cornwall   Map 1:D2

Royal Hotel   *Tel* 01872-270345
Lemon Street   *Fax* 01872-242453
Truro TR1 2QB   *Email* reception@royalhotelcornwall.co.uk
                     Website www.royalhotelcornwall.co.uk

'Strongly endorsed' in 2008, this 200-year-old Grade II listed inn, in
the centre of the cathedral city is liked for its 'relaxed atmosphere'.
Lynn Manning is the owner, Nicola Manning the manager; their
'lively young staff treated us like real humans', said one visitor.
Renovation continues: 15 bedrooms were refurbished this year, new
carpets laid on stairs and corridors throughout, and (less welcome to
some visitors) a 'state-of-the-art music system' has been installed to
'suit the clientele'. Modern brasserie-style food is served from 11 am
to 10 pm in the restaurant, where wooden tables are 'reasonably far
apart' (some on a platform). Typical dishes: Italian tomato and butter
bean broth; sweet chilli beef sizzler with mixed vegetables. 'Good
service; generous helpings.' 'My room at the rear was quiet, with
good-quality fittings; housekeeping was good and the bed was
comfortable. At breakfast there were newspapers, a buffet with a large
choice, and the food was good.' Wi-Fi is available throughout. The
bar, open until midnight, serves 'funky' cocktails. (*Michael Lewis*)

Bedrooms: 43, 9 apartments in stable block, 1 suitable for &. *Open*: all year
except 24–30 Dec. *Facilities*: lounge, bar, restaurant, boardroom. *Background
music*: in bar and restaurant. *Location*: central. *Smoking*: not allowed. *Children*:
all ages welcomed. *Dogs*: not allowed. *Credit cards*: all major cards. *Prices*: b&b
£49.50–£89 per person, full alc £35. *V*

TUNBRIDGE WELLS Kent   Map 2:D4

Hotel du Vin Tunbridge Wells   *Tel* 01892-526455
13 Crescent Road   *Fax* 01892-512044
Tunbridge Wells *Email* reception@tunbridgewells.hotelduvin.com
TN1 2LY   *Website* www.hotelduvin.com

'Stylish, reasonably priced, informal. A chain hotel that offers good
value, professionalism and personal service.' Trusted *Guide* correspondents stayed in 2008 in this 18th-century Grade II listed building
(extended in the 1830s by Decimus Burton, known for the Palm
House, Kew Gardens). Part of the Hotel du Vin group (owned by
Marylebone Warwick Balfour), it is managed by Andy Roger.

'Reception is cheerful and efficient.' 'Aura of French chic.' The quietest bedrooms overlook Calverley Park. 'We were upgraded to a large room, fairly austere but comfortable and well equipped. The big bathroom had a large walk-in shower. A roll-top bath – awkward to get in and out of – was for some reason in the bedroom.' A standard room, not very large, 'had so many accessories (minibar, DVD-player, etc) that there was little storage space; no drawers'. Singles can be very small. Booking is necessary for the 'lively' bistro where 'meals were well prepared, exceptionally good value. Interesting, reasonably priced wine list a plus point, so was the outdoor dining in fine weather.' Chef Paul Nixon offers daily specials and a seasonally changing *carte* (dishes like guinea fowl with lentils; truffle-stuffed chicken with red wine jus). (*David and Kate Wooff, Richard and Catriona Smith*)

Bedrooms: 34, 4 in adjacent cottage. *Open*: all year. *Facilities*: lift, ramps, 2 lounges, bar, snooker room, bistro, private dining/meeting rooms, civil wedding licence, 1-acre grounds (cigar shack, small vineyard). *Background music*: none. *Location*: central, opposite Assembly Hall. *Smoking*: not allowed. *Children*: all ages welcomed. *Dogs*: not allowed in bistro. *Credit cards*: all major cards. *Prices*: room £115–£325, breakfast £9.95–£13.50, set menu £17.50, full alc £49, Christmas/New Year packages.

See also SHORTLIST

ULLSWATER Cumbria   Map 4: inset C2

Howtown Hotel   *Tel* 01768-486514
Ullswater, nr Penrith CA10 2ND

🦢 *César award in 1991*

In an 'idyllic, tranquil' setting on the eastern shore of Lake Ullswater, this simple guest house has many fans. This year's praise: 'A real joy, antidote to the chain or pretentious hotel.' 'As good as ever.' 'Pure gold, no ostentation.' Jacquie Baldry, whose family have owned the house for more than a century, runs it with her son, David. Regular visitors like the lack of frills (no phones, TV or radio in the bedrooms), and the 'house drills' like the gong that calls guests to dinner at 7 pm, and breakfast at 9 am (this can cause queues at the buffet table). Most of the 'simple but pleasant' bedrooms have lake views; four have their bathroom 'one hop across the corridor'. In the main building, early morning tea is brought to the room, and there is an evening turn-down service. 'Dinner is the work of a good cook rather than a star-chasing chef,' says a seasoned reporter. 'Very enjoyable, the sort of food you would like on a seven-day holiday rather than for a special occasion.' Sunday has a set lunch and a cold supper. Tea can be taken by the fire in winter, in summer in the garden facing the wooded hills. A substantial picnic can be provided. (*Alastair Kameen, Trevor B Lee, Ann Duncan*)

Bedrooms: 13, 4 in annexe, 4 self-catering cottages for weekly rent. *Open*: Mar–Nov. *Facilities*: 3 lounges, TV room, 2 bars, dining room, 2-acre grounds, 200 yds from lake (private foreshore, fishing), walking, sailing, climbing, riding, golf nearby, unsuitable for &. *Background music*: none. *Location*: 4 miles S of Pooley Bridge, bus from Penrith station 9 miles. *Smoking*: not allowed. *Children*: all ages welcomed (no special facilities). *Dogs*: not allowed in public rooms. *Credit cards*: none. *Prices*: [2008] b&b £72 per person, set dinner £22, 1-night bookings sometimes refused.

Sharrow Bay

Ullswater
nr Penrith CA10 2LZ

Tel 01768-486301
Fax 01768-486349
Email info@sharrowbay.co.uk
Website www.sharrowbay.co.uk

Sixty years old this year, this is the original country house hotel, founded by Francis Coulson and Brian Sack. Spectacularly set on the eastern shore of Ullswater, it is backed by gardens and woodland. A Relais & Châteaux member, it is now owned by the von Essen group and managed by Andrew King. Few changes have been made: the decor is still traditional (swagged curtains, cherubs, ornaments, open fires), dinner is still at 8 pm ('but we are more flexible now'); breakfast at 9 am. 'We much enjoyed our stay,' say visitors in 2008, though they found the atmosphere in the public rooms 'strangely cool: guests did not speak much to each other'. The 'chintzy' bedrooms in the main house are quite small ('ours, immediately above the water, had good views from both bathroom and bedroom'), but there are spacious rooms in the garden annexe and in *Bank House* up the hill (transport provided). Other rooms are in an Edwardian lodge ('ours had a nice little sitting area looking over fields with lambs and ewes'). The restaurant has held a *Michelin* star for 11 years, for the 'richly flavoured classic English cooking' of chef Colin Akrigg, now working with Mark Teasdale, eg, terrine of guinea fowl and pork with pear and saffron chutney; halibut with shrimp risotto, buttered spinach; Francis Coulson's icky-sticky toffee pudding. But one couple commented

that the menu, which hardly changed from day to day, had no vegetarian alternatives. Staff are mostly young and foreign. 'There can be
long waits at meals.' (*Jill and Mike Bennett, and others*)

Bedrooms: 24, 6 in garden, 4 in lodge, 6 at *Bank House* (1¼ miles), 1 on ground
floor (ramp, wide doors). *Open*: all year. *Facilities*: 3 lounges, 2 dining rooms in
main house, 2 lounges, breakfast room in *Bank House*, civil wedding licence,
12-acre grounds (gardens, woodland, ½-mile lake shore, safe bathing, pier).
Background music: none. *Location*: E shore of Ullswater, 2 miles S of Pooley
Bridge. *Smoking*: not allowed. *Children*: not under 10. *Dogs*: only guide dogs
allowed. *Credit cards*: Amex, MasterCard, Visa. *Prices*: b&b £160–£350 per
person, d,b&b £200–£390, cookery classes, Christmas/New Year packages,
1-night bookings refused weekends.

See also SHORTLIST

ULVERSTON Cumbria   Map 4: inset C2

 The Bay Horse   *Tel* 01229-583972
Canal Foot   *Fax* 01229-580502
Ulverston   *Email* reservations@thebayhorsehotel.co.uk
LA12 9EL   *Website* www.thebayhorsehotel.co.uk

César award: Cumbrian inn of the year

'An honest, unpretentious inn', once a staging post for coaches
crossing the sands of Morecambe Bay. 'Stunning position; tides race
in and out; great birdlife.' Owner/chef Robert Lyons and manageress
Lesley Wheeler, now in their 21st year, have 'an effortless charm that
disguises deep attention to detail', says a devotee. 'They care for their
guests in a no-fuss way.' Inspectors agreed: 'Exemplary welcome;
help with luggage, offer of tea.' The small, simple bedrooms might be
'in the best of time warps' (chintzy curtains, etc), but 'why change
what you do well?' 'Towels are big, beds comfortable (made during
breakfast), duvet changed for conventional bedding when we asked,
room serviced during dinner, free Wi-Fi.' Six rooms, each with little
terrace, have the views ('you can enjoy it from bed'). Drinks in the bar
(a popular local) at 7.30 pm precede dinner at 8 in the panoramic
conservatory restaurant. 'Outstanding cooking' by Robert Lyons and
Kris Hogan ('no *nouvelle cuisine* here,' they say, 'just real food that
tastes how it should'). 'Excellent starters (shrimp, avocado and mango
salad; minced veal with egg custard); then salt marsh lamb and sea

bass; delicious vegetables, good vegetarian choices. Watching the tide as you dine is such fun.' Breakfast (no buffet) has fruit, good cooked dishes, leaf tea, 'nothing packaged'. 'The huge chemical plant nearby did not spoil our pleasure.' (*Lynn Wildgoose, and others*)

Bedrooms: 9. *Open*: all year, restaurant closed Mon midday (light bar meals available). *Facilities*: bar lounge, restaurant, picnic area, unsuitable for &. *Background music*: classical/'easy listening'. *Location*: 8 miles NE of Barrow-in-Furness. *Smoking*: not allowed. *Children*: not under 12. *Dogs*: not allowed in restaurant. *Credit cards*: Amex, MasterCard, Visa. *Prices*: [2008] b&b £42.50–£80 per person, full alc £45, bargain breaks, Christmas/New Year packages, 1-night bookings refused Christmas.

VENTNOR Isle of Wight   Map 2:E2

The Hambrough
Hambrough Road
Ventnor PO38 1SQ

Tel 01983-856333
Fax 01983-857260
Email info@thehambrough.com
Website www.thehambrough.com

Victorian villa in 'fantastic' position, on quiet road above the harbour, and by Ventnor's cascade gardens. New manager this year, Daniel Edwards. 'Delightful stay. Spacious elegant room, simple lines, good colour scheme (white, beige, brown and grey),' says visitor in 2008. 'Where else can you watch a storm from large bathtub by window?' 'Superb breakfast (not a buffet), with home-baked bread.' Bar lounge, restaurant, terrace on 3 levels; background music all day. Parking. Unsuitable for &. No smoking. No children under 10. No dogs. Diners, MasterCard, Visa accepted. 7 bedrooms. Prices: [2008] b&b £78–£105 per person, set dinner £30–£38.50, Christmas/New Year packages, 1-night bookings refused most weekends, bank holidays. *V*

The Wellington Hotel
Belgrave Road
Ventnor PO38 1JH

Tel 01983-856600
Fax 01983-856611
Email enquiries@thewellingtonhotel.net
Website www.thewellingtonhotel.net

'An excellent base for a civilised seaside break', this 'stunningly located' hotel is built into cliffs above a safe, sandy beach. The manager is Marios Porfiropoullos. 'We were impressed by the willingness to put guests first,' says a visitor, who liked 'the positive response to our request for sheets and blanket instead of a duvet'. The decor is contemporary (bare floorboards in public areas); redecoration throughout took place in late 2007. A 'smallish' bedroom was 'elegantly done; it was a delight to sit on our balcony in the sun, and take in the magnificent view' (all but two rooms face the sea). In the 'equally elegant', spacious dining room (two floors below the bedrooms), chef Roman Gigov uses mainly local produce. 'The menu didn't change during our stay, but the kitchen was flexible, adapting dishes to our preferences.' 'There is a shortage of parking (a few cramped spaces between hotel and road, otherwise the municipal car park, 200 yards away). People who have trouble with stairs should note that there is no lift and the hotel has many levels.' (*JB*)

Bedrooms: 28, some on ground floor. *Open*: all year, restaurant closed midday. *Facilities*: reception lounge, bar, restaurant, sun deck, civil wedding licence, steps to beach, unsuitable for &. *Background music*: classical/modern in restaurant. *Location*: 5 mins' walk from centre. *Smoking*: allowed in 14 bedrooms. *Children*: all ages welcomed. *Dogs*: not allowed. *Credit cards*: all major cards. *Prices*: b&b £55–£90 per person, d,b&b £75–£110, full alc £30, ferry-inclusive breaks, Christmas/New Year packages, 1-night bookings refused Sat in season. *V*

See also SHORTLIST

VERYAN-IN-ROSELAND Cornwall   Map 1:D2

The Nare   *Tel* 01872-501111
Carne Beach   *Fax* 01872-501856
Veryan   *Email* office@narehotel.co.uk
nr Truro TR2 5PF   *Website* www.narehotel.co.uk

❦ *César award in 2003*

Above a beautiful bay in the Roseland peninsula, this unashamedly old-fashioned hotel has been owned by one family for 20 years. Mrs Bettye Grey has handed management to her grandson, Toby Ashworth. 'They are always to be seen keeping a sharp eye on things,' say trusted correspondents (hoteliers who revisited after a 40-year gap). 'Difficult to find a better example of a family-run hotel.' Other visitors agree: 'Service is excellent across the board.' 'Staff who've been there many years seem to remember us.' The public rooms 'are a joy, plenty of areas for socialising or for privacy'. In this rambling building, the bedrooms vary in size. 'Our excellent twin-bedded room had a breathtaking view over the garden and out to sea.' Soundproofing may not be perfect: 'Creaking floorboards above us were a problem.' Nine bedrooms have been refurbished this year. Dinner in the main restaurant is a formal affair, with jacket and tie 'preferred' for men. Suppers and light lunches are recommended in the less formal *Quarterdeck* restaurant (alfresco in summer): 'Good food, pleasant service.' A hot tub has been installed by the renovated outdoor swimming pool. (*Dennis and Angela Marler, Sara and John Leathes, John and Ann Smith*)

Bedrooms: 39, some on ground floor, 1 suitable for &. *Open*: all year. *Facilities*: lift, ramps, lounge, drawing room, sun lounge, bar, billiard room, light lunch/supper room, 2 restaurants, conservatory, indoor swimming pool (hot tub, sauna), gym, 5-acre grounds (garden, heated swimming pool, tennis, croquet, children's play area, safe sandy beach), concessionary golf at Truro golf club. *Background music*: none. *Location*: S of Veryan, on coast. *Smoking*: not allowed. *Children*: all ages welcomed. *Dogs*: not allowed in public rooms. *Credit cards*: Amex, MasterCard, Visa. *Prices*: [2008] b&b £109–£315 per person, d,b&b £124–£330, set dinner £45, special breaks, Christmas/New Year packages.

WAREHAM Dorset   Map 2:E1

The Priory   *Tel* 01929-551666
Church Green   *Fax* 01929-554519
Wareham   *Email* reservations@theprioryhotel.co.uk
BH20 4ND   *Website* www.theprioryhotel.co.uk

César award in 1996

'High standards in a lovely setting,' says a report in 2008 on this small hotel in a 'delightful small town'. Visitors over more than 30 years found 'regular staff, attentive as ever; newcomers being well trained'. Other praise: 'It meets our needs: freshly squeezed orange juice; staff address you by name; good lights for reading in bed, room serviced while you dine; no muzak.' It is owned by Anne Turner with brother-in-law Stuart, and managed by her son, Jeremy Merchant. Approached across a green with coloured Georgian houses, and a flagstoned court-yard, the 16th-century former priory has a 'charming quirkiness'. 'The garden is beautifully maintained, terrace in front, lawn sloping down to the River Frome.' The bedrooms vary in size and aspect, 'all very comfortable, and well equipped with luxuries'; some are in a boathouse. 'Our standard room was lovely, though the bathroom was cramped.' Public rooms are in 'country house style'. An upstairs lounge faces garden, river and meadows. Drinks in the beamed drawing room precede dinner in the stone-vaulted Abbots' Cellar.

Lunch is served in the Garden Room or alfresco in fine weather. The modern cooking of the new chef, Jon Newing, is 'excellent: delicious venison'. (*Ian Malone, Nigel and Jennifer Jee, Gordon Franklin*)

Bedrooms: 18, some on ground floor (in courtyard), 4 suites in Boathouse. *Open*: all year. *Facilities*: ramps, lounge, drawing room (pianist Sat evening), bar, 2 dining rooms, 4-acre gardens (croquet, river frontage, moorings, fishing), bicycle hire, unsuitable for &. *Background music*: none. *Location*: town centre. *Smoking*: not allowed. *Children*: not under 14. *Dogs*: only guide dogs allowed. *Credit cards*: all major cards. *Prices*: [to 31 Mar 2009] b&b £112.50–£172.50 per person, d,b&b £137.50–£197.50, set dinner £39.95, off-season breaks, Christmas/New Year packages, 1-night bookings refused weekends.

WARMINSTER Wiltshire   Map 2:D1

Crockerton House
Crockerton Green
Warminster BA12 8AY

Tel 01985-216631
Email stay@crockertonhouse.co.uk
Website www.crockertonhouse.co.uk

'All is fresh and clean' at this 'gorgeous' Grade II listed Georgian house which has been 'painstakingly restored' and 'tastefully decorated' by owners Christopher and Enid Richmond. 'Inherited antiques and new furnishings are in keeping'; old features judiciously preserved. 'Chris is a pleasant front-of-house,' said inspectors. 'Our large, light room, with king-size bed and big windows overlooking the gardens, was a pleasant place to sit and read.' Two of the bedrooms have a bathroom *en suite*. The Heytesbury Suite's windows face the front and rear gardens; the Silk Room overlooks a lane running down to an old mill. The Officer's Room has a bathroom adjacent. All rooms have flat-screen TV and Wi-Fi. Visitors who arrive before 5 pm are given free tea, at a large table under a tree in the garden if weather permits. An Aga-cooked dinner, at 8, is served by arrangement (main courses like organic chicken and wild mushroom pie); no licence; bring your own wine. 'Breakfast was elegantly presented. Excellent bread, home-made preserves'; also freshly squeezed juice, organic cereals, eggs, bacon, etc. The grounds, with hedges, herbaceous borders, orchard and kitchen garden, face meadows that lead down to the River Wylye, in a designated area of outstanding natural beauty.

Bedrooms: 3. *Open*: all year except Christmas/New Year. *Facilities*: drawing room, dining room, 1¼-acre garden, unsuitable for &. *Background music*: none. *Location*: 2 miles S of Warminster. *Smoking*: not allowed. *Children*: not under 12. *Dogs*: not allowed. *Credit cards*: MasterCard, Visa. *Prices*: [2008] b&b £44.50–£119 per person, set dinner £30, reduced rates for longer stays, 1-night bookings refused weekends.

WARTLING East Sussex   Map 2:E4

Wartling Place   *Tel* 01323-832590
Wartling, Herstmonceux   *Email* accom@wartlingplace.prestel.co.uk
nr Eastbourne   *Website* www.countryhouseaccommodation.co.uk
BN27 1RY

With views to the South Downs, this early 18th-century Grade II
listed ex-rectory is now an upmarket B&B, run by its 'kind and caring'
owners, Barry and Rowena Gittoes. Painted white, it stands in a large,
'immaculate' landscaped garden. Staircases in this former rest home
have short, wide flights. Prints and pictures hang on walls. The
'beautifully finished', spacious bedrooms have cream carpet,
Egyptian cotton bedlinen, large, fluffy towels, flat-screen TV and
DVD-player. The two best rooms have an antique four-poster bed.
Any road noise is mitigated by padded blinds and thick curtains. Wi-
Fi is available. The 'exceptional' breakfast, served between 8.30 and
9 am (9.30 at weekends), includes fruit, kedgeree, omelettes, waffles
with maple syrup, full English, freshly baked rolls. In the elegant
lounge, with bay windows, settees, chairs and antiques, drinks are
taken from an honesty bar. An evening meal is available by arrangement; for dining out, *The Lamb*, an 'excellent' gastropub almost
opposite (refurbished this year), is recommended, or the *Sundial* in
Herstmonceux. Returning guests get a 'one-off package: three nights
for the price of two'. More reports, please.

Bedrooms: 4, also self-catering cottage. *Open*: all year. *Facilities*: lounge/dining
room with honesty bar and CD-player, 3-acre garden, unsuitable for &, except
ground floor of cottage. *Background music*: classical all day. *Location*: 3 miles N
of Pevensey. *Smoking*: not allowed. *Children*: all ages welcomed. *Dogs*: not
allowed. *Credit cards*: Amex, MasterCard, Visa. *Prices*: b&b £55–£100 per
person, set dinner £37.50, 1-night bookings sometimes refused Sat.

WARWICK Warwickshire   Map 3:C6
See SHORTLIST

We say 'Unsuitable for &' when a hotel tells us that it cannot
accommodate wheelchair-users. We do not have the resources
to inspect such facilities or to assess the even more
complicated matter of facilities for the partially disabled. We
suggest that you discuss such details with the hotel.

WATERMILLOCK Cumbria   Map 4: inset C2

Rampsbeck   *Tel* 01768-486442
Watermillock on Ullswater   *Fax* 01768-486688
nr Penrith CA11 0LP   *Email* enquiries@rampsbeck.co.uk
                              Website www.rampsbeck.co.uk

Tom and Marion Gibb have sold their popular hotel on the shores of
Lake Ullswater, but she will continue to run it 'for at least three
years'. 'The new owners have injected capital to allow improvements,' she tells us. 'They want everything to continue as before;
staff remain the same.' A 'hands-on' manageress, she is 'present at
least 12 hours a day', one visitor tells us, 'performing all manner of
tasks, serving at table, collecting used china and glasses from the
lounges'. The white 18th-century house has 'lovely gardens with
unusual plants and well-tended lawns'. Public rooms 'retain their
original feel: rich colours, reproduction lamps and furniture, ornaments, large fireplaces', but some guests find the dining room decor
'a bit odd'. The best bedrooms look over fields to the lake. 'Ours, in
tip-top condition, had voluminous storage space; fresh water and fruit
replenished daily.' Modern bathrooms have 'excellent lighting and
plumbing'. 'Good housekeeping.' Andrew McGeorge, the long-
serving chef, serves meals of 'a high standard' if sometimes 'a bit
fancy'. Modern dishes include baked goat's cheese with red onion
marmalade; roasted turbot with curried cauliflower confit. 'Outstanding desserts.' Breakfast, fully served, 'has comprehensive choice;
extra helpings of juice'. (*Edwin Prince, Richard Mayou, Diana Goodey,
Christian Bartoschek*)

Bedrooms: 19. *Open*: all year except 3 weeks in Jan. *Facilities*: 2 lounges, bar,
restaurant, civil wedding licence, 18-acre grounds (croquet), lake frontage
(fishing, sailing, windsurfing, etc), unsuitable for &. *Background music*: none.
Location: 5½ miles SW of Penrith. *Smoking*: not allowed. *Children*: young
children not allowed in restaurant at night. *Dogs*: allowed in 3 bedrooms, hall
lounge. *Credit cards*: MasterCard, Visa. *Prices*: [2008] b&b £65–£140 per person,
d,b&b £108–£183, set dinner £45, Christmas/New Year packages, 1-night
bookings occasionally refused weekends.

Italicised entries are for hotels on which we need more
feedback – either because we are short of detailed or recent
reports, or because we have had ambivalent or critical
comments.

WELLS Somerset   Map 1:B6

Canon Grange   *Tel* 01749-671800
Cathedral Green   *Email* canongrange@email.com
BA5 2UB   *Website* www.canongrange.co.uk

Friendly B&B run by Annette and Ken Sowden in 15th-century listed house
on cathedral green, facing magnificent west front (floodlit at night). Ask for a
room (No. 3 or No. 4) with that view (also seen from the breakfast table).
Exposed beams, wood panelling, walnut furniture. Sitting room, dining
room (church music). 5-acre garden. Breakfast English, vegetarian or
'lighter' (for dieters); evening meal by arrangement (£18–£20). No smoking.
No dogs. Amex, MasterCard, Visa accepted. 5 bedrooms with period decor
(1 family, 1 on ground floor). Prices: [2008] b&b £25–£40 per person,
1-night bookings sometimes refused Sat. More reports, please.

WEST STOKE West Sussex   Map 2:E3

West Stoke House   *Tel* 01243-575226
West Stoke, nr Chichester   *Fax* 01243-574655
PO18 9BN   *Email* info@weststokehouse.co.uk
                             Website www.weststokehouse.co.uk

🍲 *César award in 2008*

'Relaxed and unstuffy', this white-painted Georgian mansion stands
in large grounds on the edge of the South Downs. It has been
renovated in idiosyncratic style by Rowland and Mary Leach: he is a
'charmingly eccentric owner, with out-of-control hair, who wears
baggy shorts all year round'. With their 'supremely professional'
manager, Richard Macadam, they run it informally as a restaurant-
with-rooms. Chef Darren Brown was awarded a *Michelin* star in 2008 for
his 'superb' modern British, French-influenced cooking (eg, roasted
fillet of sea bass, asparagus, tagliatelle, courgette flower and crab
mousse, shellfish foam; toffee soufflé, banana and lime ice cream,
praline custard). The public rooms have antiques on polished floors,
plenty of art, much of it local. Drinks are taken in the large lounge
(with red walls and chairs, yellow curtains). The blue-walled dining
room, once a ballroom, has a musicians' gallery, a large chandelier,
tables 'properly laid with white tablecloths, good cutlery and glass'.
The bedrooms have French antiques, big bed, modern fabrics. 'Ours
was large, thoughtfully furnished; trendy fittings; flat-screen
TV/DVD; powerful shower (no bath); superb views. Everything

exuded quality.' English breakfast, served until 10 am, has fruit, cereals, yogurts, croissants, 'excellent' coffee, 'thick-cut bacon'. Weddings and other celebrations are often held.

Bedrooms: 8. *Open*: all year except Christmas, restaurant closed Sun evening/ Mon/Tues. *Facilities*: lounge, restaurant, ballroom, civil wedding licence, 5-acre grounds (garden games), unsuitable for &. *Background music*: soft, in restaurant. *Location*: 3 miles NW of Chichester. *Smoking*: not allowed. *Children*: all ages welcomed. *Dogs*: not allowed in public rooms. *Credit cards*: Amex, MasterCard, Visa. *Prices*: [2008] b&b £65–£115 per person, set dinner £45, New Year package, 1-night bookings refused Sat.

WESTON-SUPER-MARE Somerset   Map 1:B6
See SHORTLIST

WHITBY North Yorkshire   Map 4:C5
See SHORTLIST

WHITEWELL Lancashire   Map 4:D3

The Inn at Whitewell
Forest of Bowland
nr Clitheroe BB7 3AT

Tel 01200-448222
Fax 01200-448298
Email reception@innatwhitewell.com
Website www.innatwhitewell.com

'Stunningly set', high above the River Hodder, this old inn, owned by the Duchy of Lancaster and managed by Charles Bowman, has views across the Forest of Bowland. Family antiques and old paintings are everywhere, and it has an art gallery. It is liked for the quirky style and food and service in the restaurant and bar. But two readers this year, though 'on balance we would stay again', commented on 'the lack of welcome' at Reception, which 'doubles as a retail outlet'. 'This is more a gastropub with rooms than a hotel.' Log fires warm the public rooms, and the busy bar, popular with locals, 'has a delightful ambience'. The riverside dining room 'is a touch more formal'. Local ingredients are used by chef Jamie Cadman in dishes like Whitewell fish pie; roast goose breast with *choucroute*. The river-facing bedrooms have 'delightful views'; less appealing rooms face the car park. 'No tea-making facilities, but room service starts at 7 am.' 'Good breakfasts: freshly squeezed orange juice, good fruit, porridge with cream and honey, full English.' The inn owns seven miles of fishing for salmon, trout, etc. Children are welcomed, and 'many dogs are regular customers'.

Bedrooms: 23, 4 (2 on ground floor) in coach house, 150 yds. *Open*: all year. *Facilities*: 2 bars, restaurant, board room, orangery, civil wedding licence, 5-acre garden, 7 miles fishing (ghillie available), unsuitable for &. *Background music*: none. *Location*: 6 miles NW of Clitheroe. *Smoking*: not allowed. *Children*: all ages welcomed. *Dogs*: not allowed in dining room. *Credit cards*: MasterCard, Visa. *Prices*: b&b £48–£160 per person, full alc £38.

WHITSTABLE Kent   Map 2:D5

Windy Ridge   *Tel* 01227-263506
Wraik Hill   *Email* scott@windyridgewhitstable.co.uk
Whitstable CT5 3BY   *Website* www.windyridgewhitstable.co.uk

In a garden on a small country road, Hugh and Lynda Scott's characterful conversion of two farm cottages has panoramic views of town and sea. 'The pleasure of this place is how comfortable it feels, unlike many anonymous hotels,' wrote visitors with three young children, who appreciated the 'welcome and help given' by the Scotts. One of the gargoyles on the front wall is reputedly from Canterbury Cathedral; there are beamed ceilings, a wood-burning stove in the 'cosy' lounge, and cast iron fireplaces. The bedrooms 'have been refurbished to a very high standard'. One has a four-poster bed, and there are two 2-room family suites (one with a living area, the other with private access from the garden). 'Great value.' 'The dining room, facing the garden and estuary, is lovely.' Breakfast, 'done superbly', has healthy and vegetarian options and meat from local butchers. An evening meal is available by arrangement, and the Scotts 'went out of their way to help with restaurant bookings'. 'We get fantastic sunsets,' they say. Wi-Fi is available. (*NG, and others*)

Bedrooms: 10, 3 on ground floor, 1 suitable for &. *Open*: all year except part Nov. *Facilities*: lounge, bar, dining room, meeting/conference facilities, civil wedding licence, ½-acre garden (gazebo). *Background music*: at breakfast. *Location*: 1½ miles from centre, off A299. *Smoking*: not allowed. *Children*: not under 9. *Dogs*: allowed by prior arrangement, in 1 bedroom only. *Credit cards*: MasterCard, Visa. *Prices*: b&b £42.50–£53 per person, 3-night rates, Christmas/ New Year packages, 1-night bookings refused weekends in season. *V*

WILLINGTON Cheshire   Map 3:A5
See SHORTLIST

WILMINGTON East Sussex   Map 2:E4

Crossways Hotel
Lewes Road
Wilmington BN26 5SG

Tel 01323-482455
Fax 01323-487811
Email stay@crosswayshotel.co.uk
Website www.crosswayshotel.co.uk

'Professional, unpretentious, friendly', 'very comfortable', this pretty house in a village in the Cuckmere valley has a loyal following among visitors to nearby Glyndebourne: 'Staying here makes our yearly treat even more enjoyable.' The owners, David Stott ('front man and chef, how does he do it all?') and Clive James, are 'model hosts, warm, unflappable, generous; they seem always to have room in the fridge for vast Glyndebourne picnics'. No guest lounge, but bedrooms contain 'every appliance imaginable: TV, clock, knick-knacks galore'. Some rooms have a sofa; one has a balcony. 'We felt slightly in a time warp with 1960s furnishings.' The four-course *prix-fixe* dinner menu, served in an intimate dining room, changes monthly: 'Delicious, spicy sweet potato soup; smoked fish salad; main courses elegant, in conservative idiom: first-class local rack of lamb with four vegetables.' 'Breakfast, in a sunny room with a collection of cheese dishes, is hugely enjoyable, some of the best eggs and bacon'; 'nice, tart fruit salad'. 'Conversations across tables are normal. Warmth and friendliness turns clients into valued guests.' The large garden, with pond, rabbits and herb garden, runs down to a main road which is busy, even at night. (*Richard Parish, Ann Lawson Lucas, FM*)

Bedrooms: 7, also self-catering cottage. *Open*: all year except 24 Dec–22 Jan, restaurant closed midday and Sun/Mon. *Facilities*: breakfast room, restaurant, 2-acre grounds (duck pond), unsuitable for &. *Background music*: in restaurant. *Location*: 2 miles W of Polegate on A27. *Smoking*: not allowed. *Children*: not under 12. *Dogs*: not allowed. *Credit cards*: Amex, MasterCard, Visa. *Prices*: b&b £57.50–£72 per person, set dinner £36.95.

WINCHELSEA East Sussex   Map 2:E5

The Strand House
Tanyard's Lane
Winchelsea TN36 4JT

Tel 01797-226276
Fax 01797-224806
Email info@thestrandhouse.co.uk
Website www.thestrandhouse.co.uk

Below the 'delightful' old town, this small guest house, composed of two Grade II listed buildings (one 13th-century, the other Tudor), was bought by Mary Sullivan and Hugh Davie in June 2007. Visitors who stayed six weeks later were 'impressed by the standards'. Others wrote of 'friendliness and enthusiasm'. Inspectors agreed: 'A wonderful hostess, energetic, always kind, never inquisitive.' There are new soft furnishings, improved beds, new flat-screen TVs. 'Our bedroom was small but delightful, with large inglenook fireplace, French windows on to the garden. Flowery fabrics, brass bedhead; a minuscule shower.' Some rooms are up steep steps. 'Ceilings exceptionally low: beams can leave an impression on taller visitors, my husband walked with a permanent stoop.' In the evening, Mary Sullivan in chef's clothing 'takes orders then disappears into the kitchen. The food is good without being *haute cuisine*; three choices for the first two courses. Delicious mushroom soup; very fresh sea bass. A different menu each night.' 'Afternoon tea a real treat.' 'Friendly local staff.' 'Only drawback: constant muzak.' Bedrooms are serviced during breakfast, which has 'all manner of cooked dishes'. The house stands well back from a main road: most guests 'didn't find traffic noise a problem'. (*Sue Lyon, Ann and Michael Maher, and others*)

Bedrooms: 10, 1 on ground floor. *Open*: all year. *Facilities*: reception, lounge, bar, breakfast room, civil wedding/partnership licence, 1-acre garden, unsuitable for &. *Background music*: jazz/big bands/crooners in public rooms. *Location*: 300 yds from centre, 2 miles SW of Rye. *Smoking*: not allowed. *Children*: not under 5. *Dogs*: allowed by arrangement, but not in public rooms. *Credit cards*: Amex, MasterCard, Visa. *Prices*: b&b £32.50–£75 per person, d,b&b £57.50–£105, set dinner £27.50, special breaks, Christmas/New Year packages, 1-night bookings refused weekends Apr–Sept, Christmas/New Year.

WINCHESTER Hampshire   Map 2:D2
See SHORTLIST

WINDERMERE Cumbria   Map 4: inset C2

Gilpin Lodge
Crook Road
nr Windermere LA23 3NE

Tel 015394-88818
Fax 015394-88058
Email hotel@gilpinlodge.co.uk
Website www.gilpinlodge.co.uk

❦ *César award in 2000*

Surrounded by moors, woodlands and gardens, this Edwardian country house hotel (Relais & Châteaux) is run in hands-on but informal style by the Cunliffe family. Barney Cunliffe is manager; his father, Richard, is 'a dominant figure in the dining room'. 'Like being in someone's lovely home, with discreet but attentive family members to look after you,' says a returning fan in 2008. 'Perfect as ever; service delightfully friendly,' wrote another. The main lounge has been redecorated, and there is a new champagne bar with patio. Chef Chris Meredith may have lost his *Michelin* star, but a trusted correspondent insists: 'The food gets better all the time. Tasty starters, eg, lobster ravioli, sausage of pike with watercress and crayfish.' Main courses include turbot poached in red wine. Light lunches are served in the lounge. Each bedroom is named after a local beauty spot; some have a four-poster, some a whirlpool bath. The six garden suites have a contemporary decor. 'Even the smaller rooms are comfortable.' A backpack with maps and books of walks is provided for hikers. 'Breakfast is a leisurely affair with fruity starters, a great collection of warm dishes.' 'Expensive, but worth it.' (*Wolfgang Stroebe, David and Bridget Reed, James and Lesley Blood, Anne and Denis Tate*)

Bedrooms: 20, 6 in orchard wing. *Open*: all year. *Facilities*: ramps, bar, 2 lounges, 4 dining rooms, 22-acre grounds (ponds, croquet), free access to nearby country club (swimming pool, sauna, squash), golf course opposite, unsuitable for &. *Background music*: none. *Location*: on B5284, 2 miles SE of Windermere. *Smoking*: not allowed. *Children*: not under 7. *Dogs*: not allowed (kennels at nearby farm). *Credit cards*: all major cards. *Prices*: b&b £115–£175 per person, d,b&b £135–£195, set dinner £47, Christmas/New Year packages, 1-night bookings sometimes refused weekends.

Holbeck Ghyll   *Tel* 015394-32375
Holbeck Lane   *Fax* 015394-34743
Windermere LA23 1LU   *Email* stay@holbeckghyll.com
                                      Website www.holbeckghyll.com

'If you are looking for ambience, great food, friendly, attentive service, and wonderful views, you can't go wrong here,' say visitors who celebrated their silver wedding at David and Patricia Nicholson's luxurious Lakeland hotel (Pride of Britain). Others wrote of the 'warm welcome' (help with luggage). 'We like the evening turn-down service.' 'Pricey but worth it.' 'Superb views. Staff are pleasant, if sometimes a little voluble.' Built as a hunting lodge by Lord Lonsdale in 1888, the house stands in large grounds, with streams, wildlife, tennis, which slope down to the lake. There is a small spa. A four-bedroom house and a three-bedroom lodge have now opened in the grounds. A lake-view room was 'clean, comfortable, with lovely bathroom'. 'Impeccable' public rooms have 'a baronial feel': stained glass, open fires, wood panelling, antiques; also free Internet access.

There are two dining rooms, one oak-panelled, the other with French windows that lead on to a terrace for alfresco meals. Chef David McLaughlin has a *Michelin* star: 'We enjoyed every meal: good starters (salmon and crab pasta; gravadlax and truffled potato salad; small cups of soup). Lamb, beef and venison served pink and tender.' Breakfast has a large buffet, good cooked dishes. 'Booking can be a hassle.' (*Mark and Patricia Jacques, ST*)

Bedrooms: 33, 1 suitable for &, 10 (1 with kitchenette) in lodge and houses. *Open*: all year except 4–23 Jan. *Facilities*: ramp, 2 lounges, bar, restaurant, function facilities, civil wedding licence, small spa (sauna, steam room, massage, etc), 7-acre grounds (streams, ponds, woods to lake shore, tennis, putting, croquet, jogging track). *Background music*: in 1 lounge. *Location*: 3 miles N of Windermere, off road to Ambleside. *Smoking*: not allowed. *Children*: not under 8 in restaurant. *Dogs*: not allowed in public rooms. *Credit cards*: Amex, MasterCard, Visa. *Prices*: b&b £110–£275 per person, d,b&b £125–£300, set dinner £55, Christmas/New Year packages, 1-night bookings refused Sat. *V*

See also SHORTLIST

WINSTER Derbyshire   Map 3:B6

The Dower House
Main Street
Winster, nr Matlock
DE4 2DH

Tel 01629-650931
Email fosterbig@aol.com
Website www.thedowerhousewinster.com

In a conservation village in the Peak District national park, this Grade II listed 16th-century former dower house is run as a 'country house B&B' by John and Marsha Biggin. 'A most enjoyable stay,' says a visitor this year endorsing earlier praise. 'Bedrooms are generously proportioned and beautifully warm.' One has window seats facing the main street, another a stone fireplace and views through mullioned windows of the 'lovely walled garden'. One room has an *en suite* shower room, the others have a private, spacious bathroom. The guests' sitting room has sofas, 'lots of pictures', and an honesty bar. In the dining hall (with original beams, sash windows, part stone floor and wood fire), breakfast includes home-made muesli, fresh fruit, wholemeal and granary bread, dry-cured bacon, 'sausages from our award-winning farm butcher' and preserves from Chatsworth's farm shop. 'Delicious, particularly the local oatcake cushioning perfectly poached eggs.' A gate gives private access to the village churchyard. The driveway's entrance is 'rather narrow: be careful if you have a large car'. The 'cheerful' *Bowling Green* pub in the village serves 'generous, reasonable' food. The 'plague village' of Eyam, close by, is worth a visit. (*JK, and others*)

Bedrooms: 4. *Open*: all year except Christmas/New Year. *Facilities*: sitting room, bar, dining room, ¼-acre walled garden (pond), unsuitable for &. *Background music*: occasional classical, in dining room. *Location*: 3 miles W of Matlock. *Smoking*: not allowed. *Children*: not under 12. *Dogs*: allowed in courtyard only. *Credit cards*: none. *Prices*: b&b £47.50–£75 per person, 1-night bookings refused Fri/Sat in season.

WOLD NEWTON East Yorkshire   Map 4:D5

The Wold Cottage
Wold Newton, nr Driffield
YO25 3HL

Tel/Fax 01262-470696
Email katrina@woldcottage.com
Website www.woldcottage.com

In landscaped grounds with views to the Yorkshire Wolds, this red brick Georgian mansion (once a city gentleman's retreat) has been 'lovingly restored' by Katrina and Derek Gray. They offer 'country house accommodation'. 'Friendly, informative and most helpful', they welcome visitors with tea and cake. 'My room in the converted barn was spacious and well equipped,' one admirer wrote. Extras include dressing gowns, hot-water bottle, fresh milk in a flask. Mrs Gray uses local produce (vegetables from the garden) for dinner, served by arrangement, by candlelight, communally or at separate tables. 'Like the best home cooking on dinner-party days; very good value.' 'Breakfast was excellent, plenty of cereals, fresh fruit and yogurt, variations of full English or a variety of fish dishes, home-made bread and preserves.' (*RP, J and DM*)

Bedrooms: 5, 2 in converted barn, 1 on ground floor. *Open*: all year. *Facilities*: lounge, dining room, 3-acre grounds (croquet) in 300-acre farmland. *Background music*: at mealtimes. *Location*: just outside village. *Smoking*: not allowed. *Children*: all ages welcomed. *Dogs*: not allowed. *Credit cards*: MasterCard, Visa. *Prices*: [2008] b&b £40–£60 per person, set dinner £21.50.

The more reports we receive, the more accurate the *Guide* becomes. Please don't hesitate to write again about an old favourite, even if it is only to endorse the entry. New reports help us keep the *Guide* up to date.

WOLTERTON Norfolk   Map 2:A5

The Saracen's Head

Wolterton, nr Erpingham
NR11 7LZ

Tel 01263-768909
Fax 01263-768993
Email saracenshead@wolterton.freeserve.co.uk
Website www.saracenshead-norfolk.co.uk

A 'genuine family affair', this 'lost inn', down narrow lanes amid fields in rural Norfolk, is run by Robert Dawson-Smith with his daughter, Rachel, who also has a workshop selling retro furniture and pictures. The building is modelled on a Tuscan farmhouse. 'As always the welcome is warm,' said a regular visitor. It is not to all tastes ('too much of a pub'), but fans like the 'real' bedrooms (bright red, green or blue walls, patchwork bedspreads). Three, upstairs, have a rounded dormer window. 'Ours was fair-sized, done in bold colours.' In the public areas, filled with paintings, bric-a-brac, etc, Mr Dawson-Smith serves 'wonderful' dishes, perhaps fricassée of wild and tame mushrooms; baked Cromer crab with apple and sherry. In summer, meals are served alfresco. Breakfast ('especially good') includes freshly squeezed orange juice, fruit, fresh bread, good kippers. The Dawson-Smiths warn on their website: 'We are up for sale, but it could take yonks.' Check before booking. (*TB*)

Bedrooms: 6. *Open*: all year except 25 Dec, evening of 26 Dec. *Facilities*: lounge, 3 dining rooms, courtyard, 1-acre garden, shop, accommodation unsuitable for &. *Background music*: none. *Location*: 5 miles from Aylsham. *Smoking*: not allowed. *Children*: all ages welcomed. *Dogs*: not allowed in public areas. *Credit cards*: Amex, MasterCard, Visa. *Prices*: [2008] b&b £42.50–£45 per person, set dinner £33.50, d,b&b package on request, New Year package, 1-night bookings refused weekends.

WOODSTOCK Oxfordshire   Map 2:C2
See SHORTLIST

WOOKEY HOLE Somerset   Map 1:B6

Miller's at Glencot House   **NEW**

Glencot Lane
Wookey Hole, nr Wells
BA5 1BH

Tel 01749-677160
Fax 01749-670210
Email relax@glencothouse.co.uk
Website www.glencothouse.co.uk

'Wonderfully quirky, great fun' (say inspectors), this neo-Jacobean listed mansion is owned by the antique dealer Martin Miller (see also

Miller's Residence, London, Shortlist). He has turned it into a treasure trove of paintings, prints, cartoons, stuffed birds, stags' antlers, bits of china on dressers, porcelain-headed dolls, huge Chinese vases, rich colours, heavy fabrics and much more. Second-hand books are everywhere, piled high. The house, with its mullioned windows, carved ceilings and panelling, stands amid old trees in lovely grounds with the River Axe running through, and a cricket pitch. Manager Ben Humber heads a 'helpful staff'. 'Our quiet room had heavy, beaded curtains, a collection of teapots, a neat little bathroom (but no evening turn-down). In the charming dining room, with beamed ceiling and huge chandelier, dinner was fine, if not exceptional. Try for a window table.' The daily-changing menu has main courses like beef Wellington; steamed salmon with wild garlic. 'Breakfast had delicious croissants but poor toast and canned juices. Pity about the muzak, played all day in the public rooms. We thought the half-board rate (£110) reasonable.' There is a tiny indoor jet stream pool. Local sightseeing includes the marvellous cathedral city of Wells, Wookey Hole caves, the Cheddar Gorge, Glastonbury.

Bedrooms: 15, some on ground floor. *Open*: all year. *Facilities*: 2 lounges, restaurant, small cinema, snooker room, tiny indoor pool with jet stream, 18-acre grounds (garden, river (fishing), croquet, cricket pitch). *Background music*: all day in public rooms. *Location*: 2 miles NW of Wells. *Smoking*: not allowed. *Children*: all ages welcomed. *Dogs*: not allowed in restaurant. *Credit cards*: all major cards. *Prices*: b&b £82.50–£165 per person, set dinner £32.50, 2-day half-board rates, various packages.

WORFIELD Shropshire   Map 3:C5

The Old Vicarage
Worfield
nr Bridgnorth
WV15 5JZ

Tel 01746-716497
Fax 01746-716552
Email admin@the-old-vicarage.demon.co.uk
Website www.oldvicarageworfield.com

In large grounds in rural Shropshire, this gabled, red brick Edwardian former parsonage, owned by David and Sarah Blakstad, is 'highly recommended' this year. 'Excellent, with friendly staff, a splendid situation.' A granite terrace and manicured lawn with statues and seats around venerable elms give a 'continental air'. Most of the 'well-maintained' bedrooms have antique furniture; one has a Victorian four-poster bed, another a walnut half-tester. 'Fresh fruit, a decanter of sherry, and a jug of milk a welcome bonus.' The 'light and airy' *Orangey* restaurant has a 'smart casual' dress code (no jeans). The chef, Simon Diprose, serves 'appetising' dishes, eg, salad of crab and asparagus with oriental crab cake; saddle of lamb with dauphinoise potato. 'Each course a work of art, and delicious to eat. The menu didn't change, but there was plenty of choice for a four-day visit.' Breakfast has 'very good sausages', smoked haddock with poached egg, kippers. 'Fruit included passion fruit and figs.' The Blakstads, parents themselves, write: 'While we have limited facilities for children, we actively encourage them to stay.' (*Alan Langton, F and IW*)

Bedrooms: 14, 4 in coach house, 2 on ground floor, 2 suitable for &. *Open*: all year. *Facilities*: ramps, lounge, bar, restaurant, 2 private dining rooms, small conference facilities, civil wedding licence, 2-acre grounds (patio, croquet). *Background music*: none. *Location*: 3 miles NE of Bridgnorth. *Smoking*: not allowed. *Children*: all ages welcomed. *Dogs*: not allowed in public rooms. *Credit cards*: Diners, MasterCard, Visa. *Prices*: b&b £45–£80 per person, d,b&b £70–£110, set dinner £28.50, full alc £45, New Year package. *V*

WROXHAM Norfolk   Map 2:B5

Broad House Hotel   NEW   *Tel/Fax* 01603-783567
The Avenue   *Email* info@broadhousehotel.co.uk
Wroxham NR12 8TS   *Website* www.broadhousehotel.co.uk

'A wonderfully relaxing atmosphere. Homely, comfortable, yet smart.' Close to Wroxham Broad, this beautiful Queen Anne house stands secluded in large, 'lovely, peaceful' grounds. It opened in 2007, after extensive modernisation by owner/managers Philip and Caroline Search. Visitors in 2008 'were impressed by the careful way it has been done, and the quality of the furnishings'. Bedrooms are named after members of the Trafford family, former owners of the house. Andrew's was 'large, bright, with lovely views, huge bed, attractive fabrics, antique furniture, good lighting, vast walk-in cupboard (free-range hangers), small fridge, guide book and folder about local attractions, excellent bathroom'. The comfortable library has books, games, etc; French windows open on to the garden. 'It was pleasant to sit with an aperitif on the bar's small terrace watching wildlife (deer, rabbits, pheasants) and listening to birdsong.' The restaurant has large windows, red walls, antique chairs and tables, contemporary cutlery and china. 'We enjoyed home-grown asparagus; crab cake on aubergine caviar; excellent home-made bread; main courses not quite so good. Delicious pre-dessert of Barbados cream. Service was friendly, informal.' There is a snack menu during the day. 'Breakfast had fresh juice, excellent fruit salad; scrambled eggs were good but toast was boring.' (*Pat and Jeremy Temple*)

Bedrooms: 9. *Open*: all year, restaurant closed Sun to non-residents. *Facilities*: drawing room, library, bar, restaurant, civil wedding/function facilities, 24-acre grounds, heated swimming pool (10 by 4 metres), jetty, market garden, only restaurant suitable for &. *Background music*: classical. *Location*: 8 miles NE of Norwich (airport 5 miles). *Smoking*: not allowed. *Children*: all ages welcomed. *Dogs*: allowed in some bedrooms, not in public rooms. *Credit cards*: Amex, MasterCard, Visa. *Prices*: [2008] b&b £75–£210 per person, d,b&b £103–£210, set dinner £45–£49, special breaks, Christmas/New Year packages.

YARM North Yorkshire   Map 4:C4

Judges   *Tel* 01642-789000
Kirklevington Hall   *Fax* 01642-782878
Yarm TS15 9LW   *Email* enquiries@judgeshotel.co.uk
                       Website www.judgeshotel.co.uk

'Lovely, gentle hospitality, no mobile phones or intrusive muzak.' Praise this year for the Downs family's 'slightly old-fashioned' country hotel. Other comments: 'Atmospheric with fabulous food, charming staff with a lovely style and sense of humour.' 'Felt like home, except grander.' 'All-round excellence.' The Victorian house, once a residence for circuit judges, stands in large, peaceful, wooded grounds, with stream, birds and 'lovely, well-kept landscaped gardens' (floodlit at night). Tim Howard ('kind, supportive') is the manager. Bedrooms, 'a little old-fashioned but comfortable', have feather mattress, foot bath, video recorder with tapes, and CD-player, 'a goldfish in a small bowl and a request to feed it'. 'I liked the small touches (bath salts, needle and thread in a cushion, chocs and a liqueur).' Beds are turned down at night and shoes are shined. In the conservatory restaurant, chef John Schwarz serves modern French dishes, eg, mosaic of guinea fowl with fig purée; roast halibut saffron tagliatelle, seafood broth. 'Good service and food.' Light meals can be taken during the day in the panelled bar or the lounge, with its antiques, fire and flowers. Weddings are held. (*Maggi Savin-Baden, Michael and Eithne Dandy*)

Bedrooms: 21, some on ground floor. *Open*: all year. *Facilities*: ramps, lounge, bar, restaurant, private dining room, function facilities, business centre, civil wedding licence, 36-acre grounds (paths, running routes), access to local spa and sports club. *Background music*: none. *Location*: 1½ miles S of centre. *Smoking*: not allowed. *Children*: all ages welcomed. *Dogs*: only guide dogs allowed. *Credit cards*: all major cards. *Prices*: [2008] b&b £87.50–£197 per person, set dinner £48, full alc £57, Christmas/New Year packages. *V*

YORK North Yorkshire   Map 4:D4

Middlethorpe Hall   *Tel* 01904-641241
Bishopthorpe Road   *Fax* 01904-620176
York YO23 2GB   *Email* info@middlethorpe.com
                              Website www.middlethorpe.com

On the outskirts of the city, by the racecourse, this red brick William
III mansion is 'ideal for a traditional, relaxing weekend in a
beautifully restored country house', says a regular visitor. A Pride of
Britain member, managed by Lionel Chatard, it is owned by Historic
House Hotels Ltd (see also *Hartwell House*, Aylesbury, and
Bodysgallen Hall and Spa, Llandudno, Wales). It has a walled garden,
small lake and venerable trees; inside are antiques, period furnishings, much panelling, stucco ceilings, historic paintings. The large
best bedrooms in the main house have sitting room and gas coal fire;
cheaper rooms are in converted stables and cottages. All rooms have a
flat-screen TV/DVD-player and Wi-Fi connection. There is a smart
casual dress code (no trainers, tracksuits or shorts) in the formal
restaurant in interlinked rooms facing the 'delightful' walled garden.
Nicholas Evans's cooking was admired in 2008; he serves modern
dishes, eg, roast hand-dived Skye scallops; slow-cooked Scotch beef
rump, onion marmalade. Light meals are available in the 18th-
century drawing room. The breakfasts are liked too. Some readers
mention traffic noise in the gardens; one comments: 'It's such an
idyllic house that some might forget it is close to a city.' (*Nicholas
Hurst, John Gibbon, Jane and Martin Bailey*)

Bedrooms: 29, 17 in coach house, 2 in garden, 1 suitable for &. *Open*: all year.
Facilities: drawing room, sitting rooms, library, bar, restaurant, private dining
rooms, function facilities, civil wedding licence, 20-acre grounds (walled
garden, white garden, croquet, lake), spa (health and beauty facilities, heated
indoor swimming pool, 13 by 6 metres). *Background music*: none. *Location*:
1½ miles S of centre, by racecourse. *Smoking*: not allowed. *Children*: not
under 6. *Dogs*: only guide dogs allowed. *Credit cards*: Amex, MasterCard, Visa.
Prices: b&b (continental) £95–£225 per person, English breakfast £6.95 extra,
set dinner £43–£55, Christmas/New Year packages.

See also SHORTLIST

None of the hotels mentioned in the traveller's tales – readers'
horror stories – is included in the *Guide*.

ZENNOR Cornwall   Map 1:D1

 The Gurnard's Head   *Tel* 01736-796928
Treen, nr Zennor   *Email* enquiries@gurnardshead.co.uk
St Ives TR26 3DE   *Website* www.gurnardshead.co.uk

César award: Dining pub of the year

'We are a pub at heart,' write Charles and Edmund Inkin, owners of
this yellow-painted inn on the 'wild' north Cornish coast ('a thrilling
setting'). 'They have struck just the right note,' say inspectors in
2008. 'A congenial atmosphere; a welcome for locals and visitors
alike.' Children and dogs are welcomed too. The bedrooms have
been renovated (more powerful showers). 'Nothing fancy: rough
plaster walls in Delft blue, big bed, comfy window seat (books
underneath); a radio, no TV; functional furnishings; fluffy towels.'
Charles Inkin is 'very much in charge' three weeks out of four,
'chatting to guests, taking orders'; Andrew Wood is the 'charming'
manager. The bar has old tables and chairs, rugs on stone floor, log
fires, books everywhere; a snug with big sofas leads to the simply
furnished, candlelit restaurant. The cooking of Robert Wright, who
took over as chef in February 2008, is admired: 'Splendid starters; the
freshest hake with puy lentils, chorizo and ruby chard; a delicate Irish
moss pudding with cardamom and rose. Breakfast was well thought
out. Chilled apple juice brought by Charles; rustic breads on a side
table with a toaster, home-made marmalade, jam and lemon curd in
large jars. Excellent cooked dishes.' The brothers also own the *Felin
Fach Griffin*, Felin Fach, in Wales (*qv*).

Bedrooms: 7. *Open*: all year except 25 Dec. *Facilities*: bar area, small connecting
room with sofas, dining room, 1-acre garden, unsuitable for &. *Background
music*: CDs in bar, radio by breakfast table for guests' use. *Location*: 6 miles SW
of St Ives, on B3306. *Smoking*: not allowed. *Children*: all ages welcomed. *Dogs*:
allowed. *Credit cards*: MasterCard, Visa. *Prices*: b&b £40–£70 per person, full
alc £24, midweek offers, 'Sunday sleepover' rates.

SCOTLAND

This chapter demonstrates the richness and diversity of the accommodation scene in Scotland. It includes simple B&Bs, welcoming guest houses (including this year's *César* winner), inns which are very much part of local life as well as providing a bed for the traveller, restaurants-with-rooms making the most of wonderful local produce, and some grand hotels in magnificent buildings. Many are set in dramatic scenery; some on remote islands.

Bealach House, Duror

ABERDEEN *See SHORTLIST*   Map 5:C3

ABERFELDY Perth and Kinross   Map 5:D2
See SHORTLIST

ALYTH Perth and Kinross   Map 5:D2
See SHORTLIST

ARISAIG Highland *See SHORTLIST*   Map 5:C1

ASCOG Argyll and Bute   Map 5:D1
See SHORTLIST

AVIEMORE Highland   Map 5:C2

Corrour House   *Tel* 01479-810220
Inverdruie   *Fax* 01479-811500
by Aviemore   *Email* enquiries@corrourhouse.co.uk
PH22 1QH   *Website* www.corrourhouse.co.uk

'The rooms are lovely. Very good breakfast.' Set amid gardens
and woodland, the bay-windowed former dower house of the
Rothiemurchus estate has 'outstanding' views across to the Lairig
Ghru pass and the Cairngorms. 'A house of real antique character,
scrupulously maintained', it is run by owners Carol and Robert Still
who 'take immense trouble to make sure guests have all they need
and to give them information about the neighbourhood'. There are
open fires in the traditionally furnished lounges; bedrooms are
'chintzy'. Dinner is served to residents by prior arrangement (main
courses like pan-fried halibut with parsley sauce), and plenty of
eating places are nearby. 'View of mountains, red squirrels, and at
night you might see a deer cross the lawn.' Aviemore is ten minutes'
walk away. (*Ann Morrison, and others*)

Bedrooms: 8. *Open*: New Year–mid-Nov, dinner by arrangement (residents only). *Facilities*: lounge, cocktail bar, dining room, 4-acre gardens and woodland, unsuitable for &. *Background music*: none. *Location*: ¾ mile S of Aviemore. *Smoking*: not allowed. *Children*: all ages welcomed (under-4s stay free). *Dogs*: not allowed in public rooms or unsupervised in bedrooms. *Credit cards*: MasterCard, Visa. *Prices*: b&b £40–£55 per person, set dinner £32, reductions for 3 or more nights, New Year package, 1-night bookings refused in season.

AYR South Ayrshire *See SHORTLIST*   Map 5:E1

BALLATER Aberdeenshire   Map 5:C3

Darroch Learg   *Tel* 013397-55443
56 Braemar Road   *Fax* 013397-55252
Ballater AB35 5UX   *Email* enquiries@darrochlearg.co.uk
                            Website www.darrochlearg.co.uk

With the 'feel of a well-heeled country house', this pink-granite Victorian listed building ('an oak wood on a sunny hillside' in Gaelic) has been owned by the Franks family for over 40 years; Nigel and Fiona Franks are the 'accomplished hosts'. It stands on the slopes of Craigendarroch above the Royal Deeside village ('great views'). Tastefully decorated, it has big windows, comfortable seating, antiques, watercolours and an open fire in the lounge. The best bedrooms are in the main house; the nearby baronial and turreted *Oakhall*, with cheaper rooms and its own sitting room, is suitable for a group. Most bedrooms have good views; also bathrobes, flowers, fruit. Some have a four-poster or half-tester bed, some a terrace. In the candlelit conservatory restaurant, David Mutter, chef for 12 years, serves modern dishes like halibut with artichokes and mussel and saffron sauce. His cooking 'continues to delight', say returning visitors, and staff 'manage, without being starchy, to complement his efforts'. The wide-ranging wine list includes many half bottles, 'and due to a fixed mark-up per bottle, the better wines seem reasonably priced'. 'Great breakfasts (delicious porridge).' Fishing can be arranged on the nearby River Dee, given notice. (*JS, and others*)

Bedrooms: 17, 5 in *Oakhall*, 1 on ground floor. *Open*: All year except Christmas, last 3 weeks Jan. *Facilities*: ramp, 2 lounges, dining room, 4½-acre grounds. *Background music*: none. *Location*: On A93, ½ mile W of Ballater. *Smoking*: not allowed. *Children*: all ages welcomed. *Dogs*: not allowed in public rooms. *Credit cards*: all major cards. *Prices*: b&b [2008] £60–£125 per person, d,b&b

£95–£160, set lunch £24, dinner £45–£55, autumn, spring breaks, 2- or more night breaks, New Year package, 1-night bookings refused Easter, Braemar Gathering, New Year, Sat.

Deeside Hotel
45 Braemar Road
Ballater AB35 5RQ

Tel 013397-55420
Fax 0871 989 5933
Email mail@deesidehotel.co.uk
Website www.deesidehotel.co.uk

In the 'delightful mountainous countryside' of the Cairngorm national park, near the River Dee, this Victorian house is run as a 'home from home' by its owners, Gordon Waddell (the chef) and Penella Price. It stands on the road to Braemar, a short walk from the village centre. The 'warm welcome' and the good food, 'both at breakfast and dinner', are praised. There are log fires in the 'comfortable small lounge' and the 'well-stocked bar' (over 40 whiskies). The conservatory restaurant serves main courses like organic salmon with hollandaise sauce; rack of lamb with roasted sweet potato. Soups and ice cream are home made; many herbs and vegetables are home grown; breads, seafood and meat come from local suppliers. 'A good wine list, reasonably priced.' Breakfast options include The Haddock and The Highlander. Bedrooms are 'a mix of traditional, modern and Nordic', and are supplied with shortbread, books and quality toiletries. There are king-size beds and a two-room family suite. A children's menu is available. Pets are welcomed by arrangement. Red squirrels can be seen in the walled garden. Good for walkers ('both ambling and serious hill walking'). A member of the Green Tourism Business Scheme. 'Very reasonable rates.' (*DW*)

Bedrooms: 10, 2 on ground floor. *Open*: all year except Christmas, Jan. *Facilities*: ramp, lounge, library, bar, restaurant, 1-acre garden. *Background music*: Mozart in restaurant. *Location*: village outskirts, on road to Braemar. *Smoking*: not allowed. *Children*: all ages welcomed. *Dogs*: not allowed in upstairs bedrooms or public rooms. *Credit cards*: MasterCard, Visa. *Prices*: [2008] b&b £45–£100 per person, d,b&b £65–£125, full alc £35, reductions for 3 or more nights, New Year package, 1-night bookings sometimes refused Sat in season. **V**

The **V** sign at the end of an entry indicates a hotel that has agreed to take part in our Voucher scheme and to give *Guide* readers a 25% discount on their room rates for a one-night stay, subject to the conditions on the back of the vouchers and explained in 'How to use the *Good Hotel Guide*' (page 62).

BALQUHIDDER Stirling   Map 5:D2

Monachyle Mhor   *Tel* 01877-384622
Balquhidder   *Fax* 01877-384305
Lochearnhead FK19 8PQ   *Email* monachyle@mhor.net
                                   Website www.mhor.net

'Dinner was excellent. Staff were friendly. A nice place to stay.' 'A lovely, remote setting.' In a huge estate with a working farm, in Scotland's first national park, the Lewis family's pale-pink converted 18th-century farmhouse and its outbuildings stand at the end of a four-mile single-lane track that winds along Loch Voil. Public rooms have open fires, antiques and modern furnishings. Contemporary paintings by Melanie Lewis hang on walls. The cooking of her brother, owner/chef Tom Lewis, served in the conservatory dining room (views of loch and mountains), is a major draw: French, based on local produce and vegetables and herbs from the organic walled garden, eg, fillet of sea bass with asparagus and red wine sauce. There are inventive vegetarian dishes and good bar meals. Bedrooms vary. Three luxury suites are in converted stables: two have a steam room. Decor is bold and stylish, and there are plenty of 'audio-visual gadgets'. Some rooms have a fire. Some ceilings may be low, and one visitor complained of a lack of good reading lights. The 'excellent' breakfast includes haggis with mixed grill. 'The small sitting room and bar can get crowded.' Ducks wander round the farmyard next door. (*A Melville, and others*)

Bedrooms: 13, 1 on ground floor, 5 in courtyard. *Open*: Feb–New Year. *Facilities*: sitting room, bar, conservatory restaurant, wedding facilities, 2,000-acre estate (garden, *pétanque* pitch, clay-pigeon shooting), unsuitable for &. *Background music*: classical/jazz in bar/restaurant. *Location*: 11 miles NW of Callander. *Smoking*: not allowed. *Children*: all ages welcomed (under-2s free). *Dogs*: allowed in 2 bedrooms and in public rooms. *Credit cards*: MasterCard, Visa. *Prices*: b&b £52.50–£190 per person, d,b&b £141–£227.50, set lunch (Sun) £31, dinner £46, alc lunch weekdays, 1-night bookings refused Sat in season. *V*

How to contact the *Guide*
By mail: From anywhere in the UK, write to Freepost PAM 2931, London W11 4BR (no stamp is needed)
From outside the UK: *Good Hotel Guide*, 50 Addison Avenue, London W11 4QP, England
By telephone or fax: 020-7602 4182
By email: editor@goodhotelguide.com
Via our website: www.goodhotelguide.com

BLAIRGOWRIE Perth and Kinross   Map 5:D2

Kinloch House   *Tel* 01250-884237
Dunkeld Road   *Fax* 01250-884333
by Blairgowrie PH10 6SG   *Email* reception@kinlochhouse.com
                                 Website www.kinlochhouse.com

'Definitely a family-run hotel; we encountered the patriarch in gardener's clothing in the walled garden, and, later, his wife in Reception. Day-to-day management is by their son [Graeme], who did the welcoming, luggage carrying, etc.' On a hillside facing a wide valley, the Allen family's grand 19th-century Scottish mansion (Relais & Châteaux) stands peacefully in large grounds. With its traditional decor, oak-panelled hall, *objets d'art*, log fires, portrait gallery and ornate glass ceiling, it provides 'comfort and quality at a price'. The bedrooms are 'tastefully furnished, not fussy or twee'; many are spacious. Some have a four-poster bed and a large Victorian bath. Most showers are hand-held. At dinner, chef Andrew May serves main courses like turbot with herb ravioli and a caviar cream sauce; sea bass with shellfish risotto. Some visitors experienced long waits between courses. A copy of the menu is left in each bedroom, and guests are telephoned between 6 and 7 pm to take their order. The wine list includes 'good, well-priced house wines' and some expensive bottles. Male guests are no longer asked to wear a jacket at dinner, 'but the majority do'. The health centre (see below) is an attraction. (*Michael Forrest, David Grant, and others*)

Bedrooms: 18, 4 on ground floor. *Open*: all year except 12–28 Dec. *Facilities*: ramp, drawing room, lounge, conservatory, bar, dining room, private dining room, health centre (12 by 5-metre swimming pool, sauna, etc), wedding facilities, 25-acre grounds (walled garden, field with Highland cattle, and horses). *Background music*: none. *Location*: 3 miles W of Blairgowrie, on A923. *Smoking*: not allowed. *Children*: no under-7s in dining room at night.

Dogs: allowed by arrangement (dog units available). *Credit cards*: Amex, MasterCard, Visa. *Prices*: b&b £85–£100 per person, set lunch £19.50, dinner £27, 3-nights for the price of 2 Jan–end Mar, New Year package, 1-night bookings sometimes refused.

BOWMORE Argyll and Bute Map 5:D1
See SHORTLIST

BRACHLA Highland *See SHORTLIST* Map 5:C2

BRODICK North Ayrshire Map 5:E1

Kilmichael Country House
Glen Cloy, by Brodick
Isle of Arran KA27 8BY

Tel 01770-302219
Fax 01770-302068
Email enquiries@kilmichael.com
Website www.kilmichael.com

At the end of an unmade road in grounds patrolled by ducks and peacocks, this is said to be Arran's oldest house. It has spectacular mountain views. Owners Geoffrey Botterill ('a genial host') and Antony Butterworth ('insists he is the cook, not the chef') offer B&B with the option of dining in (residents must book). 'Warm reception. Dinner excellent,' says a visitor this year. 'Gluten-free bread specially baked for my wife.' 'Management much in evidence,' wrote another. Earlier comments: 'In the comfortable drawing rooms, we enjoyed canapés with pre-dinner drinks. The furniture, pictures, etc, collected with care around the world, contribute to the private house atmosphere.' 'Service first class.' In the conservatory dining room (open to non-residents), the three-course menu (with choice) is served with fine silver and crystal. Main courses include brill with mussels in a cream sauce; cheese and parsnip roulade (there is always a vegetarian dish). A light meal can be brought to the bedroom. Some rooms are in the main house (one has four-poster and 'bath big enough for two'). The others are in converted stables a short, if some-times muddy, walk away. All have flowers, fruit, a map, an iron, and 'a welcoming wee dram of whisky'. (*EM Arnold, David Hampshire, IMR*)

Bedrooms: 8, 3 in converted stables (20 yds), 7 on ground floor, 4 self-catering cottages. *Open*: Mar–Oct, restaurant closed midday and Tues. *Facilities*: 2 drawing rooms, dining room, 4½-acre grounds (burn). *Background music*: light classical background music during meals. *Location*: 1 mile SW of village. *Smoking*: not allowed. *Children*: not under 12. *Dogs*: not allowed in public rooms. *Credit cards*: MasterCard, Visa. *Prices*: b&b £75–£95 per person, set dinner £38.50, discounts for 3–7 nights, ferry-inclusive packages, 1-night bookings occasionally refused Sat.

CASTLEBAY Western Isles   Map 5: inset A1
See SHORTLIST

CHIRNSIDE Borders   Map 5:E3

Chirnside Hall
Chirnside, nr Duns
TD11 3LD

Tel 01890-818219
Fax 01890-818231
Email reception@chirnsidehallhotel.com
Website www.chirnsidehallhotel.com

A Dutch couple, Christian and Tessa Korsten, own and run this 'beautifully restored, elegantly decorated' Borders mansion (built in 1830). He specialises in Dutch shooting parties. 'She looked after us with great charm when we were the only other guests,' says a visitor this year. 'On a cold and dreary August night, she lit a log fire in the dining room just for us, and emphasised that we should eat at a time of our choosing. We enjoyed being cosseted in such a beautiful and peaceful location.' An earlier comment: 'The welcome is warm, with just the correct amount of personal attention.' There are 'inspiring' views across fields to the Cheviot Hills. 'Well-decorated', comfortable public rooms have bold colours, rich fabrics, marble fireplaces. The bedrooms have 'all the amenities that one expects'. One has a four-poster bed and a sofa. 'Lots of hot water.' 'Bath suitable for even the tallest person.' Some top rooms may be 'a little dark'. In the handsome small dining room (big tables, upholstered chairs), Gary Imlach serves a daily-changing four-course modern menu. 'Wonderful food: perfectly cooked local roe deer.' 'Breakfast of the same high standard: real kippers.' (*Christopher Beadle, Brian, Lesley and Fenella Knox*)

Bedrooms: 10. *Open*: all year except Mar. *Facilities*: 2 lounges, dining room, billiard room, fitness room, library/conference room, wedding facilities, 6-acre grounds, unsuitable for &. *Background music*: 'easy listening'. *Location*: 1½ miles E of village, NE of Duns. *Smoking*: not allowed. *Children*: all ages welcomed. *Dogs*: not allowed in public rooms. *Credit cards*: Amex, MasterCard, Visa. *Prices*: b&b £75–£150 per person, d,b&b £100–£180, set dinner £30, short breaks, Christmas package.

CLACHAN SEIL Argyll and Bute   Map 5:D1

Willowburn Hotel   *Tel* 01852-300276
Clachan Seil, Isle of Seil   *Email* willowburn.hotel@virgin.net
by Oban PA34 4TJ   *Website* www.willowburn.co.uk

On the little island of Seil (reached across a short, 18th-century, semi-
circular stone bridge over the Atlantic) stands this unpretentious
small hotel. Long, low and narrow, it faces the quiet waters of Clachan
Sound. The 'delightful' view, seen through picture windows in the
lounge and restaurant, is shared by all bedrooms but one. Jan and
Chris Wolfe are 'polite, friendly, hard-working hosts', says a report
this year. 'Dinner was amazing in quality and variety.' Guests come
down at 7 pm to view the menu. Local fishermen and the hotel's
garden supply Chris Wolfe's four-course dinners, 'served at a
comfortable pace, cooked to perfection', eg, selection of game birds
wrapped in filo pastry on a wild mushroom and pine nut risotto.
'Surprisingly extensive wine list; very good value.' 'Lots of chat
between tables.' 'Delicious bread' appears at dinner and breakfast.
Other praise: 'Peace and comfort.' 'Family atmosphere.' Decor is
homely. Neat bedrooms (most rooms are small), 'like a ship's cabin',
have 'good toiletries', 'comfortable bed, excellent reading lights',
'very good information pack'. Prospective canine guests get a letter
from the resident dogs and cat. Two swans, Mr and Mrs D52, often
visit *Willowburn*; so do many birds. (*John Cutler, and others*)

Bedrooms: 7, 1 on ground floor. *Open*: Mar–Nov. *Facilities*: lounge, bar, dining
room, 1½-acre grounds, shore 100 yds, unsuitable for &. *Background music*: quiet,
at night, in dining room. *Location*: 16 miles S of Oban, bus from Oban. *Smoking*:
not allowed. *Children*: not under 8. *Dogs*: not allowed in lounge, dining room.
Credit cards: MasterCard, Visa. *Prices*: [2008] d,b&b £85 per person, set dinner
£39, reductions for 3 or more nights, 1-night bookings occasionally refused.

COLONSAY Argyll and Bute   Map 5:D1

The Colonsay   *Tel* 01951-200316
Isle of Colonsay   *Fax* 01951-200353
PA61 7YP   *Email* reception@thecolonsay.com
                           Website www.thecolonsay.com

'The bar was pleasant, the food good, the hosts were courteous and
efficient,' says a visitor in 2008 to this unpretentious old inn. The only
hotel on this 'idyllic' Hebridean island (eight miles long), it has been
renovated by a group headed by the local laird and his wife, Alex and

Jane Howard. It is managed by Scott Omar. ('He and his wife, Becky, treated us like old friends.') They promise 'simple rooms, luxurious beds, sea views, whisky galore'. Spacious sitting areas have 'lots of log fires, deep sofas and chairs'. There are 'seaside colours', a large collection of early sepia photographs of the island, and 'vibrant' artwork by contemporary artists. The bar, which serves 'a healthy and delicious lunch', has 'a buzz of cheerfulness most of the day'. 'For peace and quiet there is a comfortable library.' In the informal restaurant (harbour views, wood-burning stove, white linen tablecloths), chef Kevin Hay serves 'excellent' modern cooking with a strong local accent, using shellfish, lamb and game ('our philosophy is to buy the best and cook it simply'). 'Very good continental breakfast, but we disliked having to pay extra for cooked.' Children (who stay free in their parents' room) have their own menu. On Colonsay you can 'explore wildlife and archaeological remains, bask on a splendid golden beach', play golf and tennis and go fishing. (*Guy Dehn, Robert E Halstead*)

Bedrooms: 9. *Open*: Mar–Jan. *Facilities*: conservatory lounge, log room, bar, restaurant, wedding facilities possible in 2008, accommodation unsuitable for &. *Background music*: traditional. *Location*: 400 yds W of harbour. *Smoking*: not allowed. *Children*: all ages welcomed. *Dogs*: not allowed in dining room. *Credit cards*: MasterCard, Visa. *Prices*: b&b £42.50–£60 per person, d,b&b (off-season) £70, full alc £25–£35, 1 free night for a 3-night stay Mar, Apr, Oct, Christmas/New Year packages.

CONTIN Highland   Map 5:C2

Coul House
Contin
IV14 9ES

Tel 01997-421487
Fax 01997-421945
Email stay@coulhousehotel.com
Website www.coulhousehotel.com

Regular *Guide* correspondents 'very much liked' this 'lovely house with particularly attractive public rooms'. A Georgian hunting lodge (*c.* 1821) fronted by a striking demi-octagonal porch, it stands in the hills, half a mile from the village. In its 'delightful garden' are 'some spectacular mature trees'. Extensively refurbished by the self-styled 'proud owners', Stuart and Susannah Macpherson, in 2006/7, it is managed by Chris McLeod. From a stone terrace where drinks are served, there are 'stunning' views of the Strathconon valley and the mountains beyond. There are plaster ceilings and log fires in the public rooms. In the dining room, with its 18-foot ceiling and full-height windows, Garry Kenley's three-course dinners (contemporary

Scottish cuisine) are thought 'excellent', though some guests found portions 'ridiculously large'. Main courses on a long menu include pan-fried sea bass and roast herb-scented chicken breast; vegetarians are well catered for. Service is 'excellent too'. Children and pets are welcomed. The bedrooms, individually decorated, are 'clean, comfortable, with good pillows' (some have a four-poster). Rooms on the lower floors are the most liked. (*Dale and Krystyna Vargas, and others*)

Bedrooms: 21, some on ground floor. *Open*: all year except 24–26 Dec. *Facilities*: ramp, hall, lounge, bar lounge, restaurant, conference and wedding facilities, 8-acre garden (children's play area, 9-hole pitch and putt). *Background music*: classical/Scottish/jazz in lounge bar and restaurant. *Location*: ½ mile above village, 17 miles NW of Inverness. *Smoking*: not allowed. *Children*: all ages welcomed (under-5s stay free). *Dogs*: not allowed in public rooms. *Credit cards*: all major cards. *Prices*: b&b £55–£100 per person, d,b&b £77.50–£125, full alc £42.50, weekend and midweek breaks, special events, New Year package. *V*

CRINAN Argyll and Bute   Map 5:D1

Crinan Hotel

Crinan
by Lochgilphead PA31 8SR

Tel 01546-830261
Fax 01546-830292
Email reservations@crinanhotel.com
Website www.crinanhotel.com

'Food and service are really excellent.' 'Fantastic situation, atmosphere relaxed, beautifully peaceful (no background music). Charming staff.' This white-painted hotel, where the Crinan Canal meets the Atlantic basin in a hamlet with a lighthouse, has been owned for 38 years by Nick and Frances Ryan (the artist Frances Macdonald). He is 'very much in evidence, and caring'; her large seascapes hang in the public rooms. Guests appreciate the greeting and the accommodation: 'Luggage carried to our most agreeable bedroom, more private house than hotel: spacious, with large bed, armchairs from which to admire the view, fresh flowers, ornaments; the bathroom was bright, clean, with robes.' Some rooms have a balcony. The coffee shop serves snacks all day. The panoramic *Gallery Bar* at the top serves pre-dinner drinks in summer. The panelled *Mainbrace* bar provides seafood and traditional bar lunches and suppers ('delicious fish soup'). In the 'well-proportioned' *Westward* restaurant, with candles, linen cloths and Lloyd Loom chairs, chef Scott Kennedy uses local fish, shellfish, game and meat (main courses like saddle of rabbit with black pudding, asparagus, and café au lait sauce). 'Impressive breakfast: fresh juice, just-right fruit salad, superb cooked dishes, proper toast.' Children (they have their own menu) and dogs are welcomed. (*AB, and others*)

Bedrooms: 20. *Open*: all year except Christmas. *Facilities*: lift, ramps, 2 lounges, seafood bar, rooftop bar, public bar, restaurant, coffee shop, art gallery, treatment room (health and beauty), wedding facilities, patio, safe, sandy beaches nearby. *Background music*: none. *Location*: village centre. *Smoking*: not allowed. *Children*: all ages welcomed. *Dogs*: allowed at management's discretion, not in restaurant. *Credit cards*: MasterCard, Visa. *Prices*: b&b £75–£110 per person, d,b&b £95–£155, set dinner £50, full alc (*Mainbrace*) £44.40, short breaks, New Year package.

DORNOCH Highland   Map 5:B2

Dornoch Castle Hotel   *Tel* 01862-810216
Castle Street   *Fax* 01862-810981
Dornoch 1V25 3SD   *Email* enquiries@dornochcastlehotel.com
                            Website www.dornochcastlehotel.com

Opposite 12th-century cathedral: 15th-century building, recently refurbished, managed by owner Colin Thompson. New chef in 2008, Michael Middleton. 'Very enjoyable. Comfortable, cosy rooms. Great location, very friendly staff. Good beer.' Weddings a speciality. 24 bedrooms. 2 suitable for &. 3 in garden chalets. Closed 24–26 Dec. Lounge, bar (meals served all day), Garden Restaurant; light background music all the time. Large grounds. No smoking. Dogs in some bedrooms. Amex, MasterCard, Visa accepted. Prices: [2008] b&b £42.50–£126 per person, full alc £35, New Year package.

DUNDEE *See SHORTLIST*   Map 5:D3

DUNKELD Perth and Kinross   Map 5:D2

Kinnaird   *Tel* 01796-482440
Kinnaird Estate   *Fax* 01796-482289
by Dunkeld PH8 0LB   *Email* enquiry@kinnairdestate.com
                            Website www.kinnairdestate.com

On a vast sporting estate (where guests may fish for salmon and trout in the River Tay and for trout in several lochs) stands this creeper-covered Grade B listed mansion (Relais & Châteaux). Sumptuously furnished, it has family portraits, grand piano, antiques, flowers, billiards; 'plenty of lounges where you can sit around'. The owner, Mrs Constance Cluett Ward, is American, as are many guests. Her manager is James Payne. 'The service at this well-appointed country house is friendly without being overbearing, extremely efficient,' one visitor wrote. 'Log fires, seemingly ablaze in every room, make this a visit to a home, while the art (principally wildlife, especially birds) is worth the trip in itself.' Most bedrooms are large, with a view of the valley; three are in cottages. 'Each morning a chambermaid brings tea on a tray, and lights the gas log fire.' Men wear a jacket at dinner in the elegant restaurant (frescoes and ornate ceiling), where Jean-Baptiste Bady serves a three-course set dinner using home-produced or local ingredients; *Kinnaird* has its own smokehouse and a walled kitchen garden. The wine list has many half bottles. Good breakfasts have freshly squeezed juice, and porridge can come laced with whisky. (*RG, and others*)

Bedrooms: 9, 1 on ground floor, 3 in cottages in courtyard. *Open*: all year. *Facilities*: Lift, ramp, 2 lounges, billiard room, restaurant, dining room, function/wedding facilities, beauty/therapy room, 7,000-acre estate (gardens, tennis, croquet, shooting, walking, birdwatching, salmon fishing on Tay, 3 trout lochs). *Background music*: none. *Location*: 6 miles NW of Dunkeld. *Smoking*: not allowed. *Children*: not under 12 in main dining room. *Dogs*: not allowed in house (heated kennels available). *Credit cards*: Amex, MasterCard, Visa. *Prices*: [2008] d,b&b double £225–£520, set lunch £20–£30, dinner £59–£65, Christmas/New Year packages.

DUNOON Argyll and Bute   Map 5:D1
See SHORTLIST

DUNVEGAN Highland   Map 5:C1

The Three Chimneys and   *Tel* 01470-511258
The House Over-By   *Fax* 01470-511358
Colbost, Dunvegan   *Email* eatandstay@threechimneys.co.uk
Isle of Skye IV55 8ZT   *Website* www.threechimneys.co.uk

 César award in 2001

'Beautifully set 'in north-west Skye, Eddie and Shirley Spear's award-winning restaurant-with-rooms stands across a single-track road (some day traffic, quiet at night) from Loch Dunvegan. 'Still excellent in every respect,' one regular visitor wrote. A white-painted crofter's cottage contains the two-room restaurant with its candles, dark beams and stone walls. Michael Smith's much-admired cooking on a three- or four-course menu uses much local fish and meat. Dishes include Mallaig coley and Sconser king scallops with Anna potatoes, choucroute savoy and claret jus; fillet of Lochalsh beef with root dauphinoise, purple sprouting broccoli, haggis pavé and Talisker gravy. 'Fresh ingredients, perfectly cooked and presented. Wonderful home-made breads.' The split-level bedrooms, in the house 'over-by', have sea views, stylish contemporary decor, flat-screen TV, DVD-player; there are comfortable beds, large, luxurious bathrooms and, from the windows, 'no one to see but sheep'. The 'excellent' breakfast has freshly squeezed orange juice, fruit salad, cheeses, porridge, smoked salmon, smoked venison, and a hot dish of the day. Young children are welcomed (cots, children's tea, baby-listening); two suites are good for a family. There are DVDs, CDs, books and maps. The morning room has been given new furniture and there is a new lounge area. (*ES, and others*)

Bedrooms: 6, all on ground floor in separate building, 1 suitable for &. *Open*: all year except 4–30 Jan, restaurant closed midday in winter, Sun lunch all year. *Facilities*: ramps, reception/lounge area/morning/breakfast room, bar, restaurant, garden on loch. *Background music*: none. *Location*: 4 miles W of Dunvegan on B884 to Glendale. *Smoking*: not allowed. *Children*: all ages welcomed (under-6s stay free in parents' room), no under-8s at dinner. *Dogs*: only guide dogs allowed. *Credit cards*: Amex, MasterCard, Visa. *Prices*: b&b £99.50–£132.50 per person, d,b&b £104.50–£187.50, set menus (3–4 courses) £55–£60, autumn/winter/spring breaks, Christmas/New Year packages, 1-night bookings refused Sat.

DUROR Argyll and Bute   Map 5:D1

 Bealach House   *Tel* 01631-740298
Salachan Glen, Duror   *Email* enquiries@bealach-house.co.uk
Appin PA38 4BW   *Website* www.bealach-house.co.uk

César award: Scottish guest house of the year

'A very special enterprise.' 'The very best hospitality.' Praise again for the 'perfectionist' Jim and Hilary McFadyen, who, without staff, run this small guest house, the only dwelling in the Salachan Glen. Up a one-and-a-half-mile forestry track, surrounded by woods and mountains, it is a 'handsome, well-maintained' building in large grounds with lovely views. Inside, it is 'beautifully decorated': muted colours, tasteful furnishings; 'exemplary housekeeping'. Inspectors in 2008 were warmly welcomed: 'First names used, complimentary tea with delicious cakes by a log-burning stove in the handsome lounge.' The bedrooms, though not large, are 'warmly furnished, extremely comfortable'. Bathrooms have a power shower (one also has a bath). Dinner (three courses, each with three alternatives) is communally served. Hilary McFadyen is the 'excellent' cook; her husband waits at table. 'Well-chosen ingredients, well-balanced flavours, attractively served, vegetables just right in texture, venison tender but nicely gamey, fish wonderfully fresh.' A complimentary glass or two of 'very drinkable' wine is offered (no licence; guests may bring their own). Breads, jams and ice creams are home made. The 'imaginative' breakfast had 'unusual cereals; two kinds of marmalade; banana and apple juice without peer; eggs and mushrooms exactly right; crunchy toast'. Wild birds visit a bird table; golden eagles and deer are sometimes seen. (*M and JC, and many others*)

Bedrooms: 3, 7 in annexe. *Open*: Feb–Nov. *Facilities*: lounge, conservatory, dining room, 8-acre grounds. unsuitable for &. *Background music*: occasional classical. *Location*: 2 miles S of Duror, off A828. *Smoking*: not allowed. *Children*: not under 14. *Dogs*: not allowed. *Credit cards*: MasterCard, Visa. *Prices*: b&b £40–£65 per person, set dinner £25, 2-night winter rates.

EDINBANE Highland   Map 5:C1

Greshornish House   *Tel* 01470-582266
Edinbane, by Portree   *Fax* 01470-582345
Isle of Skye IV51 9PN   *Email* info@greshornishhouse.com
                         Website www.greshornishhouse.com

'A lovely hotel. Exceptional service.' 'Most enjoyable.' 'Ambience friendly but not intrusive.' Endorsements for this handsome, listed, white manor house, 18th-century with Victorian additions, 'wonderfully set' by Loch Greshornish. Reached down a two-and-a-half-mile track, and secluded in wooded grounds, it looks across the water to Trotternish. Neil and Rosemary Colquhoun are 'hands-on, very friendly' owners. 'After a long journey we were offered delicious afternoon tea and home-made cakes.' One bedroom is the former music room, another was a drawing room; two have a four-poster; some are spacious; some, under the eaves, have a sloping ceiling; some look over the Victorian walled garden. 'Our charming room faced loch and mountains. Large, well-equipped bathroom. Breakfast and dinner very good.' In the candlelit dining room (open to non-residents), chef Colin Macdonald serves a three-course *table d'hôte* dinner based on local ingredients, eg, pan-fried Lochaber venison with Stornoway black pudding and chocolate jus. Ingredients like lobster and langoustine carry a supplement. An *à la carte* seafood lunch menu is now available. Log fires burn in the public rooms. For after-dinner entertainment there are billiards, chess, or 'a book with a malt whisky' in the drawing room. Children get reduced rates, high chairs, cots, etc. (*CLH, Richard Mayou, Caroline Mitchell*)

Bedrooms: 9. *Open*: Mar–Dec, except Christmas and Mon/Tues Nov–Mar. *Facilities*: drawing room, cocktail bar, billiard room, dining room, conservatory, 10-acre grounds (croquet, tennis), sea loch, only public rooms accessible for &. *Background music*: classical/Celtic on request. *Location*: 17 miles NW of Portree. *Smoking*: not allowed. *Children*: all ages welcomed. *Dogs*: not allowed in public rooms, or unaccompanied in bedrooms. *Credit cards*: Amex, MasterCard, Visa. *Prices*: [2008] d,b&b £95–£125 per person, set dinner £34, seasonal and 3-day breaks. *V*

EDINBURGH   Map 5:D2

Ingrams   NEW   *Tel* 0131-556 8140
24 Northumberland Street   *Fax* 0131-556 4423
Edinburgh EH3 6LS   *Email* info@ingrams.co.uk
                                              Website www.ingrams.co.uk

This 'delightful' b&b is an elegant Georgian house (built in 1812) in New Town. Its handsome stone staircase is lit by an oval cupola. Run by its owners, David and Theresa Ingram, it is 'comfortable and convenient', and furnished with antiques (the 'forthright and entertaining' host is also an antique dealer). His breakfasts, served round one large table in the 'beautiful, formal' dining room, 'are a highlight, especially the amazing porridge, a gourmet delight'. As well as 'perfectly cooked' traditional fare, there is fresh fruit salad with rose water, home-made muesli, and 'fine coffee'. There are two twin-bedded bedrooms, and a double which faces the garden. 'My room,' says a visitor this year, 'was simple, well laid out and comfortable. Housekeeping standards were impressive.' Mr T, the house cat, 'is welcoming and ever present'. Princes Street is within walking distance, and restaurants of all kinds are near. (*Michael Sassella, GH*)

Bedrooms: 3. *Open*: all year except Christmas. *Facilities*: sitting room, dining room, garden. *Background music*: baroque at breakfast if required. *Location*: New Town, 5 mins' walk from centre, parking for 3 cars, bus stop nearby. *Smoking*: not allowed. *Children*: not under 15. *Dogs*: not allowed. *Credit cards*: Diners, MasterCard, Visa. *Prices*: b&b £50–£55 per person, 3-night breaks.

The Scotsman

20 North Bridge
Edinburgh
EH1 1YT

Tel 0131-556 5565
Fax 0131-652 3652
Email reservations@thescotsmanhotel.co.uk
Website www.thescotsmanhotel.co.uk

Once the offices of the *Scotsman* newspaper, this 'fascinating' Edwardian building has been converted into a luxury city hotel. It is now part of the Eton Collection (see also *42 The Calls*, Leeds). Many baroque features have been retained, including a black-and-white marble staircase, intricate stained-glass windows, turrets and ornate ceilings. All bedrooms have good city views. There are 'big, comfortable beds', a sound system in each bathroom, 'lovely toiletries', a hatch for room service (you don't have to open the door), and an Edinburgh Monopoly board. But some visitors found the technology 'fiendishly complicated' and wondered 'whether the creators of "design hotels" ever sleep in the bedrooms'. The second-floor rooms overlooking Waverley station can get late-night noise from a sports bar. Meals are served in the *North Bridge* brasserie/bar on two levels in the newspaper's marble former reception hall. Visitors in 2008 found 'food and service excellent as were concierge and Reception services'. The breakfast buffet is 'good, if expensive', but some guests encountered linguistic problems. The Cowshed spa (see below) has a stainless-steel swimming pool. One tip: 'Approach on foot from the Market Street side of Waverley, not the Princes Street exit.' (*CH*)

Bedrooms: 69, 2 suitable for &. *Open*: all year. *Facilities*: ramps, lifts, drawing room, breakfast room, bar/brasserie, cinema, health spa (16-metre swimming pool, sauna, gym, treatment rooms, juice bar, café), wedding facilities. *Background music*: in public areas. *Location*: central, by Waverley station. *Smoking*: not allowed. *Children*: all ages welcomed. *Dogs*: only guide dogs allowed. *Credit cards*: all major cards. *Prices*: b&b double £325–£500, d,b&b double £375–£525, breakfast £18.50, full alc £35, weekend rates and packages on website, Christmas/New Year packages, 1-night bookings often refused Sat, rugby weekends.

****

Traveller's tale *Hotel in Devon* We arrived with high hopes, to be greeted by a terse young woman who proceeded to tell my husband how to dress for dinner – he doesn't even own a pair of jeans but was too polite to say so. The weekend staff were ghastly: unfriendly, pointedly rude, definitely clock-watchers. Our bedroom was plain but adequate, but there was sand in the sheets.

****

Windmill House

21 Coltbridge Gardens
Edinburgh EH12 6AQ

Tel/Fax 0131-346 0024
Email windmillhouse@btinternet.com

'Our hosts were polite, helpful and friendly. We felt like family guests.' 'A wonderful place. Like being in the country. Incredible value.' 'It is beautiful.' 'So quiet.' Though only a mile from Princes Street, Vivien and Michael Scott's imposing Georgian-style house (a Wolsey Lodge offering 'luxury B&B') has a rural hilltop setting, by a waterfall, weir and historic 17th-century windmill. It overlooks the valley of the Water of Leith, and has lovely views to the Pentlands. The stylish interior has antiques, open fires and flowers. Double doors open on to a pillared hall with atrium, wide staircase and galleried landing. The drawing room leads to a wide terrace where breakfast is sometimes served. 'Our room was immaculate.' Bedrooms are large, tastefully furnished, and supplied with complimentary whisky and mineral water (no tea/coffee-making equipment, no door lock). 'Thoroughly enjoyable' breakfasts, round a communal table in the handsome dining room, have 'a good choice of cereals, delicious fruit, generous cooked dishes'. The secure parking is appreciated. Badgers visit at twilight. The Scottish National Gallery of Modern Art, in its wooded grounds, is a neighbour. (*Gareth Evans, MC*)

Bedrooms: 3. *Open*: all year except Christmas/New Year. *Facilities*: drawing room, dining room, terrace, 2-acre garden (riverside walks), unsuitable for &. *Background music*: none. *Location*: 1 mile W of centre. *Smoking*: not allowed. *Children*: preferably over 5. *Dogs*: not allowed. *Credit cards*: none. *Prices*: [2008] b&b £55–£75 per person, 1-night bookings sometimes refused Aug.

See also SHORTLIST

EDNAM Borders   Map 5:E3

Edenwater House   NEW

Ednam, nr Kelso
TD5 7QL

Tel/Fax 01573-224070
Email jeffnjax@hotmail.co.uk
Website www.edenwaterhouse.co.uk

Visitors from Minnesota this year awarded 'the highest marks' to this old stone manse which stands peacefully in a hamlet near Kelso. 'We were the only guests most of the time, and thoroughly enjoyed life in a Scottish country house, sumptuously decorated, with collections everywhere, comfortable and beautiful furniture, all making a perfect whole.' There are lovely views over the pretty garden to the Eden Water which winds through fields and across to the Cheviots. Of the 'very comfortable' bedrooms, two have a view of the river; one has a small single room adjacent. The owners, Jacqui and Jeff Kelly, are 'talented and creative'. She formerly ran a restaurant in Edinburgh, and is 'a superb cook'. 'After a long day's hiking we looked forward to a cocktail by the fire in the beautiful lounge, sometimes with a chat with regular visitors.' In the 'exquisite' dining room (open at weekends to non-residents), the three-course no-choice candlelit dinner takes into account guests' preferences. It might include langoustine with cèpe sauce and penne poached with truffle oil; wild halibut with glazed fennel and lemon spinach; mango, raspberry and strawberry terrine with iced coconut parfait. 'Delicious' breakfasts have 'just about everything one could ask for'. (*Tara and Rick Varco*)

Bedrooms: 5. *Open*: end Jan–end Nov, dining room closed Sun. *Facilities*: drawing room, study, dining room, wedding facilities, 2-acre grounds, unsuitable for ♿. *Background music*: on request at private functions. *Location*: 2 miles N of Kelso on B6461. *Smoking*: not allowed. *Children*: not under 12. *Dogs*: not allowed. *Credit cards*: MasterCard, Visa. *Prices*: b&b £45–£65 per person, set dinner £37.50, 2-night breaks.

ELGIN Moray *See SHORTLIST*   Map 5:C2

ERISKA Argyll and Bute   Map 5:D1

Isle of Eriska
Benderloch, Eriska
by Oban PA37 1SD

Tel 01631-720371
Fax 01631-720531
Email office@eriska-hotel.co.uk
Website www.eriska-hotel.co.uk

❦ *César award in 2007*

'As comfortable and well run as ever,' writes a devotee after another 'perfect stay' at this 'remarkable place'. Other praise: 'Best hotel in the UK.' 'Everything runs like clockwork, they cannot control the weather but they faultlessly deliver everything else.' 'Service second to none, from young, polite staff.' The 19th-century baronial mansion (Pride of Britain) stands 'idyllically' on a 300-acre private island reached by a wrought iron vehicle bridge. 'More resort than hotel', it is run by 'amiable' brothers Beppo and Chay Buchanan-Smith. There are wellington boots by the entrance, large sofas, a year-round log fire, panelled lounges. Bedrooms vary from 'traditional' in the main building ('ours had sofa, decent-sized TV, huge bed, made while we breakfasted') to modern spa suites, each with conservatory and private garden with hot tub. 'All are immaculate.' Robert MacPherson's six-course dinners (male guests wear jacket and tie) are 'consistently good: wild sea bass, robust helpings of roast beef carved from the trolley; amazing selection of cheeses'. 'Lots of vegetables, fancy puds (savoury alternative); impeccable, formal waiting.' Light meals are served on a veranda. Breakfasts have 'limitless fresh orange juice'; 'wonderful haddock and kippers'. 'Morning coffee/tea and afternoon tea with cakes freely available within the tariff.' (*Roland Cassam, Michael and Maureen Heath, Anthony Bradbury*)

Bedrooms: 25, including 5 spa suites and 2 garden cottages, some on ground floor. *Open*: all year except Jan. *Facilities*: ramp, hall, drawing room, library, dining room, leisure centre (swimming pool (18 by 6 metres), gym, sauna, massage, beauty treatments, bar, restaurant), wedding facilities, 300-acre island (tennis, croquet, 6-hole par 22 golf course, marked walks, clay-pigeon shooting). *Background music*: none. *Location*: 12 miles N of Oban. *Smoking*: allowed in 16 bedrooms. *Children*: all ages welcomed, but no under-5s in swimming pool. *Dogs*: not allowed in public rooms. *Credit cards*: Amex, MasterCard, Visa. *Prices*: d,b&b (*min. advance reservation 2 nights*) £150–£269.50 per person, set dinner £39.50, weekly rates, off-season breaks, Christmas/New Year packages, 1-night bookings sometimes refused.

FORT WILLIAM Highland   Map 5:C1

The Grange   *Tel* 01397-705516
Grange Road   *Email* info@thegrange-scotland.co.uk
Fort William PH33 6JF   *Website* www.thegrange-scotland.co.uk

'Superb,' says a report in 2008. 'After being wowed by our room we took tea and shortcake, with lovely crockery and silver, in the beautiful lounge. We loved the size of our room, with big bed, fantastic walk-in shower, lovely views.' On a hill above Loch Linnhe, in attractive grounds, this white-painted Victorian Gothic house has long been run as a B&B by the 'welcoming, helpful' owners, John and Joan Campbell. 'Immaculately' and tastefully furnished, and with large windows, it is light and airy. There are log fires, antiques, fresh flowers. Each bedroom is different: the Garden Room ('the most peaceful') faces the loch; west-facing Rob Roy, with colonial-style bed, is where Jessica Lange stayed while making that film; the Turret Room has a window seat with garden and loch views and a Louis XV king-size bed; the Terrace Room, the best, with a private terrace facing the garden, has a king-size bed and Victorian slipper bath. 'We liked the little extras: towels tied up with a ribbon, decanter of sherry with lovely glassware.' Breakfast, ordered the night before, includes fruit compote, smoked haddock and potato pancakes. 'My poached eggs arrived with a flower, porridge came with whisky, cream, brown sugar and honey.' (*Charlotte Willis*)

Bedrooms: 4. *Open*: Mar–Oct. *Facilities*: lounge, breakfast room, 1-acre garden, unsuitable for &. *Background music*: none. *Location*: town centre. *Smoking*: not allowed. *Children*: not under 12. *Dogs*: not allowed. *Credit cards*: MasterCard, Visa. *Prices*: b&b double £98–£110, 1-night bookings sometimes refused.

See also SHORTLIST

FORTROSE Highland *See SHORTLIST* Map 5:C2

GATEHOUSE OF FLEET Dumfries and Galloway *See SHORTLIST*   Map 5:E2

GATESIDE Fife   Map 5:D2

Edenshead Stables   *Tel/Fax* 01337-868500
Gateside, by Cupar   *Email* info@edensheadstables.com
KY14 7ST   *Website* www.edensheadstables.com

On the edge of this small village, ruined stables have been turned into this modern building where a 'delightful couple', John and Gill Donald, supported by two Hungarian Vizslas, Rosa and Zeta, provide 'luxury B&B'. The River Eden flows past its garden, and it has fine views of open countryside and the Lomond hills. The 'air of relaxed comfort' is admired, as is the 'good value'. 'It's a bit of an Aladdin's cave,' says a visitor who 'really enjoyed' his visit in 2008. 'Far bigger inside than you'd expect.' The 'immaculate' interior is filled with 'beautiful furnishings, lovely paintings'. The 'elegant, formal' dining room has antiques and Spode china. The large, comfortable sitting room leads on to a patio, and contains books, maps and local information. The 'upmarket' bedrooms have an 'excellent' power shower *en suite*; the best room has a four-poster. Breakfast, 7.45–8.45 am (earlier by arrangement), is communally served. It includes local kippers, Arbroath smokies, oatmeal porridge, black pudding, home-made preserves. Dinner can be served to groups of four to six. Nearby are 'restaurants and inns offering good food to suit all pockets'. The one-storey house is suitable for physically disabled guests, but not wheelchair-bound ones. Many golf courses are nearby. (*Jon Hughes*)

Bedrooms: 3, all on ground floor. *Open*: Feb–mid-Dec. *Facilities*: Lounge, dining room, patio, courtyard, 3-acre grounds on River Eden, unsuitable for &. *Background music*: none. *Location*: outside village 12 miles SE of Perth, train to Ladybank/Cupar. *Smoking*: not allowed. *Children*: not under 12. *Dogs*: not allowed. *Credit cards*: MasterCard, Visa. *Prices*: b&b £38–£54 per person, set dinner £25, off-season breaks, 1-night bookings occasionally refused July/Aug.

GIFFORD East Lothian   Map 5:D3

Eaglescairnie Mains   NEW   *Tel/Fax* 01620-810491
Gifford, nr Haddington   *Email* williams.eagles@btinternet.com
EH41 4HN   *Website* www.eaglescairnie.com

In deepest country 18 miles south-east of Edinburgh, this 'impeccable' white-painted Georgian B&B looks over rolling wooded countryside. The owners, Michael and Barbara Williams, run it on ecological lines. It stands on a working farm which was bought by her grandmother in 1953; her husband now runs it with a neighbour, on a mixed arable and sheep/horse livery system. His 'sympathetic' farming methods 'seek to unite wildlife and landscape conservation with profitable modern agriculture'. 'Quiet and tranquil, yet within easy reach of Edinburgh (you can use the park and ride facility), the house is full of character,' says the nominator, a *César*-winning *Guide* hotelier. 'Tastefully and comfortably furnished, it is very personally run: guests feel more like family friends than paid residents.' There is a drawing room with coral walls and open log fire, and in summer breakfast can be taken in a conservatory. Spacious bedrooms, all with facilities *en suite* (shower over the bath), have matching curtains and fabrics and good views. No evening meal; a pub is a mile away. There are 'unlimited' golf courses within ten miles. (*John Rowlands*)

Bedrooms: 3. *Open*: all year except Christmas. *Facilities*: sitting room, conservatory, large garden (tennis) in 350-acre farmland, unsuitable for &. *Background music*: none. *Location*: 1 mile W of Gifford, 3 miles SE of Haddington. *Smoking*: not allowed. *Children*: all ages welcomed. *Dogs*: allowed by prior arrangement. *Credit cards*: MasterCard, Visa. *Prices*: [2008] b&b £35–£50 per person, discount for 4-night stay, 1-night bookings refused Fri and Sat in July/Aug.

GLAMIS Angus   Map 5:D2

Castleton House
by Glamis
DD8 1SJ

Tel 01307-840340
Fax 01307-840506
Email hotel@castletonglamis.co.uk
Website www.castletonglamis.co.uk

Run by its owners, David and Verity Webster, with manager Jacqui Soutar, this Edwardian stone country house is on a little hill on the site of a medieval fortress. Surrounded by a dry moat (grown over with trees and flowers), it stands next to a large dairy farm. Long admired for its 'well-trained staff', warm welcome (luggage carried, complimentary tea) and elegant public rooms (tasteful colour schemes, antiques, large log fires), it has a 'most attractive' conservatory restaurant as well as a more formal dining room (but there is no dress code). The new chef, Kevin MacGillivray, serves 'traditional with modern influences' dishes like spiced pork belly with balsamic braised purple cabbage. At breakfast, 'scrambled eggs were to die for'. A drawback is the position on a busy road, though screened by trees: best perhaps to ask for a bedroom at the back. The 'charming' rooms have antiques, good artwork, digital TV, flowers, mineral water, coffee and tea. For children there are special meals, a climbing frame in the garden, ducks and chickens, two Tamworth pigs, croquet, and 'space for golf and throwing frisbees'. Dogs are welcomed. The Websters also own *Raemoir House*, Banchory. (*Richard and Trisha Bright*)

Bedrooms: 6. *Open*: all year, house parties only at Christmas/New Year. *Facilities*: drawing room, library/bar, conservatory/dining room, dining room, conference facilities, wedding facilities, 10-acre grounds (stream, climbing frame, croquet, putting), only restaurant suitable for &. *Background music*: light jazz/classic swing ballads afternoon and evening in dining room and bar. *Location*: on A94 Perth–Forfar, W of Glamis. *Smoking*: not allowed. *Children*: all ages welcomed. *Dogs*: allowed. *Credit cards*: Amex, MasterCard, Visa. *Prices*: [2008] b&b £100–£150 per person, d,b&b £135–£185, set menus £35–£40, 2-for-1 packages Nov, Jan, Feb, Mar.

GLASGOW *See SHORTLIST*   Map 5:D2

GLENFINNAN Highland   Map 5:C1

Glenfinnan House   *Tel/Fax* 01397-722235
Glenfinnan   *Email* availability@glenfinnanhouse.com
by Fort William PH37 4LT   *Website* www.glenfinnanhouse.com

On the shores of Loch Shiel, this white Victorian mansion (with 18th-century origins) looks across the water to Ben Nevis and the Glenfinnan Monument (where Bonnie Prince Charlie raised the standard at the start of the 1745 Jacobite Rebellion). Owned by Jane MacFarlane-Glasow, managed by Duncan and Manja Gibson, it is locally popular for weddings, dances and celebrations. Well furnished, it has traditional decor and wood panelling. 'We are proud to have no TVs in the bedrooms,' we are told. 'Our guests can enjoy each other's company in the old-fashioned way.' The front rooms have 'superb views'; one has a four-poster. Attic rooms may be the least peaceful. 'The food was excellent: fine cuisine in the restaurant, good bar meals too (good-value choices for children).' Duncan Gibson ('we do not serve fast food') provides continental-influenced traditional Scottish dishes, eg, venison sausage with creamed potatoes and mushrooms; grilled prime Scottish beef steaks. Breakfast includes smoked salmon, haddock, kippers, but 'sliced-bread toast and carton orange juice'. Meals are accompanied by CDs of local musicians. There is Wi-Fi access, and loch cruises can be arranged. 'A very friendly bird (goose/duck cross) ruled the garden and kept dogs at bay.' (*Susan Harrison, MW Stratton*)

Bedrooms: 13. *Open*: Mar–Nov. *Facilities*: ramps, hall, drawing room, playroom, bar, restaurant, function/conference/wedding facilities, 1-acre grounds, children's playground, unsuitable for &. *Background music*: Scottish CDs, bar and restaurant. *Location*: 15 miles NW of Fort William. *Smoking*: not allowed. *Children*: all ages welcomed (under-12s accommodated free). *Dogs*: not allowed in restaurant. *Credit cards*: all major cards. *Prices*: [2008] b&b £42.50–£60 per person, d,b&b £72.50–£110, set menus £28.50–£34.50, bar meals/packed lunches, special breaks (see website). ***V***

> The terms printed in the *Guide* are only a rough indication of the size of the bill to be expected at the end of your stay. Always check the tariffs when booking.

Prince's House

Glenfinnan, by Fort William
PH37 4LT

Tel 01397-722246
Fax 01397-722323
Email princeshouse@glenfinnan.co.uk
Website www.glenfinnan.co.uk

The 'warmly welcoming' Ina Kelly greets visitors to this white-painted, gabled former coaching inn. 'She was most attentive throughout our stay,' wrote a recent guest. Her 'very pleasant' husband, Kieron, is chef. They hold a Green Tourism Silver award for eco-friendly ways. 'The atmosphere is homely, enhanced by the Kellys' two sons, much in evidence, who sometimes provide entertainment on their violins in the bar.' The bedrooms are on the first floor; best ones at the front. 'Ours was of a reasonable size, well appointed. Its bathroom contained some unusual toiletries.' Dinner is a three-course daily-changing menu in the spacious dining room (at quiet times opened for pre-booked meals only), or a blackboard menu in the bar. Modern British dishes use local ingredients, eg, loin of venison and breast of wood pigeon with creamed morels and port wine jus or, for simpler tastes, grilled fish of the day with seasonal vegetables. Bread is home baked. Desserts include some interesting ice creams. Breakfast has porridge, fruit and a cooked main course. The building is on the road to Mallaig, 'but traffic at night is minimal and no noise is heard inside. A fine base for exploring the spectacular scenery of the most westerly part of the British mainland.' (*AJG*)

Bedrooms: 9. *Open*: Mar–Dec and New Year (only restaurant Nov, Dec and Mar), closed 2 weeks Oct, Christmas. *Facilities*: lounge/bar, bar, dining room, small front lawn, only bar suitable for &. *Background music*: classical in restaurant, trad/modern in bar. *Location*: 15 miles NW of Fort William. *Smoking*: not allowed indoors (designated area outside). *Children*: all ages welcomed. *Dogs*: allowed in bar, standard bedrooms. *Credit cards*: MasterCard, Visa. *Prices*: [2008] b&b £42.50–£75 per person, d,b&b £72.50–£105, set menus £28.95–£35, bar meals, New Year package. *V*

GRANTOWN-ON-SPEY Highland   Map 5:C2

Culdearn House

Woodlands Terrace
Grantown-on-Spey PH26 3JU

Tel 01479-872106
Fax 01479-873641
Email enquiries@culdearn.com
Website www.culdearn.com

Recently given a major refurbishment by owners William and Sonia Marshall (she is the chef), this Victorian granite house is on the edge of a picturesque market town/resort in the Spey valley.

An enthusiastic visitor wrote: 'Delightful, tiny and unassuming, exceptionally comfortable. A useful stopping-off point, but also a place to rest in, like staying with old friends without the slightest pressure to be sociable.' There is a 'friendly welcome with offer of tea in the drawing room'. Bedrooms are 'charming and thoughtfully done'; bath/shower rooms 'immaculate'. Menus, served in a candlelit room (open to non-residents) with log fire, depend on local suppliers. 'Exquisitely fresh and beautifully cooked' dishes might include fillet of monkfish tail with crayfish and Parmesan sauce. Some rooms are spacious (some beds are king-size); extras include flowers and chocolates. The lounge has 'lots of easy armchairs and sofas', the original wood panelling, watercolours, antique maps. Salmon and sea-trout fishing on the Spey, as well as on private beats, with ghillie service, can be arranged. Anagach Woods adjoin the garden. (*JA*)

Bedrooms: 6, 1 on ground floor. *Open*: all year. *Facilities*: lounge, dining room, ¾-acre garden. *Background music*: pre-dinner classical in lounge. *Location*: edge of town, by Anagach Woods. *Smoking*: not allowed. *Children*: not under 10. *Dogs*: only guide dogs allowed. *Credit cards*: Diners, MasterCard, Visa. *Prices*: b&b £60–£77.50 per person, set dinner £34, spring/autumn breaks, Christmas/New Year packages, reduced rates for 4–7 nights.

See also SHORTLIST

GRULINE Argyll and Bute   Map 5:D1

Gruline Home Farm	*Tel* 01680-300581
Gruline, Isle of Mull	*Email* boo@gruline.com
PA71 6HR	*Website* www.gruline.com

On a remote peninsula of 'exceptional wild beauty', this 'handsome' conversion of a non-working Georgian/Victorian farmhouse and its outbuildings stands amid gardens and pastureland. Owned by the 'warmly welcoming' (except to children) Colin (the chef) and Angela Boocock, it faces the foothills of Ben More and surrounding country-side. Access is along a long, rough drive which leads also to the Macquarie Mausoleum where lies 'the father of Australia'. Arriving guests are given afternoon tea in the conservatory. The house is well decorated: good antique and modern furniture, a 'fantastic' chande-lier from Prague. The 'attractive' dining room (with Crown Derby china and crystal glasses) is open to non-residents. A dinner-party atmosphere is encouraged (guests are introduced to each other). The 'excellent' four-course dinner (two choices of starter and main course, sorbet in between) might include steamed and braised mallard with a spinach and celeriac tartlet; chocolate sponge pudding with chocolate sauce and ginger ice cream. No licence (bring your own wine; no corkage charged), but you are offered complimentary sherry. Breakfast, with 'outstanding' warm fruit compote, and lots of cooked dishes, is served, like dinner, on stylish crockery. 'Angela is meticulous with presentation and service.' The garden is midge-free, she promises. (*J and DM*)

Bedrooms: 3, 1 on ground floor, 5 yds from main house. *Open*: Apr–Oct. *Facilities*: lounge, conservatory, dining room, 2½-acre garden, stream. *Background music*: light classical always. *Location*: 2½ miles from Salen village, 14 miles S of Tobermory. *Smoking*: not allowed. *Children*: not under 16. *Dogs*: allowed in annexe bedroom only. *Credit cards*: MasterCard, Visa. *Prices*: d,b&b (min. 2 nights) £95–£170 per person. ***V***

INVERNESS Highland   Map 5:C2
See SHORTLIST

IONA Argyll and Bute   Map 5:D1

Argyll Hotel   *Tel* 01681-700334
Isle of Iona PA76 6SJ   *Fax* 01681-700510
                    Email reception@argyllhoteliona.co.uk
                    Website www.argyllhoteliona.co.uk

In the main village of this 'mystical' Hebridean island, this is the smaller of the two hotels, part of a row of 19th-century houses a short walk from the jetty where the ferry from Mull docks. There are 'idyllic views' from its book-filled lounges (one with open fire) and conservatory. Owners Daniel Morgan and Claire Bachellerie are ecologically committed. They are locals, so are most of their staff, 'who are delightful', according to a visitor in 2008 (though she would have appreciated help with luggage on arrival at the dock). When possible, produce and resources are acquired locally; waste is recycled or composted. The hotel's organic garden supplies most of the vegetables and herbs used in the kitchen. The food is thought 'extremely good' ('soups outstanding'): guests on half board choose three courses from chatty menus which might include bacon and smoked applewood salad; Iona lamb and chorizo casserole. 'Oddly, few vegetarian dishes. The beat music at mealtimes was not suitable for Iona, and it percolated into some bedrooms.' The wine list is 'firmly rooted in the deep and spiritual appreciation of the small French château'. Light lunches (soups and pies) are served; picnics are provided. Children are welcomed (early supper provided), so are dogs, 'but local crofters insist they be exercised on a lead'. Some bedrooms may be small (best ones are in the main house), and housekeeping may not be perfect, but they have 'good storage, pleasant watercolours, paperback books and a well-planned bathroom'.

Bedrooms: 16, 7 (cheaper) in annexe. *Open*: early Mar–early Nov. *Facilities*: 2 lounges, conservatory, TV/computer room, restaurant, large organic garden, unsuitable for &. *Background music*: in restaurant. *Location*: village centre. *Smoking*: not allowed. *Children*: all ages welcomed. *Dogs*: not allowed in dining room. *Credit cards*: Amex, MasterCard. *Prices*: [2008] b&b £35–£85 per person, d,b&b £48–£102, full alc £22, 1-night bookings sometimes refused.

KELSO Borders *See SHORTLIST*   Map 5:E3

KILBERRY Argyll and Bute   Map 5:D1

Kilberry Inn
Kilberry, by Tarbert
PA29 6YD

Tel 01880-770223
Email relax@kilberryinn.com
Website www.kilberryinn.com

'Amazing scenery, great hospitality and sublime food.' This 'tiny, red-tin-roofed building', red telephone box in front, has a 'beautiful if slightly remote' position on the Kintyre peninsula. Now a 'personally run' restaurant-with-rooms, it is on the scenic single-track road between Lochgilphead and Tarbert. 'Supremely likeable, with a touch of sophistication yet modest', according to another visitor, it has a *Michelin Bib Gourmand* for good cooking at moderate prices. Clare Johnson ('we like to keep things simple, emphasis on seafood in summer, red meat and game in winter') presides over the small kitchen. Her husband, David, 'runs front-of-house with friendly efficiency'. Beams and bare stone walls with local artworks 'give plenty of character' to the two dining rooms; 'impeccably laid' tables have crisp white tablecloths. The 'sensibly short' seasonal menu might include king scallops with puy lentils and salsa verde. Bread is home made. Breakfast includes smoothies, scrambled eggs with smoked salmon, home-made marmalade. The 'stylish, modern bedrooms' (each with shower and its own entrance) are in adjacent buildings. 'Ours was cheerful and impeccably clean.' Around are good walks, sailing, plenty of wildlife and 'fabulous sunsets'. (*Tracy Hoggarth, JR*)

Bedrooms: 4, all on ground floor. *Open*: mid-Mar–Nov Tues–Sun, also New Year. *Facilities*: bar/dining room, smaller dining room, small grounds. *Background music*: gentle, in larger dining room, lunch and dinner. *Location*: 16 miles SW of Tarbert, on B8024. *Smoking*: not allowed. *Children*: no under-12s in bedrooms (any age allowed in small dining room). *Dogs*: not allowed in public rooms, 3 bedrooms. *Credit cards*: MasterCard, Visa. *Prices*: b&b double £95, full alc £30–£35, short breaks, 2/3-night New Year package.

KILCHRENAN Argyll and Bute   Map 5:D1

Ardanaiseig
Kilchrenan
by Taynuilt PA35 1HE

Tel 01866-833333
Fax 01866-833222
Email ardanaiseig@clara.net
Website www.ardanaiseig.com

Recently voted 'Scotland's most romantic hotel', this grey stone baronial mansion stands remotely in a beautiful garden on Loch Awe. Its owner Bennie Gray, of Gray's Antiques Market in London, has filled it with antiques, bold colour schemes, tapestries and rich furnishings. The long drawing room has panelled walls painted in mottled gold. Open fires burn here and in the more intimate library bar. Many bedrooms have loch views. One has apple-green walls, one has Chinese-style lacquered furnishings and an open-plan 'bathing room' with a central bath big enough for two. Beds are large: some four-posters. A boat house has been converted into a suite with modern decor, double-height windows and a glass balustrade giving an uninterrupted view of the water. In the candlelit dining room, Gary Goldie's 'excellent' no-choice four-course dinners use local produce in dishes like venison with turnip and prune conserve, caramelised pear and Armagnac jus. Breakfast has brown toast, and honey and preserves in jars. Home-made scones appear at afternoon tea. Guests can go in the hotel's boats to its own island. In a small amphitheatre in the garden, performances of song and dance are sometimes held. Peter Webster is the 'hands-on' manager. More reports, please.

Bedrooms: 17, some on ground floor, 1 in boat house, 1 self-catering cottage. *Open*: 1 Feb–2 Jan. *Facilities*: drawing room, library/bar, restaurant, wedding facilities, 340-acre grounds on loch (formal garden, open-air theatre, tennis, croquet, safe bathing, fishing, boating). *Background music*: 'easy listening'/ classical in restaurant at dinner. *Location*: 3 miles E of Kilchrenan, by Loch Awe. *Smoking*: not allowed. *Children*: all ages welcomed, but no under-10s at dinner. *Dogs*: not allowed in public rooms. *Credit cards*: Amex, MasterCard, Visa. *Prices*: b&b £61–£202 per person, set dinner £50, spring/autumn reductions (3 nights for the price of 2), special breaks (Valentine, autumn gold, etc), Christmas/New Year packages. *V*

KILLIECRANKIE Perth and Kinross   Map 5:D2

Killiecrankie Hotel   NEW

Killiecrankie
by Pitlochry PH16 5LG

Tel 01796-473220
Fax 01796-472451
Email enquiries@killiecrankiehotel.co.uk
Website www.killiecrankiehotel.co.uk

Henrietta Fergusson, 'friendly, caring and with real spunk', bought this white Victorian former dower house in 2007; extensive refurbishment is under way. It stands in peaceful grounds at the entrance to the Pass of Killiecrankie, overlooking the River Garry; a riverside walk starts opposite, and an RSPB reserve is close by. 'Our rooms were well kept, quaint and comfortable,' one visitor wrote. 'Our children loved the games room. The cosy bar is visited by locals, which made it all the more enjoyable.' Inspectors wrote of a 'slightly perfunctory' welcome ('no help with luggage'), but a 'delightful bedroom, well decorated and furnished; exemplary housekeeping. Free tea in the comfortable, if small, sitting room. In the handsome, candlelit dining room, tables are well spaced; no muzak, thank goodness.' Mark Easton has been the chef for 13 years. His modern British cooking was found 'consistently good' by some, less so ('perhaps an off night') by others. Special diets are catered for. Breakfast had 'freshly squeezed orange juice, porridge, very good bacon and sausages, excellent toast and world-class coffee'. There is a 'lovely garden where you can sit during the long summer evenings'. Much wildlife – roe deer, red squirrels, birds, etc – is in the grounds and beyond. (*Charlotte Holden, and others*)

Bedrooms: 10, 2 on ground floor. *Open*: early Mar–3 Jan. *Facilities*: ramp, sitting room, bar with conservatory, dining room, breakfast conservatory, 4½-acre grounds, unsuitable for &. *Background music*: occasionally, at quiet times. *Location*: hamlet 3 miles W of Pitlochry. *Smoking*: not allowed. *Children*: all ages welcome (under-4s stay free in parents' room). *Dogs*: not allowed in eating areas at food service times, or in some bedrooms. *Credit cards*: Amex, MasterCard, Visa. *Prices*: b&b £70–£80 per person, d,b&b £94–£104, set dinner £31–£38, Christmas/New Year packages. *V*

KILLIN Perth and Kinross   Map 5:D2

Ardeonaig Hotel   *Tel* 01567-820400
South Road Loch Tay   *Email* info@ardeonaighotel.co.uk
by Killin FK21 8SU   *Website* www.ardeonaighotel.co.uk

♥ *César award in 2007*

Reached up a narrow road, in an isolated situation, this white-painted
inn has views over Loch Tay to Ben Lawers. 'If you want to get away
from it all, this is the place,' one correspondent wrote. *Ardeonaig* has
many fans, drawn by the 'astonishingly good' Scottish/colonial cooking
of owner/chef, Pete Gottgens (*Michelin Bib Gourmand*). 'You are well
cared for by the South African staff.' But some would-be visitors found
the telephone response to enquiries 'abrupt'. Major redevelopment
this year has created more accommodation in five *rondawels* (spacious
round thatched lodges) and two suites, a 'state-of-the-art' kitchen and
more dining areas. Diners can choose between the Restaurant, the
Cellar, the more casual Study and the Kitchen Table ('for those who
wish to be among the action'). The exclusively South African wine list
is 'a star feature'. 'Elegant yet unfussy' public areas have a 'Cape-
colonial' feel: floorboards, rugs, prints from the host's native South
Africa. The white lounge has generous sofas; the brown snug is 'cosy';
the library, with books and board games, has the best views. Breakfast
has a 'long and interesting' menu. All the older bedrooms (some are
small) have been refurbished. Much planting has occurred in the
gardens. We'd like reports on the developments, please.

Bedrooms: 26 (5 *rondawels*, 2 garden suites), 1 suitable for &. *Open*: all year.
Facilities: ramp, lounges, library, snug, bar, 4 dining rooms, wedding facilities,
13-acre grounds on loch. *Background music*: bar, dining rooms. *Location*: S shore
of Loch Tay. *Smoking*: not allowed. *Children*: not under 12. *Dogs*: allowed in
4 bedrooms (not unattended) and bar. *Credit cards*: all major cards. *Prices*: b&b
£63.50–£98.50 per person, d,b&b £90–£125, set dinner £28.50, full alc £40,
special breaks, cookery courses, midweek/Christmas/New Year packages,
1-night bookings refused Sat in season. *V*

****

Traveller's tale *Hotel in Kent* There was a thunderstorm on
the second night of our stay. At 5 am, water started to come
in through the bedroom ceiling, fortunately not directly on
to the bed, but a long frock which couldn't fit into the
wardrobe got wet. We spend some time searching for a
bucket to hold the water.

****

KINGUSSIE Highland   Map 5:C2

The Cross at Kingussie   *Tel* 01540-661166
Tweed Mill Brae, Ardbroilach Road   *Fax* 01540-661080
Kingussie PH21 1LB   *Email* relax@thecross.co.uk
                                    Website www.thecross.co.uk

The 'special combination of location, hospitality and great food' won a Scottish 'Good for the Soul' award in 2007 for David and Katie Young's informally run restaurant-with-rooms. And the 'quality of personal attention' is praised again this year by returning visitors (regular *Guide* correspondents). The handsome, stone-built, 19th-century tweed mill stands in wooded grounds with abundant wildlife by the River Gynack in the Cairngorm national park. There is a pretty terrace where drinks are served in summer. Interiors are 'light and bright', with modern Scottish artwork. Most bedrooms are spacious, and have a king-size bed and riverside views. The rooms are 'thoughtfully equipped' (books and music, ample lighting, 'top-quality toiletries', tea-making facilities on request). David Young, a former AA hotel inspector, shares the cooking with Becca Henderson. He describes the food as 'carefully but simply prepared fresh and seasonal Scottish produce' (eg, salad of wild asparagus and broom, lobster, quail's egg, champagne vinaigrette; fillet of Scrabster hake, mussels, creamed courgette). A 'simpler option' is offered on each menu. Breakfasts have freshly squeezed juices, fruit, fresh-baked croissants, and a hot dish of the day, eg, kedgeree. Mobile phones are strictly forbidden in the restaurant. (*T and MH, and others*)

Bedrooms: 8. *Open*: mid-Feb–mid-Dec, New Year, normally closed Sun/Mon except Easter. *Facilities*: 2 lounges, restaurant, 4-acre grounds (woodland, river (no bathing/fishing), *pétanque*), only restaurant suitable for &. *Background music*: none. *Location*: 440 yds from village centre. *Smoking*: not allowed. *Children*: no toddlers or young children. *Dogs*: not allowed. *Credit cards*: Amex, MasterCard, Visa. *Prices*: [2008] b&b £60–£140 per person, d,b&b £100–£170, special breaks all year, New Year package, website offers.

KINROSS Perth and Kinross   Map 5:D2
See SHORTLIST

We ask for more reports on a hotel if we haven't received feedback from readers for some time.

KIRKCOLM Dumfries and Galloway   Map 5:E1

Corsewall Lighthouse
Corsewall Point
Kirkcolm, Stranraer
DG9 0QG

Tel 01776-853220
Fax 01776-854231
Email info@lighthousehotel.co.uk
Website www.lighthousehotel.co.uk

A 200-year-old listed working lighthouse has been sympathetically turned by the Ward family, Gordon, Kay and Pamela, into this 'truly unique' hotel. It stands on a windy promontory north of Stranraer, on Loch Ryan. 'A splendid place,' wrote the nominator. Some bedrooms, with shower, are in the main building (some are small). Three suites are in separate buildings (one is 'almost on the rocks'). 'Ours had an average-size bedroom and a large conservatory lounge with panoramic views.' In the restaurant (with black beams and seascapes), chef Andrew Downie's daily-changing five-course dinner 'was spot on for cooking and service; meat and fish of excellent quality; everything freshly cooked and hot. You could tell from the attention to detail and non-fussy but thoughtful presentation that the kitchen was staffed by people who took pride in the product. Good choice at breakfast too, including Buck's Fizz. Warm welcome. Helpful staff seemed to enjoy what they were doing. We never had to say which room we were in: they knew, though the hotel was full. Quite remote and not for those who want the bright lights.' The last mile or so is down a roughish track, 'so not for the nervous driver'. (*LW*)

Bedrooms: 10, some on ground floor, 1 suitable for &, 3 suites in grounds. *Open*: all year. *Facilities*: 2 small lounges, restaurant, function/conference facilities, wedding facilities, 20-acre grounds (golf, pony trekking, birdwatching, walking nearby). *Background music*: radio in morning, CDs at night. *Location*: 5 miles N of Stranraer. *Smoking*: not allowed. *Children*: all ages welcomed. *Dogs*: not allowed in bedrooms. *Credit cards*: all major cards. *Prices*: b&b £65–£130 per person, d,b&b £75–£150, set menu £32.50, full alc £38, 3-night midweek breaks, Christmas/New Year packages, 1-night bookings refused Sat in season.

KIRKCUDBRIGHT   Map 5:E2
Dumfries and Galloway

Gladstone House
48 High Street
Kirkcudbright DG6 4JX

Tel/Fax 01557-331734
Email hilarygladstone@aol.com
Website www.kirkcudbrightgladstone.com

'Clean, bright and welcoming.' 'Wonderful value for money.' In a conservation area of this 'pleasant little town which most people rush past on the A75', this small guest house is run by its owners, Gordon and Hilary Cowan. The elegant, Grade II listed Georgian town house is 'beautifully decorated'. 'The fine drawing room with comfortable seating takes up most of the first floor.' Guests may use the secluded garden which supplies flowers and fruit for the house. 'Gordon greeted us with tea, cake and an update on local happenings,' say returning visitors. Evening meals, 'presented in a professional manner', are served by arrangement in a pretty room (with separate tables, fireplace, china plates on shelves in an alcove). No licence; bring your own wine. The 'excellent' breakfast has fresh fruit, 'any cooked dish you fancy', home-made rolls and jam. Bedrooms are cosy, well furnished, with a good if 'old-fashioned' bathroom. The best room is a double whose window seats overlook the impressive architecture of the high street and the maze of gardens running to the River Dee. More reports, please.

Bedrooms: 3. *Open*: all year. *Facilities*: drawing room, dining room, ½-acre garden, unsuitable for &. *Background music*: none. *Location*: town centre. *Smoking*: not allowed. *Children*: normally no children under 14 ('but we are flexible'). *Dogs*: not allowed. *Credit cards*: MasterCard, Visa. *Prices*: b&b £33–£43 per person, set dinner £21, 3-night breaks or longer.

See also SHORTLIST

KIRKTON Dumfries and Galloway   Map 5:E2

Wallamhill House
Kirkton
Dumfries DG1 1SL

Tel/Fax 01387-248249
Email wallamhill@aol.com
Website www.wallamhill.co.uk

'Better than many five-star hotels', according to one fan, this modern, single-storey B&B has a 'stunning' setting in a peaceful farming village north of Dumfries. The 'excellent hosts', Gordon and Margaret Hood, provide a generous breakfast (last orders taken at 8.30 am), with choice of fruit and cereals, and freshly cooked hot dishes. 'Gordon did the honours, padding around in his chef's over-alls and socks.' 'Everything comes on a grand scale': there is a large, well-furnished drawing room with a writing desk, and a big garden with croquet. All four 'huge, comfortable' bedrooms are on the ground floor. They have 'magnificent country views – cows grazing in the next field'; also king-size bed, power shower, large TV, video,

CD-player, sherry, biscuits, chocolates, and a fridge with water and fresh milk. 'Our enormous room had a small shower room.' There are fitness facilities, and plenty of outdoor activities available locally (see below). (*ST and others*)

Bedrooms: 3, all on ground floor. *Open*: all year except Christmas. *Facilities*: lounge, breakfast room, fitness room, sauna, steam room, 1½-acre garden (croquet), walking, cycling, fishing, golf, beaches, mountain biking nearby. *Background music*: none. *Location*: 3 miles N of Dumfries. *Smoking*: not allowed. *Children*: all ages welcomed (under-5s accommodated free). *Dogs*: not allowed. *Credit cards*: MasterCard, Visa. *Prices*: b&b £28–£40 per person.

KIRKWALL Orkney   Map 5:A3

Lynnfield Hotel   *Tel* 01856-872505
Holm Road   *Fax* 01856-870038
Kirkwall KW15 1SU   *Email* office@lynnfield.co.uk
                              Website www.lynnfieldhotel.com

Recently upgraded by Malcolm Stout and Lorna Reid (formerly of the popular *Cleaton House*, Westray, *qv*), this hotel, in Orkney's capital, stands adjacent to the Highland Park Distillery, facing the town and beyond. Twenty malts from the distillery are served in its bar. Spacious bedrooms, 'very comfortable', overlook the town. Two of the suites, Bu and Jarls, have a lounge with 'great views' and a spa bath in the bathroom. Other rooms have an antique bed and also a spa bath. All rooms have free Wi-Fi. The restaurant, with its whisky theme, faces the bay. From an extensive menu you could choose grilled beef fillet on a prune and potato cake; goat's cheese and vegetable ravioli. 'The varied wine list has some inexpensive bottles.' There is a small bar, and a residents' lounge with 'lovely squashy seating'. Mr Stout has a 'gentle, laid-back manner' and, with his Orcadian staff, runs the hotel in a 'relaxed manner'. (*ST*)

Bedrooms: 10, 1 suitable for &. *Open*: all year except 25/26 Dec, 1/2 Jan. *Facilities*: residents' lounge, bar lounge, restaurant, business/small conference/wedding facilities, small garden. *Background music*: Scottish, in restaurant. *Location*: ½ mile from centre, by Highland Park Distillery, ample parking. *Smoking*: not allowed. *Children*: not under 12. *Dogs*: not allowed in public rooms. *Credit cards*: MasterCard, Visa. *Prices*: b&b £42.50–£100 per person, full alc £35. *V*

Most hotels have reduced rates out of season, and offer breaks throughout the year.

KYLESKU Highland   Map 5:B2

Kylesku Hotel
Kylesku
by Lairg IV27 4HW

Tel 01971-502231
Fax 01971-502313
Email info@kyleskuhotel.co.uk
Website www.kyleskuhotel.co.uk

'What a beautiful location.' 'Best view from the loo in all Scotland.'
'During meals we were entertained by seals doing back-flips in the
loch.' This white-painted 17th-century former coaching inn stands on
the shore where lochs Glendhu and Glencoul meet in 'breathtaking'
north-west Sutherland ('purple mountains, huge white beaches,
incredible rock formations'). The 'hands-on' owners, Louise and
Struan Lothian (he is the chef), are 'really nice people', says a
returning visitor. 'Their staff are genuinely friendly.' There are 'magnificent views' from the lounge, 'cosy with wood-burning stove and
large library', the dining room, and the 'simple but comfortable'
bedrooms. 'Our room had cream walls and a pine-clad bathroom.'
'Our smallish annexe room had a basin in the bedroom.' The bar is
busy all day with visitors, and with locals eating in the early evening;
the menus here and in the restaurant are similar. 'Very good food,
especially the seafood', eg, grilled langoustines with garlic mayonnaise; pan-fried haddock with lemon butter. 'Breakfast the best we
had in Scotland: delicious scrambled egg and smoked salmon.' 'First-
rate fry-up.' 'Well-trained and cheerful young staff: service was faultless, and really made a difference to our stay.' Children are welcomed.
(*John and June Jennings, GC, CLH*)

Bedrooms: 8, 1 in adjacent annexe. *Open*: 1 Mar–mid-Oct, restaurant closed
Mon. *Facilities*: lounge, bar, restaurant, small garden (tables for outside eating),
unsuitable for &. *Background music*: 'easy listening' all day in bar. *Location*:
10 miles S of Scourie. *Smoking*: not allowed. *Children*: all ages welcomed. *Dogs*:
not allowed in bar, restaurant. *Credit cards*: MasterCard, Visa. *Prices*: b&b [2008]
£47–£60 per person, set dinner £25–£29, full alc (bar) £26, 3-night breaks.

LANARK South Lanarkshire   Map 5:E2

New Lanark Mill
Mill 1, New Lanark Mills
Lanark ML11 9DB

Tel 01555-667200
Fax 01555-667222
Email hotel@newlanark.org
Website www.newlanark.org

'An interesting hotel in a remarkable setting.' In a steep wooded
valley below the Falls of Clyde, this restored 18th-century cotton

mill (managed by Michael Ward) is not a typical *Guide* hotel. Owned by New Lanark Conservation Trust, it is part of a World Heritage Site, a regeneration of a cotton-manufacturing centre developed by the philanthropic socialist, Robert Owen. The complex also includes a visitor centre, shops, self-catering accommodation, a youth hostel and, new this year, extensive health and fitness facilities. The mill's original Georgian windows and barrel-vaulted ceilings have been kept. Decor is light, simple, modern, perhaps 'bland'. Spacious bedrooms, 'well furnished and clean', face the Clyde or the surrounding conservation area. There is a new head chef again, Mark Burows, who uses local ingredients when possible, eg, grilled salmon on oven-roasted vegetables. Breakfast is a 'standard' buffet. Staff are 'all very helpful'. The 'jolly' bar is busy with non-residents, and the village is popular for weddings and celebrations (check about this when booking). Ceilidhs and party nights are held in winter. The accessible Clyde walkway leads to the Falls of Clyde wildlife reserve. 'A useful stop-over en route to the Highlands.' (*Richard Mayou, and others*)

Bedrooms: 38, 5 suitable for &. *Open*: all year. *Facilities*: lounge, bar, restaurant, heated indoor swimming pool (16 by 7 metres), free access to leisure club, function/conference/wedding facilities. *Background music*: varied, in public areas. *Location*: 1 mile S of Lanark. *Smoking*: allowed in 10 bedrooms. *Children*: all ages welcomed. *Dogs*: allowed in some bedrooms, only guide dogs in public rooms. *Credit cards*: all major cards. *Prices*: b&b £59.50–£79.50 per person, d,b&b £64.50–£89.50, set dinner £27.50, special breaks, Christmas/New Year packages, 1-night bookings sometimes refused. *V*

LARGOWARD Fife   Map 5:D3

The Inn at Lathones
by Largoward, nr St Andrews
KY9 1JE

Tel 01334-840494
Fax 01334-840694
Email lathones@theinn.co.uk
Website www.theinn.co.uk

There have been changes this year in this cluster of buildings in a hamlet near St Andrews: owner Nick White has added eight bedrooms. 'They are spacious and luxurious,' he tells us, 'with wooden floor, extremely comfortable bed and wonderful bathroom.' A visitor in 2008 wrote of a 'nice room' which, thanks to 'a good deal', he thought 'good value'. He also appreciated the 'good service'. A new chef, Paul Gibson, now provides 'gastropub-style' food. Guests may eat in the lounge, the restaurant or the stables, 'so they can decide how relaxed they want to be'. The 400-year-old single-storey coaching inn houses the bar ('where you can mix with locals'), the restaurant and the 'cosy' lounge. The bedrooms are in adjacent buildings, a minute's walk away. 'The welcome was warm,' said inspectors. 'Our room had laminated floors, attractive light wooden Italian furniture, TV, DVD-player, etc, a decent-sized bathroom.' Breakfast, no menu, served at table, had 'excellent fresh orange juice but thin sliced toast, cooked dishes but no muesli or fruit'. Children under 12 are accommodated free. Functions and parties are often held. This is a winner of 'Best small golfing hotel in Scotland'; it is managed by Morag Peattie. (*SH*)

Bedrooms: 21, in 3 separate buildings, some on ground floor. *Open*: mid-Jan–31 Dec, for lunch only on 25 Dec, closed 26 Dec. *Facilities*: ramps, lounge, bar, restaurant, function room, 1-acre grounds. *Background music*: in lounge before dinner. *Location*: 5 miles S of St Andrews. *Smoking*: not allowed. *Children*: all ages welcomed (under-12s stay free in parents' room). *Dogs*: not allowed in public rooms. *Credit cards*: all major cards. *Prices*: b&b £45–£150 per person, full alc £45, New Year package. *V*

LOCHEPORT Western Isles   Map 5: inset A1
See SHORTLIST

LOCHINVER Highland   Map 5:B1

The Albannach   *Tel* 01571-844407
Baddidarroch   *Email* info@thealbannach.co.uk
Lochinver IV27 4LP   *Website* www.thealbannach.co.uk

High on a hill above Lochinver's working harbour, this handsome, white-painted 19th-century house stands in a walled garden with mature trees and shrubs. Its 'unpretentious and easy' owner/manager/chefs, Colin Craig and Lesley Crosfield, provide 'considerate service and imaginative cooking', say fans. Picture windows in the 'intimate' candlelit dining room look over the deep sea loch to the dome of Suilven and, beyond, the mountains of Assynt. The conservatory, the Snug (wood panelled and with an old stone fireplace) and all the bedrooms, share the view. 'No bar, but drinks can be ordered anywhere' (they might be accompanied by fresh oysters). 'Contemporary Scottish' dishes (eg, roast gilt-head bream with citrus fruits and braised fennel) are served on a five-course dinner menu (no choice; preferences discussed in advance; alternatives available). Dinner is not provided on Monday, but a seafood supper is available. The fish and shellfish come from the harbour, meat and game are local, herbs and vegetables are organically grown, bread and oatcakes are home baked. This year there is a new suite, The Byre, in the garden: it has a conservatory sitting room. The penthouse suite up steep steps is 'large and luxurious'. 'Good breakfasts.' (*R and TB, and others*)

Bedrooms: 5, 1 in byre with private patio. *Open*: Mar–Dec inclusive, no dinner on Mon (optional seafood supper). *Facilities*: ramp, snug, conservatory, dining room, 1-acre garden, 6 acres croftland, unsuitable for &. *Background music*: none. *Location*: ½ mile from village. *Smoking*: not allowed. *Children*: not under 12. *Dogs*: not allowed. *Credit cards*: MasterCard, Visa. *Prices*: d,b&b £125–£170 per person, set dinner £50, Mon supper £25, off-season breaks, Christmas/ New Year packages.

Inver Lodge
Iolaire Road
Lochinver IV27 4LU

Tel 01571-844496
Fax 01571-844395
Email stay@inverlodge.com
Website www.inverlodge.com

Robin Vestey has succeeded his parents as owner of this modern hotel (purpose-built in 1989); 'hands-on' manager Nicholas Gorton leads its 'excellent, cosmopolitan staff'. 'Stunningly set' on a hill above Lochinver's harbour, it is surrounded by the unspoiled mountains of Assynt. Picture windows create a light interior. The traditional public rooms have comfortable furniture, stags' heads, patterned carpets. The hotel's own malt whisky is served in the bar. In the restaurant, tables are reallocated daily to ensure that the 'breathtakingly beautiful' view is enjoyed by all. Chef Peter Cullen produces ambitious dinner menus of up to six courses in modern British style. The emphasis is on local meat and fish: try the Loch Freuchie rainbow trout with smoked lobster ravioli. The wine list is wide ranging and fairly priced; 'half bottles more than usually numerous'. At breakfast there is freshly squeezed juice, and cooked dishes include vegetarian haggis. The bedrooms, if not over-endowed with character, are spacious, well fitted and furnished; the best ones enjoy the views. Also appreciated: 'The bed is made whilst you breakfast, so the room is tidy when you return; the rest of the servicing is done later.' Entertainments include snooker (a full-size table), a sauna, fishing in two rivers and four lochs. (*AW, and others*)

Bedrooms: 20. *Open*: 10 Apr–1 Nov. *Facilities*: 2 lounges, bar, restaurant, 1-acre garden, wedding facilities, unsuitable for ♿. *Background music*: none. *Location*: ½ mile above village. *Smoking*: not allowed. *Children*: none under 10 in restaurant at night. *Dogs*: not allowed in public rooms except foyer lounge. *Credit cards*: all major cards. *Prices*: b&b £100–£135 per person, d,b&b £135–£175, set dinner £48, weekend and midweek breaks, special events, Christmas/New Year packages. *V*

LOCHRANZA North Ayrshire   Map 5:D1

Apple Lodge   *Tel/Fax* 01770-830229
Lochranza
Isle of Arran KA27 8HJ

❧ *César award in 2000*

The homely atmosphere (handmade artefacts, family photographs, books, teddy bears) created by John and Jeannie Boyd is one of this guest house's many attractions. The white-painted, grey-roofed former manse, near the sea (and the small ferry to Kintyre), has wonderful views. 'Warm and comfortable' bedrooms have antique fireplace, embroidery, paintings, books and local information; bathrooms are 'beautifully fitted'. Apple Cottage has its own small sitting room and kitchen. Mrs Boyd's three-course, no-choice dinner menu is discussed with guests each morning, and served with candlelight, crystal and flowers (but not on Tuesday or in July and August). She calls her cooking 'best of British'; 'we couldn't fault a thing'. Main courses ('first class over four days') might include roast lamb with garlic, coriander and rosemary and a redcurrant orange and port sauce; they come with 'a good selection of vegetables'. No licence; bring your own wine. In the surrounding countryside, deer and eagles are often sighted. 'On two days we walked in the hills from the door for four hours without touching the car,' said guests who 'have lost count of how many times we have stayed'. A golf course is adjacent. (*Joan and David Marston*)

Bedrooms: 4, 1 on ground floor. *Open*: all year except Christmas/New Year, dining room closed midday, for dinner Tues and July/Aug. *Facilities*: lounge, dining room, ¼-acre garden, unsuitable for ♿. *Background music*: none. *Location*: outside village on N side of island. *Smoking*: not allowed. *Children*: not allowed. *Dogs*: not allowed. *Credit cards*: none. *Prices*: b&b £38–£53 per person, set dinner £25, usually min. 3-night booking.

LOCKERBIE Dumfries and Galloway   Map 5:E2
See SHORTLIST

LYBSTER Highland *See SHORTLIST*   Map 5:B3

MAYBOLE South Ayrshire   Map 5:E1

Ladyburn   *Tel* 01655-740585
by Maybole KA19 7SG   *Fax* 01655-740206
                                Email jh@ladyburn.co.uk
                          Website www.ladyburn.co.uk

In a beautiful Ayrshire valley, surrounded by woods and fields, this 17th-century white former dower house is run by the 'warmly welcoming' owners Jane Hepburn and her daughter, Catriona. Its 'atmosphere of a friendly family home' and 'luxurious feel' are praised, as is the 'attention to detail'. It is well furnished, with family antiques. There is a 'light and airy' drawing room. Some bedrooms have a four-poster. Additional accommodation (good for a family) is in the 'Granny Flat', accessible from the main house but with its own entrance. Dinner (or supper) is served by arrangement: 'Good traditional Scottish home cooking, with French overtones', eg, asparagus wrapped in smoked salmon with a horseradish cream; gigot of lamb roasted with garlic, wine and a smattering of cream. The Hepburns hold an alcohol licence. A picnic lunch can be supplied. In spring, rhododendrons, azaleas and bluebells grow in the large garden: part of Scotland's Garden Scheme, it has three national rose collections. *Ladyburn*'s guests may walk in the grounds of the magnificent adjacent Kilkerran estate. Shooting parties, weddings and functions are catered for. Turnberry's golf courses are a short drive away; salmon fishing can be arranged. (*BA*)

Bedrooms: 5. *Open*: all year but restricted opening Nov–Mar. *Facilities*: drawing room, dining room, wedding/function facilities, 5-acre garden (croquet), unsuitable for &. *Background music*: none. *Location*: 14 miles S of Ayr. *Smoking*: not allowed. *Children*: not under 16 in main house. *Dogs*: only guide dogs allowed. *Credit cards*: Amex, MasterCard, Visa. *Prices*: b&b £60–£85 per person, supper (2 courses) from £17.50, dinner (3 courses) from £26.

MELROSE Borders *See SHORTLIST*   Map 5:E3

MUIR OF ORD Highland   Map 5:C2

The Dower House   *Tel/Fax* 01463-870090
Highfield   *Email* info@thedowerhouse.co.uk
Muir of Ord IV6 7XN   *Website* www.thedowerhouse.co.uk

❧ *César award in 2008*

'It's like a miniature treasure chest,' a reporter wrote of this gabled, one-storey *cottage-orné*. It stands in a 'large, beautiful' wooded garden (with monkey puzzle trees, shrubs, a large goldfish pond and a miniature orchard) bordered by the rivers Beauly and Conon. Inside are Persian rugs, Chinese vases, antiques, chintzy wallpaper, flowery fabrics, potted plants, stacked bookcases, creating a 'much-loved' feel. The lounge has an open fire, a piano, and a bar cupboard full of malt whiskies. Other comments: 'Like staying in a family home.' 'I felt totally pampered.' The owners, Robyn and Mena Aitchison, 'are friendly but don't interfere'. She calls herself 'owner, waitress, cleaner'; he is an 'excellent self-taught cook', who describes his no-choice menu as 'gutsy modern British cooking', eg, breast of guinea fowl with wild mushrooms and herbs. 'Magnificent puddings' include hot raspberry soufflé. Guests are expected to dine in, in the 'most attractive' dining room with its 'gleaming mahogany tables'. 'Dietary requests speedily dealt with.' Generous breakfasts include fresh fruit salad, local honey, home-laid eggs. All the 'cosy' bedrooms face the garden; all have a large bed and a well-equipped bathroom; the suite has a sitting room. Children are welcomed. (*GM, and others*)

Bedrooms: 4, all on ground floor. *Open*: all year except Christmas. *Facilities*: lounge, dining room, 5-acre grounds (small formal garden, swings, tree house), unsuitable for ♿. *Background music*: none. *Location*: 14 miles NW of Inverness. *Smoking*: not allowed. *Children*: no under-5s at dinner (high tea at 5). *Dogs*: not allowed in public rooms. *Credit cards*: MasterCard, Visa. *Prices*: b&b £60–£80 per person, set dinner £38.

We say 'Unsuitable for ♿' when a hotel tells us that it cannot accommodate wheelchair-users. We do not have the resources to inspect such facilities or to assess the even more complicated matter of facilities for the partially disabled. We suggest that you discuss such details with the hotel.

NEWTON STEWART
Dumfries and Galloway
Map 5:E1

Kirroughtree House   *Tel* 01671-402141
Newton Stewart DG8 6AN   *Fax* 01671-402425
Email info@kirroughtreehouse.co.uk
Website www.kirroughtreehouse.co.uk

❦ *César award in 2003*

'It never changes. Staff delightful, food excellent, rooms comfortable.'
'A warm welcome, everyone very helpful.' In a beautiful, 'superbly
tranquil' setting, the McMillan group's imposing white, bow-
windowed mansion stands in large grounds by the Galloway Forest
Park. It has three oak-panelled lounges hung with oil paintings, and a
wooden 'modesty staircase' (panels prevent glimpses of a lady's
ankles). 'Free afternoon tea on arrival was delivered with "silver
service" style. Our front room was large and well appointed.' 'Our huge
room on the second floor was well furnished, had all the usual extras,
marvellous views and a great bath.' All rooms are supplied with sherry
and fruit. Men are required to wear a jacket at dinner. The cooking is
'very good if not gourmet, with a welcome flexibility if an item didn't
suit'. 'Charming' chef Rolf Mueller's modern British menus, served
with white linen, crystal and bone china, have three courses (with 'pre-
starter') and might include sea bream on couscous with aubergine
caviar and sauce velouté. 'Our preferences are carefully recorded; our
drinks appear as soon as we go for dinner.' 'Breakfast is really good.' Jim
Stirling is the long-serving, able manager. (*Evelyn Schaffer, Peter Buckley,
Michael and Maureen Heath, David Morrell*)

Bedrooms: 17. *Open*: mid-Feb–2 Jan. *Facilities*: lift, 2 lounges, 2 dining rooms,
8-acre grounds (gardens, tennis, croquet, pitch and putt). *Background music*:
none. *Location*: 1½ miles NE of Newton Stewart. *Smoking*: not allowed.
Children: not under 10. *Dogs*: allowed in lower ground-floor bedrooms only, not
in public rooms. *Credit cards*: Amex, MasterCard, Visa. *Prices*: [2008] b&b
£60–£120 per person, d,b&b £80–£155, set dinner £35, 2-night breaks (golf,
garden), Christmas/New Year packages, 1-night bookings sometimes refused.

NORTH BERWICK East Lothian   Map 5:D3
See SHORTLIST

Report forms (Freepost in UK) are at the end of the *Guide.*

OBAN Argyll and Bute   Map 5:D1

Lerags House
Lerags, by Oban
PA34 4SE

Tel 01631-563381
Email stay@leragshouse.com
Website www.leragshouse.com

'We are a two-person show, offering very personal service,' writes
Bella Miller. She is the cook at this handsome grey stone house which
she runs informally ('in the space between home and hotel') with her
husband, Charlie. It stands in a mature garden by Loch Feochan.
Hungarian Vizsla dogs Libby and Rex contribute to the 'warm
welcome'. 'The standard of service was immaculate,' say visitors this
year. 'Good-size room, bathroom excellent. Food inventive and
artistic, ingredients fresh, cooking perfect. Charlie is attentive and
friendly.' An earlier guest wrote: 'Excellent value.' The Australian
owners have run *Lerags* since 2001. Guests stay on half-board terms:
the three-course dinner ('Scottish with Australian flair') might
include guinea fowl with Stornoway white pudding, Dijon cream and
courgette. No choice, but 'Bella is flexible to guests' preferences'.
Public rooms and bedrooms are comfortably furnished, decorated in
white with stylish touches of colour. 'Our spacious suite had lovely
views. Bed one of the best ever, beautifully made, with crisp, white
linen.' The breakfast menu includes waffles, kippers, porridge and
'full Scottish'. Visitors with 'limited disability' can be accommodated.
Because of fire regulations, guests may be required to be off the
premises between 11 am and 4 pm if the Millers have to go out. (*Dale
and Krystyna Vargas*)

Bedrooms: 6. *Open*: Easter–Dec, closed Christmas, limited access to the house
11 am–4 pm. *Facilities*: sitting room, dining room, wedding facilities, 1-acre
grounds, unsuitable for &. *Background music*: various, dining room. *Location*:
5 miles S of Oban, by Loch Feochan. *Smoking*: not allowed. *Children*: not
allowed. *Dogs*: not allowed. *Credit cards*: MasterCard, Visa. *Prices*: [2008] d,b&b
£79–£105 per person, 1-night bookings refused holiday weekends.

The Manor House
Gallanach Road
Oban PA34 4LS

Tel 01631-562087
Fax 01631-563053
Email info@manorhouseoban.com
Website www.manorhouseoban.com

On a rocky headland on the south shore of Oban bay, half a mile from
the town centre, this hotel was found 'excellent' by visitors again this
year. A listed Georgian stone house, now owned by Leslie and

Margaret Crane, it was built as the principal residence of the Duke of Argyll's estate in 1780. It has period decor and spectacular views over Oban's busy harbour to the Morvern hills and the Isle of Mull. Binoculars are provided in each 'well-appointed', 'cosy' and 'spotless' bedroom (most of them enjoy the view), also Wi-Fi. Some rooms are small. 'Service is very good.' In the candlelit dining room, chef Patrick Freytag serves a five-course menu: 'Up to standard, and substantial.' Main courses include supreme of chicken in Riesling and spinach sauce with herb risotto. The admired breakfasts have fresh orange juice, 'excellent scrambled eggs with smoked salmon'. The bar (a popular local) provides 'good lunches' and has good views. A sunroom is new this year. In fine weather, lunch and drinks are served on a panoramic terrace. (*Richard Mayou, D and JM*)

Bedrooms: 11. *Open*: all year except 25/26 Dec. *Facilities*: 2 lounges, bar, restaurant, wedding facilities, ½-acre grounds, unsuitable for &. *Background music*: 'easy listening'. *Location*: ½ mile from centre. *Smoking*: not allowed. *Children*: not under 12. *Dogs*: not allowed in public rooms. *Credit cards*: Amex, MasterCard, Visa. *Prices*: [2008] b&b £52–£93 per person, d,b&b £81–£123, set dinner £36, New Year package.

PEAT INN Fife   Map 5:D3

The Peat Inn
Peat Inn, by Cupar
KY15 5LH

Tel 01334-840206
Fax 01334-840530
Email stay@thepeatinn.co.uk
Website www.thepeatinn.co.uk

Geoffrey Smeddle was formerly head chef of Terence Conran's *étain* restaurant in Glasgow. Two years ago, he and his wife, Katherine (the 'particularly friendly' front-of-house), took over this famous old coaching inn at the crossroads of this tiny village near St Andrews. They have renovated the restaurant, and work on the split-level suites in the *Residence*, a separate adjacent building, is in progress (new carpets and curtains, better showers). A visitor who knew the inn under its previous owners was pleased with the new set-up: 'Our meal was very good: beautifully cooked halibut main course. Our room was very pleasant, with a good bed, a fine view from the upstairs living area.' Earlier, inspectors found food and service 'exceptional', the atmosphere 'most relaxing'. The staff, many of whom have been here for years, are 'cheerful and local'. Guests gather in a lounge (with log fire) before dinner, which is served in three 'discreet' rooms, with big windows, widely spaced tables and a cream and brown decor. 'A splendid breakfast, delivered to the room, included fresh juice, boiled eggs, toast and croissants.' (*David Grant, and others*)

Bedrooms: 8 suites, all on ground floor in annexe. *Open*: all year except Christmas, 1–16 Jan, and Sun/Mon. *Facilities*: Ramp, lounge, restaurant, 1-acre garden. *Background music*: none. *Location*: 6 miles SW of St Andrews. *Smoking*: not allowed. *Children*: all ages welcomed. *Dogs*: not allowed in public rooms. *Credit cards*: Amex, MasterCard, Visa. *Prices*: b&b £77.50–£130 per person, set lunch £18, dinner £34, tasting menu £50, full alc £52, 3 nights for the price of 2 Nov–Mar, special breaks, New Year package.

PEEBLES Borders *See SHORTLIST*   Map 5:E2

PERTH Perth and Kinross   Map 5:D2
See SHORTLIST

PITLOCHRY Perth and Kinross   Map 5:D2
See SHORTLIST

PLOCKTON Highland   Map 5:C1

Plockton Hotel   *Tel* 01599-544274
41 Harbour Street   *Fax* 01599-544475
Plockton IV52 8TN   *Email* info@plocktonhotel.co.uk
                          Website www.plocktonhotel.co.uk

'Lovely setting, sea loch and hills around.' On the palm-fringed waterfront of one of the prettiest villages in Scotland (National Trust), this is part of a terrace of mainly white-painted, stone-built houses. Accommodation is in one building; the bar – a popular local – and restaurant are in an adjoining one; a cottage annexe is a few doors along. There are spectacular views over Loch Carron to the Applecross hills beyond. 'Good value for money,' says a visitor this year. The Pearson family owners head an 'exceptional' staff. The chintzy lounge bar, the restaurant and the bedrooms have 'Mackintosh-inspired fabrics and furniture'. 'Our room was lovely, large, modern.' Another room was smaller, with small bed, and there is a 'dark, wall-facing' room in the annexe. Alan Pearson provides 'good pub food (good seafood choices)'. Blackboard specials complement the extensive menu. 'Service excellent, though they were busy.' 'Very good breakfasts.' There is a garden in front across a small road, and a rear terraced garden with waterfall. This lively place has weekly bar entertainments, and the restaurant has a ceilidh dance floor. After 25 years, the Pearsons have put the hotel on the market: check the position before booking. (*CLH, June Brannan, and others*)

Bedrooms: 15, 1 suitable for &. 4 in annexe. *Open*: all year except 25 Dec. *Facilities*: ramps, small lounge, lounge bar, public bar, snug, restaurant, wedding facilities, front and rear gardens. *Background music*: Scottish traditional throughout public areas. *Location*: village waterfront. *Smoking*: not allowed. *Children*: all ages welcomed. *Dogs*: allowed in public bar only. *Credit cards*: Amex, MasterCard, Visa. *Prices*: b&b £55–£80 per person, full alc £35, autumn, winter, spring breaks.

POOLEWE Highland *See SHORTLIST*   Map 5:B1

PORT APPIN Argyll and Bute   Map 5:D1

The Airds Hotel
Port Appin PA38 4DF

Tel 01631-730236
Fax 01631-730535
Email airds@airds-hotel.com
Website www.airds-hotel.com

'Not cheap, but good value' is the general verdict on this white-painted former ferry inn, now a luxury hotel owned by Shaun and Jenny McKivragan with Robert McKay as manager. 'Food, housekeeping and staff all excellent.' It has 'wonderful views' over Loch Linnhe. There is an 'assortment of wellies by the front door'. The lounges have 'squashy, comfy seating' and landscape paintings. The conservatory at the front, where pre-dinner drinks are served, is 'light and airy'. The bedrooms have floral fabrics, antiques, flat-screen TV and DVD-player. 'Our room at the back was nicely decorated. Two built-in cupboards, gleaming bathroom with power shower, never-ending hot water.' Room 5, 'very elegant', has a 'fabulous, roomy bathroom'. Wi-Fi is available. In the restaurant, picture windows face the water. Award-winning chef Paul Burns serves modern French dishes ('with a hint of Scottish'), eg, halibut fillet with cream herb mash and shellfish sauce. 'Fine, fresh ingredients beautifully arranged.' Service is by 'female staff, mainly East European, kilted at night'. Breakfasts are 'excellent' (fresh juice; home-made jams; 'very good kippers'), as are packed lunches and afternoon tea (with home-made scones). A small paved area and lawn are across the road. (*M and DM, and others*)

Bedrooms: 11, also self-catering cottage. *Open*: all year except 2 days a week Nov, Dec, Jan. *Facilities*: 2 lounges, conservatory, snug bar, restaurant, wedding facilities, 1-acre garden (croquet, putting), unsuitable for &. *Background music*: none. *Location*: 25 miles N of Oban. *Smoking*: not allowed. *Children*: all ages welcomed, but no under-9s in dining room at night (high tea at 6.30). *Dogs*: allowed by prior agreement; not in public rooms. *Credit cards*: Amex, MasterCard, Visa. *Prices*: [2008] d,b&b £122.50–£351 per person, off-season breaks, Christmas/New Year packages.

PORT CHARLOTTE Argyll and Bute   Map 5:D1

Port Charlotte Hotel
Main Street
Port Charlotte
Isle of Islay PA48 7TU

Tel 01496-850360
Fax 01496-850361
Email info@portcharlottehotel.co.uk
Website www.portcharlottehotel.co.uk

On the waterfront of this pretty conservation village of white-washed cottages, this small hotel has views across Loch Indaal (the distinctive Paps of Jura form a backdrop). Recently upgraded by 'competent' owners Grahame and Isabelle Allison, it is attractively furnished, with oriental rugs, polished wood floors, 'nice antique furniture' and contemporary Scottish art. Live traditional music is a feature in the bar, popular with locals (one couple admired a 'talented local young fiddler'). It stocks 118 single malts, and serves evening meals. Hotel guests are advised to book a table at the busy restaurant, where the chef, Rangasamy Dhamodharan, serves a three-course menu with much local produce. 'The best lobster we have had; oysters, too, were outstanding.' The bedrooms are 'fine, if a little on the small side'; nine of them have sea views. 'Excellent breakfasts.' You can reach a sandy beach from the small garden. As well as peaty malt whiskies, Islay, warmed by the Gulf Stream, has many deserted beaches, and is a paradise for birdwatchers. (*Dale and Krystyna Vargas, EM Arnold, Robert E Halstead*)

Bedrooms: 10, 2 on ground floor. *Open*: all year except 24–26 Dec. *Facilities*: lounge, lounge bar (traditional live music), restaurant, wedding facilities, small garden (bar meal service). *Background music*: traditional. *Location*: village centre, parking. *Smoking*: not allowed. *Children*: all ages welcomed. *Dogs*: not allowed in bedrooms. *Credit cards*: MasterCard, Visa. *Prices*: [2008] b&b £65–£85 per person, full alc £40, 3 nights for the price of 2 Oct–Mar.

PORTPATRICK
Dumfries and Galloway

Map 5:E1

Knockinaam Lodge
Portpatrick
DG9 9AD

Tel 01776-810471
Fax 01776-810435
Email reservations@knockinaamlodge.com
Website www.knockinaamlodge.com

'Really excellent,' writes a correspondent who visited this luxury hotel twice this year. 'It is worth taking the long and increasingly bumpy track to reach the private drive. I was the only guest but was treated royally.' Shielded by cliffs and wooded hills, this grey stone 19th-century hunting lodge is owned by the 'delightful' David and Sian Ibbotson. 'Beautifully decorated', it has rich fabrics, antiques, oak panelling, open fires. Churchill met Eisenhower secretly here during World War II: you can stay in his bedroom, the largest, with its enormous bath ('stool provided so you can climb in'). 'There are some fine single malts in the bar.' 'Superb dinner.' In the formal, candlelit dining room, smart casual dress (no denim) is preferred. Chef Tony Pierce's four-course dinner (no choice until dessert or cheese) earns a *Michelin* star. Classical/modern Scottish dishes include sea bass with asparagus and a champagne and chive butter sauce. Vegetarians are well catered for. 'Portions small but satisfying.' 'Divine scrambled eggs at breakfast.' In fine weather there are tea, drinks and barbecues on the lawn. There is a tree house for children, who are welcomed here. *Knockinaam* has its own sandy cove. Good walking and country pursuits. (*Robert Gower*)

Bedrooms: 10. *Open*: all year. *Facilities*: lounge, bar lounge, restaurant, wedding facilities, 40-acre grounds (sand/rock beach 50 yds), only restaurant suitable for &. *Background music*: classical in restaurant. *Location*: 2 miles S of Portpatrick. *Smoking*: not allowed. *Children*: no under-12s in dining room after 7 pm (high tea at 6). *Dogs*: not allowed in public rooms, some bedrooms. *Credit cards*: Amex, MasterCard, Visa. *Prices*: d,b&b £100–£225 per person, set menu £55, reductions for 3 or more nights off-season, Christmas/New Year packages. *V*

PORTREE Highland   Map 5:C1

Viewfield House   *Tel* 01478-612217
Portree   *Fax* 01478-613517
Isle of Skye IV51 9EU   *Email* info@viewfieldhouse.com
                                       Website www.viewfieldhouse.com

César award in 1993

In large wooded grounds in Skye's capital, this baronial pile (Georgian with Victorian additions) has been the Macdonald family's home for over two centuries. Nowadays, the 'affable' Hugh Macdonald runs it, entertaining paying guests in house party style. They enjoy the 'faded grandeur' and the 'Gothic' air of the 'interesting and comfortable' public rooms, which have changed little over the years. There are family pictures, stags' antlers, Indian brass and other imperial relics, Persian rugs on polished wooden floors. 'Our huge bedroom had four windows overlooking the gardens and bay. It was furnished with antiques, books, two writing desks; the vast bathroom had a new walk-in power shower as well as a claw-footed bath and two washstands.' The 'absence of hotel-type notices' is liked. There is no hotel-style Reception or bar, but drinks are served more or less on request. No formal evening meal, but simple hot dishes and salads are available throughout the evening (home-made soups, cheese platter, etc). 'Breakfast has plenty of fresh and dried fruit, Mallaig kippers, fresh juices.' 'Don't miss the ground-floor cloakroom, a unique "antique" experience.' There is Wi-Fi Internet access throughout, and a small office for guests' use. Children are welcomed. (*J and D A, and others*)

Bedrooms: 11, 1 on ground floor suitable for &. *Open*: Easter–mid-Oct. *Facilities*: ramp, drawing room, morning/TV room, dining room, 20-acre grounds (croquet, swings). *Background music*: none. *Location*: S side of Portree. *Smoking*: not allowed. *Children*: all ages welcomed. *Dogs*: not allowed in public rooms except with permission of other guests (except guide dogs). *Credit cards*: MasterCard, Visa. *Prices*: [2008] b&b £40–£60 per person, full alc £30, 3- to 5-day rates, 1-night group bookings sometimes refused. *V*

See also SHORTLIST

ST ANDREWS Fife *See SHORTLIST*   Map 5:D3

ST OLA Orkney   Map 5:A3

Foveran	*Tel* 01856-872389
St Ola	*Fax* 01856-876430
Kirkwall KW15 1SF	*Email* foveranhotel@aol.com
	Website www.foveranhotel.co.uk

'Caring staff, good bedroom, excellent breakfasts, good dinners.' In their simple, single-storey hotel overlooking Scapa Flow, the Doull family provide 'traditional Orcadian hospitality' and are holders of a green tourism award. The feeling is 'relaxed yet professional', say *Guide* correspondents. There is 'a warm welcome with tea'. The well-equipped bedrooms, decorated in blond woods, are 'small but immaculate and comfortable'. 'Not posh, and without the gimmicks that many hotels provide these days.' Pre-dinner drinks are served by a fire in the lounge. In the restaurant, 'large, light and airy', with well-spaced tables and fine views, Paul Doull's 'consistently good' cooking is enjoyed by 'a constant flow of locals' as well as residents. The emphasis is on local produce: 'Memorable mutton one day, sole and monkfish another.' 'The wine list is fairly short, but sensible enough.' The service from 'a splendid team of youngsters' is praised. 'One waitress produced guide books for us without prompting.' Orkney is a 'marvellous place' with abundant wildlife and fascinating archaeological sites'. (*John Barnes, Richard and Catriona Smith*)

Bedrooms: 8, all on ground floor. *Open*: mid-Apr–early Oct, by arrangement at other times, only restaurant Christmas/New Year, restaurant closed Sun evening end Sept–early June. *Facilities*: lounge, restaurant, wedding facilities, 12-acre grounds (private rock beach). *Background music*: Scottish, in evening, in restaurant. *Location*: 3 miles SW of Kirkwall. *Smoking*: not allowed. *Children*: all ages welcomed. *Dogs*: not allowed. *Credit cards*: MasterCard, Visa. *Prices*: b&b £49.50–£67 per person, d,b&b £72–£89.50, full alc £32, 1-night bookings sometimes refused.

The Hotelfinder (page 17) highlights hotels in a wide range of categories.

SCARISTA Western Isles   Map 5:B1
See SHORTLIST

SCOURIE Highland *See SHORTLIST*   Map 5:B2

SHAPINSAY Orkney   Map 5:A3

Balfour Castle   *Tel* 01856-711282
Shapinsay   *Fax* 01856-711283
KW17 2DY   *Email* info@balfourcastle.co.uk
    Website www.balfourcastle.com

On a small hill outside Shapinsay harbour, this magnificent turreted 19th-century castle was once the Orkney summer home of the Balfour family. It claims to be 'the most northerly castle hotel in the world'. 'A Victorian time warp', it is run by owner Patricia Lidderdale (her father, Captain Tadeusz Zawadski, a Polish cavalry officer, bought it in 1961). 'A fascinating place'; 'We loved it,' said recent visitors. The handsome drawing room looks over the water to St Magnus Cathedral and Kirkwall; French doors lead to a conservatory; there is a small bar in the oak-panelled library, and a small chapel where weddings are held. The no-choice (with vegetarian options) three-course communal dinners are 'simple and fresh'. Fiona Lovatt, the chef, 'is a mine of information; we learnt a lot as she chatted through the main course'. Most bedrooms are large; one has a four-poster bed with the carved coat of arms of the Balfour family; another has a small turret and a large brass bed. Bathrooms have 'lashings of hot water'. In the 'beautiful grounds' are a wood, and a walled garden which produces 'particularly good' fruit and vegetables. Shapinsay has a wealth of birds, seals, wild flowers, good walks. (*R and TB*)

Bedrooms: 6. *Open*: Apr–Sept. *Facilities*: drawing room, library, dining room, breakfast room, conservatory, billiard room, chapel, wedding facilities, 30-acre grounds (beaches, fishing, wildlife walks), unsuitable for &. *Background music*: none. *Location*: 5 mins' walk from harbour, ferry (20 mins) to Shapinsay from Kirkwall; they will meet. *Smoking*: not allowed. *Children*: not under 12. *Dogs*: not allowed. *Credit cards*: Diners, MasterCard, Visa. *Prices*: [2008] d,b&b £110–£130 per person, 10% discount for 5 or more nights.

SHIELDAIG Highland   Map 5:C1

Tigh an Eilean
Shieldaig, Loch Torridon
IV54 8XN

Tel 01520-755251
Fax 01520-755321
Email tighaneilean@keme.co.uk

❧ *César award in 2005*

'What a small hotel should be.' 'Hands-on owners, unpretentious, very friendly. Pleasant general rooms. Lovely dining room overlooking the water. Lunch and dinner really good. Bedroom large enough with good-size bathroom. I couldn't fault the service.' Praise again for Christopher and Cathryn Field's small hotel with 'glorious' views across the sea to Shieldaig Island (a sanctuary for ancient pines). All the bedrooms now have a small sitting area with table and chairs. 'Ours had loch views.' In two 'comfortable lounges', the honour bar is 'a nice touch', and 'tasty' canapés come with pre-dinner drinks. The dining room serves a three-course menu with choice (main courses like pork tenderloin with corn risotto; sole with grapes and Gewürztraminer cream), and there is a new, informal first-floor restaurant, *The Coastal Kitchen*, which focuses on 'our fantastic local seafood simply cooked' and pizzas from a wood-fired oven. It has sea views and a panoramic roof terrace. Generous cooked breakfasts have freshly squeezed juice, 'excellent yogurt', smoked haddock, etc. There is free Wi-Fi Internet access. Children are well catered for. The Fields have rebuilt the adjacent village pub, which serves 'good, inexpensive' food. 'Its facilities are now much better.' Around are 'lovely scenery, peace, quiet and good walks'. (*Richard Mayou, CLH*)

Bedrooms: 10. *Open*: Mar–end Oct. *Facilities*: 2 lounges (1 with TV and wood-burning stove), bar/library, village bar (separate entrance), 2 restaurants, drying room, wedding facilities, small front courtyard, roof terrace, unsuitable for ♿. *Background music*: none. *Location*: village centre. *Smoking*: not allowed. *Children*: all ages welcomed (under-13s stay free in parents' room). *Dogs*: not allowed in public rooms. *Credit cards*: Amex, MasterCard, Visa. *Prices*: [2008] b&b £75–£80 per person, d,b&b £115–£120, bar meals, set dinner £44 for non-residents, full alc £30, reductions for 3 or more nights. *V*

****

Traveller's tale *Hotel in Wiltshire* At breakfast, staff were oblivious to items missing off the buffet table as guests stood waiting for things to appear. Service was slow, and yesterday's crumbs were on the carpet.

****

SKIRLING Borders   Map 5:E2

Skirling House   *Tel* 01899-860274
Skirling, by Biggar ML12 6HD   *Fax* 01899-860255
                                        Email enquiry@skirlinghouse.com
                                        Website www.skirlinghouse.com

♕ *César award in 2004*

'Once in a while, one happens on perfection. Hospitality students should be trained at places like this.' 'Our 20th visit to this jewel. Wonderful ambience.' 'Excellent value.' 'Magnificent.' Again there is much praise for this fine Arts and Crafts house (Wolsey Lodge) on the green of a tiny village amid lovely Borders countryside. Built in 1908 as the summer retreat of a Scottish art connoisseur, it contains 'a stunning collection of artworks', lots of books, fresh flowers. The drawing room has a 16th-century carved wood ceiling, full-height windows, a log fire and a baby grand piano. The owners, Bob and Isobel Hunter, who provide 'exemplary attention', are supported by 'perfectly behaved four-legged animals'. 'The warmest of welcomes: tea and delicious fruitcake. Breakfasts as good as you get' (fresh orange juice, French toast with caramelised apples and black pudding, home-made jams and marmalades). 'We love the beautifully fitted bedrooms with every conceivable extra. Meals, cooked by Bob [four courses, no choice; preferences discussed] are innovative and delicious': main courses include game casserole; chicken breast with wild apricots. There are 'interesting options' for vegetarians. 'Good wine list.' Children are welcomed. (*Alastair Kameen, Revd Peter Cannon, Peter Buckley, Gwyn Morgan*)

Bedrooms: 5 plus 1 single available if let with a double, 1 on ground floor suitable for ♿. *Open*: Mar–Dec. *Facilities*: ramps, drawing room, library, conservatory, dining room, 5-acre garden (tennis, croquet) in 100-acre estate with woodland. *Background music*: none. *Location*: 2 miles E of Biggar, by village green. *Smoking*: not allowed. *Children*: all ages welcomed. *Dogs*: allowed by arrangement, not in public rooms or unattended in bedrooms. *Credit cards*: MasterCard, Visa. *Prices*: [2008] b&b £47.50–£70 per person, d,b&b £77.50–£100, set dinner £32. *V*

The more reports we receive, the more accurate the *Guide* becomes. Please don't hesitate to write again about an old favourite, even if it is only to endorse the entry. New reports help us keep the *Guide* up to date.

SLEAT Highland   Map 5:C1

Toravaig House
Knock Bay, Sleat
Isle of Skye
IV44 8RE

Tel 0845-0551117
Fax 01471-833231
Email info@skyehotel.co.uk
Website www.skyehotel.co.uk

'I really loved it,' writes a visitor this year, admiring the 'cosy
atmosphere and fabulous food' at this handsome, white-painted
1930s building. Beautifully set on the coast road, close to the
Armadale ferry, it has been renovated by Anne Gracie and Kenneth
Gunn (a former captain of the *Hebridean Princess* cruise ship). 'They
are much in evidence, hands on, greeting guests, making small talk,
waiting at table.' The interior is decorated in 'strong, but not intimi-
dating' colours, and there is 'handsome lighting'. The drawing room
has a log fire and comfortable seating. In the 'pleasing' dining room,
'the menu uses flowery language, but the cooking of chef Peter
Woods is accomplished' (local meat, haggis and seafood). 'Background muzak was fortunately subdued.' Rooms vary: 'Ours was
small, but comfortable.' 'Ours faced the car park; nicely decorated, it
had effective reading lights, armchairs, good fabrics; spotless,
compact bathroom.' Breakfast had an 'underwhelming buffet; good
marmalade and butter in proper pots; excellent bacon but poor toast'.
The staff, in neat black uniforms, were thought 'agreeable and
professional'. Captain Gunn takes guests on trips on his 42-foot yacht.
(*Morag Young, Penny Tapsfield, and others*)

Bedrooms: 9. *Open*: all year. *Facilities*: lounge, dining room, wedding facilities,
1-acre grounds, unsuitable for &. *Background music*: traditional Scottish/jazz.
Location: 3 miles N of Armadale. *Smoking*: not allowed. *Children*: not allowed.
Dogs: not allowed. *Credit cards*: MasterCard, Visa. *Prices*: b&b £70–£120 per
person, d,b&b £95–£150, set dinner £40, seasonal offers, midweek breaks,
Christmas/New Year packages.

STRONTIAN Highland   Map 5:C1

Kilcamb Lodge
Strontian
PH36 4HY

Tel 01967-402257
Fax 01967-402041
Email enquiries@kilcamblodge.co.uk
Website www.kilcamblodge.co.uk

'Always good, now better.' Sally Fox 'really knows how to run a hotel',
say visitors this year to this Georgian building (one of the oldest stone
houses in Scotland, with sympathetic Victorian additions). She and

her husband, David, are its 'friendly', 'hands-on' owners; their staff are 'all excellent' (Phillip Fleming is the 'caring' general manager). Splendidly set, surrounded by woodland and hills, *Kilcamb Lodge* has its own beach on Loch Sunart. 'Beautifully furnished', it has open fires, fresh flowers and 'spacious, comfortable period lounges'. 'Expensively excellent'; 'tremendous atmosphere' were earlier comments. In the 'cosy red dining room', chef Mark Greenaway serves a short four-course menu of modern dishes 'of a high standard', eg, confit duck leg with hot orange jelly and beetroot carpaccio. The best bedrooms are large, with 'enormous bed, window seat and loch view'. 'Quality linen and towels.' Breakfast has newly baked croissants, a good selection of cereals, free-range eggs, steak. Dogs are welcomed: 'no flowerbeds or ornamental gardens to worry about', and you might find some 'doggy treats' in your bedroom. Much wildlife can be seen on the Ardnamurchan peninsula (most easily reached by a short ferry crossing). There are red deer, otters, eagles and whale-watching trips. (*David Morrell, Robert E Halstead, and others*)

Bedrooms: 10, 7 in annexe. *Open*: Feb–end Dec, closed 2 days a week Feb, Nov. *Facilities*: drawing room, lounge bar, dining room, wedding facilities, 22-acre grounds (loch frontage, beach (safe bathing), fishing, boating), unsuitable for &. *Background music*: jazz/classical/piano. *Location*: edge of village. *Smoking*: not allowed. *Children*: not under 12. *Dogs*: not allowed. *Credit cards*: MasterCard, Visa. *Prices*: b&b [2008] £80–£122.50 per person, set dinner £48, off-season breaks, Christmas/New Year packages. *V*

SWINTON Borders *See SHORTLIST*   Map 5:E3

TAYNUILT Argyll and Bute   Map 5:D1
See SHORTLIST

TIGHNABRUAICH Argyll and Bute   Map 5:D1

An Lochan   *Tel* 01700-811239
Shore Road   *Fax* 01700-811300
Tighnabruaich PA21 2BE   *Email* info@anlochan.co.uk
                                     Website www.anlochan.co.uk

Named in Gaelic 'by the small loch', Roger and Bea McKie's white, bay-windowed seafront hotel stands across a small road from the shore in an unspoilt fishing village on the Kyles of Bute. Both restaurants and all but three bedrooms look across the sea to Bute. Visitors this year wrote of 'a warm welcome with complimentary tea and cake, a well-appointed room with an excellent view and a spacious bathroom, helpful staff, good breakfast'. Chef Paul Scott, who arrived in January 2008 and works with the McKies' daughter, Louise, describes his cooking as modern European 'with a twist'. In the wooden-floored *Deck* brasserie, and the intimate and more formal *Crustacean* restaurant, *à la carte* dishes include roast halibut with salsify, mushrooms and liquorice foam. There is a simple menu in the *Snug Bar*, which is popular with locals (eg, wild mushroom risotto; steak sandwich). Bold colours are used in the 'attractive and comfortable' public rooms, which have local paintings and sculptures, books and family memorabilia, and also in the 'immaculate' bedrooms. Golf, sailing, windsurfing, fishing and cruises can be arranged. (*Peter Buckley, and others*)

Bedrooms: 11. *Open*: all year except 20–27 Dec. *Facilities*: 2 lounges, bar, 2 restaurants, treatment room, ½-acre grounds, 100 yards from sea (shingle beach, moorings, pontoon), only restaurant and bar suitable for &. *Background music*: relaxation/jazz/Scottish. *Location*: on shore road. *Smoking*: not allowed. *Children*: all ages welcomed (no charge for extra bed). *Dogs*: allowed by arrangement (£3 a night), in public rooms only after meal service. *Credit cards*: Diners, MasterCard, Visa. *Prices*: b&b £62.50–£95 per person, full alc £45, d,b&b rates for 2 or more nights, New Year package.

TIRORAN Argyll and Bute   Map 5:D1

Tiroran House   *Tel* 01681-705232
Tiroran, Isle of Mull   *Fax* 01681-705240
PA69 6ES   *Email* tiroran-house@btinternet.com
    Website www.tiroran.com

'More private house than hotel' is how Laurence and Katie Mackay describe their white-fronted Victorian home. It stands in large grounds on the shores of Loch Scridain, near Mull's highest mountain, Ben More. Visitors praise the 'wonderful surroundings', the 'warm welcome' (with complimentary tea and scones). 'Such a friendly atmosphere.' 'A well-appointed bedroom with excellent views.' Each room is different: 'Ours was spacious; very peaceful.' Both sitting rooms have a log fire, fresh flowers; one has a polished wooden floor. In the small dining room or the adjacent conservatory (shaded by an indoor vine), Katie Mackay serves 'wonderful' dinners: three courses (with three options each) using fresh local produce (lobster, lamb, venison and fish). Breakfast, in the conservatory, has home-made muesli, breads, marmalade and preserves, and free-range eggs. Children are welcomed: under-12s have an early supper. A burn with waterfalls runs through the secluded gardens which lead to a private beach; otters, red deer and eagles can be seen. 'Mobile phones don't work very well here,' we are told. (*CH Hay, G and TH*)

Bedrooms: 7, 2 on ground floor. *Open*: generally all year except Christmas/New Year. *Facilities*: 2 sitting rooms, dining room, conservatory, wedding facilities, 17½-acre grounds (burn, beach with mooring). *Background music*: traditional/ 'easy listening'. *Location*: N side of Loch Scridain. *Smoking*: not allowed. *Children*: all ages welcomed, usually no under-12s in dining room. *Dogs*: allowed in 2 bedrooms, not in public rooms. *Credit cards*: MasterCard, Visa. *Prices*: [2008] b&b £109–£135 per person, d,b&b £117.50–£175.

TOBERMORY Argyll and Bute   Map 5:D1
See SHORTLIST

TORRIDON Highland   Map 5:C1

The Torridon   *Tel* 01445-791242
Torridon, by Achnasheen   *Fax* 01445-712253
IV22 2EY   *Email* info@thetorridon.com
                                             Website www.thetorridon.com

'Perfect; we felt relaxed and pampered,' writes a visitor to this turreted former shooting lodge, 'superbly' and remotely set by Loch Torridon, at the foot of Ben Damph. Now a luxury hotel (Pride of Britain), it is run by owners Rohaise and Daniel Rose-Bristow with manager Robert Ince. 'Friendly staff looked after us without being over-attentive.' Original features have been retained in the 'beautiful' public rooms, which retain a 'sense of Victorian grandeur'. There are patterned ceilings, traditional furnishings, wood panelling, big open fireplaces. Bedrooms are well furnished too; some have a king-size bed and a claw-footed freestanding bath; two have a four-poster. 'In a recently refurbished room I sat in the bath with a cup of tea, looking at the spectacular Torridon mountains.' 'Superb house-keeping.' Chef Kevin John Broome serves 'excellent' 'classic British' dinners on a three-course menu (eg, steamed wild bass with noodles and caviar velouté) in the panelled dining room. 'We had a leisurely and substantial meal without feeling that portions were too large.'

'First-class breakfast': porridge with whisky, kippers, haggis, 'delic-ious' raspberry jam. An activities manager suggests outings. This is a popular wedding venue. The recently refurbished *Torridon Inn*, in former stables and sheds, provides accommodation for 'the budget traveller'. (*Ann Morrison, and others*)

Bedrooms: 19, 1 on ground floor suitable for ♿, 1 suite in adjacent cottage. *Open*: all year except Jan, Mon/Tues Nov–Mar. *Facilities*: ramp, lift, drawing room, library, whisky bar, dining room, wedding facilities, 58-acre grounds (croquet, kitchen garden, river, nature walk, loch). *Background music*: classical at night in dining room. *Location*: On W coast, 10 miles SW of Kinlochewe. *Smoking*: not allowed. *Children*: no under-10s in dining room in evening (high tea provided). *Dogs*: allowed in cottage only. *Credit cards*: Amex, MasterCard, Visa. *Prices*: b&b £70–£197.50 per person, d,b&b £110–£237.50, set dinner £40, special breaks, Christmas/New Year packages.

ULLAPOOL Highland   Map 5:B2

The Ceilidh Place
14 West Argyle Street
Ullapool IV26 2TY

Tel 01854-612103
Fax 01854-613773
Email stay@theceilidhplace.com
Website www.theceilidhplace.com

'A joyous place, full of character and originality', liked for its 'relaxed atmosphere' and 'genuine friendliness'. Jean Urquhart has for many years presided over this unusual bookshop/café/pub/restaurant/hotel, winner of a 'Good for the Soul' award in 2005. Effie MacKenzie is the general manager. It includes a wholefood shop and an arts centre with plays, poetry readings and exhibitions by Scottish artists. 'The bookstore is a real one: serious titles and genuine literature.' The lounge has games, books, a small pantry with free tea and coffee and an honesty bar. The furniture is crafted from local materials. Recent visitors found the accommodation 'eminently satisfactory. Simple, spacious room, functionally laid out. Surprising touches: thick bathrobes, hot-water bottles. Pleasant younger staff; reasonable restaurant.' Scott Morrison's 'Scottish eclectic' menu, which 'changes according to what the fishermen catch and what is ripe in the garden', includes Loch Broom prawns grilled with garlic and cumin butter; shepherd's pie. Vegetarian dishes are a speciality. Ceilidhs are often held. In summer the café serves meals all day; in winter, food and drink are served in the parlour. Ullapool, a pleasant fishing port and holiday resort, was laid out in a grid pattern in the 18th century. (*SH*)

Bedrooms: 13, 10 with facilities *en suite*, plus 11 in bunkhouse across road. *Open*: all year. *Facilities*: bar, parlour, café/bistro, restaurant, bookshop, conference/ function/wedding facilities, 2-acre garden, only public areas suitable for ♿. *Background music*: 'eclectic' in public areas. *Location*: village centre, large car park. *Smoking*: not allowed. *Children*: all ages welcomed. *Dogs*: not allowed in public rooms. *Credit cards*: Amex, MasterCard, Visa. *Prices*: [2008] b&b £41– £68 per person, full alc £32.50, New Year package. *V*

See also SHORTLIST

WALKERBURN Borders   Map 5:E2

Windlestraw Lodge   *Tel* 01896-870636
Tweed Valley   *Email* reception@windlestraw.co.uk
Galashiels Road   *Website* www.windlestraw.co.uk
Walkerburn EH43 6AA

In an elevated position, facing the Traquair and Elibank forests and the Tweed valley, this Edwardian house was built as a wedding present for the local mill owner. It is now the home of chef Alan Reid and his wife, Julie. They 'achieve the perfect balance of friendly interest with efficiency', says a regular visitor who also wrote of 'romantic and elegant', candlelit, open-plan public rooms. The wood-panelled dining area has 'breathtaking views'. 'Tasteful decor (*objets d'art*, family photos). Lovely open fires. Smart, comfortable bedrooms. Superb food.' Local ingredients are used in dishes like venison on redcurrant and thyme jus and crushed pink potatoes. 'Small cups of intensely flavoured soups at the start of each meal.' On a birthday visit, 'personal touches like flowers and a card made the day special'. The Mackintosh master bedroom has a king-size brass bed and original bathtub. At breakfast, the continental version has smoked venison, cheese and fruit, and cooked dishes include porridge with honey and cream; boiled eggs with 'soldiers'; smoked haddock and poached eggs. The Reids cater for house parties, private meetings and small weddings; they offer one-to-one cookery lessons, and can arrange golf, fishing, shooting and mountain biking. (*AMC*)

Bedrooms: 6, all on first floor. *Open*: all year except 2 days Christmas, 2 days New Year, 2 weeks Feb, 1 week June, 1 week Oct. *Facilities*: lounge, sun lounge, drawing room, dining room, 'exclusive use for small weddings', 2-acre grounds, unsuitable for ♿. *Background music*: none. *Location*: outskirts of village, 2 miles E of Innerleithen. *Smoking*: not allowed. *Children*: no under-10s at dinner (high teas 5–6 pm). *Dogs*: not allowed in public rooms. *Credit cards*: MasterCard, Visa. *Prices*: [2008] b&b £65–£85 per person, d,b&b £105–£125, set menu £42.

WESTRAY Orkney   Map 5:A3

Cleaton House   *Tel* 01857-677508
Pierowall   *Fax* 01857-677442
Westray KW17 2DB   *Email* info@cleatonhouse.co.uk
                                       Website www.cleatonhouse.co.uk

Westray, one of the most northerly Orkney isles, has miles of sandy beaches, and the second-largest breeding seabird colony in the UK (puffins between May and August). Alone on a promontory, this handsome mansion faces the little island of Papa Westray. Both small hotel and local pub, it is owned by the 'hospitable' Lynne and Tony Thorpe. Their 'high standards' are admired. 'Accommodation is luxurious. Lynne's cooking is out of this world,' said one visitor. 'She presents local produce, such as the great Orkney beef and freshly caught clams and crayfish, to perfection.' Seafood comes with 'delicately flavoured sauces'. Vegetables and herbs are home grown in the walled garden. The 'elegant' dining room has linen tablecloths, cut-glass goblets, coat of arms and pictures of the Stewart family, who built the house in 1850. The bar serves simple meals. The 'comfortable, well-furnished' lounge has board games and a collection of Orcadian literature. 'Our excellent bedroom had all mod cons (very fancy TV) and good views.' Shutters keep out the light of the long summer nights. Guests can be met at the ferry or airstrip, and can be driven to remote parts of the island so they can walk back. Pets are welcomed. (*JL Craven, and others*)

Bedrooms: 6, 1 on ground floor suitable for &. *Open*: all year except Nov. *Facilities*: ramps, residents' lounge, lounge bar, restaurant, 2-acre garden (bowls), sandy bay, sea ½ mile. *Background music*: in lounge bar if required. *Location*: 2 miles SE of Pierowall village, ferry/small plane from Kirkwall (they will meet). *Smoking*: not allowed. *Children*: all ages welcomed. *Dogs*: allowed in lounge only. *Credit cards*: MasterCard, Visa. *Prices*: [2008] b&b £45–£60 per person, d,b&b £75–£90, special breaks, Christmas/New Year packages.

If you dislike piped music, why not join Pipedown, the campaign for freedom from piped music? It is at 1 The Row, Berwick St James, Salisbury SP3 4TP. *Tel* 01722-690622, www.pipedown.info.

WHITHORN Dumfries and Galloway   Map 5:E2

The Steam Packet Inn	*Tel* 01988-500334
Harbour Row	*Fax* 01988-500627
Isle of Whithorn	*Email* steampacketinn@btconnect.com
Newton Stewart DG8 8LL	*Website* www.steampacketinn.com

'Alastair Scoular is quietly dedicated to running this delightful quayside inn with comfortable rooms and a popular restaurant – well patronised by locals.' Praise for this family-owned (for 26 years) pub in a pretty seafaring village in the Isle of Whithorn (actually not an island, but the tip of the Machars peninsula). Tea and coffee are served all day. The 'consistently good' blackboard menus (changed twice daily) of chef Callum Harvey are served in the 'small, busy' bars, the 'bright, cheerful' dining room ('tables nicely laid') and the conservatory. They use fish from the harbour ('cooked to perfection: king scallops, monkfish, lemon sole'); steaks from Inverurie. 'Dishes designed for hearty appetites.' 'Very good bread rolls at dinner, but poor toast at breakfast which was otherwise entirely satisfactory, particularly the marmalade, home made by Mrs Scoular senior. Her husband acts as PR officer, appearing most mornings, enquiring if guests are enjoying their stay.' The best bedroom is spacious, with large picture windows, seating area, modern bathroom, big bed: 'Good value.' The Scoulars have bought the adjacent pub, doubling the number of rooms. The area has interesting archaeological remains, 'wonderful coastal walks along springy turf, and some beautiful gardens'. (*Michael Blanchard, June Brannan*)

Bedrooms: 14, 7 in adjacent pub. *Open*: all year except 25 Dec. *Facilities*: 2 bars, 2 restaurant areas, small garden, unsuitable for &. *Background music*: none. *Location*: village centre, 9 miles S of Wigtown. *Smoking*: allowed in bedrooms. *Children*: all ages welcomed. *Dogs*: not allowed in restaurant. *Credit cards*: MasterCard, Visa. *Prices*: b&b £25–£40 per person, d/b&b £50–£60, set menu £25, full alc £35.

WALES

Many of our Welsh hotels take considerable pride in their national identity. Menus are often written in Welsh as well as English, as visitors are encouraged to embrace the local culture. The *Portmeirion Hotel* at Portmeirion, and *Y Goeden Eirin*, a small guest house at Dolydd, near Caernarfon, with a committed green philosophy, are fine examples of this. Our Welsh *César* award this year goes to *Gliffaes*, a traditional, family-run sporting hotel at Crickhowell on the River Usk. Excellent chefs in many of our Welsh entries make the most of wonderful local ingredients.

Gliffaes, Crickhowell

ABERAERON Ceredigion   Map 3:C2

Harbourmaster Hotel   *Tel* 01545-570755
Pen Cei, Aberaeron   *Fax* 01545-570762
SA46 0BA   *Email* info@harbour-master.com
                          Website www.harbour-master.com

🏵 *César award in 2005*

The bilingual owners, Glyn and Menna Heulyn, and their staff are
'friendly and helpful', says a visitor to this bright blue building.
'Superbly located', on the quay of this 'lovely old town', it has a 'real
buzz, combining local pub with restaurant and rooms'. 'The dining
room was full in the evenings: excellent gastropub food; good choice
of wines by the glass.' Chef Stephen Evans serves 'modern Welsh'
dishes, eg, lamb shank with celeriac purée and balsamic sauce; rabbit
braised in cider. The Georgian building has been 'brilliantly updated'
in modern yet locally sympathetic fashion. 'Our lovely room was filled
with things that were a pleasure to use.' 'Ours had a squashy sofa on
which to crash out and stare at boats and the sea. It was peaceful,
while plenty of bustling went on below. Outstanding breakfast,
especially the muesli and cooked dishes.' 'Service was relaxed and
seemingly effortless.' The cottage two doors down (where children
under five may stay) is 'well furnished and equipped'. In 2008 a conversion of an adjacent grain warehouse opened. It includes a spacious
bar where meals are served, and four more bedrooms, and has created
more restaurant space in the original building. (*Bianca Emberson, FR*)

Bedrooms: 13, 2 in cottage. *Open*: all year except 25 Dec, restaurant closed Mon
midday. *Facilities*: bar, restaurant, pebble beach (safe bathing nearby), only bar
and restaurant suitable for ♿. *Background music*: 'modern, relaxed'. *Location*:
central, on harbour. *Smoking*: not allowed. *Children*: under-5s in cottage only.
Dogs: not allowed. *Credit cards*: MasterCard, Visa. *Prices*: b&b £55–£60 per
person, d,b&b £80–£85, set dinner £29, 1-night bookings refused Fri and Sat.

ABERGAVENNY Monmouthshire   Map 3:D4

The Angel Hotel   *Tel* 01873-857121
15 Cross Street   *Fax* 01873-858059
Abergavenny NP7 5EN   *Email* mail@angelhotelabergavenny.com
                      Website www.angelhotelabergavenny.com

The Griffiths family, who own this 'lively hotel' (William and
Charlotte Griffiths are the managers), have extensively refurbished

the public areas of what is 'unquestionably the social hub' of this old market town. Bedroom renovation will start in 2009. The function rooms are often busy with weddings and other events, making this 'certainly not the place for a quiet weekend', said inspectors. But it has many attractions, including a 'lovely drawing room with good armchairs and sofas', where afternoon teas, with fine china, good linen and fresh-baked pastries are served from 3 to 5 pm. The *Foxhunter* bar is '*the* gathering place, big log fire, very busy at night' (it serves lunches and suppers). In the elegant dining room, 'large helpings of good comfort food were served at a nice pace' (dishes like pot-roast guinea fowl with savoy cabbage; roast rump of Welsh lamb). This old coaching inn has no lift, and sloping corridor floors. 'Our superior double had modern, neutral colours, flat-screen TV, free Wi-Fi, smallish double bed, excellent bathroom.' Front rooms could be affected by street noise. For families there are interconnecting rooms. 'Breakfast was a basic buffet with packaged juices, OK cooked dishes.'

Bedrooms: 32, 2 in adjacent mews. *Open*: all year except 25 Dec. *Facilities*: ramps, lounge, bar, restaurant, conference/function facilities, courtyard, civil wedding licence, free use of nearby gym, facilities for ♿ planned. *Background music*: occasional 'easy listening'. *Location*: town centre. *Smoking*: not allowed. *Children*: all ages welcomed. *Dogs*: not allowed in restaurant. *Credit cards*: Amex, MasterCard, Visa. *Prices*: b&b £47.50–£65 per person, d,b&b £69.50–£92, full alc £35, short breaks, Christmas/New Year packages.

ABERSOCH Gwynedd   Map 3:B2

Porth Tocyn Hotel
Bwlch Tocyn
Abersoch LL53 7BU

Tel 01758-713303
Fax 01758-713538
Email bookings@porthtocyn.fsnet.co.uk
Website www.porth-tocyn-hotel.co.uk

❧ *César award in 1984*

For 60 years the Fletcher-Brewer family have run their family-friendly hotel in the Lleyn Peninsula. Facing Cardigan Bay and the Snowdonia mountains ('few dining rooms could have such a magnificent view'), it is near some beautiful beaches. In the grounds are a heated swimming pool, sun loungers, and 'secret corners' for taking tea. The rambling structure of former lead miners' cottages has 'grown organically' over the years. A conservatory and many sitting rooms provide space to relax inside ('fine old furniture, pictures, books, interesting knick-knacks'). Some bedrooms are interconnected. Nick Fletcher-Brewer's 'welcoming, idiosyncratic style' remains the same, says a visitor this year. Other fans wrote of the 'ever-present proprietor and excellent, young, well-trained staff'. 'On entering, you immediately feel at home.' A three-generation family on a return visit again enjoyed 'comfortable, relaxed accommodation and delicious food'. John Bell and Louise Fletcher-Brewer run the kitchen (a *Good Food Guide* entry for 51 years). 'Very good fish dishes'; 'good cheeseboard'. Main courses include roast monkfish stifado; mignons of Welsh beef fillet with wild mushrooms and truffle jus. But the breakfast toast was 'boring'. Some soft furnishings, carpets, etc, have been upgraded this year. (*Andrew Clarke, Mr and Mrs K Robinson, Lloyd Wilkinson, Jelly Williams, and others*)

Bedrooms: 17, some on ground floor. *Open*: before Easter–end Oct, occasional closures in low season. *Facilities*: ramp, sitting rooms, children's rooms, cocktail bar, dining room, 25-acre grounds (swimming pool, 10 by 6 metres, heated May–end Sept, tennis), beach (5 mins' walk, sailing), fishing, golf, riding nearby, telephone to discuss disabled access. *Background music*: none. *Location*: 2 miles outside village. *Smoking*: not allowed. *Children*: no tiny children at dinner (high tea at 5.30 pm). *Dogs*: by arrangement, not allowed in public rooms. *Credit cards*: MasterCard, Visa. *Prices*: b&b £45–£90 per person, cooked breakfast £6, set menus £32.50–£39, off-season breaks, walking breaks, 1-night bookings sometimes refused. ∗**V**∗

ABERYSTWYTH Ceredigion   Map 3:C3

Gwesty Cymru   NEW
19 Marine Terrace
Aberystwyth SY23 2AZ

Tel 01970-612252
Fax 01970-623348
Email info@gwestycymru.co.uk
Website www.gwestycymru.co.uk

Georgian Grade II listed seafront hotel on Victorian promenade, facing sea. Recently transformed by owners Huw and Beth Roberts into 'sleek, modern' restaurant-with-rooms that 'oozes quality'. 'Judicious use of Welsh materials': slate; furniture handmade from Welsh oak; oil paintings by local artist, Welsh poetry in 8 'well-equipped' bedrooms (some in eaves, 'a long climb'; some, above kitchen, might be hot). Closed Christmas/New Year. Small bar/ restaurant in basement ('first-rate meals'), terrace (drinks served); background music; unsuitable for ♿. Private, secure parking (book in advance). No smoking. 'Well-behaved children welcomed.' Guide dogs only. MasterCard, Visa accepted. Prices: [2008] b&b £42.50–£75 per person, full alc £30–£40.

Our new website works in tandem with the printed *Guide*.

BEAUMARIS Anglesey   Map 3:A3

Ye Olde Bulls Head
Castle Street
Beaumaris, Anglesey
LL58 8AP

Tel 01248-810329
Fax 01248-811294
Email info@bullsheadinn.co.uk
Website www.bullsheadinn.co.uk

Five hundred years old, with ancient beams and creaking staircases,
this former medieval staging inn for coaches to Ireland has small,
'smartly cosy', quiet bedrooms named after Dickensian characters
(the writer once stayed here). 'Our room, one of the nicest we have
stayed in, had a small but perfectly formed bathroom,' says a visitor in
2008. Others liked the 'very comfortable' Loft suite, 'reached up
steep stairs'. Owner/managers Keith Rothwell and David Robertson
create a 'good atmosphere'. Reception is 'warmly welcoming'. The
residents' lounge is 'luxuriously appointed'. The bar, a popular local,
has a rare 17th-century brass water clock, antique weapons, the
town's oak ducking seat, a fire in winter. In the 'more contemporary'
restaurant, chef Craig Yardley serves modern dishes like venison with
pheasant and bacon parcel, parsnip purée. Simon Doyle, chef in the
'airy' brasserie in converted stables, provides, eg, fish and chips;
chicken supreme with herb crème fraîche; also special dishes for
children. 'Food good but tables for two a bit cramped.' Service is
'good', if sometimes 'brisk'. Thirteen more, cheaper, bedrooms were
due to open in late 2008 in the Grade II listed building adjacent.
Contemporary in style, they will have Wi-Fi and air conditioning;
upstairs ones reached by a lift. (*Jenny Buckley, Robin and Heather
Harrison, Michael and Eithne Dandy*)

Bedrooms: 13, 2 on ground floor, 1 in courtyard, 13 more, adjacent, due to open
end 2008. *Open*: all year, closed for accommodation 25/26 Dec, 1 Jan. *Facilities*:
lounge, bar, brasserie, restaurant, sea 200 yds, unsuitable for &. *Background
music*: 'easy listening' in brasserie. *Location*: Central. *Smoking*: not allowed.
Children: no under-7s in restaurant or bedroom suites. *Dogs*: not allowed. *Credit
cards*: Amex, MasterCard, Visa. *Prices*: b&b £52.50–£85 per person, set dinner
(restaurant) £38.50–£40.

How to contact the *Guide*
By mail: From anywhere in the UK, write to Freepost PAM
2931, London W11 4BR (no stamp is needed)
From outside the UK: *Good Hotel Guide*, 50 Addison Avenue,
London W11 4QP, England
By telephone or fax: 020-7602 4182
By email: editor@goodhotelguide.com
Via our website: www.goodhotelguide.com

BODUAN Gwynedd   Map 3:B2

The Old Rectory   *Tel/Fax* 01758-721519
Boduan   *Email* thepollards@theoldrectory.net
nr Pwllheli LL53 6DT   *Website* www.theoldrectory.net

Roger and Gabrielle Pollard have for many years run this small, pale
yellow B&B. 'An elegant, comfortable, well-loved home in a quiet
location,' one couple called it: it stands in large grounds amid
woodland in the Lleyn peninsula. The 'very kind hosts' 'obviously
enjoy sharing their beautifully restored former Georgian rectory with
visitors'. It has 'large, attractive' public rooms with antique family
furniture and paintings by contemporary artists. A log fire is lit in the
drawing room on cold days. 'Spacious, well-equipped' bedrooms are
individually styled: 'Ours, shining clean, had tea-making facilities,
complimentary sherry, and fine views over fields.' Some bathrooms
have a roll-top bath. Breakfast, 'well cooked and elegantly presented',
includes porridge, compotes made from home-grown fruit, smoked
salmon, home-made breads, jam and marmalade. Dinner reservations
for guests can be made at local restaurants. Babies under one stay free;
cots and high chairs are provided. There is good walking from the
bottom of the drive. Nearby are three golf courses, Bodnant Gardens,
coastal footpaths, and splendid sandy beaches. (*MCW*)

Bedrooms: 3, also self-catering cottage. *Open*: all year except Christmas week.
Facilities: drawing room, dining room, 3½-acre grounds, unsuitable for &.
Background music: none. *Location*: 4 miles NW of Pwllheli. *Smoking*: not
allowed. *Children*: all ages welcomed, under-1s stay free, babysitting by
arrangement. *Dogs*: allowed in grounds only. *Credit cards*: none. *Prices*: b&b
£42.50–£85 per person, 1-night bookings refused bank holidays.

BRECHFA Carmarthenshire   Map 3:D2

Tŷ Mawr   *Tel* 01267-202332
Brechfa SA32 7RA   *Email* info@wales-country-hotel.co.uk
                    Website www.wales-country-hotel.co.uk

On their second visit to this 'very relaxing' place, *Guide* readers were
again enthusiastic. The owners, Annabel Viney and Stephen
Thomas, are 'a friendly, hard-working couple' who provide 'good
value'. He is the chef, serving 'good bistro-style cooking with local
ingredients and home-grown vegetables'. She ('intelligent, respon-
sive and helpful') 'uses a curious system which enables the guests to
enjoy differing menus daily'. Try the grilled Cardigan Bay sea bass on

a bed of creamed cauliflower, or Welsh lamb loin with apricot stuffing. 'Breakfasts were good too.' The 16th-century farmhouse stands by the 'gently bubbling' River Marlais, in a village on the edge of the Brechfa forest. An inspector found both house and grounds attractive, and the bedrooms are liked: 'Our room was fairly plain, but very comfortable. It had two chairs (so often a double has only one). In perfect weather, we sat on the patio with our drinks, watching the river.' The micro-brewery has been turned into a new 'superior' bedroom. Portia, the 'soft and gorgeous' Turkish rescue dog, will take guests for a walk. (*GC, and others*)

Bedrooms: 6, 1 on ground floor. *Open*: all year. *Facilities*: sitting room, bar, breakfast room, restaurant, 1-acre grounds, unsuitable for &. *Background music*: classical, in restaurant. *Location*: village centre. *Smoking*: not allowed. *Children*: not under 12. *Dogs*: not allowed in restaurant. *Credit cards*: Amex, MasterCard, Visa. *Prices*: b&b £49–£68 per person, d,b&b £70–£90, set menus £24–£29, seasonal breaks, Christmas/New Year packages. *V*

BRECON Powys *See SHORTLIST*   Map 3:D3

BROADHAVEN Pembrokeshire   Map 3:D1

The Druidstone
nr Broadhaven
Haverfordwest SA62 3NE

Tel 01437-781221
Email enquiries@druidstone.co.uk
Website www.druidstone.co.uk

Jane Bell, with husband Rod, has long presided over this 'idiosyncratic' 'family holiday centre' in a 'stunning cliff-top position above a huge, almost deserted beach'. Son Angus is head chef. 'An institution to many, it has bags of character,' said one fan. 'The slightly rough-around-the-edges feel only adds to the welcome eccentricity. The perfect antidote to over-priced designer hotels.' But one couple, visiting during a time of staff shortages, reported 'inconsistent standards'. Mrs Bell writes: 'Our policy is to look after families without making them feel uncomfortable about bringing children; this does mean that the place suffers wear and tear.' Four bedrooms have private facilities (there are three shared bathrooms); the two penthouse bedrooms each have a balcony facing Cardigan Bay. Self-catering cottages in the grounds include the tiny Roundhouse, an 'Eco Hut', which derives its energy from the sun. 'Good, unpretentious' food is served in the 'cosy' bar: used by locals, it opens on to a sea-facing terrace and garden – so does the restaurant which serves 'good bistro-style meals' (a *Good Food Guide* entry for many years). The children's high tea is 'always interesting'. Pets are welcomed, so long as they get on with Jake, the donkey. Popular for weddings and parties. More reports, please.

Bedrooms: 11, also 5 holiday cottages. *Open*: all year, restaurant closed Mon. *Facilities*: sitting room, TV room, bar (occasional live music), farmhouse kitchen, restaurant, small conference/function facilities, civil wedding licence, 22-acre grounds, sandy beach, safe bathing 200 yds, unsuitable for &. *Background music*: in bar. *Location*: 7 miles W of Haverfordwest. *Smoking*: not allowed. *Children*: all ages welcomed. *Dogs*: not allowed in restaurant. *Credit cards*: Amex, MasterCard, Visa. *Prices*: b&b £45–£74 per person, full alc £30, courses, conferences, Christmas/New Year/midweek packages, 1-night advance bookings refused for Sat.

CAERNARFON Gwynedd   Map 3:A2
See SHORTLIST

CAPEL GARMON Conwy   Map 3:A3

Tan-y-Foel Country House   *Tel* 01690-710507
Capel Garmon   *Fax* 01690-710681
nr Betws-y-Coed LL26 0RE   *Email* enquiries@tyfhotel.co.uk
                                   Website www.tyfhotel.co.uk

'Stylish in a contemporary way' (understated earth tones, lavish fabrics), this 17th-century stone house has a 'wonderful' setting, high on wooded hills in the Snowdonia national park. It is popular with walkers. 'If you want a really peaceful location, this is for you,' writes one enthusiastic guest. 'Exceptional standards,' says another. The 'highly professional' owners, Peter and Janet Pitman, and their daughter, Kelly ('charming; front-of-house, waitress, hostess'), run it as a guest house, without other help. Perhaps because of this, it has 'strict rules' (say inspectors): breakfast is between 8 and 9 am, dinner 7.30–8 pm. 'Very comfortable' bedrooms, in muted shades, have flat-screen TV, DVD/CD-player; some have a 'magnificent view' of the valley; one has a four-poster bed; two (one is a converted hayloft) have their own external entrance. There are 'spacious, well-equipped' bathrooms. Mrs Pitman's modern British dishes use organic ingredients in a daily-changing menu with two choices of each course (eg, sea bass with saffron potatoes, black olive and tomato paste). 'Food cooked with passion and elegance, so good it is not to be missed.'

'Quality of materials exceptional. Breakfast scrambled eggs were perfect.' 'Car essential,' the Pitmans warn. (*Gordon Hands, Mr and Mrs C Carr, Terry O'Keeffe, and others*)

Bedrooms: 5, 1 on ground floor. *Open*: mid-Jan–Nov, dining room closed midday. *Facilities*: lounge, breakfast room, dining room, 6-acre grounds, unsuitable for &. *Background music*: none. *Location*: 2 miles from Betws-y-Coed, 1½ miles off A470. *Smoking*: not allowed. *Children*: not under 12. *Dogs*: only guide dogs allowed. *Credit cards*: MasterCard, Visa. *Prices*: [2008] b&b £74.50–£155 per person, set dinner £44, 3-night midweek offer, 1-night bookings refused weekends, bank holidays, pre-booking essential.

CARDIFF   Map 3:E4

Jolyon's
5 Bute Crescent, Cardiff Bay
Cardiff CF10 5AN

Tel/Fax 029-2048 8775
Email info@jolyons.co.uk
Website www.jolyons.co.uk

In Cardiff's regenerated docklands, this 'intriguing' boutique hotel is a converted Georgian seamen's lodge opposite the New Millennium Centre, home of the Welsh National Opera. Jolyon Joseph, the owner/manager, is 'laid back' and 'very personable', say reporters. Bedrooms (some with views of Cardiff Bay) have 'contemporary touches enhanced by antiques'. They include one in Moroccan style; one with an Edwardian feel; one with a big wet room; one with a large panoramic balcony. 'The chrome-fitted bathroom was a joy, modern yet cosy; a leaf-shaped bath, fluffy towels, lots of hot water.' All rooms have Wi-Fi, digital TV. Downstairs, the 'friendly' *Bar Cwtch* (Welsh for 'cuddly') with wood-burning stove serves speciality beers, wines from a short, eclectic list, and snacks. A wood-burning oven produces home-made pizzas (Hot Smooch; Sexy Mermaid; Veg Out, etc). The 'generous' breakfast has a buffet (mueslis, fruit, compotes, pastries, etc); full Welsh or scrambled eggs and smoked salmon to order. Fourteen more bedrooms and a conference room are planned for 2009. (*G and MA, and others*)

Bedrooms: 6, 1, on ground floor, suitable for &. *Open*: all year. *Facilities*: residents' lounge, bar, live music sometimes, terrace. *Background music*: varied. *Location*: Cardiff Bay waterfront, under 2 miles from centre. *Smoking*: not allowed. *Children*: not under 16. *Dogs*: not allowed. *Credit cards*: all major cards. *Prices*: [2008] b&b double £110–£140, full alc £25, Christmas/New Year packages. *V*

See also SHORTLIST

CONWY   Map 3:A3

Sychnant Pass House NEW	*Tel* 01492-596868
Sychnant Pass Road	*Fax* 01492-585486
Conwy LL32 8BJ	*Email* bre@sychnant-pass-house.co.uk
	Website www.sychnant-pass-house.co.uk

Bre (Irish) and Graham (the chef, Welsh) Carrington-Sykes, with their young son, Conor, and manager Joanne Scott, run their 'handsome, well-kept' Edwardian home in the foothills of Snowdonia national park with enthusiasm. The resident three cats and two dogs 'will be delighted to share their garden with your pets', they say. Children are welcomed (swings and a swimming pool in the garden, games indoors). The bedrooms, named after TS Eliot's 'practical cats', vary greatly. Three are small, two have a private deck with hot tub, some have a balcony. 'To say that the house is generously furnished is an understatement,' writes an inspector. 'Lots of furniture, a huge library of books, DVDs, etc, every wall covered to the ceiling with pictures, many of dogs and cats. Our bedroom was well supplied (fridge, ironing board, complimentary sherry, etc), soft toys much in evidence.' The welcome is 'genuinely warm', with complimentary tea. 'Dinner was substantial' (traditional British: main courses like roast rack of lamb). 'Breakfast the usual buffet, with offers of full English.' The front porch has 'wonderful' views to the Vale of Conwy (this is a designated area of 'outstanding natural beauty'). The family also offer accommodation in *Pentre Mawr House*, nearby.

Bedrooms: 12. *Open*: Feb–Dec, closed Christmas. *Facilities*: 2 lounges, restaurant, indoor swimming pool, gym, civil wedding licence, terraces (hot tub, sauna, tanning room). *Background music*: soft, in lounges. *Location*: 2 miles SW of Conwy by A457. *Smoking*: not allowed. *Children*: all ages welcomed. *Dogs*: not allowed in restaurant. *Credit cards*: MasterCard, Visa. *Prices*: b&b £47.50–£75 per person, d,b&b £65–£102.50, set menu £30, New Year package, 1-night bookings usually refused Sat.

CRICKHOWELL Powys   Map 3:D4

Glangrwyney Court	*Tel* 01873-811288
Glangrwyney, Crickhowell	*Fax* 01873-810317
NP8 1ES	*Email* info@glancourt.co.uk
	Website www.glancourt.co.uk

'Comfortable, indeed opulent', this 'very upmarket' B&B is run by Christina and Warwick Jackson in their Grade II listed family home. It stands on the edge of the Brecon Beacons national park in 'beautiful, peaceful' gardens (ancient magnolias and Japanese acer trees a feature) amid parkland. 'Christina and her two daughters were excellent hosts,' said one visitor. The Georgian house has a cantilevered staircase of architectural significance, and an arched window with views of the Black Mountains. There are log fires in the lounge and the library with its 'well-stocked' honesty bar. 'Lots of comfy sofas.' The bedrooms in the house all face the garden and surrounding scenery. They are 'spacious and attractively furnished in country house style'. The master suite has a steam shower; one twin room has a spa bath. Some beds are king-size. In the garden are 'secret sitting areas', and patios where summer drinks can be served (the Jacksons hold an alcohol licence). An evening meal ('very good, all local produce') is available by arrangement for groups (weddings and other functions are held). There is 'ample scope for eating nearby'. (*MK, S and JS*)

Bedrooms: 9, 1, on ground floor, in courtyard, also self-catering cottages. *Open*: all year. *Facilities*: sitting room, library/honesty bar, dining room, civil wedding licence, 3-acre garden (croquet, boules, tennis) in 33-acre parkland, river 500 yds (fishing by arrangement), unsuitable for &. *Background music*: at dinner if requested. *Location*: 2 miles SE of Crickhowell, off A40. *Smoking*: not allowed. *Children*: all ages welcomed. *Dogs*: allowed in cottages only. *Credit cards*: MasterCard, Visa. *Prices*: b&b £35–£85 per person, set dinner (by arrangement, groups only) £15–£25, off-season discounts, 1-night bookings sometimes refused. *V*

 **Gliffaes**
Crickhowell
NP8 1RH

Tel 01874-730371
Fax 01874-730463
Email calls@gliffaeshotel.com
Website www.gliffaes.com

César award: Welsh country hotel of the year

'The comfort and peacefulness of the house and its surroundings, combined with the unaffected approach, made our stay memorable.' 'A happy and enjoyable place.' 'We have watched the improvements over the years with delight.' 'Lovely gardens. Good walks from the door.' Praise this year and last for this smart sporting hotel run by Susie and James Suter (the third generation of the hotel's family owners) with her parents, Mr and Mrs Brabner. Their staff, 'a mix of locals and young people from around the world', are 'charming and willing', says another visitor. The 19th-century Italianate building stands in large wooded grounds on a private stretch of the trout- and salmon-laden River Usk (fishing courses arranged). There are attractive indoor sitting areas, particularly the conservatory. Most of the comfortable bedrooms are large; the best have balcony and river view. *Gliffaes* subscribes to the Slow Food Movement, sourcing 65 per cent of ingredients from within 75 miles. Chef Stephan Trinci's 'better than average' food included 'canon of Welsh lamb, sautéed courgettes, honey and thyme jus, cooked to perfection; outstanding lemon tart'. 'Copious breakfasts.' Children are welcomed. Environmental responsibilities are taken seriously (recycling, composting, local errands by bicycle, laundry dried on a line, etc). (*Helen and Peter Walker, Franz Kuhlmann, and others*)

Bedrooms: 23, 4 in annexe (1 on ground floor). *Open*: all year except 2–31 Jan. *Facilities*: ramp, 2 sitting rooms, conservatory, bar, dining room, civil wedding licence, 33-acre garden (tennis, croquet, fishing, ghillie available). *Background music*: jazz in bar in evenings. *Location*: 3 miles W of Crickhowell, off A40. *Smoking*: not allowed. *Children*: all ages welcomed. *Dogs*: not allowed indoors. *Credit cards*: all major cards. *Prices*: [2008] b&b £46.25–£84 per person, d,b&b £80.25–£118, set dinner £35, fishing courses, website deals, Christmas/New Year packages, 1-night bookings refused weekends, bank holidays.

See also SHORTLIST

DALE Pembrokeshire   Map 3:D1

Allenbrook   NEW   *Tel* 01646-636254
Dale   *Fax* 01646-636954
SA62 3RN   *Email* elizabeth@allenbrook.freeserve.co.uk
                                    Website www.allenbrook-dale.co.uk

In a village near the Pembrokeshire Coast national park, Colonel and Mrs Webber's guest house stands in a large, rambling garden (with peacocks, bantams, guinea fowl and geese), which leads down to the sea. 'We are definitely not a hotel,' writes the 'bonny' Elizabeth Webber. 'I make few concessions for guests. They take us as they find us.' 'It would have been cheap at one-and-a-half times the price,' say visitors this year. 'The walls are cluttered with pictures and prints of horses and hounds and hunting scenes, some witty, others poignant. Our charming, large bedroom combined Victorian luxury with modern comforts: fireplace, half-tester bed, comfy chairs, good lighting, flat-screen TV; bathroom almost as big, just as comfortable, with another fireplace, a large maroon-coloured bath on legs. The guest lounge was straight out of Trollope, and the intimacy of the house was enhanced by family photographs, Staffordshire dog statues, collections of birds' eggs, etc. We shared a breakfast table with a different couple each morning. The meal was made memorable by Mrs Webber's offer of a couple of boiled guinea fowl eggs; we enjoyed them so much she gave us another two to take home.' Dale holds the sunshine record for mainland Britain. (*Tony and Sarah Thomas*)

Bedrooms: 3, 1 self-catering cottage. *Open*: Feb–Dec. *Facilities*: 2 sitting rooms, breakfast room, large garden. *Background music*: 'definitely not'. *Location*: 8 miles W of Milford Haven. *Smoking*: not allowed. *Children*: not allowed. *Dogs*: not allowed. *Credit cards*: none. *Prices*: b&b £30–£40 per person.

DOLFOR Powys   Map 3:C4

The Old Vicarage   **NEW**   *Tel* 01686-629051
Dolfor, nr Newtown   *Email* tim@theoldvicaragedolfor.co.uk
SY16 4BN   *Website* www.theoldvicaragedolfor.co.uk

High in the hills of the Welsh Marches, with fine views of Montgomeryshire countryside, this small restaurant-with-rooms is an 1880s ex-vicarage. 'The tastefully furnished bedrooms have all modern comforts: flat-screen TV, sherry, chocolates. Bathrooms have underfloor heating; there are fluffy towels, excellent beds,' says the nominator. Arriving guests are offered tea with home-made bara brith. The lounge, with log fire, is decorated in period style. There are antique tables and candles in the dining room. The 'cheerful, friendly' owners, Tim and Helen Withers, formerly ran an award-winning gastropub in Wiltshire. He is the chef, serving 'wholesome, very fresh' food on a limited-choice menu based on local, sometimes organic, produce, home-grown vegetables and eggs from free-range hens. Most wines are organic too. 'A peaceful setting. Ideal walking country near the start of the Kerry Ridgeway. There is something totally natural and authentic about the place. Breakfast is first rate too.' (*John Rowlands*)

Bedrooms: 3. *Open*: all year. *Facilities*: drawing room, dining room, 2-acre garden, unsuitable for &. *Background music*: none. *Location*: 3½ miles S of Newtown. *Smoking*: not allowed. *Children*: not under 12. *Dogs*: not allowed. *Credit cards*: MasterCard, Visa. *Prices*: b&b £47.50–£65 per person, d,b&b £72.50–£90, special breaks (walking, etc), Christmas/New Year packages. *V*

DOLYDD Gwynedd   Map 3:A2

Y Goeden Eirin   *Tel* 01286-830942
Dolydd, Caernarfon   *Email* john_rowlands@tiscali.co.uk
LL54 7EF   *Website* www.ygoedeneirin.co.uk

◊ *César award in 2008*

'Good value.' 'A fine welcome. It is hard to think how things could be improved.' 'Wonderfully situated.' In a hamlet on the edge of the Snowdonia national park, John and Eluned Rowlands run their small guest house on very personal lines. 'No sign of fashionable interior design,' they promise. It is very Welsh (bilingual menus and wine list) and very green (solar panels, recycling and composting policies; organic food; fair trade tea and coffee). Guests who arrive by train can be collected from Bangor, and are encouraged to use the 'excellent local transport'. The renovated farm buildings (local granite, slate, beams, decor a mixture of traditional and modern) stand amid rough pasture with views of mountains and sea. There is under-floor heating, Wi-Fi, books, modern Welsh art, and a grand piano in the dining room, which is open to the public. Aga-cooked dishes, 'wholesome, with the occasional exotic touch', eg, lamb steak in wine and citrus sauce, use local and home-grown ingredients. No choice, but prior consultation. 'Excellent' breakfasts include local sausages, home-baked bread, home-made preserves. The 'large and bright' bedroom in the main house was liked ('glorious views, beautiful objects, large TV, good-sized bathroom'); so was a room in the purpose-built annexe ('Arts and Crafts feel'). (*OP, and others*)

Bedrooms: 3, 2 in annexe. *Open*: all year except Christmas–New Year. *Facilities*: lounge, dining room, occasional live piano music, Wi-Fi access, 20-acre pastureland, unsuitable for &. *Background music*: occasionally. *Location*: 3 miles S of Caernarfon. *Smoking*: not allowed. *Children*: not under 12. *Dogs*: not allowed. *Credit cards*: none, cash payment requested on arrival. *Prices*: b&b £40–£60 per person, set dinner £28, 1-night bookings sometimes refused weekends. *V*

ERWOOD Powys *See SHORTLIST*   Map 3:D4

FELIN FACH Powys   Map 3:D4

The Felin Fach Griffin
Felin Fach, nr Brecon
LD3 0UB

Tel 01874-620111
Fax 01874-620120
Email enquiries@felinfachgriffin.co.uk
Website www.felinfachgriffin.co.uk

Between the Brecon Beacons and the Black Mountains, Charles and Edmund Inkin's 'civilised' inn is liked for its 'relaxed atmosphere' and 'excellent food'. It stands on a main road, fronted by a large car park. With manageress Julie Bell, the brothers tell us, they have improved the accommodation side of things this year. 'Simple but comfortable' bedrooms have a Roberts Revival radio, 'luxurious bedlinen', a detailed information pack; a small TV can be provided. In the popular restaurant, chef Ricardo Van Ede uses home-grown organic ingredients in dishes like salad of squab pigeon, beetroot and beetroot sorbet; saddle of rabbit, ragout of young vegetables. 'We enjoyed the evening buzz and the welcoming bar,' one couple wrote. No residents' lounge, but there is a sitting area with comfortable leather sofas round a fireplace and a big table with newspapers. Breakfast has boiled eggs, kippers or a fry-up, DIY toast, made on the Aga from 'delicious bread', home-made preserves. Children are welcomed. There is excellent walking nearby. The Inkins write: 'We make our charges as transparent as possible. No charge for use of telephone unless it has been used a lot, nor for a travel cot or for dogs in bedrooms.' They also own *The Gurnard's Head*, Zennor, Cornwall (*qv*). (*FR, and others*)

Bedrooms: 7. *Open*: All year except 24–26 Dec, restaurant closed Mon midday. *Facilities*: bar area, dining room, breakfast room, private dining room, 1½-acre garden (stream, kitchen garden), unsuitable for &. *Background music*: CDs/radio most of the time (*Today* programme at breakfast). *Location*: 4 miles NE of Brecon, in village on A470. *Smoking*: not allowed. *Children*: all ages welcomed. *Dogs*: not allowed in dining room. *Credit cards*: MasterCard, Visa. *Prices*: b&b £42.50–£70 per person, set menus £26–£50, full alc £38, 'Sunday Sleepover', wine, fishing, shooting packages.

Deadlines: nominations for the 2010 edition of this volume should reach us not later than 15 May 2009. Latest date for comments on existing entries: 1 June 2009.

FISHGUARD Pembrokeshire   Map 3:D1

The Manor Town House   *Tel/Fax* 01348-873260
11 Main Street   *Email* enquiries@manortownhouse.com
Fishguard SA65 9HG   *Website* www.manortownhouse.com

One visitor this year writes of 'genuine warmth of welcome, a simple, quiet room and delicious bistro-style food' at this Georgian Grade II listed town house near the market square. Another praises the 'very friendly' owners, Gail and James Stewart. A group of seven women 'arrived tired and stressed', but left 'refreshed and relaxed' after a weekend of 'cosseting and home cooking'. 'The offer of tea and home-made cake, taken on a terrace facing the sea, was a delightful start.' There are 'spectacular views' from the garden and four of the bedrooms. The restaurant is in a 'homely' basement. Local, organic ingredients are used where possible for dishes such as beef braised in beer, vegetarian sausage with pesto mash. There are four choices for each of three courses. 'Everything was meticulously prepared.' 'The wines were reasonably priced.' 'Breakfasts are good.' Antiques 'give character' to the public rooms. 'Our bedroom was a comfortable size, with nice furniture, though the bathroom was small.' A gate at the bottom of the garden leads to the Coast Path. Nearest parking is 150 yards away. (*Alastair Kameen, AN Stanton, Gill Boden*)

Bedrooms: 6. *Open*: all year except Christmas, restaurant closed Wed. *Facilities*: 2 lounges, bar/restaurant, walled garden (terrace), sea (safe bathing 2 miles), unsuitable for &. *Background music*: classical at mealtimes. *Location*: near town square. *Smoking*: not allowed. *Children*: not under 12. *Dogs*: not allowed. *Credit cards*: MasterCard, Visa. *Prices*: [2008] b&b £35–£45 per person, full alc £25, New Year package, 1-night bookings sometimes refused in season.

HARLECH Gwynedd *See SHORTLIST*   Map 3:B3

HAVERFORDWEST Pembrokeshire   Map 3:D1
See SHORTLIST

HAY-ON-WYE Powys   Map 3:D4
See SHORTLIST

KNIGHTON Powys   Map 3:C4

Milebrook House   *Tel* 01547-528632
Milebrook   *Fax* 01547-520509
Knighton   *Email* hotel@milebrook.kc3ltd.co.uk
Powys LD7 1LT   *Website* www.milebrookhouse.co.uk

Covered in Virginia creeper, Beryl and Rodney Marsden's hotel/
restaurant stands amid 'very special' gardens facing the Shropshire
hills, an area of natural beauty. 'A very enjoyable place,' says a visitor
this year. 'Real log fires smoulder away in both lounge and bar; pleasant
young staff serve the food and service the rooms.' 'The quintessential
country hotel run by lovely people in a lovely house,' said a returning
visitor. But some find the noise from the nearby road a drawback: 'We
were aware of the traffic even in our pleasant, spacious room at the
back.' The restaurant faces the garden, which provides vegetables for
the kitchen. The owners' grandson, Chris Marsden, is the 'extremely
competent' chef, serving a three-course *table d'hôte* menu (main courses
like smoked haddock with fine beans and white wine cream sauce). 'An
excellent wine list: especially by the glass.' Otters and kingfishers are
to be found in and by the River Teme next to the building, and walkers
are spoilt for choice in the surrounding Welsh Marches. The 18th-
century house was once owned by Wilfred Thesiger and visited by
Emperor Haile Selassie. A non-refundable deposit of £80 per room is
required. (*Alastair Kameen, and others*)

Bedrooms: 10, 2 on ground floor. *Open*: all year, restaurant closed Mon midday.
Facilities: lounge, bar, 2 dining rooms, 3-acre grounds on river (terraces, pond,
croquet, fishing). *Background music*: none. *Location*: on A4113, 2 miles E of
Knighton. *Smoking*: not allowed. *Children*: not under 8. *Dogs*: not allowed. *Credit
cards*: MasterCard, Visa. *Prices*: b&b £51.50–£71 per person, d,b&b £83–£102,
set menu £32, full alc £37, 2/3-day breaks, Christmas/New Year packages,
1-night bookings refused weekends. *V*

LAMPETER Ceredigion   Map 3:D3
See SHORTLIST

****

    Traveller's tale *Hotel in Kent* The rooms are elegantly
    furnished and are spoiled only by warnings to guests not to
    steal anything.

****

412   WALES

LLANARMON DYFFRYN CEIRIOG   Map 3:B4
Denbighshire

The Hand at Llanarmon	*Tel* 01691-600666
Ceiriog Valley	*Fax* 01691-600262
Llanarmon Dyffryn Ceiriog	*Email* reception@thehandhotel.co.uk
LL20 7LD	*Website* www.thehandhotel.co.uk

'Terrific value for money' is provided by owner/managers Gaynor and Martin De Luchi, at this 'very pleasant place to stay', say visitors this year. Set at the head of a pretty valley beneath the Berwyn mountains, the down-to-earth and 'charming' old inn has a black-beamed bar 'popular with local farmers exchanging gossip and tourists alike (all warmly welcomed)'. There is an attractive residents' lounge. 'Roaring log fires, candles on tables.' Chef Grant Mulholland serves good, 'straightforward, hearty' fare, eg, slow-braised shoulder of Welsh lamb with pink peppercorns and Madeira sauce. Other comments: 'Everyone so friendly.' 'Housekeeping immaculate.' 'No mobile phone signal here, just peace.' Tables and chairs stand on the terrace and in the garden. Many sites of interest are nearby, and 'you can step out of the front door to walk for miles in any direction and probably not see another soul'. 'Almost any country pursuit, even white-water rafting, can be arranged,' say the owners. The 'excellent' breakfast has good cooked choice, and is served until 10 am. 'Our double-aspect room (No. 3) was warm, tastefully decorated and well equipped.' 'Ours, facing the village square, had comfortable bed and roomy bathroom.' (*Richard and Jean Green, D and JA*)

Note Not to be confused with the *Hand Hotel* at Chirk, 11 miles away.

Bedrooms: 13, 4 on ground floor. *Open*: all year, accommodation closed at Christmas. *Facilities*: ramp, lounge, bar, restaurant, games/TV room (pool, darts), civil wedding licence, terrace, ¾-acre grounds. *Background music*: none. *Location*: 10 miles W of Oswestry. *Smoking*: not allowed. *Children*: all ages welcomed. *Dogs*: not allowed in public rooms except bar. *Credit cards*: MasterCard, Visa. *Prices*: [2008] b&b £40–£70 per person, d,b&b £55–£85, set lunch (Sun) £20, full alc £30, New Year package, 1-night bookings refused bank holidays. *V*

See also SHORTLIST

Hotels do not pay to be included in the *Guide*.

LLANDOVERY Carmarthenshire   Map 3:D3

The New White Lion   NEW   *Tel* 01550-720685
43 Stone Street   *Email* info@newwhitelion.co.uk
SA20 0BZ   *Website* www.newwhitelion.co.uk

In a small town near Brecon, Gerald and Sylvia Pritchard have transformed a Grade II listed former pub on an unprepossessing side street
into a 'stylish guest house'; they promise to provide 'local historical
insight as well as comfort'. 'They are natural hosts, unpretentious,
with plenty of time to spend with their guests,' writes the nominator.
Both are locals, 'deeply interested in Welsh history, folklore and
wildlife'. The ambience is sophisticated (their daughter runs a design
company in London), but 'personal touches make it homely'. There
are chandeliers, fine fabrics, smart wallpaper. The bedrooms have
wide-screen TV and 'interesting antique pieces'. 'Ours, at the top,
was tastefully furnished if compact, its bathroom tiny, the washbasin
perhaps too small for comfort. The bed provided a wonderful night's
sleep.' Larger bedrooms are lower down. In the spacious lounge are
comfortable sofas, an open fire and an honesty bar. 'The dining room
could do with more warmth of colour, but its white-painted open
chimney is eye-catching.' Pre-booked dinners off a short menu are
served. 'Ours was satisfying, no frills but good raw materials; service
brisk and friendly. Breakfast also good: local organic sausages, good
bacon, but juice not freshly squeezed.' Denice Hill is manager; Peter
Devlin is chef. (*John Rowlands*)

Bedrooms: 6, 1 on ground floor. *Open*: all year except Christmas. *Facilities*:
lounge, dining room. *Background music*: 'easy listening'. *Location*: town centre,
17 miles W of Brecon. *Smoking*: not allowed. *Children*: all ages welcomed (cot,
early supper available). *Dogs*: not allowed. *Credit cards*: MasterCard, Visa.
Prices: [2008] b&b £50–£80 per person, set dinner £25, New Year package.

LLANDRILLO Denbighshire   Map 3:B4

Tyddyn Llan   *Tel* 01490-440264
Llandrillo   *Fax* 01490-440414
nr Corwen LL21 0ST   *Email* tyddynllan@compuserve.com
                             Website www.tyddynllan.co.uk

❦ *César award in 2006*

In the vale of Edeyrnion, facing the Berwyn mountains, this former
shooting lodge of the dukes of Westminster is an 'elegant Georgian

house in manicured grounds' (with 'lots of nice seating areas' and a pond). A regular *Guide* correspondent on his second visit found 'everything as good as ever'. Susan Webb 'is the ultimate hostess', he writes; her husband, Bryan, 'continues to produce what must be as good as any food you will find in Wales'. Earlier praise: 'Truly excellent; so peaceful.' 'Very good service.' Comfortable lounges have 'elegant drapes, soft lighting, a piano in case you need to burst into song'. The bedrooms are 'thoughtfully furnished'. 'Nicely framed paintings, masses of glossies, bathroom with beautifully tiled floor and large walk-in shower.' Some rooms have 'views across stunning scenery in two directions'. All have flat-screen TV and DVD-player. From the dinner menu you might choose rabbit with black pudding, bacon and mustard sauce, or wild bass with laverbread beurre blanc. The wine list is wide-ranging. 'Excellent breakfast'; good compote, freshly segmented pink grapefruit; delicious porridge; undyed smoked haddock; 'perfect poached eggs'. (*Gordon Hands, and others*)

Bedrooms: 13, 1 on ground floor. *Open*: all year, restaurant closed midday Mon–Thurs. *Facilities*: ramp, 2 lounges, bar, 2 dining rooms, civil wedding licence, 3-acre grounds (fishing, riding, golf), sailing, walking nearby. *Background music*: occasional, at mealtimes. *Location*: 5 miles SW of Corwen. *Smoking*: not allowed. *Children*: all ages welcomed (£20 a night). *Dogs*: not allowed in public rooms, allowed in some bedrooms (£5 a night). *Credit cards*: MasterCard, Visa. *Prices*: [2008] b&b £65–£130 per person, d,b&b £95–£160, set menus £45–£65, full alc £53, Christmas/New Year house parties. *V*

LLANDUDNO Conwy   Map 3:A3

Bodysgallen Hall and Spa   *Tel* 01492-584466
Llandudno LL30 1RS   *Fax* 01492-582519
                                      Email info@bodysgallen.com
                                      Website www.bodysgallen.com

♛ *César award in 1988*

'Terrific in almost every respect.' 'This wonderful house remains a favourite.' Owned by Richard Broyd's Historic House Hotels, and managed by Matthew Johnson, this Grade I listed, 17th-century mansion (Pride of Britain) is 'beautifully situated' outside Llandudno in a large park with a knot garden, follies, and views of Snowdonia and Conwy Castle. It has fine panelled public rooms, ancestral portraits, antiques, splendid fireplaces and stone mullioned windows, lots of places to sit (many with log fire), and a 'well-equipped' spa (guests have unlimited access); also Wi-Fi. It offers 'great old-fashioned luxury', including 'room-service breakfast in bed'. Two suites in the main building are new this year. The best bedrooms are 'large and elegant', traditionally furnished; some have a four-poster. The cottage suites (Pineapple Lodge, Gingerbread House) suit families, but only those with children over six (and the under-eights may not use the swimming pool). In the restaurant (ask for a window table), the dress code is 'smart casual, no trainer shoes'. The chef (since November 2007), Gareth Jones, serves modern dishes, eg, monkfish with cassoulet of beans and cèpes, herb gnocchi. The afternoon teas are much admired. (*AB, Richard Mayou*)

Bedrooms: 31, 16 in cottages, 1 suitable for &. *Open*: all year. *Facilities*: hall, drawing room, library, bar, dining room, conference centre, civil wedding/ partnership licence, 220-acre park (gardens, tennis, croquet), spa (16-metre swimming pool, gym, sauna, 5 treatment rooms), riding, shooting, fishing, sandy beaches nearby. *Background music*: none. *Location*: 2 miles S of Llandudno. *Smoking*: not allowed. *Children*: no children under 6 in hotel, under 8 in spa. *Dogs*: allowed in some cottages only. *Credit cards*: Amex, MasterCard, Visa. *Prices*: b&b £87.50–£197.50 per person, d,b&b £140–£165, set menu £43, special breaks, Christmas/New Year packages.

St Tudno Hotel
The Promenade
Llandudno LL30 2LP

Tel 01492-874411
Fax 01492-860407
Email sttudnohotel@btinternet.com
Website www.st-tudno.co.uk

❧ *César award in 1987*

Guests returning this year found this 'small, friendly' hotel 'as good as before, atmosphere, pleasantly relaxed, but with a high degree of professionalism. One feels cosseted without over-attentiveness.' Once frequented by Alice Liddell who inspired Lewis Carroll (it has an Alice in Wonderland suite), the Grade II listed building is opposite the town's Victorian pier, gardens and beach. The owner, Martin Bland, 'is often about and makes a point of talking to his guests'. His staff, 'both older and new', are 'well trained, helpful and professional'. Public rooms have patterned wallpaper, swagged drapery, potted plants. *The Terrace* restaurant is Italianate (murals of Lake Como, stone fountains, tented ceiling, and chandeliers). Chef Jason Stock's cooking is 'excellent, a good balance between classics brilliantly prepared, eg, stinking bishop soufflé, and modern dishes and flavours, all built around fine local produce, especially meat and seafood. Some good wines at reasonable prices.' Bedrooms have colourful wallpaper and furnishings. 'Our small second-floor room had sea view; comfortable bed, lots of hanging space; delicious shortbread and fresh milk with the tea tray; wonderful use of space in the small bathroom.' 'My single was most comfortable.' 'Lovely little swimming pool, a good way to prepare for dinner.' (*Stephen and Pauline Glover, Dorothy Brining, PGK*)

Bedrooms: 18. *Open*: all year. *Facilities*: lift, sitting room, coffee lounge, lounge bar, restaurant, indoor swimming pool (8 by 4 metres), 'secret garden', unsuitable for &. *Background music*: none. *Location*: central, on promenade opposite pier, secure car park, garaging. *Smoking*: not allowed. *Children*: all ages welcomed. *Dogs*: allowed by arrangement (£10 per night), but not in public rooms or left unattended in bedrooms. *Credit cards*: all major cards. *Prices*: [2008] b&b £42.50–£155 per person, full alc £45, special breaks, Christmas/New Year packages, 1-night bookings occasionally refused. *V*

See also SHORTLIST

LLANDWROG Gwynedd   Map 3:A2

Rhiwafallen   *Tel* 01286-830172
Llandwrog, nr Caernarfon   *Email* ktandrobjohn@aol.com
LL54 5SW   *Website* www.rhiwafallen.co.uk

There is a new dining room this year at this restaurant-with-rooms: 'We have replaced our ageing conservatory with a hardwood one with air conditioning and a modern feel,' the owners tell us. Large windows give distant views of sea and spectacular sunsets. The granite farmhouse, 'renovated to a high standard' and with 'the feel of a contemporary city house', stands well away from the Caernarfon–Pwllheli road. Kate John is the 'cheerful front-of-house', her husband Rob the chef. They 'do almost everything themselves' and create a 'welcoming atmosphere'. The spacious lounge is furnished with an emphasis on natural materials, slate, wood, subdued colours. 'Everything blends perfectly. Lots of candles, even by day (it is a bit dark).' The cooking 'is a cut above the ordinary: genuine without unnecessary flourishes; natural flavours shine through; innovative pairings of texture and flavouring. Raw materials from the best local suppliers. Home-baked bread.' Main courses include lamb in filo pastry with apricots, pistachios, bubble and squeak rösti. At breakfast, juices are freshly squeezed, and cooked dishes include pancakes, smoked salmon with organic scrambled eggs, full Welsh. Afternoon tea is included in the price. The bedrooms have oak flooring, goose-feather duvet, Egyptian cotton bedlinen, a sleek *en suite* bathroom.

Bedrooms: 5, 1 on ground floor. *Open*: all year, but closed Sun night/Mon and Christmas. *Facilities*: ramps, lounge, restaurant, 2-acre garden. *Background music*: modern 'chill-out'. *Location*: 6 miles S of Caernarfon. *Smoking*: not allowed. *Children*: no children under 12 (must have own room; standard rates). *Dogs*: not allowed. *Credit cards*: Amex, MasterCard, Visa. *Prices*: b&b double £50–£120 per person, set menu Sun lunch £19.50, dinner £29.50.

LLANGAMMARCH WELLS Powys   Map 3:D3

The Lake	*Tel* 01591-620202
Llangammarch Wells	*Fax* 01591-620457
LD4 4BS	*Email* info@lakecountryhouse.co.uk
	Website www.lakecountryhouse.co.uk

♕ *César award in 1992*

Amid 'superb scenery', in 'magnificent' grounds, the lawns of this mock-Tudor, purpose-built Edwardian hotel slope down to the River Irfon. There are swans in the lake, daffodils and lambs in spring, sightings of red kites and red-breasted mergansers. 'An idyllic few days,' says an endorsement this year. Other comments: 'Good ambience and leisure facilities.' 'Excellent food.' The large lounge has log fire, paintings, grand piano. Owner Jean-Pierre Mifsud, 'friendly but never intrusive', 'circulates the dining room chatting to guests'. Sean Cullingford serves modern dishes (eg, halibut with mousseline of foie gras; local squab with roasted fig sauce). 'Helpful young staff.' 'Service quite formal'; men are asked to wear a jacket after 7 pm. The suites in the new wing are liked: 'Fantastic. Decanter of sherry, home-made shortbread. Towels big enough to wrap an elephant in.' 'Very comfortable, big bedroom, big bathroom with separate shower.' The older rooms, though well equipped, may feel 'somewhat dated'. Breakfast, 'everything you'd expect at a country house hotel', includes the weather forecast and suggestions for outings. The 'beautiful, Scandinavian-type' spa, by the lake, has 'good-sized pool', 'small but well-equipped gym', health and beauty treatments and an outdoor whirlpool. (*Gail Crabb, GH*)

Bedrooms: 30, 12 suites in adjacent lodge, 1 suitable for &. *Open*: all year. *Facilities*: ramps, 3 lounges, billiard room, restaurant, spa (20-metre swimming pool, sauna, gym), civil wedding licence, 50-acre grounds (lake, fishing, river, tennis, croquet, 9-hole par 3 golf course, clay-pigeon shooting, archery). *Background music*: none. *Location*: 8 miles SW of Builth Wells. *Smoking*: not allowed. *Children*: no under-8s in spa, or in dining room after 7 pm (high tea provided). *Dogs*: allowed in some bedrooms (£6 a day), only guide dogs in public rooms. *Credit cards*: Amex, MasterCard. *Prices*: b&b £85–£125 per person, d,b&b (min. 2 nights) £110–£180, set menus £42–£50, Christmas/New Year packages.

LLANGOLLEN Denbighshire   Map 3:B4
See SHORTLIST

LLANRWST Conwy *See SHORTLIST*   Map 3:A3

LLANWRTYD WELLS Powys   Map 3:D3

Carlton Riverside	*Tel* 01591-610248
Irfon Crescent	*Email* info@carltonrestaurant.co.uk
Llanwrtyd Wells LD5 4ST	*Website* www.carltonrestaurant.co.uk

✥ *César award in 1998*

The 'extrovert' Mary Ann Gilchrist, and her husband, Alan, run their unpretentious, 'very pleasant' restaurant-with-rooms near the River Irfon in this old spa town. They live 175 yards away, but can be reached by intercom if not on the spot. 'The accommodation was spacious, well equipped, beautifully decorated,' say visitors this year. The Gilchrists explain their reasonable prices: 'We do not provide trouser press, room service, "free" sherry, etc, so you are not asked to pay for them.' The building, its window and door frames painted blue, 'is hard to miss'. Its interior is 'tasteful in brown and cream'. The L-shaped lounge (with bar and library) is comfortable if 'a little small' but well lit (large windows). In the 'simple but elegant' dining room, best tables face the river. The food 'was, as ever, innovative, delicious; recommended wines a superb complement' (there are many half bottles). Mrs Gilchrist, 'passionate about cooking', serves main courses like roast rack of lamb with a timbale of courgette and tomato. 'Very good vegetarian options' (discuss these in advance). There are two fixed-price menus, one with limited choice. Breakfast, 'a joy', has fresh orange juice, 'very good scrambled eggs'. (*Hilary Gledhill, Alastair Kameen, John Patterson*)

Bedrooms: 5. *Open*: all year except 22–28 Dec, restaurant closed midday except Sun, brasserie open Fri/Sat/Sun. *Facilities*: reception, bar/lounge, restaurant, brasserie, unsuitable for &. *Background music*: classical piano in bar. *Location*: town centre, no private parking. *Smoking*: not allowed. *Children*: all ages welcomed. *Dogs*: not allowed in public rooms. *Credit cards*: MasterCard, Visa. *Prices*: b&b £32.50–£50 per person, set menu £17.50–£22.50, full alc £40, gourmet breaks, New Year package, 1-night bookings occasionally refused. *V*

See also SHORTLIST

LLYSWEN Powys   Map 3:D4

Llangoed Hall   *Tel* 01874-754525
Llyswen   *Fax* 01874-754545
nr Brecon LD3 0YP   *Email* enquiries@llangoedhall.com
                                  Website www.llangoedhall.com

Sir Bernard Ashley in 1990 turned this 17th-century manor house (redesigned by Clough Williams-Ellis in 1919) into a luxury hotel: he has filled it with his 'magnificent' collection of paintings, antiques and Ashley fabrics. It stands amid lovely countryside by the River Wye, beneath the Cambrian and Black mountains. Mark Green has been the manager since December 2007. The Great Hall has log fires, the morning room a piano, the library a snooker table. The bedrooms are spacious: 'Ours had sitting area, a Victorian mirror.' 'Staff mainly Polish, with some Welsh: very polite, good sense of humour.' Dining is a formal affair (men are asked to wear a jacket and tie). Regular visitors wrote of 'friendly, relaxed service, a superb, though expensive, meal'. The cooking of chef Sean Ballington is modern British with a traditional twist, eg, rack of lamb with mustard and pistachio crust, ratatouille and rosemary jus; butternut squash risotto with butternut foam. 'But the menu doesn't change for quite a time.' *Llangoed Hall* is the hotel of choice for literary bigwigs attending the Hay-on-Wye book festival. Good local walking and fishing. More reports, please.

Bedrooms: 23. *Open*: all year. *Facilities*: 2 lounges, library/snooker room, restaurant, private dining room, function rooms, civil wedding licence, 17-acre grounds (tennis, croquet, maze, helipad), River Wye (200 yds, fishing), unsuitable for ♿. *Background music*: none. *Location*: 11 miles NE of Brecon. *Smoking*: not allowed. *Children*: all ages welcomed, no under-12s at dinner. *Dogs*: only guide dogs allowed in house (heated kennels in grounds). *Credit cards*: all major cards. *Prices*: [2008] b&b £105–£350 per person, set dinner £39.50, full alc £61.50, Christmas/New Year/Easter packages. *V*

MUMBLES Swansea *See SHORTLIST*   Map 3:E3

NANT GWYNANT Gwynedd   Map 3:A3

Pen-y-Gwryd Hotel   *Tel* 01286-870211
Nant Gwynant   *Website* www.pyg.co.uk
LL55 4NT

♚ *César award in 1995*

'Spectacularly located' among the peaks of Snowdonia, this 'delightfully eccentric' old inn 'oozes atmosphere'. Hillary and his team stayed here before climbing Everest (their signatures are scrawled on the ceiling of a bar). The 'warm-hearted' owners, Brian and Jane Pullee (supported by sons Rupert and Nicolas), 'hold the secret of *PyG*'s success', said one guest who has been coming here for 50 years. It is 'utterly charming, spotlessly clean, never twee', adds another regular. Visitors are 'immediately put at ease' and 'soon settled in the wood-panelled snug, absorbing the atmosphere'. 'Flowers in lounge and dining room. Jane Pullee makes sure that the young enjoy themselves. She organises a rota for the popular role of banging the gong for meals, and holds a touching ceremony when children have climbed Snowdon.' The 'no-frills' bedrooms have old-fashioned furniture, 'masses of bedding', 'decent bars of soap'. Only five have facilities *en suite*: 'Sliding into a Victorian bath after a day in the hills sums up a stay in this unique hotel.' Dinners, served in house-party style, are 'hearty and very acceptable fare'. 'Perfectly cooked vegetables.' There are 'scrumptious' packed lunches. Breakfast (now served from 8.30) includes porridge and kippers. The 'lovely garden' with pond and stream 'has an undesigned appearance but is well kept and blends with the surrounding scenery'. (*Jelly Williams, and others*)

Bedrooms: 16, 1 on ground floor. *Open*: all year except Nov–Feb, but open New Year, weekends Jan, Feb. *Facilities*: lounge, bar, games room, dining room, chapel, 2-acre grounds (natural unheated 60-metre swimming pool, sauna), unsuitable for ♿. *Background music*: none. *Location*: between Beddgelert and Capel Curig. *Smoking*: not allowed. *Children*: all ages welcomed. *Dogs*: allowed. *Credit cards*: MasterCard, Visa. *Prices*: [2008] b&b £40–£50 per person, set dinner £22–£28, 3-night rates, 1-night bookings sometimes refused weekends.

NEWPORT Pembrokeshire   Map 3:D1

Cnapan   *Tel* 01239-820575
East Street, Newport   *Fax* 01239-820878
nr Fishguard SA42 0SY   *Email* enquiry@cnapan.co.uk
                                        Website www.cnapan.co.uk

'Run with warmth' (says a visitor this year), this 'superb' pink-painted restaurant-with-rooms stands on the fairly quiet main street of this seaside town in the Pembrokeshire national park (the larger Newport is in Gwent). 'As room-guests,' others add, 'you are treated as extra-special.' Michael and Judith Cooper (chef with her son, Oliver) and her sister, Eluned Lloyd, head a staff who 'seem really to enjoy being there'. 'Every afternoon we were offered tea with Welsh scones in the comfortable little drawing room, log-burning stove lit for us.' The listed Georgian house is crammed with family treasures, books and games; a crowded Welsh dresser stands in the hall. 'Dinner in the restaurant, with slightly old-fashioned feel, consisted of the freshest sea bass ever. Summer lunch in the suntrap garden was a delicious Mediterranean-style series of salads with crusty breads.' Puddings, a speciality, include swirled chocolate and ginger pots. 'Vegetables especially good; service brisk, attentive, everyone showed kindness.' The small bedrooms have pine furniture, bright colours, tea/coffee-making facilities. 'Shower room a miracle of compactness, a shared bathroom available for wallowers.' The family room has an adjoining bunk-bedroom. Huge breakfasts include home-made marmalade, free-range eggs and kippers. (*Alastair Kameen, Bob and Deborah Steel*)

Bedrooms: 5. *Open*: mid-Mar–end Dec, except Christmas, restaurant closed Tues. *Facilities*: lounge, bar, restaurant, small garden, unsuitable for ♿. *Background music*: jazz/Latin/classical. *Location*: town centre. *Smoking*: not allowed. *Children*: all ages welcomed (£9 for b&b in family room). *Dogs*: only guide dogs allowed. *Credit cards*: MasterCard, Visa. *Prices*: b&b £42–£52 per person, d,b&b £71.50–£81.50, set meal £29.50, 1-night bookings refused peak season Sat.

PENARTH Cardiff *See SHORTLIST*   Map 3:E4

PENMAENPOOL Gwynedd   Map 3:B2

Penmaenuchaf Hall   NEW   *Tel* 01341-422129
Penmaenpool, nr Dolgellau   *Fax* 01341-422787
LL40 1YB   *Email* relax@penhall.co.uk
                                      Website www.penhall.co.uk

In the Snowdonia national park, this former cotton magnate's house stands amid woodland and landscaped gardens in a fine position overlooking the Mawddach estuary. Built in imposing Victorian style in the 1860s, it has 'strikingly beautiful' grounds, say inspectors, who visited when bluebells, rhododendrons and camellias were in their prime. 'A spacious, dependably comfortable place. All staff were friendly and efficient. Our bedroom was well maintained, but its decor was uncoordinated, and sound insulation was poor.' Some rooms have a four-poster bed; some a sitting area with sofa. The panelled drawing room has leather sofas and a log fire. The 'most attractive' conservatory restaurant, *Llygad yr Haul* ('eye of the sun'), has a 'smart ambience; well-dressed candlelit tables, oak panelling, slate floor, Gothic windows and Snowdonia views'. Chefs Justin Pilkington and Tim Reeve serve 'contemporary Welsh' food, using local venison; Mawddach salmon; fillet of Welsh Black beef. Herbs, salads and vegetables are home grown. 'Wine is a passion of ours,' write the 'hands-on' owners, Lorraine Fielding and Mark Watson; their list has won awards, and they run a wine club. Our inspectors thought that 'though the price of dinner was on the high side, wines were very reasonably priced'.

Bedrooms: 14. *Open*: all year. *Facilities*: ramps, reception hall, drawing room, morning room, library, bar, breakfast room, restaurant, conference room, civil wedding licence, 21-acre grounds (gardens, lake, woodland), unsuitable for &. *Background music*: classical/jazz/mellow in restaurant. *Location*: 2 miles W of Dolgellau. *Smoking*: not allowed. *Children*: babes in arms and over-6s welcome. *Dogs*: allowed in 1 bedroom and hall. *Credit cards*: Diners, MasterCard, Visa. *Prices*: b&b £70–£135 per person, d,b&b £110–£175, set dinner £42, full alc £56, Christmas/New Year packages, 1-night bookings occasional refused Sat in summer.

The 'New' label indicates hotels which are appearing in the *Guide* for the first time or have been readmitted after an absence.

PENMYNYDD Anglesey   Map 3:A3

Neuadd Lwyd
Penmynydd
nr Llanfairpwllgwyngyll
Anglesey, LL61 5BX

Tel/Fax 01248-715005
Email post@neuaddlwyd.co.uk
Website www.neuaddlwyd.co.uk

'Set against a perfect background of countryside and hills', this 'lovely place' is 'warm and welcoming, beautifully furnished', 'peaceful with wonderful views'. 'Attention to guests is professional and friendly without being deferential,' say visitors this year. The early Victorian rectory, set amid farmland, is run as a small, upmarket guest house by owners Susannah and Peter Woods. Welsh speakers, they are 'enthusiastic about Anglesey' and promote local produce in their meals. Susannah Woods and Delyth Gwynedd, who trained together at Ballymaloe cookery school in Ireland, serve a 'delicious', 'elegant and interesting' four-course no-choice dinner, eg, sea bass with a tarragon butter sauce, savoy cabbage with Carmarthen ham, puy lentils and saffron rustic potatoes. 'Home-baked breads; farmhouse butter; wonderful cheeses.' 'Wine good choice, excellent value.' The 'extremely comfortable' lounge has high-backed wooden chairs on each side of bay windows (binoculars provided). 'Pictures everywhere; attractive chandeliers.' 'Our lovely bedroom had white-painted cast iron bedstead and furniture, pink-and-white wallpaper, original black slate fireplace'; also flat-screen TV/DVD/CD-player. Bathrooms, 'tastefully done', have slipper bath, painted floor and expensive soap. 'First-class breakfast, including fruit creations, fresh orange juice, home-made compotes and cereals, creamy scrambled eggs, buttermilk scones.' (*Kevin and Yvonne McKeown, Anne Thornthwaite*)

Bedrooms: 4. *Open*: Feb–Nov, closed Sun/Mon/Tues except bank holidays. *Facilities*: drawing room, lounge, dining room, 6-acre grounds, only dining room suitable for &. *Background music*: in evening 'if requested'. *Location*: 3 miles W of Menai Bridge, train to Bangor. *Smoking*: not allowed. *Children*: not under 12. *Dogs*: not allowed. *Credit cards*: MasterCard, Visa. *Prices*: b&b £87.50–£175 per person, d,b&b £175–£195, see website for mid-week rates.

When you make a booking you enter into a contract with a hotel. Most hotels explain their cancellation policies, which vary widely, in a letter of confirmation. You may lose your deposit or be charged at the full rate for the room if you cancel at short notice. A travel insurance policy can provide protection.

PENTREFOELAS Denbighshire   Map 3:A3

Hafod Elwy Hall   NEW
Hiraethog, nr Pentrefoelas
LL16 5SP

Tel 01690-770345
Fax 01690-770266
Email enquiries@hafodelwyhall.co.uk
Website www.hafodelwyhall.co.uk

'A great place, very isolated; should be a magnet for those tired of city life who want lovely home-grown, home-cooked food, peace and quiet, nice hosts.' This 'characterful house with an Edwardian feel' stands 'far from anywhere', in a working farm on the Denbighshire mountains. 'The welcome is personal, natural, unforced,' says the nominator. The 'very green' owners, Roger and Wendy Charles-Warner, have won awards for sustainability. They produce their own lamb, pork and beef; 'eggs from our own hens, nothing bought in'. 'The cooking is country style, authentic. Delicious sucking pig.' Everything is home made; vegetables and fruit are organically grown. No liquor licence; bring your own. 'Stylish bedrooms with everything one could wish for.' Normally up to six people are catered for, but there is 'scope for flexibility'. Two bedrooms have a four-poster (one has a big cast iron bath and a thunderbox loo in its bathroom). One room is let with an adjacent small single room. There are wood-burning stoves in the bay-windowed lounge and the red-walled dining room. Original features include slate floors, bread oven, archways, old wells. A non-refundable deposit of 20% is required to ensure a booking. Not easy to find: 'Not on most satnavs.' (*John Rowlands*)

Bedrooms: 3, 1 on ground floor suitable for &. *Open*: all year. *Facilities*: 2 lounges, sun room, dining room, 60-acre grounds (private fishing). *Background music*: none. *Location*: 12 miles SE of Betws-y-Coed, 11 miles SW of Denbigh, 6½ miles N of Pentrefoelas off A543. *Smoking*: not allowed. *Children*: normally not under 16. *Dogs*: allowed in sun room and lounge 'if dry and clean and no other guest objects', not in bedrooms. *Credit cards*: MasterCard, Visa. *Prices*: b&b £35–£70 per person, d,b&b £58–£88, set dinner £18, Christmas/New Year packages, 1-night bookings refused weekends, bank holidays.

Readers' contributions, written on the forms at the back of the book or sent by email, are the lifeblood of the *Good Hotel Guide*. Our readers play a crucial role by reporting on existing entries as well as recommending new discoveries. Everyone who writes to the *Guide* is a potential winner of the Report of the Year competition (page 63), in which a dozen correspondents each year win a copy of the *Guide* and an invitation to our annual launch party in October.

PORTHKERRY Cardiff   Map 3:E3

Egerton Grey   *Tel* 01446-711666
Porthkerry, nr Cardiff   *Fax* 01446-711690
CF62 3BZ   *Email* info@egertongrey.co.uk
                                 Website www.egertongrey.co.uk

Staying here is 'a pleasure', says a report this year. 'The welcome from
staff and proprietors was superb, the public rooms are beautifully
furnished. Good dinners, an extensive wine cellar.' The grey stone
former Victorian rectory stands in the wooded Vale of Glamorgan and
has views through a viaduct to the Bristol Channel. Its terraced
gardens are bordered by mature woodland, creating an air of tranquillity. Cardiff airport is two miles away but the hotel stands in its own
valley, and few guests have been bothered by this. Earlier visitors
described how Richard Morgan-Price, co-owner with Huw Thomas,
'though coping with a busy restaurant, came to carry our bags and lead
us to our room'. Most bedrooms are spacious, and have colourful wallpaper and fabrics, thick carpet, antique or repro furniture. There are
antiques, interesting objects and squashy sofas in the lounges. Dinner
(modern British cooking by Andrew Lawrence) is served by candlelight in the panelled former billiard room. Main courses include
venison with swede tian, blueberry and cassis sauce; lemon sole filled
with salmon mouse. Breakfast has 'a nice choice of well-cooked
classics'. Children are welcomed. Small weddings and functions are
held. (*RB, and others*)

Bedrooms: 10. *Open*: all year. *Facilities*: 2 lounges, drawing room, library, conservatory, bar, restaurant, private dining room, function facilities, civil wedding
licence, 7-acre garden (croquet), rock beach 400 yds, only restaurant suitable
for &. *Background music*: light classical in restaurant. *Location*: 9 miles SW of
Cardiff. *Smoking*: not allowed. *Children*: all ages welcomed. *Dogs*: not usually
allowed in public rooms. *Credit cards*: Amex, MasterCard, Visa. *Prices*: b&b
£70–£100 per person, d,b&b £90–£120, full alc £33, Christmas/New Year
packages, 1-night bookings occasionally refused at weekends. ***V***

How to contact the *Guide*
By mail: From anywhere in the UK, write to Freepost PAM
2931, London W11 4BR (no stamp is needed)
From outside the UK: *Good Hotel Guide*, 50 Addison Avenue,
London W11 4QP, England
By telephone or fax: 020-7602 4182
By email: editor@goodhotelguide.com
Via our website: www.goodhotelguide.com

PORTMEIRION Gwynedd   Map 3:B3

Portmeirion Hotel   *Tel* 01766-770000
Portmeirion LL48 6ET   *Fax* 01766-770300
                              Email enquiries@portmeirion-village.com
                              Website www.portmeirion-village.com

'Can there be a more beautiful setting?' Sir Clough Williams-Ellis's 'magical Italianate village' is on the wooded hillside of a peninsula on the Snowdonia coast. Accommodation is in a Victorian hotel, in *Castell Deudraeth* (1850s folly; mock-Tudor towers and ramparts; modern interior), and in cottages and villas. Most of the hotel's public areas are 'in grand style', with Moghul-inspired decor, but recent refurbishment has given bar, restaurant and some bedrooms a 'sleek, modern' style: rooms range from the Peacock suite, with 'vast marble fireplace' and 'bed so high footstools are needed to get into it', to 'average size, done in black, grey and white' which one couple thought 'rather gloomy'. Manager Siôn Dobson Jones leads a 'long-established staff' who 'without exception make one most welcome'. Guests eat in the hotel's restaurant (lovely estuary views) or *Castell*'s brasserie ('more choice and cheaper options'); 'an efficient minibus service links the buildings'. Village rooms, each 'unique', should be chosen carefully: 'A ground-floor one can leave you vulnerable to curious eyes of day visitors'; the deluxe Anchor One and Anchor Three are liked. Weddings are often held, and 'there is a lot of climbing to get anywhere on the estate'. (*Patricia Fenn, BP, and others*)

Bedrooms: 14 in hotel, some on ground floor, 1 suitable for &, 11 in *Castell Deudraeth*, 28 in village. *Open*: all year. *Facilities*: hall, lift, 2 lounges, bars, restaurant (harpist sometimes), brasserie in *Castell*, children's supper room, function room, beauty salon, civil wedding licence, 170-acre grounds (garden), heated swimming pool (8 by 15 metres, May–Sept). *Background music*: none. *Location*: edge of Snowdonia national park, 2 miles from Porthmadog, free minibus from Minffordd station. *Smoking*: not allowed. *Children*: all ages welcomed (babysitters available). *Dogs*: not allowed. *Credit cards*: all major cards. *Prices*: b&b £85–£265 per person, d,b&b £120–£300, set lunch £17.50, dinner £37.50, full alc £45, Christmas/New Year packages.

We update the *Guide* every year. Hotels are dropped if there has been a change of owner (unless reports after the change are positive), if this year's reports are negative, or in rare cases where there has been no feedback. A lot of hotels fall by the wayside every year, and many new ones are added.

PWLLHELI Gwynedd   Map 3:B2

Plas Bodegroes   *Tel* 01758-612363
Nefyn Road   *Fax* 01758-701247
Pwllheli LL53 5TH   *Email* gunna@bodegroes.co.uk
                           Website www.bodegroes.co.uk

❦ *César award in 1992*

For 21 years, Chris Chown and his Faroese wife, Gunna, have run
this white Georgian manor house as a restaurant-with-rooms. It
stands up an avenue of beech trees in lovely wooded grounds on the
Lleyn peninsula. He has long held a *Michelin* star for his 'classically
based' use of local ingredients (eg, grilled Welsh Black beef with
mushroom and horseradish crust and oxtail sauce; lemon sole with
saltcod mash and parsley sauce); she is front-of-house. The
'gorgeous' L-shaped dining room has 'delightful illuminated display
cabinets', polished wood floors, paintings by contemporary Welsh
artists, 'perfect lighting'. 'Cooking of a very high standard,' say
visitors this year. At busy times meal service can be leisurely. The
bedrooms have a Scandinavian-style decor and flat-screen TV.
Guests are advised that two smaller attic rooms are best for a stay of
only one night, but recent visitors thought them 'cleverly designed'
and well equipped. 'We liked the view from the window seat.' Two
rooms are in a cottage, facing a tranquil courtyard garden. 'Every
shower is now a power shower.' The 'enjoyable breakfast' includes
fresh orange juice, 'perfectly cooked hot dishes, very good toast',
'delicious smoked haddock'. The wisteria-draped porch is 'a
pleasant place to sit'. (*BP, and others*)

Bedrooms: 11, 2 in courtyard annexe. *Open*: 12 Mar–22 Nov, closed Sun and
Mon nights except bank holidays. *Facilities*: lounge, bar, breakfast room,
restaurant, 5-acre grounds, unsuitable for &. *Background music*: occasional, on
quiet nights, in restaurant. *Location*: 1 mile W of Pwllheli. *Smoking*: not
allowed. *Children*: all ages welcomed. *Dogs*: not allowed in public rooms,
1 bedroom. *Credit cards*: MasterCard, Visa. *Prices*: b&b £50–£85 per person,
d,b&b £90–£125, set lunch (Sun) £18.50, dinner £42.50, midweek breaks,
1-night bookings refused bank holidays.

We say 'Unsuitable for &' when a hotel tells us that it cannot
accommodate wheelchair-users. We do not have the resources
to inspect such facilities or to assess the even more
complicated matter of facilities for the partially disabled. We
suggest that you discuss such details with the hotel.

REYNOLDSTON Swansea   Map 3:E2

Fairyhill   NEW
Reynoldston, Gower
nr Swansea SA3 1BS

Tel 01792-390139
Fax 01792-391358
Email postbox@fairyhill.net
Website www.fairyhill.net

In a quiet rural setting, this small, creeper-covered, 18th-century mansion stands in large grounds near the Gower coast (magnificent beaches). Andrew Hetherington, front-of-house, owns it with Paul Davies (the chef with Nick Jones). Service ('first class', one couple wrote) is by young men in black. All bedrooms (some are a bit small) have flat-screen TV/DVD/CD-player and free Wi-Fi. 'Our spacious room had a large bathroom, fruit bowl replenished daily. House-keeping immaculate.' 'Ours was lovely, the dinner was superb.' Imaginative modern dishes, eg, seared fillets of brill with laverbread butter sauce; roast lamb with leek and ginger mash and red wine sauce, are served on a three-course dinner menu. Most meals are enjoyed, though some visitors found the cooking 'variable' in the owners' absence. Breakfast 'has a comprehensive buffet and the usual cooked offerings'. Jam, biscuits and bread are home made; a walled garden and orchard provide vegetables, herbs and fruit. Holistic treatments can be arranged. Manicured lawns with sculptures lead to grassy areas and woodlands, a trout stream and a lake with wild ducks. Some visitors in the past found the muzak played in the public areas 'truly ghastly'; we'd like comments on this, please. (*Richard and Catriona Smith, Hilary Blakemore*)

Bedrooms: 8. *Open*: all year except 24–26 Dec, 15–23 Jan, Sun night in winter. *Facilities*: lounge, bar, 3 dining rooms, meeting room, 24-acre grounds (croquet, woodland, stream, lake), beaches (water sports 3 miles), unsuitable for ♿. *Background music*: jazz/classical/pop in lounge, bar, dining room at mealtimes. *Location*: 11 miles W of Swansea, M4 exit 47 to Gowerton. *Smoking*: not allowed. *Children*: not under 8. *Dogs*: allowed in grounds only. *Credit cards*: MasterCard, Visa. *Prices*: b&b £82.50–£250 per person, d,b&b £122.50–£290, set lunch £15.95–£19.95, set dinner from £30, 1-night bookings sometimes refused Sat.

RUTHIN Denbighshire   Map 3:A4
See SHORTLIST

ST DAVID'S Pembrokeshire
See SHORTLIST
Map 3:D1

SKENFRITH Monmouthshire
Map 3:D4

The Bell at Skenfrith
Skenfrith NP7 8UH

Tel 01600-750235
Fax 01600-750525
Email enquiries@skenfrith.co.uk
Website www.skenfrith.co.uk

In a 'wonderfully quiet', 'very beautiful' setting, deep in the Welsh Marches, Janet and William Hutchings's 17th-century coaching inn stands beside an old stone bridge across the River Monnow. Offering 'value for what is on offer', it is 'excellent and fun', and has 'friendly staff', say visitors this year. It has flagstone floors, inglenook fireplace and 'simple yet sophisticated' bedrooms. One visitor, who had booked a single room, was delighted, on a quiet weekend, to be upgraded to a 'magnificent suite, with huge, stylish bathroom, very comfortable bed, large sofa'. Another guest enjoyed the 'idyllic' experience of lying in the bath and 'watching ewes with their lambs on a green hillside'. All bedrooms have DVD- and CD-player and free Internet access. 'Beds turned down during dinner, rooms made up during breakfast' (which includes eggs Florentine; French toast; boiled egg with 'soldiers'). Children are welcomed; they have their own organic menu, and electronic listening devices are available. Chef David Hill serves modern dishes like confit of duck leg, herb mashed potato, asparagus, redcurrant jus. The 'splendid', wide-ranging wine list has many half bottles and 14 wines by the glass. (*Richard Mayou, Humphrey and Frances Norrington, MP*)

Bedrooms: 11, 8 with facilities *en suite*. *Open*: all year except last week Jan, first week Feb, also Mon Nov–Easter (not Christmas fortnight). *Facilities*: ramps, large open sitting area, restaurant, 1-acre grounds (river opposite, quad biking, archery, go-karting, clay-pigeon shooting, fishing nearby), only restaurant suitable for &. *Background music*: none. *Location*: 9 miles W of Ross-on-Wye. *Smoking*: not allowed. *Children*: small children stay free, no under-8s in restaurant in evening (supper at 6 pm). *Dogs*: not allowed in restaurant or unattended in bedrooms. *Credit cards*: MasterCard, Visa. *Prices*: b&b £55–£75 per person, set menus £15–£22.50, full alc £40, Christmas package, 1-night bookings refused weekends.

SWANSEA *See SHORTLIST*   Map 3:E3

TALSARNAU Gwynedd   Map 3:B3

Maes-y-Neuadd   *Tel* 01766-780200
Talsarnau LL47 6YA   *Fax* 01766-780211
                    Email maes@neuadd.com
                    Website www.neuadd.com

❦ *César award in 2003*

In a 'wonderful, peaceful location', this 'mansion in the meadow' is
owned by Peter and Lynn Jackson and Peter Payne, who run it with
a 'universally attentive and friendly' staff (arriving guests are given a
list of those they are likely to encounter). It stands in large, well-kept
grounds, with 'magnificent views' over Snowdonia. 'The food is
excellent; the rooms are inviting,' writes a fan. But some reporters felt
there were 'rather a lot of rules' and were less keen on the food.
'Lovely, bright' sitting areas have oak beams, antique and modern
furniture, inglenook fireplace. The bedrooms vary in size and style;
their refurbishment continues. Extras include 'a small complimentary
bottle of home-produced gin'. In the 'elegant' dining room, local and
organic produce (home-grown vegetables and herbs) are used in
dishes like chicken breast with creamed leeks, roasted root vegetables, mushroom sauce. If you prefer a simpler style of cooking, or
have a favourite dish, you may ask for it. The 'well-chosen' wine list
has a 'good range of prices'. Children have their own menu (served in
the bedroom or the family dining room), and board games, baby-
listening, etc, can be provided. Breakfast has 'a good selection of
dishes both hot and cold'. (*Gordon Hands, FR, and others*)

Bedrooms: 15, 4 in coach house, 3 on ground floor. *Open*: all year. *Facilities*: lift,
ramps, lounge, bar, conservatory, family dining room, main dining room,
business facilities, terrace, civil wedding licence, 80-acre grounds (croquet,
helipad), unsuitable for ♿. *Background music*: none. *Location*: 3 miles NE of
Harlech off B4573. *Smoking*: not allowed. *Children*: all ages welcomed but no
under-8s in main dining room at night. *Dogs*: allowed in coach house bedrooms
only, must be on a leash in grounds. *Credit cards*: MasterCard, Visa. *Prices*:
[2008] b&b double £98–£152, d,b&b double £164–£222, set lunch £16.95–£25,
dinner £30–£35, 2/3-night breaks, Christmas/New Year packages.

New reports help us keep the *Guide* up to date.

TREMADOG Gwynedd   Map 3:B3

Plas Tan-Yr-Allt
Tremadog, nr Porthmadog
LL49 9RG

Tel 01766-514545
Email info@tanyrallt.co.uk
Website www.tanyrallt.co.uk

🏆 *César award in 2008*

Known to its fans as 'Tanny', this 'exquisite and tranquil' Grade II
listed house (where the poet Shelley once spent a year) overlooks the
Glaslyn estuary. Run in house-party style by owners Michael Bewick
and Nick Golding (the chef), it has a stylish decor inside its 'cottagey'
exterior. In the bright red entrance hall with Philippe Starck 'ghost'
chairs, Percy the parrot is 'a real ice-breaker'. 'Wonderful welcome,'
says a visitor this year, 'tea and cakes on the terrace with breathtaking
views. We felt at home.' Another report tells of 'superjolly service'
and a 'spacious and chic' bedroom. Each room is different: Madocks
has a domed ceiling, white paintwork, huge modern chandelier,
metal-framed bed, 'wonderful sea views'. Shelley's Theatre has 'a
beautifully dressed four-poster, window seat, huge bathroom'. Guests
dine together at 8.15 off a set menu, at a 'fabulous' oak and slate table.
'A glorious affair, emphasis on locally sourced food', eg, roast
pancetta-wrapped cod with asparagus and lemon mayonnaise. When
dinner is not served, help is given with bookings at 'recommended
local restaurants'. The 'excellent' breakfast, 'another social affair', has
fruit salad, 'imaginative' cooked dishes, 'lashings of toast, local jams'.
No children under 16, unless you rent the entire house. (*Jill Joseph,
WA, and others*)

Bedrooms: 6. *Open*: all year except Christmas, Feb, Mon/Tues Oct–Mar.
Facilities: drawing room, library, dining room, 47-acre grounds, unsuitable for
&. *Background music*: none. *Location*: 1 mile N of Porthmadog, guests collected
by car. *Smoking*: not allowed. *Children*: not under 16. *Dogs*: not allowed. *Credit
cards*: Amex, MasterCard, Visa. *Prices*: b&b £60–£140 per person, d,b&b
£79–£178, set dinner £38.50, New Year package, 1-night bookings refused
bank holidays and peak weekends.

****

Traveller's tale *Hotel in Wales* The rooms were obviously
designed by a professional. I think it must have been a
woman because in our attic room, in order to use the loo, I
had to stick my head through a Velux roof light.

****

WHITEBROOK Monmouthshire   Map 3:D4

The Crown at Whitebrook
Whitebrook, nr Monmouth
NP25 4TX

Tel 01600-860254
Fax 01600-860607
Email info@crownatwhitebrook.co.uk
Website www.crownatwhitebrook.co.uk

'This splendid place,' writes an inspector, 'may call itself a restaurant-with-rooms, but residents are no less important than guests at table. Our room may have lacked fridge and trouser press, but nothing of consequence. The bathroom was elegant: high-tech shower as well as bath; generous towels.' The *Michelin* star is thoroughly deserved. Surrounded by woods, in Wye valley, the former 17th-century drovers' inn is in a small village near Monmouth. January 2008 saw the arrival of a new manager, David Hennigan, and general redecoration, giving a 'bright, fresh, modern look' alongside some original features. The chef, James Sommerin, serves modern British 'with French flair' cooking, eg, pan-fried hake with crab beignet, tomato fondue and sauce vierge. 'Our meal was faultless at every course, served in a formal manner, but with charm. Good value.' 'Very attentive *maître d'*.' There are 250 wines to choose from. The bedrooms, ranging from 'Executive' to 'Standard', are in a modern extension. They have a contemporary feel, under-floor heating and 'the latest technological advancements' (Internet facilities, flat-screen TV, etc). The views are extensive. Breakfast is a 'sumptuous Welsh' affair. Guests may take part in a complimentary round at a local golf club. Transport can be arranged from Bristol and Cardiff airports. (*Richard Barrett, and others*)

Bedrooms: 8. *Open*: all year except 22 Dec–6 Jan, Sun night, Mon, Tues. *Facilities*: ramp, lounge, restaurant, business facilities, 5-acre garden, River Wye 2 miles (fishing), unsuitable for &. *Background music*: light jazz in lounge. *Location*: 6 miles S of Monmouth. *Smoking*: not allowed. *Children*: welcomed 'at parental discretion'. *Dogs*: not allowed. *Credit cards*: MasterCard, Visa. *Prices*: b&b £57.50–£100, set lunch £28, dinner £45, 1-night bookings sometimes refused bank holidays.

CHANNEL ISLANDS

Close to Normandy, these *Îles Anglo-Normandes*, as the French call them, have a distinct French flavour, notably in their cooking of lunch and dinner (breakfast tends to be boldly British). The hotels vary greatly. Two of our entries (one a former *César* winner) are long-time favourites on car-free Sark; a third is on the tiny island of Herm. On the opposite end of the scale are the sumptuous *Longueville Manor*, in St Saviour, with its sophisticated restaurant, and the family-owned, family-friendly *Atlantic Hotel* at St Brelade.

The Atlantic Hotel, St Brelade

BRAYE Alderney
See SHORTLIST
Map 1: inset D6

HERM
Map 1: inset D6

The White House
Herm, via Guernsey GY1 3HR

Tel 01481-722159
Fax 01481-710066
Email hotel@herm-island.com
Website www.herm-island.com

🏆 *César award in 1987*

This beautiful, tiny island ('peaceful, particularly when day-trippers have left') has no cars, no TV, cliffs, a little harbour, pastel-painted cottages, three shops, an inn, a 10th-century chapel, birdwatching, shell gathering, bathing, fishing. Its only hotel, owned by Adrian and Pennie Heyworth, has a devoted clientele. 'Our Utopia,' one visitor wrote. Set by a beach, it is managed by Jonathan Watson: guests are met at the boat. 'Senior staff are permanent and cannot be faulted; others, from around the world, are new each season' (one couple, visiting early in the season, was critical of the service). Children 'are treated like VIPs: amazing high tea buffet, baby-listening'. Family suites have a second bedroom with bunk bed. Spacious cottage rooms have small garden and balcony, but some may be in need of refurbishment. The 'old-time' quality is liked (eg, jacket required of male diners), but 'some of the furniture is now a bit rickety'. Neil Southgate's cooking is generally enjoyed: 'Memories of Italy and France.' 'As you dine, the sun sets over Guernsey.' Bedrooms lack 'upmarket extras' (minibar, Wi-Fi, etc), but have good storage and evening turn-down service. Neighbouring islands are visible from the lounge (which has board games, free self-help tea and coffee). As we went to press, we learned that Herm island is for sale. (*Vera Tracy, Nigel and Jennifer Jee, and others*)

Bedrooms: 40, 23 in cottages, some on ground floor. *Open*: 23 Mar–4 Oct. *Facilities*: 3 lounges, 2 bars, carvery, restaurant, conference room, 1-acre garden (tennis, croquet, 7-metre solar-heated swimming pool), beach 200 yds, Herm unsuitable for ♿. *Background music*: none. *Location*: by harbour, air/sea to Guernsey, then ferry from Guernsey (20 mins). *Smoking*: not allowed. *Children*: all ages welcomed, no under-9s in restaurant at night (high teas provided). *Dogs*: only guide dogs allowed. *Credit cards*: MasterCard, Visa. *Prices*: d,b&b £80–£120 per person, bar lunches, set dinner £27.

KINGS MILLS Guernsey   Map 1: inset D5
See SHORTLIST

ST BRELADE Jersey   Map 1: inset E6

The Atlantic Hotel   `NEW`   *Tel* 01534-744101
Le Mont de la Pulente   *Fax* 01534-744102
St Brelade JE3 8HE   *Email* info@theatlantichotel.com
                          Website www.theatlantichotel.com

Facing the magnificent five-mile beach of St Ouen's Bay, this large, white, modern building is owned by Patrick Burke, managed by Jason Adams. 'An exceptional hotel with exceptional standards; satisfaction of guests is paramount,' fans wrote. The interior is luxurious: antique terracotta flagstones, wrought iron staircase, rich carpeting, urns, fountains, antiques, specially designed furniture. 'Even the corridors are beautiful.' The large lounge merges into reception. Staff are 'most helpful'. In the *Ocean* restaurant (designed 'with the coastal setting in mind'), head chef Mark Jordan (*Michelin* star) provides 'superb meals'. Dishes include scallops, puy lentils, pancetta; pot-roasted wood pigeon, risotto of cèpe mushrooms, shaved truffle. There is a leisure centre, free for guests. 'Lovely bedrooms' have terrace or balcony. Sliding windows make the most of the views. Many rooms look over the swimming pool (where light meals are served in fine weather) to pine trees and the sea beyond, others face the adjacent La Moye championship golf course. Spacious studios and suites are in a garden wing. 'Excellent breakfasts' have 'delicious fruit salad'. In summer, many guests are families (there are nursery menus and board games). The airport is ten minutes' drive away, 'but we did not notice any aircraft noise'. (*Shirley and Michael Vast, Michael and Eithne Dandy, and others*)

Bedrooms: 50, some on ground floor. *Open*: all year. *Facilities*: lift, lounge, library, cocktail bar, restaurant, private dining room, fitness centre (swimming pool, sauna), wedding facilities, garden (tennis, heated swimming pool, 10 by 3 metres), golf club and beach ½ mile. *Background music*: at dinnertime. *Location*: 5 miles W of St Helier. *Smoking*: not allowed. *Children*: all ages welcomed. *Dogs*: not allowed. *Credit cards*: all major cards. *Prices*: [2008] b&b £82.50–£207.50 per person, d,b&b £127.50–£235, set menu £45, special breaks, off-season rates, Christmas/New Year packages.

There is no VAT in the Channel Islands.

St Brelade's Bay Hotel
St Brelade JE3 8EF

Tel 01534-746141
Fax 01534-747278
Email info@stbreladesbayhotel.com
Website www.stbreladesbayhotel.com

A 'wonderful collection of paintings' hangs throughout this 'large, glamorous' hotel. 'Peaceful, idyllic,' said a devotee who has known it for half a century. 'Wonderful,' said a three-generation family group. Other comments: 'Pleasant staff, excellent food and service, tasteful decor.' 'Marvellous situation and grounds.' 'Luxurious throughout', it is run by the 'hands-on' Robert Colley (fifth-generation owner/ managing director) with manager Margriet Barnes (new this year). The long, white, modern building faces Jersey's loveliest bay: the 'beautiful beach' is across a road. Elegant public rooms have parquet floors, moulded ceilings, chandeliers, oriental rugs, formal flower arrangements. Loungers stand on lawns near the freshwater swimming pools. In summer, alfresco lunches are served, and 'afternoon tea is brought while you laze in the shade'. Bedrooms are spacious; there are some two-bedroom penthouse suites; front rooms have 'fantastic' views (most have a balcony); second-floor rooms above the kitchen might be noisy; there are communicating family rooms, cots, high chairs, and high tea for small children. Chef Franz Hacker's 'fantastic' six-course dinners include 'wonderful crab and lobster specialities'. The English breakfast is 'superb'. 'Smart casual' clothing is expected in the restaurant. Mobile phones are 'not welcome' in public areas. (*PMT, John J Wilcox, and others*)

Bedrooms: 85. *Open*: 4 Apr–3 Nov. *Facilities*: lift, ramps, lounge, cocktail bar (evening entertainment, singers disco, magician, etc, daily except Sun), restaurant (pianist 3 nights a week), toddlers' room, games room, snooker room, sun veranda, 7-acre grounds (outdoor restaurant, 2 heated swimming pools (25 by 10 metres, 1 for children) with bar and grill, sauna, mini-gym, tennis, croquet, putting, boules, children's play area), beach across road, golf nearby. *Background music*: none. *Location*: 5 miles W of St Helier. *Smoking*: on terrace and balcony only. *Children*: all ages welcomed. *Dogs*: not allowed. *Credit cards*: all major cards. *Prices*: [2008] b&b £65–£252 per person, d,b&b £30 added, set dinner £35, full alc £37, weekend breaks.

ST HELIER Jersey
See SHORTLIST

Map 1: inset E6

There is no VAT in the Channel Islands.

ST MARTIN Guernsey
See SHORTLIST

Map 1: inset E5

ST PETER PORT Guernsey
See SHORTLIST

Map 1: inset E5

ST SAVIOUR Guernsey
See SHORTLIST

Map 1: inset E5

ST SAVIOUR Jersey

Map 1: inset E6

Longueville Manor
Longueville Road
St Saviour JE2 7WF

Tel 01534-725501
Fax 01534-731613
Email info@longuevillemanor.com
Website www.longuevillemanor.com

Exuding 'a pleasant air of confidence', this is Jersey's most sumptuous hotel (Relais & Châteaux). 'Beautifully kept', the extended
13th-century manor house 'offers country house comfort'. It stands
inland from St Helier in wide grounds by a wooded valley (all windows are double glazed). Rooms are light and the decor is smart,
with traditionally swagged curtains, oriental rugs, original paintings,
antiques, repro furniture. But the atmosphere is 'unstuffy': 'guests
share the reception rooms with the house cats and dogs'. Malcolm
Lewis is the 'attentive' third-generation owner. Staff are
'effortlessly helpful'. Andrew Baird, the executive head chef, serves
main courses like grilled John Dory with sauté langoustine and
butternut squash; 'wonderful vegetarian dishes'. There is a 'superb
cheese trolley' and a 400-strong wine list. Some ingredients are
home grown. Lighter meals are also available. There is a large,
bright dining room facing the garden, and a darker panelled one.
'Our bedroom was richly decorated: a comfortable chair was set in
front of the fireplace, just like home.' Breakfast, 'a relaxed affair',
has a generous buffet, a wide choice of cooked dishes, 'proper tea'.
Lunches and afternoon teas are served by the swimming pool. The
Royal Jersey Golf Club is near. Day-trips to France can be arranged.
More reports, please.

Bedrooms: 31, 8 on ground floor, 2 in cottage. *Open*: all year. *Facilities*: lift, ramp, 2 lounges, cocktail bar, 2 dining rooms, function/conference/wedding facilities, 15-acre grounds (croquet, tennis, heated swimming pool, woodland), sea 1 mile. *Background music*: none. *Location*: 1½ miles E of St Helier by A3. *Smoking*: allowed in 5 bedrooms. *Children*: all ages welcomed. *Dogs*: not allowed in public rooms. *Credit cards*: all major cards. *Prices*: [2008] b&b £100–£335 per person, d,b&b £150–£385, light meals available, set lunch (Sun) £27.50, dinner £47.50–£70, full alc £75, winter weekend breaks, Christmas/New Year packages.

SARK   Map 1: inset E6

Hotel Petit Champ
Sark
via Guernsey GY9 0SF

Tel 01481-832046
Fax 01481-832469
Email info@hotelpetitchamp.co.uk
Website www.hotelpetitchamp.co.uk

❦ *César award in 2007*

'Our fourteenth stay. Value for money and food have always been excellent. What makes it special is the friendliness and efficiency of the staff, ably managed by Caroline and Chris Robins.' A visitor to this 'delightful' small hotel writes of 'continuing high standards'. Another regular guest was touched by the 'wonderful attention' given to a family golden wedding celebration. 'Everyone did their utmost to make it a special occasion.' The low, late Victorian granite building stands alone on a headland on Sark's west coast, facing Guernsey (superb views, spectacular sunsets). The 'old-fashioned values' and the housekeeping are praised. 'Rooms done during breakfast, beds turned down at night.' The new chef, Andrew Clayton, specialises in local lobster and crab. 'Top-notch wines at low-notch prices.' 'Scrummy breakfast': ample choice, and a weather forecast on each table. The decor is traditional. 'Our room was simply furnished, large and comfortable.' 'Ours, with balcony, had generous storage, lovely view.' 'Plenty of lounges' and games, puzzles, etc, for children. Tips not expected. A secluded beach, sandy at low tide, is a steep walk down from the hotel; many other safe beaches are near. On car-free Sark, bicycles can be hired, and hotel visitors can be met by horse and carriage. (*Alan Lyne, HJ Martin Tucker, Sophia Hartland*)

Bedrooms: 10. *Open*: Apr–early Oct. *Facilities*: 3 sun lounges, library lounge, TV room, cocktail bar restaurant, 1-acre garden (solar-heated swimming pool (5 by 13 metres), putting, croquet), Sark unsuitable for ♿. *Background music*: in bar midday and evening. *Location*: 15 mins' walk from village. *Smoking*: allowed in bedrooms. *Children*: 'must be old enough to sit with parents at dinner (6/7 yrs)'.

Dogs: guide dogs allowed, otherwise no dogs in bedrooms or restaurant. *Credit cards*: all major cards. *Prices*: b&b £47.50–£59.50 per person, d,b&b £64.50–£76.50, set lunch (Sun) £12.75, dinner £21.75, full alc £32.50. *V*

La Sablonnerie
Little Sark
Sark, via Guernsey GY9 0SD

Tel 01481-832061
Fax 01481-832408
Email lasablonnerie@cwgsy.net
Website www.lasablonnerie.com

Opened in 1948, and run 'with gusto' by its current owner, Elizabeth Perrée, this 'wonderful little hotel with wonderful food' has a loyal following. 'Stylish, idiosyncratic', it stands in 'lovely' grounds, in a quiet southern corner of the island, reached by an isthmus; cows graze in an adjacent field. Its white walls are fronted by flowers; indoors are low ceilings and oak beams. Standards are 'consistently high'. 'The enthusiastic, young, multi-ethnic staff all seemed to want us to have fun.' Canapés at the bar (where a fire burns on cold days) precede dinner in the candlelit restaurant. Chef Colin Day's dishes include saddle of venison with a fricassée of oyster mushrooms. There is a separate lobster menu. Many ingredients come from the home farm. Breakfasts can start with champagne, and they include freshly cooked 'Sark Breakfast' (porridge with cream; eggs, sausages, kippers, etc). The tea room serves 'very good lunches'. The bedrooms are 'charming but not luxurious': some are reached through a door in the bar; some spacious ones are in cottages. You should pack a dress or tie for dinner. Nearby are the natural pools of Venus and Adonis, cliffs, coves, sandy beaches. (*JB, and others*)

Bedrooms: 22, also accommodation in nearby cottages. *Open*: Easter–Oct. *Facilities*: 3 lounges, 2 bars, restaurant, wedding facilities, 1-acre garden (tea garden/bar, croquet), Sark unsuitable for &. *Background music*: classical/piano in bar. *Location*: S part of island, boat from Guernsey (hotel will meet). *Smoking*: allowed in some bedrooms. *Children*: all ages welcomed. *Dogs*: allowed at hotel's discretion, but not in public rooms. *Credit cards*: MasterCard, Visa. *Prices*: b&b £40–£80 per person, d,b&b £55.50–£97.50, set menu £25.80, full alc £39.50 (*excluding 10% service charge*).

IRELAND

The great majority of hotels in Ireland are privately owned and managed. This is why some of the *Guide*'s favourite hotels can be found in this chapter. These days, some of the staff may be recruited from various European countries, but the Irish spirit prevails. Dinner is a social event at many of the smaller places where visitors can enjoy the *craic* around a communal dinner table. This year's *César* award goes to an outstanding example, *Ballyvolane House*, Castlelyons, where Justin and Jenny Green receive guests in relaxed country house style.

Ballyvolane House, Castlelyons

ARTHURSTOWN Co. Wexford   Map 6:D6

Dunbrody Country House   *Tel* 00 353 51-389600
Arthurstown, New Ross   *Fax* 00 353 51-389601
Email dunbrody@indigo.ie
Website www.dunbrodyhouse.com

The ancestral home of the Chichester family, this elegant Georgian
mansion in 'large and tranquil' parkland has been converted into a
luxury hotel by Kevin and Catherine Dundon. He is chef/*patron*, she
runs front-of-house. 'Excellent in every way; one of the nicest
country house hotels we have stayed in,' said one visitor. 'The
Dundons and their marvellously helpful staff did everything possible
to make us comfortable.' Patrician gates lead up a long drive; a splendid chandelier hangs in the magnificent foyer; all the furniture is
antique or 'good repro'. There are open fires and fresh flowers. The
bedrooms, up three attractive staircases, have fine carpets and curtains, good furnishing, dressing gowns, flowers and apples. In the
large red dining room, 'splendid dinners' have a seasonal menu or a
daily-changing tasting menu. Typical dishes: Duncannon crab with
avocado purée; char-grilled fillet of beef with an oxtail cottage pie.
There is also an informal seafood bar and a spa. Breakfasts are
'delicious'. (*PC*)

Bedrooms: 22, 4 on ground floor, 1 suitable for &. *Open*: all year except 22–27
Dec. *Facilities*: ramps, lounge, bar, seafood bar, restaurant, terrace, 20-acre
gardens in 300-acre grounds (golf, fishing, sailing, hunting nearby).
Background music: classical/jazz. *Location*: 10 miles S of New Ross. *Smoking*:
not allowed. *Children*: not in restaurant after 8 pm. *Dogs*: only guide dogs
allowed. *Credit cards*: all major cards. *Prices*: [2008] b&b €117.50–€225 per
person, set dinner €65, special breaks, New Year package, 1-night bookings
refused winter weekends.

BAGENALSTOWN Co. Carlow   Map 6:D6

Lorum Old Rectory   *Tel* 00 353 59-977 5282
Kilgreaney, Bagenalstown   *Fax* 00 353 59-977 5455
Email bobbie@lorum.com
Website www.lorum.com

'Welcome, catering and comfort cannot be faulted' at this granite
Victorian former rectory in large grounds in the rolling land at the foot
of Mount Leinster. The owner, Bobbie Smith, is 'delightful and a
wonderful cook', we are told. She knows the locality ('and it seems

every inhabitant'). The high-ceilinged bedrooms have 'perfect pro-
portions'; three have been redecorated this year. 'She has an eye for
colour, and our four-poster bed was artfully draped without being
fussy.' 'Our room was spacious, pretty and comfortable; shower, no
bath.' One bedroom has a separate bathroom. Bobbie Smith, a member of Euro-Toques, dedicated to using local and organic produce,
serves a six-course dinner (with a sorbet and cheese); 'I plan what I am
going to cook and discuss it with the people staying,' she says. Typical
dishes: broccoli and horseradish with lime soup; roast pork stuffed
with prunes and apricots. Dinner is served communally around a large
mahogany table in the red dining room. The 'wonderful' breakfast has
fresh orange juice, a 'good full Irish, home-baked breads, much fruit –
and the feeling that you have all day to enjoy it'. Nearby are the
gardens at Kilfane, Woodstock and Altamont. (*RB, AEM*)

Bedrooms: 5. *Open*: Mar–Nov. *Facilities*: drawing room, bar, study, dining room,
18-acre garden (croquet), unsuitable for &. *Background music*: none. *Location*:
4 miles S of Bagenalstown on R705 to Borris. *Smoking*: not allowed. *Children*:
welcomed by arrangement. *Dogs*: allowed by arrangement. *Credit cards*: Amex,
MasterCard, Visa. *Prices*: b&b €80–€100 per person, set dinner €45, 10% discount for stays of more than 2 nights.

BALLYCASTLE Co. Mayo   Map 6:B4

Stella Maris   *Tel* 00 353 96-43322
Ballycastle   *Fax* 00 353 96-43965
                              Email info@stellamarisireland.com
                              Website www.stellamarisireland.com

'A splendid location. Wonderful, friendly hosts,' says a visitor in 2008
to this white 19th-century coastguard station on the wild coast of
north Mayo. It has been converted into a hotel by Frances Kelly, a
local, and her American husband, Terence McSweeney. 'The welcome, on first-name terms, is warm. They are attentive to guests
throughout,' said another guest. 'Redecoration of the public and
private rooms is of the highest standard.' Mr McSweeney is a keen
golfer (he works for the US PGA in Florida during the winter); there
are golfing books aplenty in the 100-foot-long conservatory that runs
the length of the house and faces the sea: drinks are served here and
in the bar. Each bedroom is named after a golf course. Some rooms
are small, but most have a sea view. Frances Kelly ('her cooking is a
real bonus') serves contemporary dishes using 'local, organic
artisan produce', perhaps jumbo prawns and monkfish goujons,

prawn-scented cream. 'A brief but carefully chosen wine list.' Breakfast has fresh grapefruit, home-made preserves, 'the usual cooked things attractively presented'. (*Stuart Smith, RP*)

Bedrooms: 11, 1, on ground floor, suitable for ♿. *Open*: 9 Apr–4 Oct, restaurant closed to non-residents on Mon. *Facilities*: ramps, lounge, bar, restaurant, conservatory, 2-acre grounds (golf), sea/freshwater fishing, sandy beach nearby. *Background music*: in public rooms. *Location*: 1½ miles W of village, 16½ miles NW of Ballina. *Smoking*: not allowed. *Children*: all ages welcomed (limited availability). *Dogs*: not allowed in house. *Credit cards*: Diners, MasterCard, Visa. *Prices*: [2008] b&b €125–€185 per person, full alc €57.

BALLYLICKEY Co. Cork   Map 6:D4

Seaview House   *Tel* 00 353 27-50073
Ballylickey, Bantry Bay   *Fax* 00 353 27-51555
                              Email info@seaviewhousehotel.com
                              Website www.seaviewhousehotel.com

Set back from the road above Bantry Bay, this extended, white, bay-windowed Victorian building is now a hotel, which 'runs like clock-work' under the 'sharp eye' of its owner, Kathleen O'Sullivan, say fans. 'Nothing passes her by: the gardens and house are maintained to a high standard.' Earlier praise, from a guest who stayed for a week with three generations of his family: 'Miss O'Sullivan and her excellent staff could not have been kinder. My young granddaughters were given delicious high teas, and made to feel special.' There is a library with mahogany bookcases. The lounge has an open fire. 'A lively mix of guests': they gather in the bar for drinks before dinner. No music ('absolute bliss') here or in the restaurant with its conservatory extension. Chef Eleanor O'Donovan's four-course dinner menu, priced according to number of courses taken, has wide choice (so does breakfast). Typical dishes: Bantry Bay crab salad, Marie Rose sauce; Dover sole on the bone. This year all the bedrooms have been redecorated. Those in the new wing have under-floor heating in the bathroom; sea 'glimpses' from top-floor rooms. 'A serene environment.' 'Excellent value.' (*David and Gail Crabb, PC*)

Bedrooms: 25, 2, on ground floor, suitable for ♿. *Open*: mid-Mar–mid-Nov. *Facilities*: lounge bar, library/TV room, restaurant/conservatory, 3-acre grounds on waterfront (fishing, boating), riding, golf nearby. *Background music*: none. *Location*: 3 miles N of Bantry. *Smoking*: not allowed. *Children*: all ages welcomed. *Dogs*: not allowed in public rooms. *Credit cards*: all major cards. *Prices*: b&b €70–€105 per person, set dinner €50, full alc €60, special breaks. *V*

BALLYMENA Co. Antrim   Map 6:B6

Marlagh Lodge   NEW
71 Moorfields Road
Ballymena
BT42 3BU

Tel 028-2563 1505
Fax 208-2564 1590
Email info@marlaghlodge.com
Website www.marlaghlodge.com

'A natural sense of design' is evident in the restoration by Robert and Rachael Thompson of this listed Victorian dower house which they run as a guest house. 'You won't find satellite TV or DVD-player in our bedrooms,' they say, 'each room has its own bookcase instead.' 'Wonderful quirky Victorian furniture everywhere goes well together and suits the building,' says the nominator, who felt 'very well looked after'. The Blue Room has a king-size cast iron four-poster bed, and a roll-top bath in its bathroom. The Chintz Room, in aquamarine and cream, has a spacious shower room. The Print Room, 'populated by cherubs', has brass beds; bathroom ('more cherubs') across a landing. The drawing room contains many books about Irish country houses. Guests may play the piano in the study (the Thompsons are keen musicians). Rachael Thompson's 'inventive' five-course dinners use local produce in modern dishes, eg, twice-baked goat's cheese soufflé; roast cider-marinated pork with cider, honey and clove sauce. Breakfasts, 'lavish and over-tempting', have 'excellent home-made bread', 'Tummy Warmer' (porridge with Bushmills whiskey), Ulster fry, scrambled eggs with smoked salmon. The house is just off a busy road 'but was quiet at night'. Children are welcomed. Ballymena ('middle town') is between Belfast and the nine glens of Antrim. (*Charles Goldie*)

Bedrooms: 3. *Open*: all year except Christmas/New Year, dining room closed Sun night. *Facilities*: drawing room, dining room, ½-acre garden, unsuitable for ♿. *Background music*: classical/jazz during dinner. *Location*: 1½ miles E of Ballymena. *Smoking*: not allowed. *Children*: all ages welcomed. *Dogs*: not allowed. *Credit cards*: MasterCard, Visa. *Prices*: b&b £45 per person, d,b&b £77.50. *V*

How to contact the *Guide*
By mail: From anywhere in the UK, write to Freepost PAM 2931, London W11 4BR (no stamp is needed)
From outside the UK: *Good Hotel Guide*, 50 Addison Avenue, London W11 4QP, England
By telephone or fax: 020-7602 4182
By email: editor@goodhotelguide.com
Via our website: www.goodhotelguide.com

BALLYVAUGHAN Co. Clare   Map 6:C4

Gregans Castle [NEW]   *Tel* 00 353 65-707 7005
Ballyvaughan   *Fax* 00 353 65-707 7111
                                   Email stay@gregans.ie
                                   Website www.gregans.ie

In large grounds on a hill above Galway Bay, this Georgian house, owned and managed by Simon Haden and his wife, Frederieke McMurray, returns to the *Guide* after a time without reports. 'Everything perfect; we were warmly welcomed, luggage carried,' say visitors this year. 'We were upgraded to a large ground-floor suite, with four-poster bed, small sitting room, radio, CD-player, no television (a bonus).' Open turf fires burn in the public rooms, which have paintings, and photographs of local characters. There are books and magazines in the lounge, wellingtons for visitors in the porch. The dining room, redecorated this year, has wide views of the bay and the 'magical' rock landscapes of the Burren. The chef (since February 2008), Mickael Viljanen, serves modern dishes, eg, carpaccio of venison, beetroot caviar, hazelnut vinaigrette; slow-roasted loin of sucking pig, white truffle mousseline. Vegetarians are catered for. 'The excellent wine list has a wide range of prices.' Small children are fed at 7 pm. Live classical harp or piano music accompanies dinner three evenings a week. Breakfast has a large buffet and wide choice of cooked dishes, including fish. Guided walks of the Burren, and day-trips to the Aran Islands can be arranged. (*Mr and Mrs D Ruddle*)

Bedrooms: 21, some on ground floor. *Open*: 13 Feb–29 Nov. *Facilities*: hall, lounge/library, bar, dining room (live music 3 nights a week), 15-acre grounds (ornamental pool, croquet), safe sandy beach 4½ miles, golf, riding, hill walking nearby. *Background music*: none. *Location*: 3½ miles SW of Ballyvaughan. *Smoking*: not allowed. *Children*: no under-6s in dining room at night. *Dogs*: not allowed in house. *Credit cards*: Amex, MasterCard, Visa. *Prices*: b&b €97.50–€225 per person, full alc €67.50, special breaks on website, 1-night bookings sometimes refused bank holiday weekends.

BANGOR Co. Down *See SHORTLIST*   Map 6:B6

If you dislike piped music, why not join Pipedown, the campaign for freedom from piped music? It is at 1 The Row, Berwick St James, Salisbury SP3 4TP. *Tel* 01722-690622, www.pipedown.info.

BELFAST   Map 6:B6

Ash-Rowan
12 Windsor Avenue
Belfast BT9 6EE

Tel 028-9066 1758
Fax 028-9066 3227

Popular with visiting academics and musicians, Evelyn and Sam Hazlett's old house is in a tree-lined avenue near Queen's University. Minimalists might be amazed by the public rooms which are 'happily cluttered in Edwardian style'. 'Like living in an upmarket antiques shop,' was an inspector's comment. The conservatory/sitting room has newspapers and old copies of *Picture Post*. The two large double bedrooms (No. 7 and No. 8) on the top floor are the best, each having a large bed. One has a power shower, the other (the more expensive) has a bath as well as a shower. Smaller singles have comfortable bed, linen sheets and lace-trimmed pillowcases, but one guest wrote: 'The plumbing in the next-door room trumpeted an unbooked alarm call.' The 'excellent' breakfast (ordered the night before) has 'yummy porridge with Drambuie', home-made wheaten bread, and an individual cafetière; the fish dish of the day might be kedgeree. No evening meals, but there are good nearby restaurants. 'I don't think we'll ever retire,' says Mrs Hazlett, 'though we are trying to learn to say "No" more often.' (*LP, and others*)

Bedrooms: 5. *Open*: all year except Christmas. *Facilities*: lounge, breakfast room, conservatory, ⅓-acre garden, unsuitable for &. *Background music*: none. *Location*: 1½ miles SW of centre, car park, buses. *Smoking*: not allowed. *Children*: not under 12. *Dogs*: not allowed. *Credit cards*: MasterCard, Visa (*5% service charge added*). *Prices*: [2008] b&b £48–£66 per person.

Ravenhill House
690 Ravenhill Road
Belfast BT6 0BZ

Tel 028-9020 7444
Fax 028-9028 2590
Email info@ravenhillhouse.com
Website www.ravenhillhouse.com

'Good value for money in a newly thriving city', this detached Victorian house in a leafy suburb is run as a B&B by owners Roger and Olive Nicholson, 'most helpful hosts'. It is convenient for the city, having good bus links on the busy road ('I was not disturbed by traffic'). 'It is a well-run, friendly place,' said an inspector. 'My small single bedroom was clean, well equipped and well lit; comfortable bed, with good pillows and sheets, blankets not a duvet; a clean bathroom with a good shower; just enough storage space.' There's a payphone and fresh coffee on the landing. Breakfast choices are made in the evening (cooked alternatives include an Ulster fry and several vegetarian options). 'Home-made bread, excellent fruit compote, a good buffet selection with fresh fruit.' Maps and other information are provided; many eating places are nearby.

Bedrooms: 5. *Open*: all year except Christmas/New Year, 2 weeks in summer. *Facilities*: sitting room, dining room, unsuitable for &. *Background music*: none. *Location*: 2 miles S of centre. *Smoking*: not allowed. *Children*: all ages welcomed. *Dogs*: not allowed. *Credit cards*: MasterCard, Visa (*3% surcharge*). *Prices*: [2008] b&b £37.50–£55 per person.

See also SHORTLIST

BLARNEY Co. Cork *See SHORTLIST*   Map 6:D5

BUSHMILLS Co. Antrim   Map 6:A6
See SHORTLIST

CAHERLISTRANE Co. Galway   Map 6:C5

Lisdonagh Manor House   *Tel* 00 353 93-31163
Caherlistrane, nr Headford   *Fax* 00 353 93-31528
                                     Email cooke@lisdonagh.com
                                     Website www.lisdonagh.com

In remote countryside north of Galway city, this white Georgian manor house was 'expertly restored' from a run-down state, by John and Finola Cooke. 'No shabby chic here,' said inspectors. Set in a large estate with ancient trees and a lake, it has a fine spiral staircase, and frescoes in the grand oval entrance hall, painted in 1790 by John Ryan, depicting Strength, Chastity, Vanity and Justice. First-floor bedrooms have views of lake or garden, and a period decor. 'Ours, the Yeats suite, had plenty of storage, chairs, dressing table, bright lights, a well-integrated bathroom.' Four rooms are at garden level. A pavilion suite has been created in an adjacent pyramid-shaped building where the landlord's agent once collected rent from tenant farmers: it has high stone arches; bathroom up a spiral staircase. The drawing room has a log fire and comfortable chairs. In the high-ceilinged dining room, with lake views, the South African head chef, Craig Goivea, serves a set dinner at 8 pm (vegetarian option available): portions are generous. Many other staff are South African too. Breakfast has a platter of mixed fruits and berries; 'good croissants, well-presented poached egg'. Children are welcomed. House parties and weddings are catered for.

Bedrooms: 10, 4 at garden level, suite in adjacent pavilion, 2 self-catering apartments in courtyard. *Open*: May–Oct. *Facilities*: drawing room, library with honesty bar, dining room, 200-acre estate (walled garden, kitchen garden, lake, fishing, woodland walks, horses). *Background music*: classical/jazz in public rooms. *Location*: 20 miles N of Galway city, off R333. *Smoking*: not allowed. *Children*: all ages welcomed (under-2s stay free). *Dogs*: not allowed in house. *Credit cards*: MasterCard, Visa. *Prices*: b&b €90–€175 per person, set dinner €49.

CAPPOQUIN Co. Waterford   Map 6:D5

Richmond House
Cappoquin

Tel 00 353 58-54278
Fax 00 353 58-54988
Email info@richmondhouse.net
Website www.richmondhouse.net

'A lovely place, wonderful people, delicious food and wine, extreme comfort.' Praise from a regular *Guide* correspondent for this small hotel/restaurant in a substantial Georgian house in parkland in the Blackwater valley. It is 'brilliantly' run by owners Paul and Claire Deevy; he is the award-winning chef; she the hostess 'who keeps her eye on the ball'. 'Their staff are courteous, friendly; they seem unflappable even when the restaurant is full and functions are being held.' The 'feel of a private country house' is liked. There is antique furniture throughout. An earlier comment: 'Our second-floor room was impressively large, with king-size bed, wardrobe, chest of drawers and other antique furniture; the bathroom was well proportioned and equipped.' Paul Deevy cooks modern dishes, eg, baked mussels with a fresh herb crust; roast loin of wild venison, grilled black pudding. 'There are changes to the menu every day. The long and good wine list is not overpriced.' The traditional breakfast includes freshly squeezed juice and crisp, hot toast. 'The best hotel I've stayed in for a long time. We came away with a happy feeling.' (*Brig. JF Rickett*)

Bedrooms: 9. *Open*: 16 Jan–23 Dec, restaurant closed Sun/Mon in winter. *Facilities*: lounge, restaurant, 12-acre grounds, fishing, golf, pony trekking nearby, unsuitable for &. *Background music*: 'easy listening' in restaurant. *Location*: ½ mile E of Cappoquin on N72. *Smoking*: not allowed. *Children*: all ages welcomed. *Dogs*: not allowed. *Credit cards*: all major cards. *Prices*: [2008] b&b €75–€120 per person, d,b&b €125–€180, set dinner €60. *V*

CARAGH LAKE Co. Kerry   Map 6:D4

Carrig House   *Tel* 00 353 66-976 9100
Caragh Lake   *Fax* 00 353 66-976 9166
Killorglin   *Email* info@carrighouse.com
                              Website www.carrighouse.com

In an 'idyllic location', a lakeside dell facing the MacGillycuddy Reeks, this former hunting lodge is owned and managed by Mary and Frank Slattery. The attractive yellow 1850s building stands in large grounds with camellias and azaleas, 950 species of trees, rare flowers and shrubs; also marked walks, a stream and waterfalls. 'The beautiful view is the equal, on a sunny day, of anything in the Italian lake district,' said an inspector, who was 'greeted warmly' by the 'large, dapper' host. A 'pleasant' ground-floor room, with doors leading to a patio facing the lake, 'had all you could need for a comfortable stay; so did its bathroom'. All bedrooms have been redecorated this year. The Slatterys take dinner orders in the 'cosy, handsome' drawing room with its open fire; a 'tasty appetiser' was enjoyed over drinks. The chef, John Luke, cooks in modern Irish/continental style; his extensive seasonal menu might include tequila and lime-cured salmon with pickled cucumber; medallions of Killorglin beef with roasted celeriac, cumin seeds. A pianist sometimes accompanies the meal; or there might be 'annoying background music', say visitors this year.

Bedrooms: 17, some on ground floor. *Open*: Mar–Nov, lunch not served. *Facilities*: 2 lounges, snug, library, TV room, dining room (occasional pianist), wedding facilities, 4-acre garden on lake (croquet, private jetty, boat, fishing, walks), 10 golf courses locally. *Background music*: classical in lounge and restaurant. *Location*: 22 miles W of Killarney. *Smoking*: allowed in some bedrooms 'on request'. *Children*: not under 8 (except infants under 12 months). *Dogs*: only guide dogs allowed. *Credit cards*: Diners, MasterCard, Visa. *Prices*: [2008] b&b €75–€185 per person, full alc €50. *V*

The *V* sign at the end of an entry indicates a hotel that has agreed to take part in our Voucher scheme (see page 62).

CARRICK-ON-SHANNON   Map 6:B5
Co. Leitrim

Hollywell Country House   *Tel/Fax* 00 353 71-962 1124
Liberty Hill   *Email* hollywell@esatbiz.com
Carrick-on-Shannon

In large gardens running down to the River Shannon, this rambling Georgian house stands on a rise across a bridge, just outside a pretty town famed for its angling. It is 'awash with fascinating antiques, *objets d'art*, and books'. The owners, Tom and Rosaleen Maher, are 'hospitable'; in their absence, their daughter, Claire, 'looked after us very well', said recent visitors who found the 'slightly faded' house 'welcoming and comfortable'. Two bedrooms at the back have views of the river: 'Ours was interestingly furnished, exceptionally large.' One of the front rooms has been redecorated this year. All rooms have tea/coffee-making facilities. Seating in the large drawing room is 'cleverly arranged so that groups of guests do not have to eyeball each other'. 'Breakfasts were spectacular. A tremendous range of well-presented food': fresh orange juice, cereals, fresh fruit, porridge, an Irish Fry or smoked salmon and scrambled eggs. The Mahers' two sons run an 'excellent' restaurant in the town, *The Oarsman*, a short walk away (dinner served Thursday to Saturday). (*A and MM*)

Bedrooms: 4. *Open*: Mar–Nov. *Facilities*: drawing room, dining room, 2½-acre grounds, fishing, unsuitable for &. *Background music*: none. *Location*: 500 yds NW of Carrick-on-Shannon. *Smoking*: not allowed. *Children*: not under 12. *Dogs*: not allowed. *Credit cards*: Amex, MasterCard, Visa. *Prices*: b&b €55–€80 per person, midweek breaks.

CARRIGBYRNE Co. Wexford   Map 6:D6

Cedar Lodge   *Tel* 00 353 51-428386
Carrigbyrne, Newbawn   *Fax* 00 353 51-428222
                                      Email info@cedarlodge.ie
                                      Website www.cedarlodgehotel.ie

'An ideal stopping-off point' for travellers heading south from the Rosslare ferry, Tom and Ailish Martin's low, white, modern hotel is 'well run, with good food and drink', says a long-standing visitor. 'Standards have not dropped in the last 15 years.' *Cedar Lodge* stands in award-winning gardens below the slopes of Carrigbyrne forest ('lovely walks'). 'Beautifully appointed', it has 'a happy, homely atmosphere'; bedrooms are 'comfortable and well equipped' (tea-making equipment, etc). 'They are quiet; you don't hear the traffic from the main road.' Mr Martin is a 'charming and ebullient' host, who 'has an eye for detail'; his staff are 'courteous and well trained'. In the dining room 'of great character', with its exposed brick walls and large copper-canopied log fire, Mrs Martin serves 'excellent' traditional dishes, eg, mussels and garlic; venison with blackberry sauce. The wine list is 'well researched'. (*Brig. JF Rickett, and others*)

Bedrooms: 28, some on ground floor. *Open*: 1 Feb–20 Dec. *Facilities*: ramp, lounge, lounge bar, restaurant, wedding facilities, 1½-acre garden. *Background music*: varied in lounge and restaurant. *Location*: on N25, 14 miles W of Wexford. *Smoking*: not allowed. *Children*: all ages welcomed. *Dogs*: allowed by arrangement, but not in public rooms. *Credit cards*: all major cards. *Prices*: b&b €75–€165 per person, d,b&b €125–€200, set dinner €55.

CASHEL BAY Co. Galway   Map 6:C4

Cashel House   *Tel* 00 353 95-31001
Cashel Bay   *Fax* 00 353 95-31077
                          Email res@cashel-house-hotel.com
                          Website www.cashel-house-hotel.com

❦ *César award in 2008*

Run with a 'personal touch' by the McEvilly family, this 'immaculately preserved slice of Old Ireland' stands amid 'rambling gardens, full of surprises' in a lovely, sheltered bay. Kay McEvilly 'seems never to be off-duty', says a returning visitor. 'If she is not in the dining room, she's gardening.' She 'holds court with style and charm', adds a reporter. An inspector liked 'this warm, lived-in place; I have rarely felt so relaxed in a hotel'. The 19th-century manor house, 'cleverly extended' to side and rear, has an 'appropriate country house decor, antiques in the hall and the welcoming lounge', leather seating in the big bar. Bedrooms vary in size; not all face the sea. 'Our corner room had big bed, neat sitting area, traditional furnishings, heavy drapes, a little faded.' The five-course menus of Arturo Amit and Arturo Tillo have wide choice, including locally caught fish. 'Huge prawns grilled in their shell; pan-fried turbot in a potato crust.' 'Portions just right, though you are invariably asked if you'd like a little more.' Breakfast has a big buffet with porridge, warm croissants, fresh fruits; three types of fish; leaf tea, 'super bread', home-made preserves. 'Wonderful staff.' We were saddened to hear, as we went to press, of the death of Kay McEvilly's husband, Dermot. (*Gill Holden, and others*)

Bedrooms: 32. *Open*: 1 Feb–2 Jan. *Facilities*: ramps, 2 lounges, bar, library, dining room/conservatory, 15-acre grounds (tennis, riding, small private beach). *Background music*: none. *Location*: 42 miles NW of Galway. *Smoking*: not allowed. *Children*: all ages welcomed. *Dogs*: not allowed in house. *Credit cards*: Amex, MasterCard, Visa. *Prices*: [2008] (*12½% service charge added*) b&b €95–€290 per person, set dinner €60, full alc €70, winter breaks, Christmas/New Year packages. *V*

CASTLEBALDWIN Co. Sligo   Map 6:B5

Cromleach Lodge   *Tel* 00 353 71-916 5155
Castlebaldwin, via Boyle   *Fax* 00 353 71-916 5455
                                  Email info@cromleach.com
                                 Website www.cromleach.com

🏆 *César award in 1999*

On a low hillside above Lough Arrow, this purpose-built hotel has long been popular with *Guide* readers for the 'superb service, wonderful food, and luxurious comfort'. A final phase of extensive building work was due to be completed as we went to press, involving 23 additional bedrooms linked to a function suite, taking the total to 68, high by *Guide* standards. The owners, Moira and Christy Tighe, say that the new rooms are in three suites up to 300 yards from the main building, to 'ensure privacy for all our residents; wedding guests can dance the night away while others relax'. Recent visitors welcomed the changes to the public areas: the dining area is now 'a large, light room with panoramic views over the lough'; at the rear is the glass-fronted kitchen. Mrs Tighe's modern cooking 'continues to be full of flavour and light in texture; even our vegetarian was impressed. Service well balanced.' The new bedrooms are contemporary in style; the older rooms, in the main building, are 'spotless, well appointed, with plenty of storage space'; all have 'fantastic views'. Nicholas Ryan is the general manager. Children of all ages are welcomed (babysitting, special menus). More reports, please.

Bedrooms: 68, 3 suitable for ♿. *Open*: all year except 23–25 Dec. *Facilities*: lounge, bar, dining room, spa (sauna, steam room), function rooms, wedding facilities, 30-acre grounds (forest walks, private access to Lough Arrow, fishing, boating, surfing, walking), hill climbing. *Background music*: varied in public rooms. *Location*: 3 miles E of Castlebaldwin. *Smoking*: not allowed. *Children*: all ages welcomed. *Dogs*: not allowed in public rooms. *Credit cards*: Amex, MasterCard, Visa. *Prices*: b&b €75–€249 per person, d,b&b €125–€304, set dinner €65, New Year package. *V*

CASTLEHILL Co. Mayo   Map 6:B4

Enniscoe House   *Tel* 00 353 96-31112
Castlehill, nr Ballina   *Fax* 00 353 96-31773
                                          Email mail@enniscoe.com
                                          Website www.enniscoe.com

Thirteen generations of one family have lived on the large estate on which this 'magnificent' Georgian building stands. Now a small private hotel, it is run by Susan Kellett, and her 'quiet-spoken, humorous' son, Donald John ('everybody calls me DJ'). Inspectors enjoyed their 'glimpse of this well-maintained heritage house': a massive front door opens on to a high-ceilinged hall with family portraits and fishing trophies. A huge elliptical staircase leads to the three best bedrooms, which face the lough (where guests may fish). 'Our spacious room had high canopy bed, dressing table, wardrobe; small bathroom.' Pre-dinner drinks are taken in one of two vast sitting rooms: it has 'cosy corners' and big sofas round an open fire. Dinner is served by DJ in an attractive room with well-spaced wooden tables. His mother cooks in 'good country style'. Two choices (except soup) for each of the five courses: 'earthy lamb casserole; lovely salmon with lemon cream sauce; a big dish of vegetables; splendid desserts'. Breakfast has a silver dish of porridge on the sideboard; a basket of breads and toast; 'super bacon and sausages'. The estate has a heritage centre, a walled garden with a tea room. 'Frodo, the Labrador, sometimes accompanies guests in the lovely walk through woods to the lough.' (*FK, and others*)

Bedrooms: 6, plus self-catering units behind house. *Open*: Apr–Oct, groups only at New Year. *Facilities*: 2 sitting rooms, dining room, 150-acre estate (garden, tea room, farm, heritage centre, conference centre, forge, fishing), unsuitable for &. *Background music*: none. *Location*: On R315, 2 miles S of Crossmolina. *Smoking*: not allowed. *Children*: all ages welcomed. *Dogs*: not allowed in public rooms. *Credit cards*: MasterCard, Visa. *Prices*: b&b €96–€140 per person, d,b&b €145–€188, set dinner €50, New Year package, 10% discount for 3 nights or more, 1-night bookings refused bank holiday Sat. *V*

CASTLELYONS Co. Cork   Map 6:D5

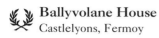

Ballyvolane House
Castlelyons, Fermoy

Tel 00 353 25-36349
Fax 00 353 25-36781
Email info@ballyvolanehouse.ie
Website www.ballyvolanehouse.ie

César award: Irish heritage home of the year

At their family home, the 'generous, hospitable' Justin and Jenny Green give guests 'a taste of country house living in the Irish way: elegant and relaxed'. In north Cork farming country, the 'beautiful, unpretentious' Georgian house stands in 'glorious' grounds with parkland, woodland and formal gardens. 'Justin gave us a friendly, informal greeting,' say inspectors. 'He showed us round before carrying our bags to our room. It had big sash windows overlooking the garden, lovely old furniture, an enormous bed, bottled water, home-made blackcurrant juice; in the large bathroom a claw-footed bath and a stag's head.' Guests help themselves to drinks from an honesty bar before the four-course no-choice dinner ('we'll think of a plan B if you don't like something'), taken at 8 pm around a huge mahogany table with silver candelabras. Teena Mahon or Jenny Green cook 'tasty' country house dishes. 'Asparagus from the walled garden; loin of local bacon (full of flavour), buttered carrots and salad leaves; gooey chocolate pudding with poached pears; fabulous local artisan cheeses.' Breakfast, 'unrushed' and served until noon, has freshly squeezed juice, poached fruits and cereals from the sideboard, 'good cooked dishes'. *Ballyvolane House* has three trout lakes in its grounds, and six miles of fishing on the River Blackwater. Children are warmly welcomed. (*DCA, and others*)

Bedrooms: 6. *Open*: 4 Jan–24 Dec. *Facilities*: hall, drawing room, honesty bar, dining room, 15-acre grounds (garden, croquet, 3 trout lakes), unsuitable for &. *Background music*: none. *Location*: 22 miles NE of Cork. *Smoking*: not allowed. *Children*: all ages welcomed. *Dogs*: not allowed in bedrooms (outhouse provided). *Credit cards*: Amex, MasterCard, Visa. *Prices*: b&b €115–€165 per person, set dinner €60, special breaks, fishing school, monthly supper club.

Make sure the hotel has included VAT in the prices it quotes.

CLIFDEN Co. Galway   Map 6:C4

The Quay House   *Tel* 00 353 95-21369
Beach Road   *Fax* 00 353 95-21608
Clifden   *Email* thequay@iol.ie
                              Website www.thequayhouse.com

🐾 *César award in 2003*

'Wonderful hosts', Paddy and Julia Foyle, run their B&B in the
former harbourmaster's house on the waterfront below this interesting little town on the western Connemara coast. Their 'easy informality' is much admired. 'They were there to greet us each evening
on return from exploring; on our last night we were invited into their
kitchen for drinks and conversation,' said one visitor. 'They make you
feel as if you have known them all their lives. He helped us change a
punctured tyre in the rain.' The house is 'amusingly eccentric'. There
are gilt-framed family portraits, Irish paintings and antiques, and
Napoleonic mementos, and a peat fire at night in the cosy drawing
room. The bedrooms in the main house have garden or bay view;
most are spacious, though ones at the top are small. The newest
section contains studios with a balcony overlooking the water. 'Our
spacious, quiet room had a kitchenette and huge bath.' The Foyles
have a licence, and sell a good selection of wines. The 'wonderful'
breakfast in the plant-filled conservatory has fresh juice, scrambled
eggs and smoked salmon, good coffee. The town has 'great pubs and
shops; we enjoyed our meal at *Foyle's* (yes, a relation)'. (*ES*)

Bedrooms: 14, 2, on ground floor, suitable for &, 7 studios (6 with kitchenette)
in annexe. *Open*: Mid-Mar–end Oct. *Facilities*: 2 sitting rooms, breakfast
conservatory, ½-acre garden, fishing, sailing, golf, riding nearby. *Background
music*: none. *Location*: harbour, 8 mins' walk from centre. *Smoking*: not allowed.
Children: all ages welcomed. *Dogs*: not allowed. *Credit cards*: MasterCard, Visa.
Prices: b&b €70–€120 per person, 1-night bookings refused bank holiday Sat.

CLONES Co. Monaghan   Map 6:B6
See SHORTLIST

The more reports we receive, the more accurate the *Guide*
becomes. Please don't hesitate to write again about an old
favourite, even if it is only to endorse the entry. New reports
help us keep the *Guide* up to date.

CONG Co. Mayo   Map 6:C4

Ballywarren House
Cross, Cong

Tel/Fax 00 353 9495-46989
Email ballywarrenhouse@gmail.com
Website www.ballywarrenhouse.com

'Thoroughly recommended' this year, David and Diane Skelton's creeper-covered replica Georgian home stands in farming country between Lough Corrib and Lough Mask. 'Delightful stay; splendid hosts, very good food.' There are open peat fires, an oak staircase, and books and magazines in the sitting room where tea with home-baked cake is taken. 'Pleasing little touches in our well-equipped and comfortable bedroom.' A room with a four-poster bed had 'good white linen; the huge bath was deep and double-ended, and there was a pile of lovely thick towels'. 'We make all our own bread and rolls from granary to walnut bread,' says Mrs Skelton, who posts her four-course *table d'hôte* menu on a blackboard, discussing likes and dislikes in advance. She cooks French/Irish dishes using local free-range and organic produce ('simple, not *haute cuisine*', she says), perhaps slow-cooked duckling on a bed of greens with mango and Madeira sauce. The wine list is entirely French. The Skeltons sometimes join guests for after-dinner drinks. Breakfast has a 'brilliant buffet spread', a choice of six cooked dishes, home-made bread, jams and marmalades; eggs come from the hens which roam the grounds. Good fishing nearby. (*John Clark, and others*)

Bedrooms: 3. *Open*: all year. *Facilities*: reception hall, 2 sitting rooms, dining room, 1-acre garden in 6-acre grounds (lake, fishing nearby), unsuitable for &. *Background music*: none. *Location*: 2 miles E of Cong. *Smoking*: not allowed. *Children*: not under 14, except babies. *Dogs*: not allowed in house. *Credit cards*: Amex, MasterCard, Visa. *Prices*: b&b €68–€136 per person, set dinner €42, 1-night bookings sometimes refused.

DERRY Co. Londonderry   Map 6:B6
See SHORTLIST

DINGLE Co. Kerry *See SHORTLIST*   Map 6:D4

All our inspections are paid for, and carried out anonymously.

DONEGAL Co. Donegal   Map 6:B5

St Ernan's House
St Ernan's Island
Donegal

Tel 00 353 74-97 21065
Fax 00 353 74-97 22098
Email res@sainternans.com
Website www.sainternans.com

On a tranquil private tidal island reached by a single-track causeway, this 'special' hotel is run by its owner, Brian O'Dowd. The white two-storey Georgian building has 'astonishingly high' ceilings, antique and period furniture and period prints plus the 'appropriate modern luxury of carpets and warm radiators'. One lounge has a grand piano, the other lots of seats and a log fire. Inspectors, for the price of a 'superior' double room, had a suite: 'Large, comfortable bed, good lighting, plenty of storage space, large, bright, warm bathroom; limited water pressure.' Dinner is served only at weekends ('no problem: Donegal town is a short, cheap taxi ride away'). In the 'gorgeous' dining room, whose high windows overlook the causeway, chef Gabrielle Doyle's short traditional menu might include mushrooms in a creamy tarragon sauce; brill with a green herb sauce. 'Perhaps a little bland. Highlight was the mix 'n' match puddings and the cheeses. Starched white tablecloths, waitresses anything but starchy.' Breakfast has freshly squeezed juices, yogurt, fruit, 'excellent smoked salmon and scrambled egg; lovely scones, but white toast and a dull fry-up'. 'The garden leads to wooded grounds with paths laid out on two levels through a profusion of wild garlic to the end of the island.'

Bedrooms: 6. *Open*: May–Sept, dining room open Fri and Sat evenings. *Facilities*: hall, 2 lounges, dining room, 1-acre grounds, unsuitable for &. *Background music*: none. *Location*: On R267, 2 miles S of Donegal town. *Smoking*: not allowed. *Children*: not under 6. *Dogs*: not allowed. *Credit cards*: MasterCard, Visa. *Prices*: [2008] b&b €125–€200 per person, set dinner €50.

See also SHORTLIST

When you make a booking you enter into a contract with a hotel. Most hotels explain their cancellation policies, which vary widely, in a letter of confirmation. You may lose your deposit or be charged at the full rate for the room if you cancel at short notice. A travel insurance policy can provide protection.

DUBLIN   Map 6:C6

Aberdeen Lodge
53–55 Park Avenue,
Ballsbridge, Dublin 4

Tel 00 353 1-283 8155
Fax 00 353 1-283 7877
Email aberdeen@iol.ie
Website www.halpinsprivatehotels.com

Providing 'good accommodation without city-centre prices', Pat
Halpin's 'well-run, comfortable' small hotel is well placed for bus and
rail connections to the centre. Ann Keane is the manager. 'When Mr
Halpin heard we suffered from bad backs and had had a poor bed the
previous night, he gave us a room with his latest, very large bed with
special mattress,' say visitors this year. Earlier guests 'were warmly
welcomed out of pouring rain, with tea and scones. Staff, of varying
nationalities, were charming. Once we had dried out, we were taken
to our room where our bags were already installed; it had goodies in
bathroom and masses of hot water. On paying, we were delighted that
there were no extras.' There is free Wi-Fi Internet access, antiques,
and a garden. Breakfast, in the 'attractive' dining room, has 'a table
with fruit, yogurt, cereals, freshly squeezed orange juice, and a tasty,
cooked selection', eg, scrambled eggs with smoked salmon. Also
'unwelcome piped music'. A limited drawing room/room-service
menu is available; there is good dining at Sandymount village ten
minutes' walk away (*Browne's* and *Mario's* are recommended). The
family owns three other hotels in Dublin, and one in Kilkee, County
Clare. (*Margaret and Patrick Filsell, Guy Dehn, and others*)

Bedrooms: 17. *Open*: all year. *Facilities*: ramps, drawing room, dining room,
½-acre garden, beach nearby. *Background music*: classical. *Location*: S of city,
close to DART station. *Smoking*: not allowed. *Children*: all ages welcomed.
Dogs: not allowed. *Credit cards*: all major cards. *Prices*: b&b €69.50–€170 per
person, set menu €25–€35, full alc €45, Christmas/New Year packages. *V*

The Clarence
6–8 Wellington Quay
Dublin 2

Tel 00 353 1-407 0800
Fax 00 353 1-407 0820
Email reservations@theclarence.ie
Website www.theclarence.ie

'Where old Dublin meets youth culture', this handsome 19th-
century waterfront building stands on the south bank of the River
Liffey in Temple Bar. Oliver Sevestre is its manager. It was restored
by Bono and The Edge, of the rock group U2, and given a 'fresh,
uncluttered decor', with specially commissioned furniture and

original artwork. Bedrooms have Egyptian cotton sheets, huge pillows, good wardrobe space, but some are small. The Penthouse suite has wide views. The wood-panelled *Octagon Bar* is the place to see and be seen in the city (it serves simple meals from 11 am to 5.30 pm), but residents can retreat to the *Study*, a large, 'pleasant' lounge with writing table and leather chairs and sofas. French/Irish cooking is served in the formal *Tea Room Restaurant*, eg, breast of squab pigeon, wild mushroom ravioli, Madeira caviar: an *à la carte* breakfast is also taken here. 'Everything delicious; attentive waiters.' Mathieu Melin is executive chef. Temple Bar is busy with revellers, especially at weekends, so noise can be a problem. The owners hope to carry out a major redevelopment; subject to planning permission, *The Clarence* is set to close for renovation for two years in summer 2009. (*J and MB, and others*)

Bedrooms: 49. *Open*: all year except 24–26 Dec. *Facilities*: lounge, bar, restaurant. *Background music*: in public rooms. *Location*: S bank of Liffey, in Temple Bar, valet parking. *Smoking*: allowed in 5 bedrooms. *Children*: all ages welcomed. *Dogs*: only guide dogs allowed. *Credit cards*: all major cards. *Prices*: [2008] b&b €115–€299.50 per person, d,b&b (min. 2 nights) €144.50–€350, set dinner €39, full alc €85, special packages, New Year package.

See also SHORTLIST

DUNFANAGHY Co. Donegal   Map 6:A5

The Mill   *Tel/Fax* 00 353 74-913 6985
Figart   *Email* themillrestaurant@oceanfree.net
Dunfanaghy   *Website* www.themillrestaurant.com

César award in 2007

The food 'is the main point of visiting' this 'friendly place in a lovely setting', an informal restaurant-with-rooms in a modest, white, late 19th-century former flax mill, outside a small Atlantic coastal village. Susan Alcorn is the 'vivacious hostess' at the former home of her grandfather, Frank Egginton, a watercolour artist whose work is displayed in the public rooms. Her husband, Derek, is the chef whose imaginative seasonal menus have a bias towards fish. Try the 'magnificent' house speciality, upside down fish pie, which might have lobster, crab claws, cockles and salmon in a creamy sauce inside a mashed potato case. Desserts are 'mouth-watering', and service in the two-tier dining room is cheerful. It is often busy; tables need to be booked ahead. One visitor complained of 'raucous pop music'. Drinks and after-dinner coffee are served in a sitting room with open fire or a conservatory which faces a lake. The bedrooms are simple with a mix of furniture, TV on a wall bracket. Breakfast has 'an above-average buffet with treats like rhubarb compote, carrageen milk mousse; lovely home-made breads and preserves; super bacon and sausage'. 'Remarkable value.'

Bedrooms: 6. *Open*: mid-Mar–mid-Dec, weekends only off-season. *Facilities*: sitting room, conservatory, restaurant, 1-acre grounds (lake, beach ½ mile), only restaurant suitable for &. *Background music*: in lounge and restaurant. *Location*: at Figart, ½ mile W of Dunfanaghy. *Smoking*: not allowed. *Children*: all ages welcomed. *Dogs*: not allowed. *Credit cards*: Amex, MasterCard, Visa. *Prices*: [2008] b&b €52.50–€75 per person, set dinner €45.

DUNGARVAN Co. Waterford   Map 6:D5

The Tannery Restaurant & Townhouse   *Tel* 00 353 58-45420
10 Quay Street   *Fax* 00 353 58-45814
Dungarvan   *Email* info@tannery.ie
                                                       Website www.tannery.ie

The Irish celebrity chef Paul Flynn runs his restaurant, *The Tannery*, in a converted leather warehouse in this small seaside town. His wife, Máire, is front-of-house. Diners can stay in 'ultra-modern, well-thought-out' bedrooms in *The Townhouse*, in nearby Church Street. 'My room was compact but comfortable,' said an inspector. 'The bed, probably the biggest I have seen, could have held four people. Louvred window shutters can be set at whatever level you like. Spacious shower room.' In the restaurant on two levels, where Mr Flynn can be seen through glass as he cooks, 'we enjoyed some fine food'. 'Excellent bread' with olives and pesto is followed by dishes like roast rump of lamb with creamed butter beans, spinach, wild garlic and Parmesan; seared scallops with cauliflower cream, French beans, artisan chorizo. 'A jug of iced water was provided; a good wine list.' Breakfast is a 'DIY affair' in the bedroom: yogurt, fruit purée and fresh fruit in a fridge; a bag with bread and pastries is hung on the door last thing at night. 'Very good value, but don't expect a sea view.' Children are welcomed.

Bedrooms: 7. *Open*: all year except 2 weeks end Jan, 1 week Sept, restaurant closed Sun/Mon. *Facilities*: restaurant, private dining room, unsuitable for &. *Background music*: 'appropriate' CDs. *Location*: town centre. *Smoking*: not allowed. *Children*: all ages welcomed. *Dogs*: not allowed. *Credit cards*: all major cards. *Prices*: [2008] b&b €60–€80 per person, set dinner €60, early bird menu €28, full alc €110.

See also SHORTLIST

DUNKINEELY Co. Donegal   Map 6:B5

Castle Murray House   *Tel* 00 353 74-973 7022
St John's Point   *Fax* 00 353 74-973 7330
Dunkineely   *Email* info@castlemurray.com
                              Website www.castlemurray.com

'Good food, nice staff, pretty good value for a fine location.' An inspector's comments on Marguerite Howley's small hotel/ restaurant. It has a splendid view over St John's Point and the ruined castle from which the bay takes its name. Dinner orders are taken in a 'splendid long narrow seating area' facing the sea. Seafood is a speciality on the lengthy menu of chef Remy Dupuy, whose style is modern French. 'Delicious starter of prawn and monkfish baked in garlic butter; generous helpings of good grilled sea bass; excellent lamb and pigeon; jugs of iced water were supplied. The staff, all non-Irish, were attentive.' The only let-down: 'Awful piped music.' But 'the volume was turned down at dinnertime'. The themed bedrooms (African, Oriental, etc) on the first and second floors (no lift) are generally thought 'comfortable', but a family room was 'disappointing (pine-effect dressing table, harsh lighting)'. Breakfast has freshly squeezed orange juice, 'nice muesli, porridge and fresh fruit salad; proper coffee, preserves and butter; a substantial fry'.

Bedrooms: 10. *Open*: all year except Christmas, Jan. *Facilities*: bar, restaurant, civil wedding licence, 2-acre garden, unsuitable for &. *Background music*: jazz. *Location*: 1 mile SW of village. *Smoking*: not allowed. *Children*: all ages welcomed. *Dogs*: not allowed in public rooms. *Credit cards*: MasterCard, Visa. *Prices*: b&b €60–€85 per person, d,b&b €50 added, New Year package.

Most hotels have reduced rates out of season, and offer breaks throughout the year. It is always worth checking for special deals on the hotel's website or by telephone.

ENNISCORTHY Co. Wexford   Map 6:D6

Salville House   *Tel/Fax* 00 353 92-35252
Salville   *Email* info@salvillehouse.com
Enniscorthy   *Website* www.salvillehouse.com

Mature beech trees stand on the lawn of this Victorian country
house on a hilltop overlooking the River Slaney and the Blackstairs
mountains. Gordon Parker, who runs it with his wife, Jane, is 'evi-
dently passionate about food', writes a visitor this year. Regular visitors like the 'home from home' feel and 'ambience of warmth, both
literal and metaphysical'. 'Jack the Dalmatian was pleased to see
us.' Three of the bedrooms (Pink, Yellow, Blue) are in the main
house; most rooms are spacious. 'Pink is well done, though its
bathroom reminds me of my schooldays.' 'Our lovely, bright room
had large bed, good bathroom.' The 'excellent' dinners must be
booked the evening before: likes and dislikes taken into account for
a four-course no-choice menu served at 8 pm and using local meat
and fish and organic ingredients from the garden. 'Fillet of beef a
highlight; puddings irresistible.' Bring your own wine; no corkage
charge. Early suppers are provided for guests attending the Wexford
opera festival. Breakfast has fresh orange juice, fruit compote,
toasted oats and honey; full Irish or smoked haddock with rösti and
poached egg. The grass tennis court in the garden is 'definitely not
Wimbledon standard', write the Parkers. (*Roderic Rennison, Simon
and Pearl Willbourn*)

Bedrooms: 5, 2 in apartment at rear. *Open*: all year except Christmas, dining
room closed Sun. *Facilities*: drawing room, dining room, 5-acre grounds
('rough' tennis, badminton, croquet), golf nearby, beach, bird sanctuary
10 miles, unsuitable for &. *Background music*: none. *Location*: 2 miles S of town.
Smoking: not allowed. *Children*: all ages welcomed. *Dogs*: allowed by arrangement, but not in public rooms, bedrooms. *Credit cards*: none. *Prices*: b&b
€55–€65 per person, set dinner €40, New Year package.

GALWAY Co. Galway *See SHORTLIST* Map 6:C5

We say 'Unsuitable for &' when a hotel tells us that it cannot
accommodate wheelchair-users. We do not have the resources
to inspect such facilities or to assess the even more
complicated matter of facilities for the partially disabled. We
suggest that you discuss such details with the hotel.

GLIN Co. Limerick   Map 6:D4

Glin Castle   *Tel* 00 353 68-34173
Glin   *Fax* 00 353 68-34364
                                          Email knight@iol.ie
                                          Website www.glincastle.com

'Great fun, way over the top', this Georgian Gothic castle, set on the
Shannon estuary, is the country seat of Desmond FitzGerald, the 29th
Knight of Glin. 'An elegant, welcoming place', it is much liked by *Guide*
readers. 'A bit pretentious – staff in livery – but it is lavish and comfortable,' says a visitor this year. Bob Duff, the 'welcoming and entertaining' manager, runs it with 'great attention to detail'. 'More historic
house than hotel', it has secret doorways, Corinthian pillars, an unusual
flying staircase. The drawing room has an Adam-influenced plaster
ceiling; huge windows face the garden. The Knight (his formal title)
sometimes joins visitors for the 'excellent' dinner cooked by Eddie
Baguio and Seamus Hogan. They serve modern dishes, eg, grilled
marinated quail; venison and wild boar ragout with Montbéliard
sausage. Breakfasts are 'excellent'. The bedrooms have four-poster bed,
chaise longue, porcelain plates and Irish prints on walls, river or garden
views. 'Ours had a huge, hard bed, with heavenly linen sheets; enormous bathroom with a bath large enough for a cow.' The background
music, even at breakfast, is not to all tastes. 'Madly expensive, but a
great treat.' (*Jennifer Hicks, David and Gail Crabb, and others*)

Bedrooms: 15. *Open*: 1 Mar–30 Nov. *Facilities*: hall, drawing room, sitting room,
library, dining room, 500-acre estate (5-acre garden, tennis, croquet, tea/craft
shop, parkland, dairy farm, clay-pigeon shooting), on Shannon estuary boating
(fishing), golf nearby, unsuitable for &. *Background music*: classical, dining
room. *Location*: edge of village, 32 miles W of Limerick. *Smoking*: not allowed.
Children: not under 10. *Dogs*: not allowed. *Credit cards*: all major cards. *Prices*:
b&b €155–€310 per person, set dinner €60, off-season rates, house
parties. *V*

GOREY Co. Wexford   Map 6:D6

Marlfield House   *Tel* 00 353 53-942 1124
Courtown Road   *Fax* 00 353 53-942 1572
Gorey   *Email* info@marlfieldhouse.ie
                                          Website www.marlfieldhouse.com

'A lovely place' (a comment in 2008), the former home of the Earls of
Courtown, owned by Ray and Mary Bowe, is run as a luxury hotel

(Relais & Châteaux) by their daughters, Margaret and Laura. 'Antiques and pictures abound', contributing to the 'elegant charms' of the Regency building. It has a grand marble hall, a lounge with open fire, spectacular flower displays. 'After a warm greeting we were shown to a large ground-floor room with a welcoming coal-effect gas fire and French windows opening on to the lovely grounds. Fruit and a bucket of ice were thoughtful extras.' Earlier praise: 'Faultless; wonderful care and attention from the family.' In the 'glorious' dining room (with frescoes and a large domed conservatory), chef Colin Byrne serves classic dishes with modern influence, eg, chicken mousseline sausage with pancetta; hake in a garlic and herb broth. 'A delight, exquisitely presented, a challenge to the appetite. Service impeccable, balancing formality with friendly conversation.' Breakfast has a 'super buffet with fresh fruit salad, compotes, a choice of beautifully cooked dishes, leaf tea'. In the wooded grounds are a lake with ducks, geese and swans, and a wildfowl reserve. Nearby are sandy beaches and golf. (*Paul and Rosalind Bench*)

Bedrooms: 20, 8 on ground floor. *Open*: Mar–Dec. *Facilities*: reception hall, drawing room, library/bar, restaurant with conservatory, function/conference facilities, wedding facilities, 36-acre grounds (gardens, tennis, croquet, wild fowl reserve, lake), sea (sandy beaches, safe bathing 2 miles), fishing, golf, horse riding nearby. *Background music*: classical in restaurant. *Location*: 1 mile E of Gorey. *Smoking*: not allowed. *Children*: no under-10s at dinner. *Dogs*: allowed by arrangement, but not in public rooms. *Credit cards*: all major cards. *Prices*: b&b €127.50–€382.50 per person, set dinner €68, Christmas/New Year packages, 1-night bookings sometimes refused Sat. **V*** (not Sat)

HOLYWOOD Co. Down   Map 6:B6

Rayanne House   *Tel/Fax* 028-9042 5859
60 Demesne Road   *Email* rayannehouse@hotmail.com
Holywood BT18 9EX   *Website* www.rayannehouse.co.uk

'High standards of comfort and food' are found at this Victorian building which is run as a guest house by owners Conor and Bernadette McClelland. In an elevated position above this attractive small town on the Belfast Lough, it has wide landings, sweeping stairs, 'display cabinets, bookshelves and ornamental bits and pieces everywhere; a wonderful Art Deco theme'. The McClellands are continuing with improvements: they tell us that they will be modernising all the bedrooms during 2008 (there already is Wi-Fi Internet access). Many rooms look over the town and across the lough to the Antrim hills. A recently added ground-floor room is equipped for disabled visitors. Conor McClelland, who worked as a chef in New York, has won awards for the breakfast, which must be ordered the evening before. It has an array of interesting dishes, eg, chilled raspberry porridge; warm crêpes with banana and maple syrup. He serves meals by arrangement for a minimum of ten people. More reports, please.

Bedrooms: 11, 1, on ground floor, suitable for &. *Open*: all year, restaurant closed Sun. *Facilities*: 2 lounges, dining room, wedding/conference facilities, 1-acre grounds. *Background music*: classical/jazz in dining room. *Location*: 1 mile from town centre, 6 miles E of Belfast, train to Holywood. *Smoking*: not allowed. *Children*: all ages welcomed. *Dogs*: not allowed. *Credit cards*: MasterCard, Visa. *Prices*: b&b £51–£85 per person, set dinner £45 (*10% service charge added*).

KENMARE Co. Kerry   Map 6:D4

Shelburne Lodge   *Tel* 00 353 64-41013
Cork Road   *Fax* 00 353 64-42135
Kenmare   *Email* shelburnekenmare@eircom.net
                              Website www.shelburnelodge.com

The oldest house in the area, this handsome 18th-century farmhouse, just outside Kenmare, is run as a B&B by owners Tom and Maura Foley. They also own *Packies*, a popular restaurant in town, a 'short, flat walk away'. They are 'fabulous hosts', says a report in 2008, 'friendly, polite, obliging'. Tea and home-baked cake may be served on arrival. The 'elegant, spacious' house is filled with antiques and modern art; there are log fires and comfortable seating in the drawing room and library, striking colour schemes on the landing, and in some of the bedrooms. These are spacious and have polished wooden floor, fresh flowers and water; one has 'stripped pine, a cosy alcove, attractive repro furniture, a small bathroom'; an 'even nicer' room at the front has a large bathroom. 'Ours was spacious and spotless'. Some rooms are in a coach house. In a large and airy yellow room, Tom Foley presides at breakfast ('the best I have had in any hotel') which has freshly squeezed juice, home-made jams and bread, traditional cooked dishes, and fresh fish. In the grounds are a grass tennis court, a small orchard and a pretty herb garden. *Mulcahy's* (see below) is also recommended for an evening meal. (*Rob Lacey*)

Bedrooms: 9, 2 in coach house. *Open*: mid-Mar–early Oct. *Facilities*: drawing room, library, breakfast room, 3-acre garden (tennis), golf adjacent, unsuitable for &. *Background music*: none. *Location*: on R569 to Cork, ½ mile E of centre. *Smoking*: not allowed. *Children*: all ages welcomed. *Dogs*: not allowed. *Credit cards*: Diners, MasterCard, Visa. *Prices*: b&b €65–€120 per person.

Virginia's Guesthouse
36 Henry Street
Kenmare

Tel 00 353 64-41021
Fax 00 353 64-42415
Email virginias@eircom.net
Website www.virginias-kenmare.com

An 'engaging, helpful couple', Neil and Noreen Harrington, run their friendly little guest house above *Mulcahy's*, a popular restaurant in this lively little town between the Beara and Iveragh peninsulas. All the bedrooms have been updated this year and given new bedlinen; none has a bath; there are power showers. The rooms at the front overlook Henry Street with its food shops, pubs and restaurants. There is a library with tea- and coffee-making facilities. The 'very good' breakfast, ordered the evening before (when a time is agreed), has creamy organic porridge, interesting cooked dishes (eg, poached free-range eggs in a herby mushroom nest). All bread, preserves and chutneys are home-made. 'Pleasant accommodation at budget prices.'

Bedrooms: 8. *Open*: all year except 24/25 Dec. *Facilities*: library, breakfast room, unsuitable for &. *Background music*: classical in breakfast room. *Location*: central. *Smoking*: not allowed. *Children*: not under 12. *Dogs*: not allowed. *Credit cards*: MasterCard, Visa. *Prices*: b&b €35–€85 per person, 3-night off-season breaks, New Year package, 1-night bookings refused bank holidays.

See also SHORTLIST

KILCONNELL Co. Galway   Map 6:C5

Ballinderry Park
Kilconnell
nr Ballinasloe

Tel/Fax 00 353 90-968 6796
Email info@ballinderrypark.com
Website www.ballinderrypark.com

'Lovely place, fine food, a very pleasant bedroom,' says a visitor returning in 2008 to this 'beautifully proportioned' Georgian home, 'a fine stopping place for any aficionado of the Irish country house'. The 'charming' owners, George and Susie Gossip, have painstakingly restored the building from ruin, with 'taste and imagination' (he once trained as an architect). 'Beautiful wood panelling' is in many of the rooms. There is an honesty bar in the 'cosy' lounge. 'George buzzes around tending to everyone's whim, dispensing bonhomie.' He is assisted by a 'pleasant young Polish couple'. 'An excellent cook', he lectures on game off-season at the famous cookery school at *Ballymaloe House*, Shanagarry (*qv*). He serves a 'simple, straightforward', set 'but flexible' four-course dinner (tastes are discussed and vegetarians catered for). It is taken communally by candlelight in the 'impressive' blue-walled dining room. 'I was served woodcock, shot on the land by the man himself. Our bedroom was not large, but warm (electric blanket in the bed); a cleverly installed bathroom.' Breakfast has 'good ingredients; freshly squeezed orange juice, wheaten bread (baked by the Polish lady)'. (*Esler Crawford*)

Bedrooms: 4. *Open*: mid-Mar–30 Sept, closed Christmas, groups only at New Year (other times by arrangement). *Facilities*: hall, drawing room, dining room, 40-acre garden, fishing, horse riding nearby, unsuitable for &. *Background music*: none. *Location*: 7 miles W of Ballinasloe. *Smoking*: not allowed. *Children*: all ages welcomed. *Dogs*: 'allowed if well behaved, must sleep in enclosed lobby outside bedroom'. *Credit cards*: MasterCard, Visa. *Prices*: b&b €80–€125 per person, set dinner €55.

KILLARNEY Co. Kerry   Map 6:D4
See SHORTLIST

KILLYBEGS Co. Donegal   Map 6:B5
See SHORTLIST

KILMALLOCK Co. Limerick   Map 6:D5

Flemingstown House   *Tel* 00 353 63-98093
Kilmallock   *Fax* 00 353 63-98546
                                   Email info@flemingstown.com
                                   Website www.flemingstown.com

❧ *César award in 2005*

Endorsed by visitors again this year ('a very enjoyable stay'), this 'flawless' guest house is run by owner Imelda Sheedy-King on a working dairy farm near an important medieval town. She is 'the heart and soul of the place', the 'perfect hostess, attending to every detail'. The 18th-century building, 'comfortable rather than luxurious', has a 'cosy lounge with mostly 19th-century pieces'. The bedrooms are spacious; some have a king-size bed and 'superb' views across fields to the Ballyhoura mountains. 'Our well-lit room had a cheerful air, a crystal chandelier.' A self-catering lodge in the grounds is new this year. Dinner, in a room with big stained-glass windows, is highly recommended, but 'give plenty of notice that you wish to dine, and bring your own wine'. Mrs Sheedy-King's five-course menu features traditional dishes from the farmhouse kitchen; her sister's own Cheddar cheese might be offered. If she is not cooking, there is a 'good restaurant and pub with food' nearby. Breakfast has home-made breads, cheeses, jams and cakes; fresh juices and a range of cooked dishes including pancakes with banana and grapes. Families are accommodated. Visitors can explore the farm and watch the cows being milked. (*GR Smith, PH*)

Bedrooms: 5, 1 self-catering lodge. *Open*: Mar–Oct. *Facilities*: lounge, dining room, 2-acre garden in 100-acre farm (golf, riding, fishing, cycling nearby), unsuitable for &. *Background music*: 'easy listening' in dining room. *Location*: on R512, 2 miles SE of Kilmallock. *Smoking*: not allowed. *Children*: all ages welcomed. *Dogs*: not allowed in house. *Credit cards*: MasterCard, Visa. *Prices*: b&b €60–€70 per person, set dinner €45.

KINSALE Co. Cork *See SHORTLIST*   *Map* 6:D5

LAHINCH Co. Clare *See SHORTLIST*   Map 6:C4

LETTERFRACK Co. Galway   Map 6:C4

Rosleague Manor   *Tel* 00 353 95-41101
Letterfrack   *Fax* 00 353 95-41168
                                        Email info@rosleague.com
                                        Website www.rosleague.com

'We keep going back because we love it,' says a devotee of this Georgian manor house on Connemara's Atlantic coast. It has a lovely setting, looking out across 'exquisite' gardens to sea and mountains. Owned by Edmund Foyle, it is managed by his son, Mark. He 'turns his hand to anything, carrying luggage and making tea on our arrival; carrying out essential repairs, and being regularly on hand to set the tone that makes *Rosleague* so uniquely relaxing'. The elegant lounges have log and turf fires, paintings, antiques and *objets d'art*. 'Our large first-floor room overlooked the bay; it was nicely decorated in blue and yellow; adequate storage space; huge Victorian roll-top bath, but we would have liked bigger towels.' A recently refurbished downstairs suite is 'vast'. Pre-dinner drinks are served in a new hardwood conservatory in an internal courtyard with trees and shrubs. In the 'handsome' dining room (fine furniture and silverware), Pascal Marinot's daily-changing four-course dinners involve 'straightforward, often classic, treatment of top-quality ingredients. Friendly service.' 'Wine list patchy but value for money.' 'Delicious fish options at dinner and breakfast.' The latter, 'always well done', also has freshly squeezed juice, fresh and stewed fruits, crisp toast and grills. (*Ann Walden, and others*)

Bedrooms: 20, 2 on ground floor. *Open*: 15 Mar–15 Nov. *Facilities*: 2 drawing rooms, conservatory/bar, dining room, 30-acre grounds (tennis), unsuitable for &. *Background music*: none. *Location*: 7 miles NE of Clifden. *Smoking*: not allowed. *Children*: all ages welcomed. *Dogs*: only 'well-behaved dogs' allowed in public rooms, with own bedding in bedrooms. *Credit cards*: Amex, MasterCard, Visa. *Prices*: b&b €80–€140 per person, set dinner €48, 1-night bookings refused bank holidays. *V*

LISDOONVARNA Co. Clare   Map 6:C4

Sheedy's   *Tel* 00 353 65-707 4026
Lisdoonvarna   *Fax* 00 353 65-707 4555
                                        Email info@sheedys.com
                                      Website www.sheedys.com

In a spa resort best known for its annual match-making festival in September, this yellow building, in neat grounds, has been owned by John Sheedy's family since the 18th century. He and his wife, Martina, run 'a very friendly but efficient ship', say recent visitors. 'It fully lived up to its outstanding reputation.' Bedrooms, in the main house and a modern extension, are 'well cared for': 'Ours was spacious, cool, decorated in excellent taste.' They have been given a new TV/DVD-player this year ('not that I watch any,' says Mrs Sheedy). She is the 'hands-on, charming' manageress. Her husband is 'an accomplished cook' using fresh local ingredients for his modern dishes, eg, prawn soup with coconut and chilli; roast rack of Burren lamb with pearl barley, smoked bacon. Bar meals might include crab claws in garlic, chilli and ginger butter. Breakfast, served at table, has 'real' juice, home-made preserves, good teas, interesting cooked dishes. Nearby is the Burren, a limestone landscape rich in unusual plant life and historical sites, and the Cliffs of Moher. (*A and MM*)

Bedrooms: 11, some on ground floor, 1 suitable for &. *Open*: 12 Apr–30 Sept, restaurant closed 1 night a week in Mar/Apr ('please phone'). *Facilities*: ramp, sitting room/library, sun lounge, bar, restaurant, 1½-acre garden (rose garden). *Background music*: jazz at dinner. *Location*: 20 miles SW of Galway. *Smoking*: not allowed. *Children*: all ages welcomed. *Dogs*: not allowed. *Credit cards*: MasterCard, Visa. *Prices*: [2008] b&b €70–€120 per person, d,b&b €120–€175, full alc €70, 1-night bookings refused Sept.

LONGFORD Co. Longford   Map 6:C5
See SHORTLIST

MILTOWN MALBAY Co. Clare   Map 6:C4

Admiralty Lodge   *Tel* 00 353 65-708 5007
Spanish Point   *Fax* 00 353 65-708 5030
Miltown Malbay   *Email* info@admiralty.ie
                              Website www.admiralty.ie

In good golfing country on the coast of Clare, this much-extended Georgian country house is run by owner/managers Pat and Aoife O'Malley, 'very much in evidence'. 'More like a fine restaurant-with-rooms than a hotel,' says a visitor this year. 'The food is good, the restaurant well run, and the staff are charming and attentive.' The lounges are decorated in neo-Georgian style, 'a clubby look with leather furniture' is one view; another visitor thought they 'lacked atmosphere'. The bedrooms have flat-screen TV, CD-player and air conditioning. 'Our room was spacious, clean and comfortable; a shame it overlooked the car park.' 'A high standard of housekeeping, with evening turn-down.' The chef, David Godin, serves modern dishes, eg, remoulade of crab with mild curry flavour; rack of lamb with a cannelloni of aubergines. A pianist often plays the baby grand in the dining room: 'We found the meandering playing intrusive; it seemed popular with others.' Breakfast has a 'well-cooked' traditional grill or smoked salmon and scrambled eggs. (*AW, and others*)

Bedrooms: 11. *Open*: Mar–Dec. *Facilities*: ramps, 3 lounges, bar, restaurant (pianist at night), ½-acre grounds (helipad, beach 2 mins' walk), golf, fishing nearby. *Background music*: 'easy listening' morning and evening. *Location*: 2 miles SW of village. *Smoking*: not allowed. *Children*: not under 4. *Dogs*: only guide dogs allowed. *Credit cards*: Amex, MasterCard, Visa. *Prices*: [2008] b&b €75–€160 per person, set dinner €55, Christmas/New Year packages. ***V***

Prices may change – always check them when booking.

MOUNTRATH Co. Laois   Map 6:C5

Roundwood House
Mountrath

Tel 00 353 57-873 2120
Fax 00 353 57-873 2711
Email roundwood@eircom.net
Website www.roundwoodhouse.com

🏆 *César award in 1990*

'The perfect home from home,' writes a visitor who first stayed 20 years ago at this 18th-century Palladian villa below the Slieve Bloom mountains. It is run in relaxed style by Rosemarie and Frank Kennan who have long been restoring the house, which they bought from the Georgian Society. 'They made us as welcome as ever. The decor may be "battered" but it would not be the same if it became smart.' The Kennans, 'gracious and unaffected' hosts, sometimes join guests for drinks after dinner when 'good company and conversation abound'. The two-storey main hall has creaking floorboards, an eclectic collection of books, furniture and ornaments. The first-floor Blue Bedroom, large and high-ceilinged, is 'very comfortable'. Mrs Kennan's cooking is widely praised: her no-choice menus are based on 'what is available in the market, perhaps black olive and mushroom pâté; rack of lamb with fennel, rosemary and aubergine. Children are welcomed (there is a 'wet day' nursery with toys) and encouraged to feed the donkeys, ducks, horses, etc. Around are 'shimmering trees and meadows, bluebells and blackberries'. A coach house, forge and cottage have been turned into self-catering units. (*Roderic Rennison*)

Bedrooms: 10, 4 in garden annexe. *Open*: all year except Christmas. *Facilities*: drawing room, study/library, dining room, playroom, table tennis room, 20-acre grounds (garden, woodland), golf, walking, river fishing nearby, unsuitable for &. *Background music*: none. *Location*: 3 miles N of village. *Smoking*: allowed in 4 bedrooms. *Children*: all ages welcomed. *Dogs*: not allowed. *Credit cards*: all major cards. *Prices*: b&b €90–€120 per person, set dinner €55. ***V***

MULTYFARNHAM Co. Westmeath   Map 6:C5

Mornington House
Multyfarnham

Tel 00 353 44-937 2191
Fax 00 353 44-937 2338
Email stay@mornington.ie
Website www.mornington.ie

'Grand yet homely', this old Anglo-Irish house has been owned by one family since 1858. Its present incumbents, Warwick and Anne

O'Hara ('wonderful, welcoming hosts, great conversationalists'), entertain guests on a house-party basis, with meals served around one large table. Set in grounds with ancient trees, near the fish-filled Lough Derravaragh, it has much original furniture, family portraits, strong colours on walls, oriental rugs. Visitors help themselves to drinks in the 'pleasant, light' drawing room where a turf or log fire burns in cold weather. Mrs O'Hara's country house cooking, using vegetables, fruit and herbs from the walled garden, is much admired. Her four-course, no-choice dinner might include Irish Guinness stew, 'cheesecake sublime, like a soufflé'. Vegetarians are 'particularly welcome', but should give advance notice. Mr O'Hara cooks the 'very good' breakfast: fresh orange juice; 'superb home-made muesli and brown bread; a full Irish Fry'; linen napkins. Bedrooms are 'a bit idiosyncratic'. 'Ours was large, quiet, with plenty of light.' More reports, please.

Bedrooms: 5. *Open*: Apr–Oct. *Facilities*: drawing room, dining room, 50-acre grounds (croquet, bicycle hire), unsuitable for &. *Background music*: none. *Location*: 9 miles NW of Mullingar. *Smoking*: not allowed. *Children*: all ages welcomed. *Dogs*: not allowed in house. *Credit cards*: all major cards. *Prices*: b&b €75–€95 per person, set dinner €45, 3-night breaks.

NEWPORT Co. Mayo   Map 6:B4

Newport House   *Tel* 00 353 98-41222
Newport   *Fax* 00 353 98-41613
Email info@newporthouse.ie
Website www.newporthouse.ie

Overlooking the Newport estuary, in a village on lovely Clew Bay, this creeper-covered Georgian mansion, liked for its 'unstuffy' atmosphere, is run by owners Thelma and Kieran Thompson, and manageress Catherine Flynn, 'like a large private home'. Many of the 'helpful' staff are local. 'It feels as every country house hotel should but rarely does,' said one visitor. It has a grand staircase with lantern and dome, fires in the public rooms with their fine plasterwork and chandeliers. Bedrooms have been redecorated and bathrooms updated this year. Some rooms are in self-contained units, good for a family. The rooms in two houses in a courtyard are popular with dog-owners and 'angling guests': *Newport House* is famous for its fishing, holding rights on the Newport River ('all our fish are wild'). A ghillie is generally available; a picnic lunch can be provided; there is a drying room, and freezing or smoking of the catch can be arranged. In the formal dining room, chef

John Gavin's admired cooking is country house/French in style, eg, avocado terrine wrapped in wild smoked salmon; chicken breast stuffed with Cashel blue cheese. Breakfast, with freshly squeezed orange juice, 'was our best in Ireland: incomparable eggs Benedict'. 'Not cheap, but good value.' More reports, please.

Bedrooms: 16, 5 in courtyard, 4 on ground floor. *Open*: 19 Mar–14 Oct. *Facilities*: sitting room, bar, dining room, restaurant, billiard/TV room, table-tennis room, 15-acre grounds (walled garden, private fishing on Newport River), golf, riding, walking, shooting nearby, unsuitable for &. *Background music*: none. *Location*: in village 7 miles N of Westport. *Smoking*: allowed in 8 bedrooms. *Children*: all ages welcomed. *Dogs*: allowed in courtyard bedrooms, not in public rooms. *Credit cards*: Amex, MasterCard, Visa. *Prices*: b&b €114–€190 per person, d,b&b €176–€252, set dinner €65.

OUGHTERARD Co. Galway   Map 6:C4

Currarevagh House   *Tel* 00 353 91-552312
Oughterard   *Fax* 00 353 91-552731
                            Email rooms@currarevagh.com
                             Website www.currarevagh.com

❧ *César award in 1992*

The younger generation is to the fore at the Hodgson family's early Victorian manor house, which has had an entry in every edition of the *Guide*. It stands in parkland and woodland on Lough Corrib. June Hodgson has stepped out of the kitchen to run front-of-house with her son, Henry. His wife, Lucy, now does the cooking, serving a four-course no-choice menu based on fresh local produce, perhaps crab cake; confit of duck with caramelised beet; chocolate parfait; Irish cheeses. Visitors love the family's 'easy Irish charm', the 'unchanging quality of welcome, atmosphere and food'. There is much to do in the area: 'The Hodgsons will helpfully advise, but you are welcome to spend the day in the house and gardens.' The lavish afternoon tea served in the drawing room (4.30–6 pm) includes sandwiches, scones and cakes. An 'Edwardian' buffet breakfast has kedgeree, black pudding. Bedrooms have fresh flowers and hot-water bottles, many have 'wonderful views'. Beds are 'properly made with blanket and sheets'. *Currarevagh* has its own boats and ghillies for fishing on Lough Corrib and there can be 'a fairly heavy fishing ethos', but 'non-fishing is entirely acceptable'. (*Richard Parish*)

Bedrooms: 15, 2 on ground floor in mews. *Open*: 10 Apr–17 Oct. *Facilities*: sitting room/hall, drawing room, library/bar with TV, dining room, 180-acre grounds (lake, fishing, ghillies available, boating, swimming, tennis, croquet), golf, riding nearby, unsuitable for &. *Background music*: none. *Location*: 4 miles NW of Oughterard. *Smoking*: allowed in 2 bedrooms. *Children*: all ages welcomed. *Dogs*: allowed in all areas. *Credit cards*: MasterCard, Visa. *Prices*: b&b €75–€110 per person, d,b&b €120–€150, set dinner €49. *V*

RAMELTON Co. Donegal   Map 6:B5

Frewin   *Tel/Fax* 00 353 74-915 1246
Rectory Road   *Email* flaxmill@indigo.ie
Ramelton   *Website* www.frewinhouse.com

'Small and stylish, peaceful and relaxing', this Victorian ex-rectory stands in mature wooded grounds outside a Georgian port at the mouth of the River Lennon. The owners, Regina and Thomas Coyle, have renovated it 'with flair', retaining period features, an elegant staircase, stained glass and a library. The hostess is 'warmly welcoming', says a visitor this year. 'My double room had an extra single bed and an adjoining large, comfortable sitting room, good lighting, bottled water, fruit, tea, coffee and biscuits; the only minus was the small shower room.' In the 'atmospheric' dining room, Mrs Coyle serves a 'simple but satisfactory' dinner by arrangement; and 'a couple of reasonable restaurants are within walking distance'. Breakfast, taken communally around a large table, was 'good, with home-made muesli, fresh fruit salad, warm home-baked bread and freshly squeezed juice; proper butter and three types of jam; good tea and coffee; also a full fry-up'. There is a small antique shop in the courtyard. (*Esler Crawford, and others*)

Bedrooms: 4. *Open*: 2 Jan–20 Dec. *Facilities*: sitting room, library, dining room, 2-acre garden, golf, horse riding, beaches nearby, unsuitable for &. *Background music*: none. *Location*: outskirts of town. *Smoking*: not allowed. *Children*: 'not suitable for young children.' *Dogs*: not allowed. *Credit cards*: MasterCard, Visa. *Prices*: b&b €65–€100 per person, set dinner €50.

RATHMULLAN Co. Donegal   Map 6:B5

Rathmullan House   *Tel* 00 353 74-915 8188
Rathmullan   *Fax* 00 353 74-915 8200
                                    Email info@rathmullanhouse.com
                                    Website www.rathmullanhouse.com

The Wheeler family, 'very much in evidence', are owner/managers of this informal country hotel, a handsome, white 1800s mansion a few minutes' walk from the village. It stands in 'superb', well-maintained gardens which lead to a long sandy beach on Lough Swilly (an inlet of the sea). 'Everything runs smoothly in a supremely comfortable and cosseting environment,' says a fan. A wheelchair-user, who felt well cared for, adds: 'Sound management, well-trained staff, attentive not over-attentive.' Spacious public rooms have high ceilings, chandeliers, antiques, marble fireplaces, log fires, oil paintings, lots of books. Bedrooms vary: older ones are 'classic country house', some with a lough view, some with a balcony. Ten newer rooms are spacious and have restful colours and under-floor heating. Families are welcomed, and one bedroom has a 'room' for a dog. A Derry man, Ian Orr, came this year from the renowned *River Café* in London to become head chef in *The Weeping Elm*, a conservatory-style dining room with a tented ceiling. He serves modern dishes, eg, ravioli of roast butternut squash and mascarpone cheese; wild sea bass with sautéed spinach, leeks and fennel. We would welcome reports on his cooking. There's a large indoor swimming pool and a resident masseuse. (*JMR Irving, EC*)

Bedrooms: 32, some on ground floor, 2 suitable for ♿. *Open*: all year except 20–27 Dec. *Facilities*: ramps, 4 lounges, library, TV room, cellar bar/bistro, restaurant, 50-ft indoor swimming pool (steam room), small conference centre, 10-acre grounds (tennis, croquet), direct access to sandy beach (safe bathing), boating, golf, riding, hill walking nearby. *Background music*: none. *Location*: ½ mile N of village. *Smoking*: allowed in some bedrooms by prior request. *Children*: all ages welcomed. *Dogs*: allowed in 1 dog-friendly bedroom, but not in public rooms. *Credit cards*: Amex, MasterCard, Visa. *Prices*: b&b €110–€165 per person, set dinner €60, full alc €85, special breaks. ***V***

See also SHORTLIST

RECESS Co. Galway   Map 6:C4

Lough Inagh Lodge   NEW   *Tel* 00 353 95-34706
Recess   *Fax* 00 353 95-34708
                                       Email inagh@iol.ie
                          Website www.loughinaghlodgehotel.ie

On the shores of a freshwater lough beneath the Twelve Bens mountain range in western Connemara, Máire O'Connor's former fishing lodge is liked for its informality ('like a family home', says one of several nominators). An American visitor was greeted by the manager, Dominic O'Móráin, with 'a warm handshake and smiles, just in time for tea and scones before a peat fire'. There are open fires in the drawing room, the library and the oak-panelled bar, which has a separate entrance and tiled floor for fisherfolk. Each of the spacious bedrooms has a separate dressing room. 'Our room had views over lough and mountains; its recently renovated bathroom had fluffy robes and towels and luscious soaps and oils.' In the restaurant, Julie Whorley's cooking is admired (seafood and game a speciality). 'The smoked salmon and local beef were very good; home-made bread at all meals. I enjoyed an avocado and crab salad at lunch.' Pets are welcomed. Many outdoor activities are nearby. (*MG Norkett, Edward J Walshe, Victoria Mishcon*)

Bedrooms: 13, 4 on ground floor. *Open*: Mar–mid-Dec. *Facilities*: bar, drawing room, library, dining room, small conference facilities, 12-acre grounds, fishing, shooting, golf nearby. *Background music*: none. *Location*: on R344, 4 miles N of Recess. *Smoking*: allowed in 1 bedroom. *Children*: all ages welcomed. *Dogs*: allowed. *Credit cards*: all major cards. *Prices*: b&b €105–€159 per person, d,b&b €150–€200, full alc €65, special breaks.

RIVERSTOWN Co. Sligo   Map 6:B5

Coopershill   *Tel* 00 353 71-916 5108
Riverstown   *Fax* 00 353 71-916 5466
                                    Email ohara@coopershill.com
                                    Website www.coopershill.com

✿ *César award in 1987*

'In pristine condition, unlike some of its Irish peers', this magnificent Palladian mansion stands on a large estate on the River Arrow (fishing is available), with extensive woodland, a large farm, deer, sheep and peacocks. It has been owned by the O'Hara family since it was built in 1774. Simon O'Hara has taken over management from his parents, Brian and Lindy, though his mother still does the cooking 'assisted by an able kitchen staff'. She and her three dogs 'warmly welcomed' recent visitors with afternoon tea. The public rooms have original 18th-century furniture, family portraits, etc; stags' heads and hunting trophies hang on walls. Bedrooms retain their original dimensions; many have a four-poster bed, some have a freestanding Victorian bath. One room has its bathroom down the corridor (bathrobes and slippers provided). Dinner, a leisurely candlelit affair starting some time around 8.30 pm, is taken at separate tables in the elegant dining room with family silver and glass. Traditional dishes include fillet of

Donegal brill with a mustard and tarragon sauce; loin of Riverstown lamb with redcurrants. The 'fine breakfast' has fresh orange juice, leaf tea with a strainer, 'superior porridge'. Children are welcomed. (*F and RB*)

Bedrooms: 8. *Open*: Apr–Oct, off-season house parties by arrangement. *Facilities*: 2 halls, drawing room, TV room, dining room, snooker room, 500-acre estate (garden, tennis, croquet, woods, farmland, river with trout fishing), unsuitable for &. *Background music*: none. *Location*: 11 miles SE of Sligo. *Smoking*: not allowed. *Children*: all ages welcomed. *Dogs*: not allowed in house (accommodation in stables). *Credit cards*: all major cards. *Prices*: b&b €109–€171 per person, d,b&b €166–€228, set dinner €59, discounts for 3 or more nights.

ROSSLARE Co. Wexford   Map 6:D6

Churchtown House	*Tel* 00 353 53-913 2555
Tagoat	*Fax* 00 353 53-913 2577
Rosslare	*Email* info@churchtownhouse.com
	Website www.churchtownhouse.com

The extensive grounds, 'cultivated and wilderness', and the interior space are distinctive features of this white Georgian house, say visitors this year. The 'delightful' owners, Austin and Patricia Cody, are 'open and approachable' and welcome children with kindness. Fine original Irish paintings hang on the walls and there are 'tasteful modern *objets d'art*' in rooms and passages. 'Our bedroom, on the ground floor, had a big comfortable bed, fierce shower, ample storage, good lighting.' 'We liked the pre-dinner gathering where we met other guests.' The four-course no-choice dinner ('good food at fair prices') is served at separate tables. 'Wholesome dishes', with ingredients sourced where possible from Wexford, include carrot and ginger soup; roast fillet of pork with rosemary and plum sauce. There is a short wine list, including some half bottles. An early supper is served for guests attending the Wexford opera festival. Breakfast has 'good yogurt, prunes, various egg dishes, and bacon'; it can be provided for visitors catching an early ferry from Rosslare. (*S and PW, M and PF*)

Bedrooms: 12, 5 on ground floor. *Open*: mid-Mar–31 Oct, dinner served Tues–Sat, supper on Sun and Mon. *Facilities*: 2 lounges, 2 dining rooms, private dining room, 8-acre grounds (golf, fishing, riding), beaches nearby, unsuitable for &. *Background music*: none. *Location*: on R736, 2½ miles S of Rosslare. *Smoking*: not allowed. *Children*: all ages welcomed. *Dogs*: not allowed in house. *Credit cards*: MasterCard, Visa. *Prices*: b&b €65–€110 per person, set dinner €42.50, 2/3-day breaks.

SCHULL Co. Cork   Map 6:D4

Rock Cottage
Barnatonicane
Schull

Tel/Fax 00 353 28-35538
Email rockcottage@eircom.net
Website www.rockcottage.ie

♥ *César award in 2004*

'We wished we had stayed longer,' says a visitor this year to Barbara Klötzer's elegant slate-sided Georgian hunting lodge in large grounds among grassy hillocks, one of which has 'stunning' views of Dunmanus Bay. 'She sees that you are thoroughly welcome and well looked after. This is a much-loved house with a warm atmosphere. After walking and exploring, we would come back to crash out and read, or snooze in the garden.' The 'sunny and uncluttered' building has fine furnishings, flowers, and an eclectic collection of paintings, prints and ornaments. Two bedrooms are 'spacious and airy, with a sitting area'. 'Ours was comfortable, decorated in Tyrolean style. Ms Klötzer is an accomplished cook; breakfasts and dinners were all fabulous and imaginatively put together.' Her three-course menu, based on fresh local produce (lamb, fish and shellfish), has no choice. 'Let me know your preferences, otherwise it is a surprise,' she says. Breakfast includes 'freshly squeezed orange and lemon juice, home-baked bread, lavish fruit platter with Greek yogurt, blissfully soft scrambled eggs', or a continental version with cold meats and local cheeses. Hens, dogs and cats roam the working farm next door. (*Jennifer Hicks*)

Bedrooms: 3, also 1 self-catering cottage. *Open*: all year (advance notice essential for Sun night). *Facilities*: lounge, dining room, 17-acre grounds, unsuitable for &. *Background music*: when guests want it. *Location*: 8 miles NW of Schull. *Smoking*: not allowed. *Children*: not under 10. *Dogs*: only disability dogs allowed. *Credit cards*: MasterCard, Visa. *Prices*: b&b €65–€95 per person, set dinner €45, 1-night bookings refused in winter.

SHANAGARRY Co. Cork   Map 6:D5

Ballymaloe House
Shanagarry

Tel 00 353 21-465 2531
Fax 00 353 21-465 2021
Email res@ballymaloe.ie
Website www.ballymaloe.ie

♥ *César award in 1984*

The veteran Myrtle Allen ('what a star') still presides at her family's renowned hotel/restaurant in this ivy-clad Georgian house. Filled with original paintings and books, and with the 'atmosphere of a cultured private home', it stands in large grounds on a farm which supplies the kitchen. Daughter-in-law Hazel is manager; another daughter-in-law, Darina, the food writer, runs the nearby cookery school, with its famous *potager*. At the heart of the enterprise is the 'fantastic, faultless food'. Jason Fahey, head chef, serves country house cooking in a series of small dining rooms: perhaps spring mimosa salad; wild garlic and watercress tart; glazed Gubbeen ham with Irish Mist sauce. 'No piped music, just the sound of people talking and laughing.' Mrs Allen might be seen carving at the 'magnificent' Sunday lunch buffet. Bedrooms in the main house are largest; some open on to the garden. Some rooms are in a Norman keep. Some rooms may be a bit cramped. Breakfast includes fresh juices, porridge, 'very good marmalade and kippers'. (*MH, and others*)

Bedrooms: 34, 9 in adjacent building, 4 on ground floor, 5 self-catering apartments. *Open*: all year except 24–26 Dec, 2 weeks mid-Jan. *Facilities*: drawing room (live traditional music on Sat), 2 small sitting rooms, conservatory, 7 dining rooms, conference facilities, 40-acre grounds (farm, gardens, tennis, swimming pool, 10 by 4 metres, heated in summer, 6-hole golf course, croquet, children's play area, craft shop), cookery school nearby, sea 3 miles (sand and rock beaches). *Background music*: none. *Location*: on L35 Ballycotton road, 20 miles E of Cork. *Smoking*: not allowed. *Children*: all ages welcomed. *Dogs*: not allowed. *Credit cards*: all major cards. *Prices*: b&b €110–€195 per person, d,b&b €174–€255, set dinner €70, special breaks, New Year package.

STRAFFAN Co. Kildare   Map 6:C6

Barberstown Castle   NEW   *Tel* 00 353 1-628 8157
Straffan   *Fax* 00 353 1-627 7027
                          Email info@barberstowncastle.ie
                          Website www.barberstowncastle.ie

In a village 30 minutes' drive from Dublin, this large hotel, furnished with antiques, is purpose-built around a 13th-century castle linked to an Elizabethan house and a refurbished Victorian extension. Richard Millea is the manager. 'We were looked after very well by friendly staff of various nationalities,' writes a correspondent, reintroducing it to the *Guide*. 'Our surprisingly large bedroom was nicely decorated and well equipped.' 'Efficient turn-down service during dinner.' There are log fires in the public areas. In the restaurant in the castle keep, head chef Bertrand Malabat serves French/Irish dishes 'of gourmet standard', eg, lobster, scallop and basil sausage; roast Irish beef fillet, swede and potato purée, caramelised endive. Lighter meals and afternoon tea are available in the *Tea Room* (open 10 am until 7 pm), which has a terrace facing the attractive landscaped gardens. Many activities are available in the large grounds (see below). 'A limited amount of noise from the nearby road, but not enough to disturb unduly.' Free Wi-Fi is available. (*Sir John Hall*)

Bedrooms: 59, 21 on ground floor, 3 suitable for &. *Open*: all year, except 24–26 Dec, Jan, 1 week at Easter. *Facilities*: ramps, lift, bar, 2 lounges, restaurant, tea room, terrace, banqueting/conference/wedding facilities, business centre, 20-acre grounds (walking, archery, clay-pigeon shooting), fishing, golf, horse riding nearby. *Background music*: in lounges and restaurant. *Location*: village 12 miles W of Dublin. *Smoking*: not allowed. *Children*: all ages welcomed. *Dogs*: not allowed. *Credit cards*: Amex, MasterCard, Visa. *Prices*: b&b €120–€210 per person, tasting menu €75–€80, full alc €85, special breaks.

STRANGFORD Co. Down   Map 6:B6
See SHORTLIST

THURLES Co. Tipperary   Map 6:C5

Inch House   *Tel* 00 353 504-51348
Inch, Thurles   *Fax* 00 353 504-51754
      Email mairin@inchhouse.ie
      Website www.inchhouse.ie

The feel of 'old-style living' is liked by visitors to this Georgian mansion reached up a long drive on a working farm in peaceful Tipperary countryside ('lovely views'). John and Nora Egan, who restored the house from a derelict state, run it with their children as a 'country house and restaurant'. 'Like staying with a family,' was a recent comment. Daughter Mairin runs the front-of-house 'with efficiency'. 'She welcomed us and invited us to relax in the drawing room while a tray of tea was brought with delicious home-made profiteroles.' The 'magnificent' public rooms are mostly decorated in Adam style, though the drawing room has William Morris decor, 'country house furniture', and a huge stained-glass window. The dining room, elegant in red and green, is popular with locals; the chef, Michael Galvin, serves 'European dishes with an Irish influence', eg, goat's cheese ciabatta; sea bass with nibbed almonds and a fennel cream sauce. The large bedrooms have 'quirky charm'. Breakfast has fruit, yogurt, home-made jams and soda bread. More reports, please.

Bedrooms: 5. *Open*: all year except Christmas/New Year/Easter, restaurant closed Sun and Mon nights. *Facilities*: ramp, drawing room, bar, restaurant, chapel, conference/function facilities, 2-acre garden on 250-acre farm (golf, riding, fishing nearby), unsuitable for &. *Background music*: Irish. *Location*: on R498, 4 miles W of Thurles. *Smoking*: not allowed. *Children*: no under-10s in restaurant. *Dogs*: only guide dogs allowed. *Credit cards*: MasterCard, Visa. *Prices*: b&b €70–€80 per person, set dinner €55.60.

WATERFORD Co. Waterford   Map 6:D5

Foxmount Country House
Passage East Road
Waterford

Tel 00 353 51-874308
Fax 00 353 51-854906
Email info@foxmountcountryhouse.com
Website www.foxmountcountryhouse.com

'A most relaxed place', David and Margaret Kent's creeper-covered 17th-century house is on a working farm ('though you would hardly know it'). Mrs Kent, 'friendly without being imposing', cooks an award-winning breakfast, with home-made scones, preserves and bread, porridge with cream and honey, a cheese plate, and 'scrambled eggs as good as it gets'. She will recommend Waterford restaurants for dinner. Guests can take tea in front of the log fire, and bring their own pre-dinner drinks. The bedrooms face the grounds or the herb garden. 'Ours was clean and homely, with fruit, pretty view, lovely towels in the huge bathroom.' There is a hard tennis court in the garden, and ten golf courses within five to 40 minutes' drive. More reports, please.

Bedrooms: 4. *Open*: Mar–Oct. *Facilities*: sitting room, dining room, 3-acre grounds (tennis). *Background music*: none. *Location*: 2 miles W of Waterford. *Smoking*: not allowed. *Children*: all ages welcomed. *Dogs*: not allowed. *Credit cards*: none. *Prices*: b&b €55–€65 per person.

See also SHORTLIST

SHORTLIST

This Shortlist is designed mainly to fill gaps in our maps. Because our selection of hotels for main entries in the *Guide* is based on quality and character rather than on location, we have a limited choice in some towns and cities (or in some cases no hotels at all). We have looked for hotels, inns, guest houses and B&Bs which we believe provide reasonable accommodation in these areas. Some are more business-oriented than the places that we include in the main section. We also feature establishments that may qualify for a full entry in later editions of the *Guide*. They include new nominations that we have not yet checked, recent openings on which as yet we have no reports, and hotels which have had a full entry in the past but have no recent reports, or mixed reviews. We welcome readers' comments on all the hotels on the Shortlist. Those places which do not also have a full entry in the *Guide* are indicated on the map by a triangle.

LONDON   Map 2:D4

Apex City of London, 1 Seething Lane, EC3N 4AX. *Tel* 0845-365 0000, www.apexhotel.co.uk. In side street near Tower of London, hi-tech, large, contemporary hotel (stainless steel, marble, grainy wood). Managed by Yousif Al-Wagga. Panoramic views. *Addendum* restaurant and gastro bar; background music; business facilities; gym; sauna. Garden. Wi-Fi; free local telephone calls. 130 bedrooms. B&B (continental) from £52 per person. (Underground: Tower Hill)

base2stay, 25 Courtfield Gardens, SW5 0PG. *Tel* 0845-262 8000, www.base2stay.com. In pillared, white stucco town house, managed by Mr Khalil. Smart, modern rooms. No frills; kitchenettes and state-of-the-art equipment. Reception, lobby (background music). 67 bedrooms (some on ground floor, some with bunk beds): £93–£197. Breakfast 'box' £3.95. (Underground: Earls Court, Gloucester Road)

B+B Belgravia, 64–66 Ebury Street, SW1W 9QD. *Tel* 020-7259 8570, www.bb-belgravia.com. Elegant contemporary interior in town house owned by Penny Brown. Lounge with fire, open-plan kitchen/breakfast room; complimentary tea/coffee. Free Wi-Fi and bicycles. No background music. Small garden. 17 bedrooms (2 family; 1 suitable for &). B&B £57.50–£99 per person. (Underground: Victoria)

The Berkeley, Wilton Place, SW1X 7RL. *Tel* 020-7235 6000, www. the-savoy-group.com. Large, luxury designer hotel overlooking Hyde Park, managed by Klaus Kabelitz. 'Phenomenally well-trained staff make it a personal, comforting place for a relaxing stay.' *The Blue Bar*, *Pétrus* restaurant, *Boxwood* café, *The Caramel Room* (afternoon tea); health club and spa; swimming pool (spectacular views over Knightsbridge); meeting rooms/private dining room. 214 bedrooms: single from £249, double from £139.50. Breakfast £26. (Underground: Hyde Park Corner, Knightsbridge)

The Bingham, 61–63 Petersham Road, Richmond, TW10 6UT. *Tel* 020-8940 0902, www.thebingham.co.uk. Ruth and Samantha Trinder's riverside hotel in 2 Georgian town houses. Contemporary decor; 'sophisticated atmosphere'. Cocktail bar ('a delightful space in which to relax'), restaurant (large windows; river views), terrace (alfresco dining). Background music; occasional live music. Landscaped gardens. Wedding/function facilities. Children welcomed. 15 bedrooms. B&B £60–£137.50 per person; D,B&B £92–£169.50. (Underground: Richmond, 10 mins' walk)

Church Street Hotel, 29–33 Camberwell Church Street, SE5 8TR. *Tel* 020-7703 5984, www.churchstreethotel.com. In gritty Camberwell, Spanish/Greek brothers José and Mel Raido's 'amazing', idiosyncratic

B&B. Staid grey outside, a riot of Hispanic colour, patterned Mexican tiles and religious paraphernalia within. 'Fantastic artwork; familial but luxurious atmosphere.' Honesty bar in lounge. Organic breakfast. No background music. Wi-Fi. 30 bedrooms (some shared bathrooms). 'Good value.' B&B £45–£100 per person. (Underground: Oval)

City Inn Westminster, 30 John Islip Street, SW1P 4DD. *Tel* 020-7630 1000, www.cityinn.com. Large, contemporary hotel (City Inn group) by Tate Britain, managed by Simon Morpuss. Lounge (ruby-red decor; background music); modern art; *City* café; gym. Wi-Fi. 460 bedrooms: £199–£299. Breakfast £13–£17. Weekend breaks. (Underground: Pimlico)

County Hall Premier Travel Inn, Belvedere Road, SE1 7PB. *Tel* 0870-238 3300, www.premiertravelinn.com. 'Basic, but has all you need; helpful staff.' Well-located, budget hotel in old County Hall building by London Eye, across river from Houses of Parliament. Managed by Nuno Sacramento. Lift, lobby, bar, restaurant; background music. 314 uniform bedrooms: £104–£117. Breakfast £7.50. (Underground: Waterloo)

Covent Garden Hotel, 10 Monmouth Street, WC2H 9HB. *Tel* 020-7806 1000, www.coventgardenhotel.co.uk. Theatrical splendour (Royal Opera House nearby) at this Firmdale hotel (Tim and Kit Kemp), managed by Helle Jensen. Drawing room, library, bar, *Brasserie Max*; meeting rooms; screening room; gym; beauty treatments. No background music. 58 bedrooms: £235–£1,150. Breakfast £19.50. (Underground: Covent Garden)

Dorset Square Hotel, 39 Dorset Square, NW1 6QN. *Tel* 020-7723 7874, www.dorsetsquare.co.uk. Regency residence facing garden square, site of Thomas Lord's first cricket ground. Owned by Luxury Hotel Partners, managed by François Touzin. Grand country house interior. Dorset country produce in *The Potting Shed* restaurant. Lounge, bar. Live jazz on Fri nights. 37 bedrooms: £175–£260. Breakfast £13.50–£15.75. (Underground: Marylebone)

The Draycott, 26 Cadogan Gardens, SW3 2RP. *Tel* 020-7730 6466, www.draycotthotel.com. Between Knightsbridge and Chelsea, 3 Edwardian buildings with period interior to match. Owned by Adrian Gardiner, managed by John Hanna. 2 drawing rooms, breakfast room. No background music. Afternoon tea at 4 pm. champagne at 6, hot chocolate drink at bedtime. Garden. Children welcomed. 35 bedrooms: (*excluding VAT*) £140–£770. Breakfast £16.50–£21.50. (Underground: Sloane Square)

Dukes Hotel, 35 St James's Place, SW1A 1NY. *Tel* 020-7491 4840, www.dukeshotel.com. In quiet courtyard: discreet Mayfair hotel, part of Gordon Campbell Gray's group (see also *One Aldwych*, main entry).

Michael Voight is manager. Traditional English style plus latest technology (Wi-Fi, etc). Drawing room, bar, restaurant, 24-hour room service; health club; courtyard garden. No background music. 90 bedrooms: £155–£775. Breakfast £17–£22. (Underground: Green Park) **Haymarket Hotel**, 1 Suffolk Place, SW1Y 4BP. *Tel* 020-7470 4000, www.haymarkethotel.com. Part of Firmdale group, managed by Marianne Clave. Vivid contemporary interior, in 3 John Nash-designed buildings near Theatre Royal. Lift, drawing room, library, bar, *Brumus* restaurant; background music. Indoor swimming pool, gym. 50 bedrooms: £250–£2,250. Breakfast £18.50. (Underground: Green Park, Piccadilly)

High Road House, 162 Chiswick High Road, W4Y 1PR. *Tel* 020-8742 1717, www.highroadhouse.co.uk. Private members' club and (Soho House group) hotel in Chiswick, managed by Kelly Taylor. Retro-modern style. Bar, brasserie; games room (red leather sofas, pool table, football table, board games; 'Playground' has plasma screens, DVDs, Wi-Fi); background music. 14 (small, white wood-panelled) bedrooms: £140–£160. English breakfast £9. (Underground: Turnham Green)

The Hoxton, 81 Great Eastern Street, EC2A 3HU. *Tel* 020-7750 1000, www.hoxtonhotels.com. Buzzy hotel owned by Sinclair Beecham (co-founder of Pret A Manger), managed by David Taylor. Radical preferential early booking system (£1 room sale), inexpensive phone calls, free Wi-Fi. Lift. Huge lobby, sitting area, bar, brasserie *Hoxton Grille*; background music; business facilities; shop. Courtyard. Children welcomed. 205 bedrooms. B&B (Pret Lite breakfast) £29.50–£99.50 per person. Full breakfast £8.50. (Underground: Old Street)

Kensington House, 15–16 Prince of Wales Terrace, W8 5PQ. *Tel* 020-7937 2345, www.kenhouse.com. Quietly situated near Kensington Gardens: 19th-century stucco-fronted town house, managed by Antonio Sola. Contemporary interior. Informal dining in *Tiger Bar*; 24-hour room service. No background music. 41 (mainly small) bedrooms. B&B (continental) £70–£150 per person. (Underground: High St Kensington) **Knightsbridge Hotel**, 10 Beaufort Gardens, SW3 1PT. *Tel* 020-7584 6300, www.knightsbridgehotel.com. Filled with quirky artwork, and with contemporary decor, in peaceful tree-lined cul-de-sac near shops. Managed by Anna Jackson for Firmdale group. Lounge, library, bar. No background music. Room service. 44 bedrooms: £170–£595. Breakfast £16.50. (Underground: Knightsbridge)

Knightsbridge Green Hotel, 159 Knightsbridge, SW1X 7PD. *Tel* 020-7584 6274, www.thekghotel.co.uk. Under new ownership, refurbished in uncluttered contemporary style, now managed by Ardal

O'Hanlon: B&B near South Kensington museums and Knightsbridge shops. Reception (background music), lift, lounge; business centre, Wi-Fi. 28 bedrooms (some suitable for ♿): £150–£250. Room-service breakfast £5.50–£12. (Underground: Knightsbridge)

Lord Milner, 111 Ebury Street, SW1 9QU. *Tel* 020-7881 9880, www.lordmilner.com. Owned by Anton and Amber Engelbrecht: small town house hotel, convenient for Victoria rail and coach stations. Lift, reception (seating round fireplace). Background music ('soft hits'). Wi-Fi. 11 bedrooms: £115–£255. Breakfast £11.50. (Underground: Victoria).

Malmaison, Charterhouse Square, EC1M 6AH. *Tel* 020-7012 3700, www.malmaison.com. Former nurses' hostel, in quiet Clerkenwell square, managed by Anthony Thwaites. Informal style; funky decor. Bedrooms in lilac, dove and earth tones. Cosy corners with plump silk and velvet cushions in opened-up original vaults for dining. Bar, brasserie; background music; gym. Dogs welcome (£10 charge). 97 bedrooms: £155–£555. Breakfast £16.95. (Underground: Farringdon, Barbican)

Mandeville Hotel, Mandeville Place, W1U 2BE. *Tel* 020-7935 5599, www.mandeville.co.uk. Large, style-conscious hotel in Marylebone (Summit Hotels & Resorts), managed by Alexander Watenphul. Bold colours, mirrors, abstract art; green policy. *de Vigne* bar, *de Ville* organic restaurant; function facilities. Background music. 142 bedrooms (6 suitable for ♿): £255–£800. Breakfast £16.50–£21.50. (Underground: Bond Street)

The Mayflower, 26–28 Trebovir Road, SW5 9NJ. *Tel* 020-7370 0991, www.mayflowerhotel.co.uk. Owned by Mayflower group, town house hotel decorated in 'funky' Anglo-Indian style: oak-panelled Reception, marble floors; hand-carved wooden beds, oriental antiques, plush fabrics, bright colours. Lounge/juice bar, attractive breakfast room. Tropical garden. 48 bedrooms (some are small; all have Wi-Fi). No background music. B&B (continental buffet): £85–£155 per person. (Underground: Earl's Court)

Miller's Residence, 111A Westbourne Grove, W2 4UW. *Tel* 020-7243 1024, www.millershotel.com. A treasure trove of antiques and curios: 3-storey guest house owned by Martin Miller (of *Miller's Antiques* guides), managed by his daughter, Cara. Large candlelit drawing room/breakfast room/bar (complimentary drinks; classical background music; guests may bring their own food and drink). 8 bedrooms, named after British poets. Children welcomed. B&B (continental, *excluding VAT*) £82.50–£115 per person. (Underground: Notting Hill Gate, Bayswater, Queensway)

Montagu Place, 2 Montagu Place, W1N 2ER. *Tel* 020-7467 2777, www.montagu-place.co.uk. Intimate hotel in 2 Grade II listed Georgian town houses. Managed by Victor Phillips. Modern brown/beige interior retaining some original features (fireplaces, wood panelling). Lounge, bar, breakfast room. No background music. Wi-Fi. 16 bedrooms: (*excluding VAT*) £169–£235. Breakfast £4.95–£13.95. (Underground: Marylebone, Baker Street)

Number Sixteen, 16 Sumner Place, SW7 3EG. *Tel* 020-7589 5232, www.numbersixteenhotel.co.uk. 'Great location with a neighbourhood feel.' Peacefully located, white stucco mid-Victorian terraced building (Firmdale group), managed by Alison Huxley. Decorated with flair. Lift, drawing room, library, conservatory. No background music. Court-yard garden with fountain. 42 bedrooms: £120–£270. Breakfast £16.50. (Underground: South Kensington)

Portobello Gold, 95–97 Portobello Road, W11 2QB. *Tel* 020-7460 4910, www.portobellogold.com. Michael Bell's quirky restaurant-with-rooms on street famed for Saturday market. Lots of stairs. Live music on Sun. Bar, conservatory restaurant with sliding roof (lively atmosphere); Internet café; function facilities. 8 bedrooms: with continental breakfast £70–£170. (Underground: Notting Hill Gate)

Royal Park Hotel, 3 Westbourne Terrace, W2 3UL. *Tel* 020-7479 6600, www.theroyalpark.com. Elegant conversion of 3 listed Georgian town houses, managed by Gareth Rowlands. Victorian and Georgian antiques; plain-painted walls in Regency colours. Four-poster and half-tester beds. Drawing room. Background music. Small room-service menu. 48 bed-rooms (*excluding VAT*): £150–£230. (Underground: Paddington)

San Domenico House, 29–31 Draycott Place, SW1X 0HJ. *Tel* 020-7581 5757, www.sandomenicohouse.com. Extravagantly decorated, ornately furnished boutique hotel in red brick Chelsea house, owned by Marisa Melpignano and staffed by Italians. Lobby, lounge, dining room, exten-sive room service; fitness/massage rooms; roof terrace. No background music. 16 bedrooms: (*excluding VAT*) £210–£360. Breakfast £12–£18. (Underground: Sloane Square)

Sanctuary House, 33 Tothill Street, SW1H 9LA. *Tel* 020-7799 4044, www.fullershotels.com. Near Houses of Parliament, good-value B&B (Fuller's Hotels) with refurbished rooms above traditional ale and pie house (where breakfast is served). Managed by Sol Yepes. 'Staff terrific, friendly, thoughtful. We loved the real feather quilts.' 34 bedrooms: £120–£205. Breakfast £6.50–£10.95. (Underground: St James's Park)

Searcy's Roof Garden Rooms, 30 Pavilion Road, SW1X 0HJ. *Tel* 020-7584 4921, www.30pavilionroad.co.uk. In small Knightsbridge street: quaint, friendly B&B in Georgian town house, managed by Dimitrios Neofitidis. No public rooms. Large roof garden. Function facilities. Free Wi-Fi. 10 bedrooms. B&B (continental) £55–£120 per person. (Underground: Sloane Square)

Shaftesbury Hotel, 65–73 Shaftesbury Avenue, W1D 6EX. *Tel* 020-7871 6000, www.shaftesburyhotellondon.co.uk. In theatreland, Best Western hotel managed by Sheetal Sohri. Ultra-modern, well-equipped interior. Lift. 24-hour room service. Lounge, *Premier* bar, restaurants (*RV* Indian restaurant); background music; fitness room; conference facilities. Wi-Fi. 67 bedrooms (some small; some suitable for &): £115–£279. (Underground: Piccadilly Circus, Leicester Square)

The Soho Hotel, 4 Richmond Mews, off Dean Street, W1D 3DH. *Tel* 020-7559 3000, www.sohohotel.com. Stylish (granite, oak, glass bathrooms) luxury hotel (Firmdale group), managed by Carrie Wicks. Lift, drawing room, library, *Refuel* bar/restaurant; background music; 4 private dining rooms; 2 screening rooms. 85 bedrooms (some suitable for &): £280–£2,750. Breakfast £18.50. (Underground: Leicester Square)

The Stafford, 16–18 St James's Place, SW1A 1NJ. *Tel* 020-7493 0111, www.thestaffordhotel.co.uk. In quiet backwater off St James's Street, large luxury hotel (Shire Hotels Limited), managed by Stuart Procter. 'Excellent staff. Good breakfast.' Lounge, American bar (food served), restaurant; lift. Courtyard. No background music. Children welcomed. Access to nearby fitness studio. Parking (charge). 105 bedrooms (11 in Carriage House; 26 in mews; 1 suitable for &): (*excluding VAT*) £270–£1,200. Breakfast £23.50. (Underground: Green Park)

Threadneedles, 5 Threadneedle Street, EC2R 8AY. *Tel* 020-7657 8080, www.theetoncollection.com. Opulent conversion of 1856 banking hall near Bank of England. Part of Eton Collection, managed by Julian Payne. Original stained-glass dome towers over reception lounge (background music). Bar, *Bonds* restaurant (closed weekends); 3 meeting rooms; conference facilities. 69 bedrooms (some suitable for &): £125–£525. Breakfast £19. (Underground: Bank)

Tophams, 24–32 Ebury Street, SW1W 0LU. *Tel* 020-7730 3813, www.zolahotels.com. Reopened summer 2008 after £4 million reburbishment (now part of Zola Hotels); Paul Fizia, formerly of *Knightsbridge Green Hotel* (*qv*), is manager. Luxury B&B hotel in handsome stucco-fronted house. 2 lounges, bar, breakfast room; lift; small business centre. No background music. 48 bedrooms. B&B £98.50–£180 per person. (Underground: Victoria)

The Victoria, 10 West Temple Sheen, SW14 7RT. *Tel* 020-8876 4238, www.thevictoria.net. Unpretentious gastropub in London suburbs, refurbished by new owners Paul Merrett and Greg Bellamy. Restaurant, conservatory. Background music. Wi-Fi. Garden (children's play area).

Some noise from Heathrow flight path. Parking. 7 small bedrooms (in rear annexe). B&B (continental) £42.50–£75 per person. (Near Richmond. Train: Mortlake, 5 mins' walk)

ENGLAND

BATH Somerset   Map 2:D1
Aquae Sulis, 174–176 Newbridge Road, BA1 3LE. *Tel* 01225-420061. Short bus trip from abbey (or 30-min riverside stroll); Park & Ride close by. Peaceful hotel run by owners David and Jane Carnegie in Edwardian house, traditionally furnished. 2 lounges (1 computer room); background music. Wi-Fi. Patio garden. Parking. 14 bedrooms (some family). B&B £32.50–£99 per person.

The Ayrlington, 24–25 Pulteney Road, BA2 4EZ. *Tel* 01225-425495, www.ayrlington.com. Simon and Mee-Ling Roper's elegant listed Victorian house with oriental touches, near centre. Bar, breakfast room; background music. Wi-Fi. Award-winning walled garden; views over city. Parking. Spa breaks. 14 bedrooms. B&B £50–£92.50 per person.

Dorian House, 1 Upper Oldfield Park, BA2 3JX. *Tel* 01225-426336, www.dorianhouse.co.uk. 10 mins' downhill walk to centre, B&B in characterful Victorian stone house, owned by cellist Tim Hugh and wife, Kathryn. Lounge (open fire), breakfast room/music library; classical background music. Wi-Fi. Garden. Parking. 11 bedrooms (named after musicians; some have four-poster). B&B £39.50–£95 per person.

Dukes Hotel, Great Pulteney Road, BA2 4DN. *Tel* 01225-787960, www.dukesbath.co.uk. Owned by Alan Brookes and Michael Bokenham, managed by Tina Paradise: elegant Grade 1 Palladian-style town house (lots of stairs), with contemporary comforts. Lounge, bar, *Cavendish* restaurant (modern menus; background music). Patio garden. 17 bedrooms (1 on ground floor). B&B £65.50–£125 per person; D,B&B £65.50–£125.

Harington's Hotel, 8–10 Queen Street, BA1 1HE. *Tel* 01225-461728, www.haringtonshotel.co.uk. 'Great position' in quiet cobbled street near abbey: hotel formed from group of 17th-century houses, owned by Melissa and Peter O'Sullivan. Bar/café, restaurant; background music. Patio. Children welcomed. Reserved parking nearby. 13 bedrooms, 3 self-catering apartments. B&B £49–£148 per person.

The Kennard, 11 Henrietta Street, BA2 6LL. *Tel* 01225-310472, www.kennard.co.uk. Georgian town house just over Pulteney Bridge, run by owners Giovanni and Mary Baiano. 'Location perfect for walking everywhere.' 2 sitting areas, breakfast room. No background music. Garden. 12 bedrooms (2 singles share a bathroom). B&B £49–£70 per person.

Paradise House, 86–88 Holloway, BA2 4PX. *Tel* 01225-317723, www.paradise-house.co.uk. Fine city views from Annie and David Lanz's listed Georgian house with Victorian extension, in quiet cul-de-sac, 7 mins' walk (down steep hill, longer coming back) from centre. Drawing room, breakfast room. Classical background music all day. Wi-Fi. 11 bedrooms (4 on ground floor, 2 in annexe in ½-acre landscaped garden). B&B £37.50–£95 per person.

BATHFORD Somerset   Map 2:D1

Eagle House, Church Street, BA1 7RS. *Tel* 01225-859946, www. eaglehouse.co.uk. In peaceful surroundings, 3 miles outside Bath, elegant B&B in listed Georgian mansion, home of John and Rosamund Napier. Drawing room, breakfast room. No background music. 2-acre grounds: croquet lawn, grass tennis court, tree house, sand pit. Wi-Fi. Children, and dogs (by arrangement) welcomed (resident dog and cat). 8 bedrooms (2 in garden cottage). B&B (continental) £29–£104 per person. Cooked breakfast £4.80.

BELFORD Northumberland   Map 4:A3

Waren House, Waren Mill, NE70 7EE. *Tel* 01668-214581, www. warenhousehotel.co.uk. Above natural bird sanctuary of Budle Bay, Georgian house in wooded grounds. 'Enthusiastically decorated' by owners Anita and Peter Laverick: crammed with antique dolls, soft toys, old paintings. Drawing room, library, dining room (good cooking by chef Steven Owens). No background music. 6-acre garden. 13 bedrooms (1 suitable for &). B&B £56.50–£143 per person; D,B&B £84–£140.

BERWICK-UPON-TWEED NorthumberlandMap 4:A3

Marshall Meadows, TD15 1UT. *Tel* 01289-331133, www. marshallmeadows.co.uk. England's most northerly hotel, managed for Classic Lodges by Mr Catterell. 400 yds from Scottish border, off A1, 2 miles N of centre. Georgian building in 15-acre landscaped gardens and woodland. Lounge, bar, 2-tiered restaurant with oak-panelled gallery; soft background music; terrace; conference/function facilities. Parking. 19 bedrooms (farmland or garden views). B&B £62.50–£85 per person.

BEVERLEY East Yorkshire   Map 4:D5

Tickton Grange, Main Street, Tickton, HU17 9SH. *Tel* 01964-543666, www.ticktongrange.co.uk. Whymant family's Georgian house in 4-acre rose garden, 3 miles NE of Beverley, off A1035 (Hull and York within easy reach). *Champagne* restaurant; background music. Wi-Fi. Function/

civil wedding facilities. Children welcomed. Parking. 20 bedrooms (some on ground floor). B&B £52.50–£92.50 per person; D,B&B £82.50–£122.50.

BIRMINGHAM West Midlands   Map 2:B2

Hotel du Vin Birmingham, 25 Church Street, B3 2NR. *Tel* 0121-200 0600, www.hotelduvin.com. Ornate red brick Victorian building imaginatively converted from disused eye hospital (*trompe l'oeil* stonework, sweeping staircase, granite pillars). Managed by Mark Davies. 2 bars, bistro (background music); billiard room; lift; spa; courtyard. 66 contemporary bedrooms (5 suitable for &). Around central courtyard. Room £150–£425. Breakfast £9.95–£13.50.

BLACKBURN Lancashire   Map 4:D3

The Millstone at Mellor, Church Lane, Mellor, BB2 7JR. *Tel* 01254-813333, www.millstonehotel.co.uk. 3 miles NW of Blackburn, in attractive village in Ribble valley: stone-built former coaching inn retaining quaint style. Owned by Shire Hotels, run by chef/*patron* Anson Bolton. Residents' lounge (log fire), bar, *Millers* restaurant ('excellent food'; emphasis on Lancashire produce); no background music. Parking. 23 'above-average' bedrooms (6 in courtyard; 1 suitable for &). B&B £49.50–£109 per person; D,B&B £65.50–£131.

BLACKPOOL Lancashire   Map 4:D2

Number One St Lukes, 1 St Lukes Road, South Shore, FY4 2EL. *Tel* 01253-343901, www.numberoneblackpool.com. Stylish B&B in handsome period house on regenerated South Shore. Modern bathrooms; state-of-the-art gadgetry. No background music. Large garden. Ample parking. 3 bedrooms. B&B from £60 per person. Proprietors Mark and Claire Smith also own *Number One South Beach* on promenade (14 bedrooms, bar, restaurant).

Raffles Hotel & Tea Room, 73–77 Hornby Road, FY1 4QJ. *Tel* 01253-294713, www.raffleshotelblackpool.co.uk. Within walking distance of the sights: small, flower-fronted, bay-windowed hotel, run by owners Ian Balmforth (chef) and Graham Poole. Lounge, bar, traditional English tea room (closed mid-week in winter); classical background music. Parking. 17 bedrooms plus 3 apartment suites. B&B from £32 per person.

BONCHURCH Isle of Wight   Map 2:E2

Winterbourne Country House, Bonchurch Village Road, PO38 1RQ. *Tel* 01983-852535, www.winterbournehouse.co.uk. In tranquil sea-facing gardens 2 miles E of town: B&B run by owner Michael Sharrock in house where Dickens wrote *David Copperfield*. 2 lounges, breakfast room, snug; classical background music; terrace. Garden: swimming pool, stream, private path to small beach. 7 bedrooms. B&B £55–£95 per person.

BOSCASTLE Cornwall   Map 1:C3
Trerosewill Farmhouse, Paradise, PL35 0BL. *Tel* 01840-250545, www.trerosewill.co.uk. Coastline views from Steve and Cheryl Nicholls's B&B on 40-acre farmland (with badger sett); member of Green Tourism Business Scheme. Local produce at breakfast. 2 lounges (1 in annexe), conservatory dining room; video library. No background music. 1-acre garden; summer house; hot tub. 8 bedrooms. B&B £33.50–£45 per person.

BOURNEMOUTH Dorset   Map 2:E2
Urban Beach, 23 Argyll Road, BH5 1EB. *Tel* 01202-301509, www.urbanbeachhotel.co.uk. 5 mins' walk from Boscombe beach, contemporary style in Victorian building run by 'laid-back' owners Mark and Fiona Cribb with manager James Fowler. Bar, bistro (local produce, home-made bread); background music. Wi-Fi. Complimentary use of local gym. 12 bedrooms. B&B £47.50–£85 per person.

BOWNESS-ON-WINDERMERE   Map 4: inset C2
Lindeth Howe, Lindeth Drive, Longtail Hill, LA23 3JF. *Tel* 015394-45759, www.lindeth-howe.co.uk. Overlooking lake, Stephen Broughton's imposing country house owned by Potter family 1902–1913 (Beatrix wrote tales of Timmy Tiptoes and Pigland Bland here). Traditional interior. Lounge, library, bar, restaurant (classical background music); sun terrace; leisure centre (swimming pool, sauna, fitness room). 6-acre garden. 36 bedrooms. B&B £65–£125 per person. Dinner £38.

BRIGHTON East Sussex   Map 2:E4
Fivehotel, 5 New Steine, BN2 1PB. *Tel* 01273-686547, www.fivehotel.com. Near The Lanes, Caroline and Simon Heath's contemporary B&B in period town house in Kemp Town Regency square. 2 public rooms. No background music. Organic breakfasts; free Wi-Fi; sea views. 10 bedrooms. B&B £35–£75 per person.
Grey's, 11 Charlotte Street, BN2 1AG. *Tel* 01273-603197, www.greyshotel.co.uk. A stone's throw from beach, 5 mins' stroll in to centre, contemporary B&B with muted decor in Kemp Town Georgian house, run by owner Terry Sessions. Breakfast room. No background music. 9 bedrooms. B&B £45–£69 per person.

Hotel Una, 55–56 Regency Square, BN1 2FF. *Tel* 01273-820464, www.hotel-una.co.uk. Owned by Zoran Mericevic and Jelena Popic, unpretentious balance of old with new (stripped wood, dark leather furniture, lots of art) in Regency building with views of West Pier. 'Clubby' bar (background music), breakfast room, beauty salon, conference facilities. Lift. 20 bedrooms (named after rivers; sauna, whirlpool in 2 suites). B&B £55–£125 per person.

BRISTOL   Map 1:B6

Avon Gorge Hotel, Sion Hill, BS8 4LD. *Tel* 0117-973 8955, www.theavongorge.com. In Clifton village, with panoramic views of the gorge and Brunel's Suspension Bridge. Managed by Mark Passmore. 'Superb position.' Lounge/*White Lion* bar; *Bridge* café; terrace; wedding/function facilities, background music. Wi-Fi. Children welcomed. Facilities for &/deaf visitors. 'Breakfast was excellent; staff efficient and friendly.' Complimentary daily passes to Clifton College Fitness Centre nearby. Limited parking. 76 bedrooms. £57.50–£105 per person.

The Berkeley Square Hotel, 15 Berkeley Square, Clifton, BS8 1HB. *Tel* 0117-925 4000, www.cliftonhotels.com. On Georgian square, close to zoo. Part of small Clifton Hotels group, managed by William Palmer. Lounge (light, airy; dashing decor; artwork), *The Square* cocktail bar; *Lower Deck* for light meals; dining room; lift; background music. Parking. 43 bedrooms (Wi-Fi, DVD/CD-player, etc): £57.50–£129 per person. Breakfast £9–£12.

Hotel du Vin Bristol, The Sugar House, Narrow Lewins Mead, BS1 2NU. *Tel* 0117-925 5577, www.hotelduvin.com. 'Wonderful eclectic', imaginatively converted Grade II listed old warehouses (part of MWB group) in centre, managed by Steve Lewis. Library, bar (background music), bistro; billiard room. Lift. Small courtyard. Secure (limited) parking. 40 'well-equipped' bedrooms: £145–£215. Breakfast £9.95–£13.50.

BROCKENHURST Hampshire   Map 2:E2

Thatched Cottage, 16 Brookley Road, SO42 7RR. *Tel* 01590-623090, www.thatched-cottage.co.uk. In New Forest national park, restaurant-with-rooms ('refined cuisine') in 400-year-old timber-framed thatched cottage run by Matysik family. 'Indulgent' afternoon teas. Lounge, dining room. Garden. 5 bedrooms. B&B £40–£90 per person. Dinner £15–£60.

BUDE Cornwall   Map 1:C3

Bangors Organic, Poundstock, EX23 0DP. *Tel* 01288-361297, www.bangorsorganic.co.uk. On unspoiled north Cornish coast 5 miles

S of town: Gill and Neil Faiers's organically run, carbon-neutral 'B&B &
Restaurant': home-grown produce; solar-heated water, green electricity,
wood fires. Background music 'when requested'. No smoking in
grounds. Widemouth Bay beach nearby. 5-acre garden and farmland.
4 contemporary bedrooms (2 suites in coach house; 1 suitable for &).
B&B £50–£70 per person. Dinner £30.

BUDLEIGH SALTERTON Devon   Map 1:D5
Downderry House, 10 Exmouth Road, EX9 6AQ. *Tel* 01395-442663,
www.downderryhouse.co.uk. Don and Amanda Clarke's 'benchmark
luxury' B&B in 'tastefully decorated' 1920s detached house on outskirts
of seaside resort. Drawing room, dining room. No background music.
Room-service supper tray menu and full wine list available. Wi-Fi. 1-
acre garden: terrace; croquet. 5 bedrooms. B&B: £39.50–£89 per person.

BUNGAY Suffolk   Map 2:B6
Earsham Park Farm, Old Railway Road, Earsham, NR35 2AQ. *Tel*
01986-892180, www.earsham-parkfarm.co.uk. 'Top-notch' Victorian
farmhouse on 600-acre working farm (arable crops, free-range pig herd),
sweeping views over Waveney valley. Informally run by Bobbie and
Simon Watchorn. 'Fabulous breakfasts.' 3 miles NW of town, up ½-mile
drive off A143. Lounge, dining room; background music. Garden. 3
bedrooms. B&B £35–£48 per person.

BURY ST EDMUNDS Suffolk   Map 2:B5
Ounce House, Northgate Street, IP33 1HP. *Tel* 01284-761779,
www.ouncehouse.co.uk. Simon and Jenny Pott's Victorian merchant's
house on fine residential street. Family feel: chintzy drawing room with
photographs and knick-knacks. Breakfast and 3-course dinner (by
arrangement) served communally. Drawing room, snug/bar/library,
dining room. No background music. Children welcomed. 3 bedrooms
(quietest 2 face ½-acre walled garden). B&B £45–£85 per person.
Ravenwood Hall, Rougham, IP30 9JA. *Tel* 01359-270345, www.
ravenwoodhall.co.uk. Off A14 (some traffic noise), 3 miles SE of Bury.
Historic home (Tudor origins; inglenook fireplaces) of Craig Jarvis, in
7-acre grounds (garden, croquet, heated swimming pool, woodland).
Yvonne Howland manages. Child-friendly, pet-friendly. Ramps, lounge,
bar (informal meals); 'easy-listening'/classical background music; restaurant, garden dining room; Edwardian pavilion for conferences/weddings.
14 bedrooms (7 in mews, some on ground floor). B&B £60–£130 per
person. Dinner £30.

BUXTON Derbyshire   Map 3:A6

Grendon, Bishops Lane, SK17 6UN. *Tel* 01298-78831, www. grendonguesthouse.co.uk. ½ mile NE of centre, Hilary and Colin Parker's welcoming, spacious guest house, on quiet country lane leading to Goyt Valley hills. Lounge, breakfast room; terrace. No background music. 1-acre garden overlooking golf course. Parking. 5 bedrooms. B&B £32–£45 per person.

CAMBER East Sussex   Map 2:E5

The Place, Camber Sands, New Lydd Road, nr Rye, TN31 7RB. *Tel* 01797-225057, www.theplacecambersands.co.uk. 'Excellent situation', across road from famous sandy beach 3 miles SE of Rye. Red-roofed, white, single-storey building, now owned by WAW Leisure Ltd, managed by Matt Collins. Light interior; brasserie (seasonal produce; soft background jazz); conference facilities. Terrace. Children welcomed. 18 bedrooms (all on ground floor). B&B £45–£82.50 per person.

CAMBRIDGE Cambridgeshire   Map 2:B4

Hotel Felix, Whitehouse Lane, Huntingdon Road, CB3 0LX. *Tel* 01223-277977, www.hotelfelix.co.uk. Contemporary style inside extended late Victorian, yellow brick mansion, on edge of city: business people's hotel, managed by Shara Ross. Small lounge, bar, *Graffiti* restaurant (modern Mediterranean cooking; background music); function facilities. 4-acre garden, terrace. Parking. 52 bedrooms (4 suitable for &). B&B (continental) £90–£145 per person. Cooked breakfast £7.50. Dinner from £28.

Hotel du Vin Cambridge, Trumpington Street, CB2 1QA. *Tel* 01223-227330, www.hotelduvin.com. Managed by Denis Frucot: modern conversion of 5 old town houses. Interesting architectural features (exposed brickwork, reconditioned fireplaces, vaulted cellar); 'rambling feel'. Library, bar, bistro (open-style kitchen); terrace. No background music. Wi-Fi. 41 bedrooms with trademark modern bathroom (monsoon shower, etc): £135–£325. Breakfast £9.95–£13.50.

CANTERBURY Kent   Map 2:D5

ABode Canterbury, 30–33 High Street, CT1 2RX. *Tel* 01227-766266, www.abodehotels.co.uk. In pedestrian precinct (directions needed) near cathedral: contemporary hotel, part of group developed by chef Michael Caines. Managed by Stephen Gee. Champagne bar, 'chic' restaurant, traditional tavern (background music). Wi-Fi. 77 bedrooms, contemporary, well equipped (LCD TV, DVD-player, broadband; wet room; tuck box); choice of 'comfortable', 'desirable', 'enviable', 'fabulous': £89–£250. Breakfast £13. Tasting menu £58.

Ebury Hotel, 65–67 New Dover Road, CT1 3DX. *Tel* 01227-768433, www.ebury-hotel.co.uk. Near cathedral, Henry Mason's solid Victorian house (*c.* 1840) with original features. 'Large, spacious bedrooms; friendly staff; very good food.' Lounge, restaurant (French cuisine); indoor swimming pool. Background music. Wi-Fi. 2-acre grounds: 1 acre garden. Charlie the labradoodle ('trainee receptionist') has his own web page. 15 bedrooms; self-catering cottages. B&B £42.50–£85 per person; D,B&B £70–£105.

Magnolia House, 36 St Dunstan's Terrace, CT2 8AX. *Tel* 01227-765121, www.magnoliahousecanterbury.co.uk. Isobelle Leggett's late Georgian guest house in residential street ½ mile from centre. Dinner by arrangement. Sitting room, dining room (background music). Walled garden. Parking. 7 bedrooms (some four-poster beds). Wi-Fi. B&B £47.50–£65 per person. Dinner £35.

CARTMEL Cumbria   Map 4: inset C2

Uplands, Haggs Lane, LA11 6HD. *Tel* 01539-536248, www.uplands.uk.com. Now owned by Anthony de Clerck: restaurant-with-rooms in white pebble-dashed house outside village near Grange-over-Sands. 'Professional, courteous welcome, excellent food.' 2-acre landscaped garden with views of Leven Estuary on Morecambe Bay. Breakfast room, dining room ('background music not normally played'). 5 bedrooms (garden or estuary view). B&B £55–£65 per person.

CHELTENHAM Gloucestershire   Map 3:D5

The Big Sleep, Wellington Street, GL50 1XZ. *Tel* 01242-696999, www.thebigsleephotel.com. Bright, shiny budget accommodation in former Inland Revenue building in centre (sister of *The Big Sleep*, Cardiff, see Shortlist). Managed by Scott Thorley. Lobby with seating (background music); breakfast room. Wi-Fi. Function facilities. Parking. 62 bedrooms (some for families, some suitable for &). B&B (continental) £32.50–£45 per person.

The Cheltenham Townhouse, 12–14 Pittville Lawn, GL52 2BD. *Tel* 01242-221922, www.cheltenhamtownhouse.com. Adam and Jayne Lillywhite's contemporary B&B, decorated in cream, caramel and coffee shades. 10 mins' walk from Pittville Pump Rooms. 'Good location; comfortable, quiet.' Lift. Lounge (honesty bar), breakfast room (background music); sun deck. Children welcomed. Parking. 21 rooms (5 serviced apartments in annexe). B&B £34.50–£79 per person.

Thirty Two, 32 Imperial Square, GL50 1QZ. *Tel* 01242-771110, www.thirtytwoltd.com. Overlooking Imperial Gardens in listed Regency terrace: B&B with sophisticated contemporary interior (show-case for designer-owners Jonathan Sellwood and Jonathan Parkin). Drawing room, breakfast room (soft background music). 4 bedrooms. B&B £84.50–£139 per person.

Hotel du Vin Cheltenham, Parabola Road, GL50 3AQ. *Tel* 01242-588450, www.hotelduvin.com. Contemporary conversion of Georgian house in fashionable Montpellier district, managed by Tom Ross. Spacious public areas around showpiece spiral staircase. Bar, bistro; function facilities; alfresco dining. No background music. Spa, beauty treatment rooms. 49 bedrooms: £145–£285. Breakfast £9.95–£13.50.

CHESTER Cheshire   Map 3:A4
The Chester Grosvenor, Eastgate, CH1 1LT. *Tel* 01244-324024, www.chestergrosvenor.co.uk. 'Unashamedly luxurious' hotel owned by Duke of Westminster, managed by Ross Grieve. Near Roman walls and cathedral: timbered facade (Grade II listed), elegant interior (doormen, marble lobby, chandeliers, grand staircase). Lounge, brasserie, *The Arkle* restaurant (*Michelin* star). Background music. Function facilities. Spa (steam room, herb sauna, relaxation room). 80 bedrooms and suites: (*excluding VAT*) £195–£850. Breakfast £19. Dinner £35–£59.

CHICHESTER West Sussex   Map 2:E3
The Ship, North Street, PO19 1NH. *Tel* 01243-77800, www.shiphotelchichester.co.uk. Within old city walls (5 mins' walk from theatre), refurbished Georgian building (Grade II listed), now owned by WAW Leisure Ltd (see also *The Place*, Camber, also shortlisted); man-aged by Liz Darvill. Circular Adam staircase. Lift, bar, 2-tier brasserie with conservatory (light oak floor, tub seating), background music; conference/wedding facilities. Parking. 36 bedrooms (on 3 floors; some family). B&B £60–£95 per person.

CHIDDINGFOLD Surrey   Map 2:D3
The Swan Inn, Petworth Road, GU8 4TY. *Tel* 01428-682073, www.theswaninn.biz. Converted 15th-century inn, now dining pub, on main road of leafy village N of Petworth on A283. Run by owner Daniel Hall and family with manager William Allen. 'Uniformly modern, with a style of its own, comfortable, well-equipped bedrooms, jolly and helpful staff.' Bar, restaurant (traditional/modern British cooking by Darren Tidd); background music. Wi-Fi throughout. Large garden. Easy

parking. Children welcomed. 11 bedrooms (front ones hear traffic). B&B £32.50–£72.50 per person.

CHRISTCHURCH Dorset   Map 2:E2

Captain's Club Hotel, Wick Ferry, Wick Lane, Mudeford, BH23 1HU. *Tel* 01202-475111, www.thecaptainsclub.net. 'Buzzing, happening place.' Striking contemporary hotel (chic metal and glass construction) owned by Robert Wilson and Timothy Lloyd. On River Stour at Christchurch Quay; panoramic river views. Bar, *Tides* restaurant; terrace (alfresco dining); function facilities. Background music. Spa (pool; treatments). Lift. 29 'superbly appointed' bedrooms (2 suitable for &). B&B from £99.50 per person.

Waterford Lodge, 87 Bure Lane, Friars Cliff, Mudeford, BH23 4DN. *Tel* 01425-282100, www.bw-waterfordlodge.co.uk. Hooper family's hotel (Best Western), '4 mins' stroll from natural coastline', 2 miles SE of Christchurch. Lounge, bar (light meals; background music), garden-facing restaurant; free Wi-Fi; conference/wedding facilities. Parking. 18 bedrooms (3 on ground floor). B&B £37.50–£75 per person.

COOKHAM DEAN Berkshire   Map 2:D3

The Inn on the Green, The Old Cricket Common, SL6 9NZ. *Tel* 01628-482638, www.theinnonthegreen.com. Stylish restaurant-with-rooms in 1-acre grounds, 3 miles NW of Maidenhead. Owned by chef Garry Hollihead with Mark Fuller and Andy Taylor. Lounge/bar, 3 dining rooms (*Lamp Room, The Stublie, Conservatory*); background music; alfresco summer dining in Mediterranean-style courtyard. 'Dinner very good; decent wine list with bonus of bin ends.' Hot tub. Parking. 9 bedrooms (4 on ground floor). B&B £47.50–£115 per person.

DARLINGTON Co. Durham   Map 4:C4

Headlam Hall, nr Gainford, DL2 3HA. *Tel* 01325-730238, www.headlamhall.co.uk. Surrounded by farmland, Robinson family's traditionally furnished 17th-century country house in lower Teesdale hamlet. 3 lounges, bar, restaurant (classical background music). Spa (pool, sauna, gym, treatment rooms; lift). Terraces; 4-acre walled garden: lake, tennis, 9-hole golf course, croquet. 40 bedrooms (16 in mews or coach house; 7 in spa; 2 suitable for &). B&B £55–£155 per person. Dinner £38.

DARTMOUTH Devon   Map 1:D4

Browns, 27–29 Victoria Road, TQ6 9RT. *Tel* 01803-832572, www.brownshoteldartmouth.co.uk. In centre, informal town house hotel refurbished in contemporary style by owners Clare and James Brown. New manager and chef in 2008, Robin Tozer and Phil Kelly. Lounge bar, bar, restaurant ('local food with Mediterranean twist'). Background music throughout. 10 bedrooms. B&B £60–£85 per person.

Dart Marina, Sandquay Road, TQ6 9PH. *Tel* 01803-832580, www. dartmarina.com. Stylish hotel, owned by Richard Seton, on waterfront overlooking marina. 'Staff one of its major strengths, helpful, friendly.' Contemporary decor. Lift. 2 lounges, 2 bars, *River* restaurant ('very good food'; terrace: alfresco dining), *Wildfire* bistro; background music. Spa (pool, gym, treatments). Parking. Pebble beach. Children welcomed. 49 bedrooms ('very comfortable'; all with river view, some with balcony or French window; 1 suitable for &). B&B £62.50–£155 per person; D,B&B from £110.

DEDHAM Essex   Map 2:C5

Dedham Hall, Brook Street, CO7 6AD. *Tel* 01206-323027, www. dedhamhall.demon.co.uk. Guest house/restaurant/art school in cluster of old buildings (15th-century cottage, 18th-century house, Dutch barn), long run by owners Wendy and Jim Sarton. 2 lounges, 2 bars, *The Fountain House* restaurant. No background music. 6-acre garden. 20 bedrooms (16 in annexe for painting holidays). B&B £50–£55 per person; D,B&B £77.50–£82.50.

Maison Talbooth, Stratford Road, CO7 6HN. *Tel* 01206-322367, www.milsomhotels.com. 'Expanded and revitalised' in 2008, Milsom family's Victorian mansion (tranquil setting; spectacular views over Stour valley), managed by Bridget Stanley. Ramp. Large drawing room, *Garden Room* (breakfasts, light lunches). Guests may eat at the family's restaurant *Le Talbooth*, and hotel/brasserie, *milsom's*, both nearby. No background music. 4-acre grounds: heated swimming pool complex (sun deck terrace, hot tub); tennis court; beauty treatment rooms. 12 bedrooms (3 new ones on 2nd floor). B&B (continental) £95–£275 per person. Dinner £52.

DONCASTER South Yorkshire   Map 4:E4

Mount Pleasant, Great North Road, DN11 0HW. *Tel* 01302-868696, www.mountpleasant.co.uk. Handy for airport and racecourse, Mr McIlroy's large low-rise hotel (Best Western) with spacious accommo-dation. 4 lounges, 3 bars. Restaurant ('excellent food and service') faces 'pleasant garden'. Background music. Wi-Fi. *therapié* health and wellness centre; function facilities. Parking. 56 bedrooms (plus 8 self-catering cottages). B&B £45–£145 per person.

DOVER Kent   Map 2:D5

Loddington House, 14 East Cliff, CT16 1LX. *Tel* 01304-201947, www.
loddingtonhousehotel.co.uk. 'Comfortable, hospitable, non-preten-
tious; dinner was superb': mother and son Kathy and Robert Cupper's
seafront Regency Grade II listed guest house. Harbour views; convenient for terminals; 10 mins' walk from centre. Lounge (balcony with sea
view), dining room (evening meal by arrangement, £25). No background music. Small garden. 6 bedrooms (4 *en suite*; rear ones quietest).
B&B £32.50–£55 per person.

The White Cliffs Hotel, High Street, St. Margaret's-at-Cliffe, CT15
6AT. *Tel* 01304-852229, www.thewhitecliffs.com. Traditional, white,
weather-board inn with recently modernised interior, in pretty village
10 mins' drive from port. 'Delightful service from owners Oakley family
and everyone else.' Lounges, *Bay* restaurant; terrace; walled garden;
'micro spa' treatments; wedding/conference facilities. Wi-Fi. Parking.
15 bedrooms (9 in mews). B&B £49.50–£99 per person.

DURHAM Co. Durham   Map 4:B4

Grafton House, 40 South Street, DH1 4QP. *Tel* 0191-375 6790,
www.grafton-house.co.uk. Mary Parker's plush small hotel (opened
Nov 2007) on S side of river: 19th-century building in pretty street in
conservation area. 'Spectacular' views of castle and cathedral. 'Friendly.
Good, well-priced food.' Snug, dining room; light background music;
courtyard. Function facilities. Limited parking; valet service available.
10 bedrooms (1 on ground floor; 3 best ones face cathedral; some flaws:
'no drawers, no pictures, no shelf in shower'). B&B £112.50–£125 per
person. Dinner £25.

DUXFORD Cambridgeshire   Map 2:C4

Duxford Lodge, Ickleton Road, CB22 4RT. *Tel* 01223-836444,
www.duxfordlodgehotel.co.uk. Traditionally furnished 1900s red brick
house off M11, near Imperial War Museum, managed by Christine
Drury. Some motorway noise. Cambridge 20 mins' drive N. Lounge, bar
(pictures of aeroplanes and fighter pilots), *Le Paradis* restaurant;
function/wedding facilities. No background music. Garden. 15 bedrooms (4 in garden annexe). B&B £54–£93.50 per person.

EASTBOURNE East Sussex   Map 2:E4

Grand Hotel, King Edwards Parade, BN21 4EQ. *Tel* 01323-412345,
www.grandeastbourne.com. 'Lovely warm hotel. Excellent food.'
Traditional 5-star, 19th-century seafront 'white palace', managed by

Jonathan Webley. 'Vast public spaces, immaculately kept.' 'Impeccable service.' Live band at weekend; monthly teatime Palm Court quartet. Children welcomed (playroom, carers, high teas). 3 lounges, bar, *Mirabelle* and *Garden* restaurants (both with pianist; 'elegant cooking on reassuringly limited menu'); conference/function facilities; health spa; heated indoor and outdoor swimming pools; 2-acre garden: putting, etc. Parking. 152 bedrooms (many with sea view). B&B £95–£217.50 per person. Dinner from £36.

EXETER Devon   Map 1:C5
ABode Exeter, Cathedral Yard, EX1 1HD. *Tel* 01392-319955, www.abodehotels.co.uk. Opposite cathedral, boutique hotel, first in the ABode group (started by Andrew Brownsword and Exeter-born chef Michael Caines; see also shortlisted *ABode Canterbury*). Julien Wilkinson is manager. Lift, ramps. 2 bars, restaurant; background music; fitness spa. Public parking 10 mins' walk. 53 bedrooms ('modern chic'): £89–£145. Breakfast £10.50–£14.50. Dinner £60.

FALMOUTH Cornwall   Map 1:E2
Green Lawns, Western Terrace, TR11 4QJ. *Tel* 01326-312734, www.greenlawnshotel.com. In style of small French château, ivy-clad, traditionally furnished hotel, managed by Wendy Symons, ½ mile from centre. Views across Falmouth Bay. Lounge, bar, *Garras* restaurant (background music); leisure/conference/function facilities (indoor swimming pool, sauna, whirlpool). Award-winning garden: patio area. 39 bedrooms (11 on ground floor). B&B £35–£115 per person; D,B&B (min 3 nights) £50–£140.

The Greenbank, Harbourside, TR11 2SR. *Tel* 01326-312440, www.greenbank-hotel.co.uk. Overlooking Fal estuary, white hotel (said to be Falmouth's oldest), managed by Kearan McVey, 10 mins' walk from centre. 'Great harbour views. Friendly staff. Good dinners and breakfasts.' Lounge, terrace bar, *Harbourside* restaurant (fish/seafood specialities); background music; lift to 1st floor; terraces. Private quay and beach at low tide. Children welcomed. 59 bedrooms. B&B £45.50–£99 per person. Dinner £35.

FOLKESTONE Kent   Map 2:E5
The Relish, 4 Augusta Gardens, CT20 2RR. *Tel* 01303-850952, www.hotelrelish.co.uk. Contemporary interior in Sarah and Chris van Dyke's grand 1850s merchant's house in West End, ½ mile from centre. Lounge, breakfast room (Radio 2 played); unlimited coffee/tea with cake; Wi-Fi;

small terrace. Families welcomed. Direct access to private 4-acre Augusta Gardens. Parking. 10 bedrooms. B&B £45–£130 per person.

FOWEY Cornwall   Map 1:D3
Fowey Hall, Hanson Drive, PL23 1ET. *Tel* 01726-833866, www. luxuryfamilyhotels.com. High above port (estuary views): informal, family-friendly hotel (von Essen group), managed by Oliver Richards. Victorian mansion, said to be inspiration for Toad Hall (*The Wind in the Willows*). 'Luxuriously spacious, comfortable annexe bedroom; cheerful staff.' Large drawing room, library, billiard/meeting room, 2 restaurants (*Palm Court, Hansons*). 'Excellent local seafood.' Background music. Extensive wedding/function facilities. croquet, badminton, crèche, children's games room. Indoor swimming pool due to open September 2008. 36 bedrooms (8 in annexe, 6 ground floor, 2 suitable for &). B&B £60–£170 per person; D,B&B £87.50–£225.

GATWICK West Sussex   Map 2:D4
Langshott Manor, Langshott, RH6 9LN. *Tel* 01293-786680, www. alexanderhotels.co.uk. Luxury hotel within classic timber-framed Tudor house (ancient moat) 5 mins' drive from airport. Managed by Sakis Dinas. Lounge, *St Peter's* brasserie, *Mulberry* restaurant (background music); conference/wedding facilities. Peaceful, landscaped 3-acre gardens. 22 bedrooms (some in mews; some overlooking lake). B&B £115–£160 per person. Dinner £40.

GLASTONBURY Somerset   Map 1:B6
Number Three, 3 Magdalene Street, BA6 9EW. *Tel* 01458-832129, www.numberthree.co.uk. Patricia Redmond's Georgian town house B&B, in 1-acre walled garden by abbey ruins. Breakfast room. No background music. Parking. 5 bedrooms (1 on ground floor; 3 in *Garden House*). B&B £60–£105 per person.

GOLANT-BY-FOWEY Cornwall   Map 1:D3
The Cormorant, nr Fowey, NG31 6PN. *Tel* 01726-833426, www. cormoranthotel.co.uk. Clean-lined hotel in tranquil setting on hillside overlooking River Fowey. Refurbished in 2007 by new owner, antiques dealer Mary Tozer. Vertiginous views. Sitting room, bar, *à la carte* restaurant; 'subdued' background music; garden terraces; indoor swimming pool, hot tub (refurbishment planned). Wi-Fi. Parking. 14 bedrooms (all with river views; most with balcony). B&B £50–£150 per person; D,B&B £80–£180.

GRANGE-OVER-SANDS Cumbria   Map 4: inset C2

Clare House, Park Road, LA11 7HQ. *Tel* 015395-33026, www. clarehousehotel.co.uk. Read family's imposing Victorian house, with extension overlooking Morecambe Bay. 'An excellent stay.' 'Friendly welcome. Very good dinner (6.45–7.15 pm) and breakfast.' 2 lounges, dining room; no background music. ½-acre ground. Parking. 18 bedrooms ('clean, comfortable', most with bay views). B&B £50 per person; D,B&B £78.

GRANTHAM Lincolnshire   Map 2:A3

Angel & Royal, High Street, NG31 6PN. *Tel* 01476-565816, www. angelandroyal.co.uk. Furnished in country house style: ancient inn (1203), once hostel for Brotherhood of Knights Templar. Owned by Martin Wicks, managed by Bob Rammalingham. Lounge, *Angel* bar (inglenook fireplace; vast malt whisky collection; classical background music), *King's Room* restaurant, *Simply Bertie's* bistro; conference/ function facilities, civil wedding licence. 29 bedrooms (some on ground floor). B&B £55–£79 per person; D,B&B £57.50–£90.

GRASMERE Cumbria   Map 4: inset C2

Moss Grove, Ambleside, LA22 9SW. *Tel* 015394-35251, www. mossgrove.com. In 'very pretty' Lakeland village: 'posh'. informal B&B run by owner Susan Lowe with organic principles, without loss of style or luxury: natural materials (wood, glass); organic, local or fair trade produce; recycling and pollution policy. Lounge, kitchen. Latest gadgetry; Wi-Fi. No background music. 'Lovely room; reasonable value; varied clientele but definitely young-at heart.' 11 bedrooms. B&B (Mediterranean-style buffet) £62.50–£195 per person.

Rothay Garden Hotel, Broadgate, LA22 9RJ. *Tel* 015394-35334, www.rothay-garden.com. In riverside garden on N edge of village, Christopher Carss's traditional Victorian hotel, run with long-serving staff. Reopened summer 2008 after major redevelopment: 7 new bedrooms (including 5 new loft suites), 8 smaller rooms reconfigured into 5; public areas much improved. 2 lounges, bar, restaurant; no background music. 30 bedrooms (some on ground floor). B&B £52.50–£132.50 per person; D,B&B £90–£178.

GREAT BIRCHAM Norfolk   Map 2:A5

The King's Head, Lynn Road, PE31 6RJ. *Tel* 01485-578265, www. the-kings-head-bircham.co.uk. Modern styling in Victorian inn, 8 miles from Brancaster Beach; Sandringham close by. Managed by Rachel Lake and Davy Gallagher. Lounge, bar (village pub), restaurant (alfresco in summer); background music; TV accompanies good breakfast; function facilities; courtyard. 12 bedrooms (king-size beds, play station, CD/DVD-player, Internet). B&B £55–£185 per person; D,B&B £80–£235.

GREAT LANGDALE Cumbria   Map 4: inset C2
Old Dungeon Ghyll, Great Langdale, LA22 9JY. *Tel* 015394-37272, www.odg.co.uk. Remote (3 miles from village), 300-year-old mountain hotel, owned by National Trust, run by 'welcoming' Jane and Neil Walmsley. Lounge, residents bar, public *Hiker's Bar* (old cow stalls); live music occasionally; no background music, dining room, drying room. 1-acre garden. Fell walkers, climbers, cyclists, children, dogs welcomed. 13 bedrooms (5 with shared facilities). B&B £50–£55 per person; D,B&B £72.50–£77.50.

GREAT YARMOUTH Norfolk   Map 2:B6
The Old Vicarage, The Street, Hemsby, NR29 4EU. *Tel* 01493-731557, www.theoldvicaragehotel.net. Chef/proprietor Jason and Justine Ingram's restaurant-with-rooms; handsome 1850s red brick house in large grounds 10 mins' drive from Great Yarmouth. Lounge/bar, dining room (open daily to residents, to non-residents Wed–Sat; Norfolk produce). Special dinners (musical, etc). B&B £80 per person. Dinner (3 courses) £29.

HARMONDSWORTH Middlesex   Map 2:D3
Harmondsworth Hall, Summerhouse Lane, Harmondsworth Village, UB7 0BG. *Tel* 020-8759 1824, www.harmondsworthhall.com. In peaceful village 7 mins from Heathrow (not on flight path), Elaine Burke's B&B in large 17th-century Grade II listed building. Grand entrance hall (stained glass), carved staircase, wood panelling. Breakfast room (radio played). Room-service snacks until 9 pm. Wi-Fi. Parking. Transport links to London from West Drayton and Heathrow. 12 bedrooms. B&B £40–£70 per person.

HARROGATE North Yorkshire   Map 4:D4
Ascot House, 53 Kings Road, HG1 5HJ. *Tel* 01423-531005, www.ascothouse.com. Run by Johnson family for 20 years, 'welcoming' hotel in handsome Victorian building, 10 mins' walk from centre. Lounge, bar, restaurant (background music); patio, balcony; function facilities, themed dinners (*Fawlty Towers*). 18 bedrooms. B&B £48.50–£79 per person; D,B&B £66–£98.50.

HASTINGS Sussex   Map 2:E5

Swan House, 1 Hill Street, TN34 3HU. *Tel* 01424-430014, www. swanhousehastings.co.uk. In Old Town, owned by Lionel Copley and Brendan McDonagh: B&B in half-timbered cottage (built 1490). Mix of antique and contemporary design (many pieces from owners' emporium, *No Eight*). Lounge/dining area; no background music. Garden; terrace. Breakfast ingredients sourced locally. 5 bedrooms. B&B £50–£95 per person.

HAWORTH West Yorkshire   Map 4:D3

Ashmount Country House, Mytholmes Lane, BD22 8EZ. *Tel* 01535-645726, www.ashmounthaworth.co.uk. 'A guest house with hotel standards', owned by Ray and Gill Capeling: stone-built former home of Dr Amos Ingham, physician to the Brontë Sisters. Near Brontë Parsonage. Traditionally furnished; mature gardens; open views; ample private parking; Yorkshire breakfasts. Picnics available. Free Wi-Fi. 8 bedrooms (some on ground floor; 2 with outdoor hot tub, 2 with whirlpool, music and 'mood lighting'). B&B £37.50–£82.50 per person.

HELMSLEY North Yorkshire   Map 4:C4

No54, 54 Bondgate, YO62 5EZ. *Tel* 01439-771533, www.no54.co.uk. Near market place: Lizzie Would's 'charming' town house B&B. Simple decor: crisp white linen, pine furniture, York stone floors; open fires. No background music. Courtyard garden. North Yorkshire Moors national park nearby. Dinner (by arrangement, £28–£35) and picnics available. 4 bedrooms (ground floor, around sunny courtyard). Breakfast includes muffins and kedgeree. B&B £35–£45 per person.

HENLEY-ON-THAMES Oxfordshire   Map 2:D3

Hotel du Vin Henley-on-Thames, New Street, YO62 5EZ. *Tel* 01491-848400, www.hotelduvin.com. Airy conversion of Georgian industrial buildings (formerly Brakspear's Brewery) round courtyard (alfresco dining). Managed by Claire Pollock. Some bedrooms on 2 levels; one has balcony with alfresco bath. Bar (background music), snug, busy bistro ('land, sea, local' menu; 'excellent wine list'). Wi-Fi. Children welcomed. Valet parking. Motor launch. 43 bedrooms (2 suitable for &): £145–£295. Breakfast £9.50–£13.50. Dinner £40.

HEREFORD Herefordshire   Map 3:D4

Castle House, Castle Street, HR1 2NW. *Tel* 01432-356321, www.castlehse.co.uk. Luxury hotel, sensitively converted from 2 Grade

II listed town houses, in gardens beside old castle moat. Owned by David Watkins, managed by Michelle Marriott-Lodge. 'Two very pleasant nights. Nice room; great staff.' Lounge, bar, restaurant; light jazz/classical background music. Lift. Garden, terrace. Parking. 15 bedrooms (1, on ground floor, equipped for &). B&B £87.50–£120 per person. Dinner £50.

HEXHAM Northumberland   Map 4:B3

The Hermitage, Swinburne, NE48 4DG. *Tel* 01434-681248, *email* katie.stewart@the meet.co.uk. Approached through grand arch and up long drive: B&B with 'true country house atmosphere', Katie and Simon Stewart's rural family home, 7½ miles N of Hexham and Corbridge. Open Mar–end Sept. 2 drawing rooms, breakfast room. No background music. 4-acre grounds: terrace, tennis. 3 bedrooms. B&B £40–£50 per person.

HOLKHAM Norfolk   Map 2:A5

The Victoria at Holkham, Park Road, NR23 1RG. *Tel* 01328-711008, www.victoriaatholkham.co.uk. Near famous sandy beach, refurbished pub, managed by Phil Lance, on Earl of Leicester's Holkham estate. 'Shabby chic' decor (ornate Indian furniture, vibrant colours). 'Well placed for walks and drives to some of the country's best bird places.' Lounge area, 3 bars, restaurant; background music. 3-acre grounds: children's play area, barbecue. 10 bedrooms (1 suitable for &) plus accommodation in 3 'follies'. B&B £60–£120 per person. Dinner £40.

HOLMFIRTH West Yorkshire   Map 4:E3

Sunnybank, 78 Upperthong Lane, HD9 3BQ. *Tel* 01484-684857, www.sunnybankguesthouse.co.uk. With 'welcoming, helpful approach', Peter and Anne White's B&B in Victorian gentleman's residence on hillside: views over Holme valley. 'Beautiful house, beautifully decorated.' 'Top-class breakfasts' in oak-panelled dining room (fire in winter; background music if requested). Wi-Fi. 2-acre wooded garden. ½ mile from centre. 5 bedrooms (2 on ground floor). B&B £37.50–£70 per person.

HOPE Derbyshire   Map 3:A6

Losehill House, Edale Road, S33 6RF. *Tel* 01433-621219, www.losehillhouse.co.uk. On outskirts of village, secluded spa hotel on side of Losehill, owned since 2007 by Paul and Kathryn Roden. Panoramic views over Hope valley. Solid, white-painted house with comfortable, modern furnishing. Drawing room, bar, restaurant; lift. 1-acre garden; terrace. Indoor swimming pool; hot tub; treatment rooms. Wedding/function/conference facilities. Footpath access to Peak District national park. 21 bedrooms (some family suites). B&B £60–£115 per person. Dinner £29.50.

HOVE East Sussex   Map 2:E4

The Claremont, 13 Second Avenue, BN3 2LL. *Tel* 01273-735161, www.theclaremont.eu. Owned by Vicki Banks and Stuart Hill: contemporary hotel in Victorian villa just off seafront: checked floor, high ceilings, chandeliers, bright colours (lots of red). Exhibitions by local artists. Drawing room, study, breakfast room (full English or vegetarian breakfast; Radio 2 played); conference/wedding/civil partnership facilities. ½-acre walled garden. 11 bedrooms (2 with four-poster). B&B £62.50–£75 per person.

HUDDERSFIELD West Yorkshire   Map 4:E3

Three Acres Inn & Restaurant, Roydhouse, Shelley, HD8 8LR. *Tel* 01484-602606, www.3acres.com. In Pennine countryside, 5 miles SE of centre: Neil Truelove and Brian Orme's smart old roadside drover's inn. *Seafood Bar*, 2 dining rooms; background music. Small function/private dining facilities. Terraced garden; decked dining terrace. Children welcomed. 20 bedrooms (1 suitable for &; 9 in adjacent cottages). B&B £45–£70 per person. Dinner from £34.95.

HULL East Yorkshire   Map 4:D5

Willerby Manor, Well Lane, Willerby, HU10 6ER. *Tel* 01482-652616, www.bw-willerbymanor.co.uk. Edwardian mansion in rural setting (Best Western), 6 miles NW of centre: run by owner Alexandra Townend. 'Breakfast in lovely room overlooking garden. Good service.' *Everglades* bar/brasserie (alfresco dining), *Icon* restaurant ('food a bit complicated'). Background music. Health club (swimming pool, gym, etc), crèche; extensive business/function facilities. 3-acre gardens. Parking. 63 bedrooms (1 suitable for &). B&B £50–£99 per person; D,B&B £70–£119.

INKPEN Berkshire   Map 2:D2

The Crown & Garter, Great Common, Inkpen, nr Hungerford, RG17 9QR. *Tel* 01488-668325, www.crownandgarter.com. Owned by Gill and Chris Hern: traditional 17th-century red brick inn (real ales). Simple accommodation (white-painted floorboards, pine furniture) in L-shaped chalet-style annexe on courtyard garden. Bar (inglenook fireplace, beams; occasional quiet background music), restaurant. Garden; patio (alfresco dining). Parking. 8 bedrooms (some on ground floor). B&B £45–£59.50; D,B&B £62.50.

IPSWICH Suffolk   Map 2:C5

Salthouse Harbour Hotel, 1 Neptune Quay, IP4 1AS. *Tel* 01473-226789, www.salthouseharbour.co.uk. Owned by Robert Gough: contemporary warehouse conversion (exposed brickwork, industrial pillars) on waterfront. 'Splendid view over quay.' Spacious bedrooms: 'mine was quiet, well lit'. 'Friendly reception staff. Pleasant public rooms.' Brasserie (Mediterranean 'all day' dishes; background music). Courtyard. 43 bedrooms (some with balcony). B&B £80–£155 per person; D,B&B from £90.

KESWICK Cumbria   Map 4: inset C2

Dalegarth House, Portinscale, CA12 5RQ. *Tel* 017687-72817, www.dalegarth-house.co.uk. 'Friendly reception' from Bruce and Pauline Jackson, chef/proprietors of country hotel (Edwardian house), 1 mile W of Keswick. 'Out-of-this-world views.' Traditional decor. 'Outstanding' locally sourced food. Cumbrian breakfast. Lounge, bar (quiet background music), dining room. Garden. Parking. 10 bedrooms. B&B £37–£40 per person; D,B&B £55–£60.

Lyzzick Hall, Underskiddaw, CA12 4PY. *Tel* 017687-72277, www.lyzzickhall.co.uk. On lower slopes of Skiddaw, former home of wealthy textile merchant, now country hotel with Spanish owner, Mr Fernandez. 'Glorious setting' (views of mountains) 1½ miles N of town. 2 lounges, bar, restaurant (English with Spanish influence); background music; heated indoor swimming pool, sauna, whirlpool. Extensive grounds. 31 bedrooms (sound insulation not always perfect). B&B £60–£77 per person; D,B&B £78–£95.

KING'S LYNN Norfolk   Map 2:A4

Congham Hall, Lynn Road, Grimston, PE32 1AH. *Tel* 01485-600250, www.conghamhallhotel.co.uk. In 'exceptionally peaceful' setting, Georgian country house (von Essen hotels), managed by Julie Woodhouse. On 30-acre estate (famous herb garden), 6 miles E of King's Lynn. Front rooms face walled garden and cricket pitch; lawns and parkland at rear. Lounge, *Orangery* restaurant; terrace. No background music. Clay pigeon shooting. 14 bedrooms. B&B £99–£192.50 per person; D,B&B £160–£245.

KINGSBRIDGE Devon   Map 1:D4

Buckland-Tout-Saints, Goveton, TQ7 2DS. *Tel* 01548-853055, www.
tout-saints.co.uk. William and Mary manor house in 'glorious' rural
setting 2½ miles NE of Kingsbridge. Now owned by Sir Peter Rigby,
who also owns *Mallory Court*, Bishop's Tachbrook; still managed by Julie
Hudson. Wood-panelled public rooms, open fires; traditional bedrooms,
contemporary bathrooms. 4½-acre garden and woodland. Lounge, bar,
2 attractive dining rooms; background music; function/wedding facilities. 16 bedrooms (traditional or contemporary decor). B&B £60–£105
per person. Dinner £37.

Thurlestone Hotel, Thurlestone, TQ7 3NN. *Tel* 01548-560382,
www.thurlestone.co.uk. In 'unique' position (bay views; coastal walks,
sandy beaches close by): large, family-friendly hotel, owned by Grose
family, managed by Julie Baugh. 4 miles SW of Kingsbridge. Lounges,
bar, *Margaret Amelia* restaurant; alfresco *Rock Pool* eating area (teas,
lunches, snacks, dinners), terrace (alfresco dining); function facilities;
leisure complex and beauty spa (indoor and outdoor heated swimming
pools, tennis, squash, badminton). No background music. 19-acre subtropical gardens. 9-hole golf course adjacent. 64 bedrooms. B&B
£61–£122 per person; D,B&B £80–£140.

KIRKBY LONSDALE Cumbria   Map 4: inset C2

Sun Inn, 6 Market Street, LA6 2AU. *Tel* 015242-71965, www.sun-inn.
info. In centre of market town, 17th-century inn (white-painted walls
hung with flower baskets), run by owners Lucy and Mark Fuller with
manager Steven Turner as 'bar, restaurant and rooms'. Flagstone and
wood floors, panelling, exposed stonework; roaring fires; modern styling.
'Fantastic service, excellent food'; background music. Children
welcomed. Dog-friendly. 11 bedrooms (contemporary, in cream, browns
and white; spacious bathrooms). B&B £45–£110 per person. Dinner £36.

KNUTSFORD Cheshire   Map 4:E3

Belle Epoque, 60 King Street, WA16 6DT. *Tel* 01565-633060,
www.thebelleepoque.com. In commuter town near Manchester,
restaurant-with-rooms in listed Art Nouveau building. Owned and run
by Mooney family for over 3 decades. Original Venetian glass floor,
marble-pillared alcoves, statuary, lavish drapes, tall glass vases and cosy
recesses. Bar, restaurant. Background jazz. Mediterranean roof garden.
Function facilities. 6 bedrooms. B&B £57.50 per person. Dinner £45.

Longview, 51 and 55 Manchester Road, WA16 0LX. *Tel* 01565-632119,
www.longviewhotel.com. With Greek owner, Lulu Ahooie: central

hotel (formerly Victorian merchant's home) looking across busy road to heath. Cellar bar, *Stuffed Olive* restaurant (eastern Mediterranean dishes/ 'British standbys'); background music. 32 bedrooms (most 'smallish'; suites have lounge and private garden). B&B £42.50–£89 per person.

LEEDS West Yorkshire   Map 4:D4

Malmaison, 1 Swinegate, LS1 4AG. *Tel* 0113-398 1000, www. malmaison-leeds.com. In Calls district, buzzy, city-centre hotel, former bus/train administration building on River Aire ('undistinguished area but convenient for station'). Managed by Andrew Creese. Bedrooms in aubergine, plum and taupe; brown hues, wood and leather downstairs. 'Very pleasant, if not polished, staff; stylish bedroom, impressive bathroom; excellent dinner; compendious wine list.' Bar with cosy alcoves, brasserie (Homegrown & Local menu; vaulted ceiling; background music); meeting rooms; wheelchair lift; high-tech gym. 100 bedrooms. B&B £85–£190 per person.

Quebecs, 9 Quebec Street, LS1 2HA. *Tel* 0113-244 8989, www. theetongroup.com. Luxury town house B&B in Grade II listed Victorian red brick building (former Leeds and County Liberal Club), 2 mins' walk from station. Managed by Stuart Ward. Grand oak staircase, stained-glass window, panelled lounge, library, bright breakfast room, conservatory; terrace. 24-hour room service. No background music. 45 bedrooms (some are small). B&B £95–£190 per person.

Woodlands, Gelderd Road, Gildersome, LS27 7LY. *Tel* 0113-238 1488, www.tomahawkhotels.co.uk. Contemporary hotel (originally residence of textile mill owner) owned by Rob Foulston and Tom Horsforth (Tomahawk group). In landscaped gardens 3 miles S of centre. Lounge, 3 dining rooms; conservatory. Background music throughout. Gardens; patio. Wedding/function facilities. 18 bedrooms, named after unusual fabrics (some on ground floor). B&B £69–£139 per person. Dinner £24.95–£29.95.

LICHFIELD Staffordshire   Map 2:A2

Swinfen Hall, Swinfen, WS14 9RE. *Tel* 01543-481494, www. swinfenhallhotel.co.uk. In 100-acre estate in rolling countryside, managed by owners Helen and Victor Wiser: Grade II-listed 18th-century manor house. 2 miles S of Lichfield on A38; 20 mins' drive from Birmingham. Period decor in 1st-floor bedrooms; 2nd-floor rooms more contemporary. Lounge, cocktail lounge, bar, restaurant, ballroom; conference/wedding facilities; classical background music. Terrace, walled vegetable garden: croquet, 2 tennis courts; formal gardens;

ornamental ponds; woodlands; flower meadows; 45-acre deer park. Children welcomed. 18 bedrooms. B&B £80–£145 per person. Dinner £42.

LINCOLN Lincolnshire   Map 4:E5

Castle Hotel, Westgate, LN1 3AS. *Tel* 01522-538801, www.castlehotel.net. Near cathedral and castle, in historic centre, owned by Worrell family: Grade II listed. 2 small lounges, bar (a popular local), *Knights* restaurant (evenings only; *à la carte*; background radio/CDs). Parking. 19 bedrooms, ('modest but clean'; some in attic, some in stables, 1 suitable for &). B&B £47–£132 per person. Dinner £24.

The Old Bakery, 26–28 Burton Road, LN1 3LB. *Tel* 01522-576057, www.theold-bakery.co.uk. Behind castle, restaurant-with-rooms owned by Alan and Lynn Ritson; son-in-law Ivano de Serio is chef. Original features of bakehouse and shop retained (brick walls, stone floors; bread ovens). Restaurant in glassed-in garden room (alfresco dining in warm weather). Modern English cooking with Mediterranean twist; homemade bread, ice cream, pasta. 'Interesting, experimental menu; huge cheese list.' Monthly cookery courses. In quiet street but there can be noise from diners. 4 simple bedrooms (2 *en suite*; 2 with private bathroom): double room with breakfast £53–£58. Dinner from £26.50.

LITTLE SHELFORD Cambridgeshire   Map 2:C4

Purlins, 12 High Street, CB22 5ES. *Tel* 01223-842643, *email* dgallh@ndirect.co.uk. B&B in musician David Hindley and wife Olga's welcoming Arts and Crafts-style home (built 1978), in village 4½ miles S of Cambridge by River Cam. Conservatory sitting room, vaulted dining room, gallery. No background music. Beautiful gardens: 2-acre mature woodland, meadow, lawn, wildlife. Sometimes closed for owners' breaks. 4 bedrooms. B&B £37–£56 per person.

LIVERPOOL Merseyside   Map 4:E2

Hard Days Night, Central Buildings, North John Street, L2 6RR. *Tel* 0151-236 1964. www.harddaysnighthotel.com. Managed by Michael Dewey: large Beatles-themed hotel in Grade II listed building in old merchant quarter (noisy location at night). Artwork and photographs devoted to the Fab Four throughout. Contemporary decor; state-of-the-art gadgetry. Brasserie, *Bar Four*, *Blake's* restaurant, art gallery. Background music. 110 bedrooms: £130–£650. Breakfast £15.95.

Malmaison, William Jessop Way, Princes Dock, L3 1QW. *Tel* 0151-229 5000, www.malmaison-liverpool.com. In regenerated area of city: ultrastylish, 11-storey, purpose-built hotel managed by Mark James.

'Stunning' river views. Minimalist decor (exposed brickwork, air-conditioning ducts, industrial metal staircase). *Plum* bar, brasserie; gym-tonic; background music; function facilities. 'Good dinners; generous breakfasts.' 24-hour room service. 131 bedrooms (wet-room showers; some circular baths): £99–£395. Breakfast £11.95–£13.95.

LOOE Cornwall   Map 1:D3

Fieldhead Hotel, Portuan Road, Hannafore, PL13 2DR. *Tel* 01503-262689, www.fieldheadhotel.co.uk. In elevated position with views across Looe Bay, Julian Peek's traditional hotel (built 1896 as private home) 15 mins' walk from centre. Lounge with huge bow window, bar, *Horizons* restaurant; 'gentle' classical background music. Free Wi-Fi. 1½-acre garden: terrace (views, parasols), heated swimming pool. Parking. 16 bedrooms (most with view, 3 with balcony). B&B £38.50–£60 per person; D,B&B £64.50–£83.

LORTON Cumbria   Map 4: inset C2

Winder Hall, Low Lorton, Cockermouth, CA13 9UP. *Tel* 01900-85107, www.winderhall.co.uk. Jacobean manor house run by owners Nick and Ann Lawler, in hamlet 4 miles S of Cockermouth. 'Green and organic' ethos: eggs, chickens, pigs vegetables and herbs from their small-holding. Informal atmosphere; family feel: children welcomed. After-noon teas. Bar, lounge, restaurant (oak-panelling, mullioned windows; quiet background music; dinner at 7.30); civil wedding licence. 6-acre grounds sloping down to River Cocker (summer house with sauna, hot tub). 7 bedrooms (fell views). B&B £46–£96 per person; D,B&B £78–£133.

LOWESTOFT Suffolk   Map 2:B6

Ivy House, Ivy Lane, off Beccles Road, Oulton Broad, NR33 8HY. *Tel* 01502-501353, www.ivyhousecountryhotel.co.uk. Converted farm owned by Caroline Coe, on southern shores of Oulton Broad. 2 sitting rooms, conservatory, *The Crooked Barn* restaurant (in 18th-century thatched, beamed barn); background music; function/conference facilities; courtyard. 4-acre garden (2 lily ponds, summer house), surrounded by 50-acre meadows. 20 annexe bedrooms (1 suitable for &). B&B £67.50–£125 per person. Dinner £29.50.

LUDLOW Shropshire   Map 3:C4

The Bringewood, Burrington, SY8 2HT. *Tel* 01568-770033, www.thebringewood.co.uk. 'In wonderful countryside with great views' just outside Ludlow (5 mins' drive): modern rustic renovation of Victorian farm building in 250-acre grounds, owned by Neil and Stephen Cocum. Lounge (exposed beams), bar (open log fire); 'elegant' *Oaktree* restaurant ('finest local produce'); patio; wedding/conference/business facilities. Background music. 12 bedrooms. B&B £50–£85 per person. Dinner £27–£32.

Dinham Hall, by the castle, SY8 1EJ. *Tel* 01584-876464, www.dinhamhall.co.uk. 'Splendidly situated': mellow stone building once used by boarders of Ludlow grammar school. Now owned by Mr and Mrs Choblet of *Overton Grange* (see below), managed by Ian Hazeldine. Country house decor. 2 lounges, bar, restaurant. No background music. 1-acre walled garden. Wedding/function facilities. Parking. 13 bedrooms (2 in cottage). B&B £70–£120 per person; D,B&B (min 2 nights) £20 added.

The Feathers, Bull Ring, SY8 1AA. *Tel* 01584-875261, www.feathersatludlow.co.uk. Now owned by a consortium, recently much refurbished, managed by Ian Taylor: landmark Ludlow building with ornate, timber-framed facade (Jacobean, Grade I listed), oak panelling; huge fireplaces, plaster ceilings. 'Welcoming. Good dinners and breakfast. Helpful staff throughout.' Lounge, bar (tea, coffee, light meals), restaurant, background music. Conference facilities. Civil wedding licence. Parking. 40 bedrooms (2 family; some in adjoining buildings; 4 four-posters). B&B £65–£75.50 per person. Dinner £46.50–£55.

Fishmore Hall, Fishmore Road, SY8 3DP. *Tel* 01584-875148, www.fishmorehall.co.uk. Owned by Penman family: symmetrical, white Regency house (former school) overlooking Ludlow, converted to 'very comfortable' boutique hotel. Pared-down decor; impressive bathrooms. 'Excellent dinner and breakfast.' Bar, sitting room, restaurant (background music); lift. Wi-Fi. Garden; terrace. Wedding/function facilities. 15 bedrooms (1 suitable for &). B&B £70–£250 per person. Dinner £46.50–£55.

Overton Grange, Old Hereford Road, SY8 4AD. *Tel* 01584-873500, www.overtongrangehotel.com. Owned by Mr and Mrs Choblet, Edwardian manor house with smart, contemporary interior, in rural location 1 mile S of Ludlow. Lounge, library, breakfast room, restaurant. Background music. 2½-acre garden. 14 bedrooms. B&B £70–£140 per person; D,B&B £110–£182.50.

LYME REGIS Dorset   Map 1:C6

Alexandra Hotel, Pound Street, DT7 3HZ. *Tel* 01297-442010, www.hotelalexandra.co.uk. Long-established hotel run by one family for over 25 years. Kathryn Richards is now the owner/manager;

refurbishment on-going. 'Excellent' position (sea views) above The Cobb. 'Obliging staff.' 'A very happy visit. Excellent rooms with sea view.' Drawing room, conservatory (light lunches), cocktail bar, restaurant ('dinner good; breakfast less so'). Background music. 1½-acre garden. Parking. Town 100 yds; beach 300 yds. 25 bedrooms. B&B £52.50–£65 per person; D,B&B £70–£85.

LYNMOUTH Devon   Map 1:B4

Shelley's, 8 Watersmeet Road, EX35 6EP. *Tel* 01598-753219, www.shelleyshotel.co.uk. Owned by 'great hosts', Jane Becker and Richard Briden: 18th-century cottage B&B in centre (Shelley honeymooned here in summer 1812). Views over Lynmouth Bay. Lounge, bar, conservatory breakfast room. No background music. 11 bedrooms (1 on ground floor). B&B £35–£100 per person.

LYTHAM Lancashire   Map 4:D2

Clifton Arms, West Beach, FY58 5QJ. *Tel* 01253-739898, www. cliftonarms-lytham.com. Overlooking Lytham green and seafront: historic beachfront hotel (Fairhaven Hotels group), managed by Mike Harrison. *Churchills* bar/lounge (brasserie menu), library/TV room, *West Beach* restaurant (background music); conference/banqueting facilities. Lift. Small garden. Parking. 48 bedrooms. B&B £62.50–£130 per person; D,B&B £79–£120.

MANCHESTER   Map 4:E3

Bewley's Hotel, Outwood Lane, Manchester Airport, M90 4HL. *Tel* 0161-498 0333, www.bewleyshotels.com. Large, modern, triple-glazed chain hotel (Moran group), managed by Allison Diggle. 10 mins' walk to Terminals 1 and 3; 24-hour shuttle service. 20 mins' drive from city. Sitting area, bar, brasserie; Wi-Fi; business facilities. No background music. Parking. 226 bedrooms (some suitable for &): £79–£89. Breakfast £8.95.
City Inn, 1 Auburn Street, M1 3DG. *Tel* 0161-242 1000, www. cityinn.com/manchester. Purpose-built chain hotel near station, managed by Darren Townsend. Contemporary design, state-of-the-art fittings. Floor-to-ceiling opening windows; a computer in each bedroom; mist-free mirrors; walk-in power showers, etc. Exhibitions by local artists. *Piccadilly* lounge, *Blue* bar, *City* café. Background music. Wi-Fi. Fitness suite. Meeting rooms. 285 bedrooms (14 suitable for &). B&B from £77.50 per person.
Malmaison, 1–3 Piccadilly, M1 3AQ. *Tel* 0161-278 1000, www.malmaison. com. Imposing building by station: buzzy atmosphere; striking red and

black decoration; dimly lit public areas. Managed by Graham Bradford. 'Friendly, efficient, professional staff.' Bar, brasserie; background music; gym. Conference facilities. Dogs welcomed. 167 bedrooms: £99–£325. Breakfast £13.95.

The Midland, Peter Street, M60 2DS. *Tel* 0161-236 3333, www.qhotels. co.uk. Next to G-Mex centre: built for Midland Railway Company (1903), ornate hotel with terracotta tiled exterior. Owned by Michael Purtill, managed by Michael Magrane. *Octagon* lounge (afternoon tea, light snacks; pianist), *Wyvern* bar, *The French* and *The Colony* restaurants; background music. Lift. Health club (gym, swimming pool, squash); function facilities. Parking (charge). 312 bedrooms. B&B £70–£260 per person; D,B&B £90–£280.

Old Trafford Lodge, Lancashire County Cricket Club, Talbot Road, Old Trafford, M16 0PX. *Tel* 0161-874 3333, www.oldtraffordlodgehotel. co.uk. Uniquely situated, purpose-built hotel beside Lancashire's test match ground. Managed by Claire Jones. Photographs of cricketing heroes; pictures of bats, balls, stumps, etc; free match tickets. Lounge, bar (sandwiches available). No background music. Parking. 68 bedrooms (36 have balcony overlooking pitch; others face car park). B&B (continental) from £37–£79 per person.

MATLOCK Derbyshire   Map 3:A6

The Red House, Old Road, Darley Dale, DE4 2ER. *Tel* 01629-734854, www.theredhousecountryhotel.co.uk. Victorian architect's country home, now David and Kate Gardiner's hotel on edge of village (on quiet road off A6). Views over Derwent valley. Next to carriage museum (horse riding, carriage driving). Many original features. 2 sitting rooms, bar, candlelit restaurant. No background music. ½-acre garden. Parking. 10 bedrooms (3 on ground floor in coach house). B&B £55–£65 per person; D,B&B £82–£92.

MIDHURST Sussex   Map 2:E3

The Spread Eagle, South Street, GU29 9NH. *Tel* 01730-816911, www.hshotels.co.uk. Attractive, traditionally furnished 15th-century coaching inn (Historic Sussex Hotels group), managed by Ted James. Residents' lounge (huge fireplaces, Tudor bread ovens), lounge bar, restaurant (inglenook fireplace), conservatory, terrace (alfresco dining); function facilities. Spa: swimming pool, gym, sauna, steam room, hot tub. No background music. 1-acre garden. Children welcomed. 39 bedrooms. B&B £85–£203 per person; D,B&B £117–£235.

MORPETH Northumberland   Map 4:B4
Eshott Hall, NE65 9EP. *Tel* 01670-787777, www.eshott.com.
Sanderson family's country home for 6 generations ('not a hotel'):
wisteria-clad, symmetrical 17th-century building. On 500-acre estate
(farm, walled garden, arboretum, formal gardens), ½ hour's drive NW of
Newcastle. 'High class. Superb furnishings. Warm, attentive staff.'
Period features, neutral colours. Drawing room, dining room (private
party atmosphere, guests eat and drink together), library, ballroom. No
background music. Weddings, house parties, small conferences a
speciality. 7 bedrooms. B&B £64–£80 per person. Dinner £35.

MUCH WENLOCK Shropshire   Map 3:C5
The Raven, Barrow Street, TF13 6EN. *Tel* 01952-727251, www.
ravenhotel.com. White-fronted 17th-century coaching inn, 12 miles SE
of Shrewsbury. 'Central yet quiet.' Managed by Kirk Heywood. Bar,
2 dining rooms 'prettily arranged' in original 15th-century almshouses
(alfresco meals in summer); classical background music. Courtyard:
small herb garden. 'Excellent service.' Parking. 15 bedrooms (some
across courtyard). B&B £60–£85 per person.

NAYLAND Suffolk   Map 2:C5
The White Hart, 11 High Street, CO6 4JF. *Tel* 01206-263382,
www.whitehart-nayland.co.uk. Owned by Michel Roux (see *Waterside
Inn*, Bray, main entry), now managed by Christine Altug with head chef
Didier Piot: 15th-century coaching inn in pretty village 6 miles N of
Colchester. Lots of character (beams, sloping floors, roaring fires).
Children welcomed. 'Friendly staff.' Lounge, bar/restaurant (home-
grown/locally sourced food); 'good breakfast'; private dining room.
Background music. Terrace; garden. Parking. 6 bedrooms (plain walls,
brightly checked fabrics). B&B £48–£109 per person. Lunch £12.90–
£17.90. Dinner £45.

NEWBURY Berkshire   Map 2:D2
The Vineyard at Stockcross, RG20 8JU. *Tel* 01635-528770, www.
the-vineyard.co.uk. 3 miles NW of centre, Sir Peter Michael's (founder
of Classic FM) 'restaurant with room to stay' (Relais & Chateaux):
former hunting lodge with eclectic art collection. Managed by Nicolas
Peth. Two *Michelin* stars for chef John Campbell. Lounge/conservatory,
bar, restaurant; no background music; function facilities. Spa: swimming
pool, gym. Landscaped garden: patio. Parking. 49 bedrooms (some on
ground floor): £172.50–£345. Breakfast £18.50. Dinner £37–£42.

NEWCASTLE UPON TYNE Tyne and WearMap 4:B4

Malmaison, The Quayside, NE1 3DX. *Tel* 0191-245 5000, www. malmaison.com. On quayside near Millennium Bridge: former warehouse converted in contemporary style (strong colours, bold prints, modern furniture); quirky touches. Managed by Lizzy Kelk. 2 lounges, café, bar, brasserie (dimly lit); background music. Lift. Spa. 122 bedrooms (most with river views; 4 suitable for &): £80–£375. Breakfast from £11.95.

NEWMARKET Suffolk   Map 2:B4

Bedford Lodge, Bury Road, CB8 7BX. *Tel* 01638-663175, www. bedfordlodgehotel.co.uk. Within easy walking distance of town, updated Georgian hunting lodge in 3-acre secluded gardens near racecourse. Managed by Noel Byrne. Lounge, *Roxanna* bar, *Orangery* restaurant; background music; extensive function/wedding/conference facilities; fitness centre (indoor swimming pool, beauty salon); 24-hour room service. 55 bedrooms (1 on ground floor). B&B £75–£170 per person. Dinner £26.50.

NEWQUAY Cornwall   Map 1:D2

The Headland Hotel, Fistral Beach, TR7 1EW. *Tel* 01637-872211, www.headlandhotel.co.uk. 'Traditional British hospitality' provided by owners for 28 years, John and Carolyn Armstrong, with manager Ivan Curtis in 'stunning location' by Fistral beach ('UK's surfing capital'). Large Victorian edifice (coastal views on 3 sides; contemporary/ traditional decor). 'Professional staff, good food.' 'My dog enjoyed his stay.' Lounges, bar, *Sand* brasserie ('casual meals by day, more intimate from 6 pm'), terrace (alfresco dining); background and live music; conference/function facilities; snooker; table tennis; 2 swimming pools, sauna; croquet; tennis; 9-hole golf approach course and putting green. Families welcomed (bunk beds, baby-listening, entertainments, etc). 104 bedrooms. B&B £42.50–£135 per person. Dinner £39.

NORWICH Norfolk   Map 2:B5

Annesley House, 6 Newmarket Road, NR2 2LA. *Tel* 01603-624553, www.bw-annesleyhouse.co.uk. In 3-acre grounds in conservation area near centre: Best Western hotel (2 Grade II listed Georgian houses). Run since 1985 by owners David and Jill Reynolds. Bar/lounge, attractive conservatory restaurant (views over water gardens and koi pond; background music); conference/function facilities. Wi-Fi. Garden. Parking. 26 bedrooms (some face main road). B&B £44–£62 per person; D,B&B £79.50–£87.

Beaufort Lodge, 62 Earlham Road, NR2 3DF. *Tel* 01603-667402, www.beaufortlodge.com. Managed by owners Aylwin and Don Shingler: B&B in handsome Victorian villa 5 mins' walk from centre. Lounge/conservatory, breakfast room (classical background music). Small garden. 10 bedrooms (3 in annexe). No credit cards. B&B £30–£70 per person.

Catton Old Hall, Lodge Lane, Old Catton, NR6 7HG. *Tel* 01603-419379, www.catton-hall.co.uk. Characterful small hotel (oak beams, mullioned windows, inglenook hearths) built 1632, in village suburb 2½ miles NE of centre. Afternoon tea; dinner by arrangement (owner Anthea Cawdron uses old family recipes). Vegetarian options at breakfast; afternoon tea by fire or on patio. Drawing room, dining room. No background music. Wi-Fi. Garden. 7 bedrooms (each with own lounge). B&B £32.50–£75 per person.

Norfolk Mead, Church Loke, Coltishall, NR12 7DN. *Tel* 01603-737531, www.norfolkmead.co.uk. Jill and Don Fleming's Georgian manor house in 8-acre grounds by River Bure, 7 miles NE of Norwich, on edge of Norfolk Broads. 'We arrived by water. Lovely stay, nice food, great staff.' Lounge, bar, restaurant; background music; conference facilities. Walled garden, unheated swimming pool; fishing lake; off-river mooring. Children welcomed. 13 bedrooms (2 beamed ones in cottage suite). B&B £60–£80 per person; D,B&B £90–£115.

NOTTINGHAM Nottinghamshire   Map 2:A3
Lace Market Hotel, 29–31 High Pavement, NG1 1HE. *Tel* 0115-852 3232, www.lacemarkethotel.co.uk. Owned by James Blick, managed by Susanne Martin: conversion of 4 Georgian and Victorian town houses (one a former lace factory), facing church of St Mary the Virgin. *Saint* cocktail bar, *Merchants* restaurant (French cuisine), *Cock & Hoop* gastropub. Background music. Contemporary, minimalist decor. Free access to nearby health club. Wedding/function facilities. 'Excellent continental breakfast, friendly staff.' 42 bedrooms: £99–£249. Breakfast £14.95. Dinner £45.

Restaurant Sat Bains, Lenton Lane, NG7 2SA. *Tel* 0115-986 6566, www.restaurantsatbains.com. On city outskirts, *Michelin*-starred restaurant with 8 sleek bedrooms. Run by eponymous chef/*patron* and wife Amanda. Lounge, bar, restaurant (dinner only, closed Sun/Mon), Tasting Room, conservatory, courtyard. Background music. B&B £45–£115 per person; D,B&B from £110. Tasting menu £65.

OTTERBURN Northumberland   Map 4:B3
Otterburn Tower, NE19 1NS. *Tel* 01830-520620, www.otterburntower.com. On 32-acre estate, fronted by terraced lawns amid woodland,

owner/manager Robin Goodfellow's fortified country house on ancient site (founded 1086 by cousin of William the Conqueror). Oak panelling, Florentine marble fireplace. 2 drawing rooms, bar, breakfast room, restaurant (farm produce), garden room; classical background music; wedding/function facilities; private stretch of River Rede (fishing). Children welcomed. 'Excellent value for money.' 30 mins' drive from Newcastle. 18 bedrooms (1 suitable for &.). B&B £65–£95 per person, D,B&B £85–£115.

OXFORD Oxfordshire   Map 2:C2
Burlington House, 374 Banbury Road, OX2 7PP. *Tel* 01865-513513, www.burlington-house.co.uk. In leafy Summertown, 1½ miles from centre: B&B in handsome Victorian house on busy road. 'Most welcoming' resident manager, Nes Saini. 'Small, attractive' sitting room, 'pleasant' breakfast room (home-made bread and granola). Wi-Fi. No background music. Small rear oriental garden. Parking. 12 bedrooms (3 on ground floor). 'Mine, stylish, characterful, had lovely bathroom, green outlook.' B&B £42.50–£65 per person

Cotswold House, 363 Banbury Road, OX2 7PL. *Tel* 01865-310558, www.cotswoldhouse.co.uk. 2 miles N of centre on busy road (reliable bus service): Derek and Hilary Walker's B&B in Cotswold stone building. Lounge, breakfast room (fresh fruit; home-made muesli; vegetarian options). No background music. Wi-Fi. Garden. Parking. 8 bedrooms (1 on ground floor). B&B £45–£67 per person.

The Randolph, Beaumont Street, OX1 2LN. *Tel* 0870 400 8200, www.randolph-hotel.com. Oxford institution (Victorian Gothic) by Ashmolean Museum, now high-comfort chain hotel (Macdonald group) with 'attentive manager', Michael Grange. 'Spick and span. Well-equipped bedroom. Good breakfast.' Lounge (pianist on Sat), *Morse* bar, restaurant (classical background music); lift; cellar spa (vaulted ceilings, Italian tiling, candlelight; thermal suite, hydrotherapy bath, relaxation room). Children welcomed. 151 bedrooms (1 suitable for &.). B&B £79.50–£270 per person; D,B&B £109.50–£330.

PENRITH Cumbria   Map 4: inset C2
The George, Devonshire Street, CA11 7SU. *Tel* 01768-862696, www.georgehotelpenrith.co.uk. In centre, 300-year-old coaching inn with traditional decor. Part of Grange family's small Lakeland group; managed by Wayne Bartholomew. Lounges (background music at night), *Oak* bar, candlelit *Devonshire* restaurant (ornate ceiling); wedding/function/conference facilities. Free day membership of local swimming

pool and gym. Parking. Lake Ullswater 4 miles. 35 bedrooms. B&B: £53–£103 per person; D,B&B £89–£122.

Westmorland Hotel, nr Orton, CA10 3SB. *Tel* 01539-624351, www. westmorlandhotel.com. Secluded modern hotel just off M6 (Tebay Motorway Services, Junction 38), managed by Martin Richardson. 'Ideal stopover.' 'What a find. Welcoming, friendly, efficient, reasonably priced, clean.' Contemporary design blended with traditional materials. 'Dramatic' moorland and mountain views. Bar (log fires), lounge, split-level dining room ('excellent dinner'); background music; Wi-Fi; function facilities. 50 bedrooms. B&B £47–£100 per person; D,B&B £69–£119.

PENZANCE Cornwall   Map 1:E1

Hotel Penzance, Britons Hill, TR18 3AE. *Tel* 01736-363117, www. hotelpenzance.com. With 'wonderful views' over harbour and bay to St Michael's Mount, Stephen and Yvonne Hill's 'relaxing' hotel, managed by Andrew Griffiths. Conversion of two 1920s houses. 3 lounges, conservatory, *Bay* restaurant (background music). Children welcomed. Local art displays. Small subtropical garden: heated outdoor swimming pool. 24 bedrooms (2 on ground floor). B&B £50–£80 per person; D,B&B £70–£102.

PETERSFIELD Hampshire   Map 2:E3

JSW, 20 Dragon Street, GU31 4JJ, *Tel* 01730-262030. 'Sensational' modern British cooking (*Michelin* star) by Jake Watkins (served Tues–Sat, booking essential). White-painted former coaching inn in centre of pleasant market town. Restaurant, rear courtyard (alfresco dining). 3 bedrooms upstairs ('comfortable, minimalist'). B&B £42.50–£55 per person. Dinner £27–£43.

PLYMOUTH Devon   Map 1:D4

Bowling Green Hotel, 9–10 Osborne Place, Lockyer St, The Hoe, PL1 2PU. *Tel* 01752-209090, www.bowlinggreenhotel.co.uk. Owned by Tom Roberts: small B&B in Georgian house facing 'Drake's bowling green', 5 mins' walk from Barbican. Views across Plymouth Hoe. Lounge, TV room, breakfast room, conservatory. No background music. Parking. 12 bedrooms. B&B £34–£48 per person.

POOLE Dorset   Map 2:E1

Hotel du Vin Poole (formerly *The Mansion House*), Thames Street, BH15 1JN. *Tel* 01202-685666, www.hotelduvin.com. Reopening summer

2008 after refurbishment: Georgian town house (1779) in quiet cul-de-sac near church and quay. Bar, bistro; alfresco dining; function facilities; roof garden. No background music. Parking. 38 bedrooms: £170–£450. Breakfast £11.95–£13.95.

READING Berkshire   Map 2:D3
The Forbury, 26 The Forbury, RG1 3EJ. *Tel* 08000-789789, www.theforburyhotel.co.uk. Striking modern design meets old civic grandeur: central hotel in 100-year-old County Hall building. Managed by David Reed. Up-to-the-minute equipment; artwork by French and British painters and sculptors. Lounge, grand salon, library, *Cerise* restaurant, cellar dining room; background music; cinema; lift; small 'secret' garden; function facilities. 23 bedrooms. B&B from £115 per person; D,B&B £150.

ROCK Cornwall   Map 1:D2
St Enodoc, nr Wadebridge, PL27 6LA. *Tel* 01208-863394, www.enodoc-hotel.co.uk. Family-friendly hotel, now managed by Kate Simms, in 'super position' on Camel estuary. 2 lounges, TV room, bar/restaurant (classical background music); playroom; games/billiards room; sauna, heated outdoor swimming pool. Terrace; ½-acre garden. Bright, colourful decor; 'exceptional bathrooms'. Sandy beach nearby. 20 bedrooms. B&B £65–£185 per person; D,B&B £90–£120.

ROSS-ON-WYE Herefordshire   Map 3:D5
The Hill House, Howle Hill, HR9 5ST. *Tel* 01989-562033, www.thehowlinghillhouse.com. Duncan and Alex Stayton's 17th-century house high above Forest of Dean (views of Black Mountains). Quirky style (ghosts promised); eco-friendly. Organic local produce (free-range hens; home-grown vegetables); Aga-cooked, vegetarian-friendly breakfasts; packed lunch/evening meal by arrangement. Morning room, lounge, bar (background music), restaurant; hot tub; sauna (charges); cinema (DVD film library). Garden; 4½-acre woodland. 5 bedrooms. B&B £25–£35 per person. Dinner £10–£15.

Pencraig Court, Pencraig, HR9 6HR. *Tel* 01989 770306, www.pencraig-court.co.uk. Overlooking River Wye, managed by owners Malcolm and Liz Dobson: yellow-painted Georgian country house, traditionally furnished. 4 miles SW of town. 3½-acre garden (croquet) and woodlands; lovely views. 2 lounges, dining room (classical background music; garden produce). Dogs welcomed (by arrangement). 11 bedrooms (1 family). B&B £43–£75 per person. Dinner £28.

RYE East Sussex   Map 2:E5
Durrant House, 2 Market Street, TN31 7LA. *Tel* 01797-223182, www. durranthouse.com. Jilly Mitchell and William Bilecki's 'very friendly' small, central guest house. White-painted Georgian facade, hanging flower baskets. Lounge with honesty bar, breakfast room (vegetarian options; background CDs/radio). Small garden: 'exhilarating views' over Romney Marsh to sea. 5 bedrooms (1 can be family; 1 four-poster). B&B £47.50–£70 per person.

ST IVES Cornwall   Map 1:D1
Blue Hayes, Trelyon Avenue, TR26 2AD. *Tel* 01736-797129, www. bluehayes.co.uk. On Porthminster Point, overlooking bay and harbour, small luxury hotel in 1920s house owned by Malcolm Herring. 2 lounges, bar, dining room; terrace (panoramic views). Civil wedding licence. No background music. Small garden: gate leading to South West Coast Path. Parking. 6 bedrooms (some with balcony, roof terrace, patio). Small function facilities. B&B £75–£155 per person. Supper £15.

The Garrack, Burthallan Lane, TR26 3AA. *Tel* 01736-796199, www. garrack.com. Creeper-clad building on hill overlooking Porthmeor beach, a short, steep walk from town. Owned for over 40 years by Kilby family. 'As good as ever, excellent value.' Lounge, restaurant (recent makeover; Cornish produce; background music); leisure centre (gym, sauna, indoor swimming pool). 2-acre garden: sun terrace. Parking. 18 bedrooms (2 suitable for ♿). B&B £60–£105 per person; D,B&B £77–£150.

The Porthminster, The Terrace, TR26 2BN. *Tel* 01736-795221, www. porthminster-hotel.co.uk. Above famous beach, Victorian building in subtropical gardens overlooking bay and Godrevy Lighthouse. Owned since Jan 2008 by Christchurch Hotels, managed by Ben Young. Traditional interior. Lift. Lounge, bar, cocktail bar, restaurant (Cornish fare; fish and seafood); background music; function/wedding/business facilities. Wi-Fi. Heated indoor swimming pool, garden (outdoor pool). 42 bedrooms (some family). B&B £50–£140 per person; D,B&B £60–£150.

SALISBURY Wiltshire   Map 2:D2
Leena's, 50 Castle Road, SP1 3RL. *Tel* 01722-335419. Leena and Malcolm Street's budget B&B in Edwardian house on busy Amesbury road (double glazing), 15 mins' riverside walk from centre. Lounge, breakfast room. No background music. Children welcomed. Garden. Parking. 6 bedrooms (1 on ground floor). B&B £30–£32 per person.

Milford Hall, 206 Castle Street, SP1 3TE. *Tel* 01722-417411, www. milfordhallhotel.com. 5 mins' walk from centre: Georgian mansion with modern extension, owned by Hughes family. Lounge, bar, *brasserie@206* (in grounds); conference/business/wedding facilities; Masonic festival weekends; Wi-Fi; background music. Parking. 34 bedrooms. B&B £66–£112 per person.

Spire House, 84 Exeter Street, SP1 2SE. *Tel* 01722-339213, www.salisbury-bedandbreakfast.com. Near cathedral: Lois and John Faulkner's B&B in 18th-century Grade II listed town house. Full English or healthy breakfast. No background music. Walled garden. Parking opposite. 4 bedrooms. B&B £35–£70 per person.

SCARBOROUGH North Yorkshire   Map 4:C5

Interludes, 32 Princess Street, YO11 1QR. *Tel* 01723-360513, www.interludeshotel.co.uk. Listed Georgian building in Old Town conservation area, run by theatre buffs Ian Grundy and Bob Harris. 'Eccentrically decorated' (thespian memorabilia); 2 resident cats. Lounge, dining room (background music: light classical/stage shows); small patio. 5 bedrooms (4 with sea views). B&B £26–£36 per person. Pre-theatre meal ('simple but tasty') £14.

Phoenix Court, 8/9 Rutland Terrace, YO12 7JB. *Tel* 01723-501150, www.hotel-phoenix.co.uk. On headland overlooking North Bay, 2 Victorian terrace houses run as guest house by owners Alison and Bryan Edwards. Refurbishment continues. Lounge, bar area, dining room (background radio during breakfast). Car park. 16 bedrooms (9 with sea views, 1 on ground floor). Local and fair trade produce at breakfast. B&B £25–£40 per person.

SHEFFIELD South Yorkshire   Map 4:E4

The Leopold, Leopold Street, S1 2JG. *Tel* 0114-252 4000, www.leopoldhotel.co.uk. Sleekly converted old school building in revitalised Leopold Square area. Now large hotel, owned by Irish PREM group, managed by George Arizmendi. Quirky decor: sombre colours, school memorabilia (old photos, ranks of coat pegs). Bar, restaurant, terrace; 24-hour room service. Background music. Conference/function facilities. 90 bedrooms (6 suitable for &). B&B £49.50–£169 per person.

SHIPSTON-ON-STOUR Warwickshire   Map 3:D6

The George, High Street, CV36 4AJ. *Tel* 01608-661453, www.thefabulousgeorgehotel.com. Old coaching inn, restored in contemporary style by owner Sue Hawkins 'without spoiling traditional look of attractive building'. Very popular. 'Operates well in all it sets out to do.' Library bar, main bar (log fires, sash windows on to market square), brasserie, private dining/meeting room. Background music. 'Laid-back, relaxing. Good dinners and breakfasts.' 16 bright bedrooms. B&B £60–£145 per person.

SHREWSBURY Shropshire   Map 3:B4
Chatford House, Bayston Hill, Chatford, SY3 0AY. *Tel* 01743-718301, www.chatfordhouse.co.uk. In hamlet 5 miles S of city, comfortable B&B in Grade II listed farmhouse run by owners Christine and Rupert Farmer. Views of The Wrekin. Home-made cake and damson gin. Local ingredients used for Aga-cooked breakfast. Sitting room, dining room (piano CDs). Garden. Children welcomed. No credit cards. 3 bedrooms. B&B £30–£45 per person.

SIDMOUTH Devon   Map 1:C5
Victoria Hotel, The Esplanade, EX10 8RY. *Tel* 01395-512651, www.victoriahotel.co.uk. 'First-class welcome and attention.' Majestic hotel (Brend Group), managed by Matthew Raistrick. In 5-acre grounds on hill at W end of esplanade (views across bay). Long-serving staff. Lounges, restaurant; background music; snooker; gym; outdoor/indoor swimming pool, whirlpool, sauna, solarium; tennis, putting. Families welcomed. 61 bedrooms ('comfortable, well equipped', some with sea views and balcony). B&B £77.50–£140 per person.

SOUTHWOLD Suffolk   Map 2:B6
The Swan, Market Place, IP18 6EG. *Tel* 01502-722186, www.adnamshotels.co.uk. 300-year-old building on market square, managed for Adnams by Jade Arnold. Traditional decor. Lift. 2 lounges, bar, restaurant; function facilities. No background music. Garden. Parking. Beach 200 yds. 42 bedrooms (1 suitable for &; 17 dog-friendly garden rooms round old bowling green). 'The short stay was a great success – accommodation good, staff helpful, food delicious.' B&B £76–£116 per person. Dinner £32–£37.

STANSTED Essex   Map 2:C4
Oak Lodge, Jacks Lane, Smiths Green, Takeley, CM22 6NT. *Tel* 01279-871667, www.oaklodgebb.com. In village 2 miles SE of airport: B&B in characterful 16th-century house, run by 'hugely welcoming' owners, Jan and Ron Griffiths. Lounge/TV room, dining room. Wi-Fi. No background music. 2-acre garden. Parking (moderate long-term rates). 4 bedrooms. B&B £30–£50 per person. Dinner (by arrangement) £19.

STOKE CANON Devon   Map 1:C5
Barton Cross Hotel, Huxham, EX5 4EJ. *Tel* 01392-841245, *email* bartonxhuxham@aol.com. In quiet location, 4 miles N of Exeter off A396: 'considerate host' Brian Hamilton's part-thatched 17th-century house. Low beams, gallery, inglenook fires. Ramps. Lounge, bar, restaurant. No background music. 1-acre garden. Parking. 9 bedrooms (some on ground floor). B&B £52.50–£80 per person; D,B&B £73–£98.

SUTTON COLDFIELD Warwickshire   Map 3:C6
New Hall Hotel, Walmley Rd, B76 1QX. *Tel* 0121-378 2442, www.newhalluk.com. Reputedly oldest inhabited moated manor house in England, 20 mins' drive from Birmingham. Managed by Mark Clayton. Formerly hunting lodge for earls of Warwick (Grade I listed). Lounges, bar; background music; oak-panelled *Bridge* restaurant, *Terrace* room; leisure facilities (swimming pool, whirlpool, steam room, beauty treatments, fitness room); function facilities. 26-acre grounds: tennis, 9-hole par 3 golf course. 60 bedrooms. B&B £47.50–£65 per person. Dinner from £30.

SWAY Hampshire   Map 2:E2
The Nurse's Cottage, Station Road, nr Lymington, SO41 6BA. *Tel* 01590-683402, www.nursescottage.co.uk. With 'hands-on' owner Tony Barnfield, restaurant-with-rooms in small house, once the home of successive district nurses. Sitting area, conservatory restaurant. Background music. 5 bedrooms (all on ground floor; disabled-friendly, equipped for mobility/hearing/visual impairment). 5 bedrooms. D,B&B £80–£90 per person.

SWINDON Wiltshire   Map 2:C2
The Landmark Hotel, Station Road, Chiseldon, SN4 0PW. *Tel* 01793-740149, www.landmarkhotel.com. 16 bedrooms. Light, modern hotel in rural location on Swindon outskirts, 'beautifully run' by Trevor Mitchell (owner) and Paul Heal (manager). 'Feeling of peace and space. Superb service, lovely staff.' Lounge/bar area, restaurant (background music), courtyard; small function facilities. 16 bedrooms (5 with balcony; 5 with courtyard garden access). B&B £50–£75 per person; D,B&B £60–£90.

TEIGNMOUTH Devon   Map 1:D5
Britannia House, 26 Teign Street, TQ14 8EG. *Tel* 01626-770051, www.britanniahouse.org. Blue-walled 16th-century sea captain's house

in maze of small streets 5 mins' walk from seafront, now Jennifer and Michael Gillett's 'very welcoming', 'well-run' B&B. Local ingredients at 'very good' breakfast. Sitting room (with music centre), dining room. No background music. Small walled garden. 3 bedrooms. B&B £30–£60 per person.

TETBURY Gloucestershire   Map 3:E5

The Close, 8 Long Street, GL8 8AQ. *Tel* 01666-502272, www.theclose-hotel.com. Crenellated 16th-century yeoman's house in centre, a hotel since 1974. Owned by Greene King group, managed by Colin and Val Holman. Elegant interior: panelled rooms; dramatic touches. Lounge, bar, *Garden* restaurant (Adam ceiling); background music; function/wedding facilities. Terrace: alfresco meals, fountain. Walled garden. Parking. 15 bedrooms. B&B from £52.50 per person.

THIRSK North Yorkshire   Map 4:C4

Oswalds, Front Street, Sowerby, YO7 1JF. *Tel* 01845-523655, www.oswaldsrestaurantwithrooms.co.uk. Owned by David Hawkins's IDH group, managed by Leon Moshatos: light, airy restaurant-with-rooms on quiet tree-lined street, a short walk from racecourse. North Yorkshire national park and Yorkshire dales nearby. Lounge, bar, restaurant; constant background music; function room. Parking. 16 bedrooms (5 in main house, some across courtyard or in stable block; 1 suitable for &). B&B £40–£80 per person; D,B&B £62.50–£72.50.

THORPE ST ANDREW Norfolk   Map 2:B5

The Old Rectory, 103 Yarmouth Road, NR7 0HF. *Tel* 01603-700772, www.oldrectorynorwich.com. Creeper-clad Georgian rectory (Grade II listed) 2½ miles from Norwich. Home of Sally and Chris Entwistle and Birman cats Rolo and Milli. Drawing room, dining room, conservatory; terrace. Background music. Wi-Fi. Meeting/function facilities. 1-acre garden; heated swimming pool. 8 bedrooms (3 in coach house). B&B £59–£87 per person. Dinner £24–£26.

TISBURY Wiltshire   Map 2:D1

The Compasses Inn, Lower Chicksgrove, SP3 6NB. *Tel* 01722-714318, www.thecompassesinn.com. Alan and Susie Stoneham's 14th-century pub (thatched roof, stone-paved path; views; some low ceilings) in rural setting off A30, halfway between Salisbury and Shaftesbury. Bar, dining room. Garden. No background music. 4 bedrooms (plus 3-bed cottage). B&B £42.50–£65 per person. Dinner from £31.

TOTNES Devon   Map 1:D4
Royal Seven Stars, The Plains, TQ9 5DD. *Tel* 01803-862125,
www.royalsevenstars.co.uk. 17th-century coaching inn in town centre,
renovated in contemporary style by owners Nigel and Anne Way;
managed by Margaret Stone. Environment-friendly policy. Local watering hole; light meals available all day. Lounge, 2 bars (background
music; log fires in winter); restaurant; alfresco dining; terrace; balcony.
Wi-Fi. Business facilities. Civil wedding licence. Parking. 18 bedrooms
(quietest at back). B&B £54.50–£110 per person. Dinner £30.

TUNBRIDGE WELLS Kent   Map 2:D4
Smart and Simple, 54–57 London Road, TN1 1DS. *Tel* 0845-402 5744,
www.smartandsimple.co.uk. Near centre, William Inglis's budget hotel
with stylish touches. Plainly furnished bedrooms; views over 'secret'
garden (lots of steps down) or town common. Bar, restaurant (*tapas*
dishes), conservatory; meeting rooms, small gym (£5 fee). Wi-Fi. Background music. 40 bedrooms. B&B (continental) £40–£50 per person.

ULLSWATER Cumbria   Map 4: inset C2
The Inn on the Lake, Glenridding, CA11 0PE. *Tel* 017684-82444,
www.lakedistricthotels.net. 'Superb location' at rugged end of Lake
Ullswater: 15-acre grounds leading to shore; access to footpath network
to mountains. Large, traditional hotel (Lake District group), managed
by Gary Wilson. Lounge, 2 bars, *Lake View* restaurant ('dishes elaborate;
delicious without exception; very good breakfasts; smart, courteous
staff'); background music; conference/function/wedding facilities. Parking. 46 bedrooms. B&B £69–£110 per person; D,B&B £92–£133.

VENTNOR Isle of Wight   Map 2:E2
The Royal Hotel, Belgrave Road, PO38 1JJ. *Tel* 01983-852186,
www.royalhoteliow.co.uk. Owned by William Bailey, managed by
Jennie McKee, classic seaside hotel (largest on island), used by Queen
Victoria as annexe to Osborne House. 5 mins' walk from centre.
2 lounges, bar, restaurant, conservatory; resident pianist peak season
weekends. 2-acre landscaped gardens: terrace, heated swimming pool,
children's play area. Sandy beach nearby (hilly walk). Parking. 55 bedrooms (some suitable for &). B&B £80–£130 per person. Dinner £36.

WARWICK Warwickshire   Map 3:C6
Northleigh House, Five Ways Road, Hatton, CV35 7HZ. *Tel* 01926-
484203, www.northleigh.co.uk. Viv and Fred Morgan's white-painted

B&B in countryside 4 miles N of Warwick. Children and dogs welcome. Sitting room (log fire), dining room. Organic breakfasts. No background music. 1-acre garden. 7 bedrooms (1 suitable for &). B&B £35–£50 per person. Family-style evening meal by arrangement £7.

WESTON-SUPER-MARE Somerset   Map 1:B6

Beachlands, 17 Uphill Road North, BS23 4NG. *Tel* 01934-621401, www. beachlandshotel.com. Overlooking sand dunes (300 yds from beach) and 18-hole golf course, traditional hotel owned by Charles and Beverly Porter. 2 lounges, bar, restaurant; background music. 10-metre indoor swimming pool, sauna; function/business facilities. Wi-Fi. Children welcome. Garden. Parking. 21 bedrooms (some on ground floor). B&B £59–£70 per person. Dinner £22.50.

Church House, 27 Kewstoke Road, Kewstoke, BS22 9YD. *Tel* 01934-633185, www.churchhousekewstoke.co.uk. By Norman church, former residence of vicar of Kewstoke, now Jane and Tony Chapman's immaculate B&B. Peaceful location; sea views to Wales. Dining room (home-made preserves; eggs from own free-range hens). No background music. Wi-Fi. Garden. 5 bedrooms. B&B £37.50–£55 per person.

WHITBY North Yorkshire   Map 4:C5

Bagdale Hall, 1 Bagdale, YO21 1QL. *Tel* 01947-602958, www.bagdale. co.uk. Central hotel in 3 historic buildings, owned by John Cattaneo, managed by Michael Fagg. Lounge, bar, restaurant. No background music. Children welcomed. 6 bedrooms in *The Hall* (Tudor manor house steeped in character: mullioned windows, beamed ceilings, carved wooden over-mantels; four-poster beds). 8 bedrooms in *No 4* (Georgian town house). 12 bedrooms in *The Lodge* (detached Georgian mansion with more modern furnishings). 1 room suitable for &. B&B £45–£75 per person.

Dunsley Hall, Dunsley, YO21 3TL. *Tel* 01947-893437, www.dunsleyhall. com. Victorian mansion built for shipping magnate, in hamlet 2½ miles NW of Whitby. Run by owner Bill Ward: traditional country house ambience (oak panelling, stained glass window with seafaring scene, inglenook fireplace, four-posters). Lounge, *Pyman's* bar (background music), fine-dining restaurant. 4-acre landscaped gardens: putting, croquet, tennis; hotel's working farm nearby. Sea 1 mile. Parking. 26 bedrooms (8 in new wing, some suitable for &). B&B £74.50–£90 per person.

WILLINGTON Cheshire   Map 3:A5

Willington Hall, CW6 0NB. *Tel* 01829-752321, www.willingtonhall. co.uk. 'Beautifully situated, wonderfully quiet' 19th-century building owned by Diana and Stuart Begbie. In 17-acre formal gardens and parkland at foot of Willington hills, 3½ miles NW of Tarporley, 10 miles E of Chester. Original features, antiques, family portraits; traditionally furnished. Lounge, 2 bars (light meals), restaurant (*à la carte/table d'hôte*); terrace; wedding/function facilities. No background music. 10 bedrooms. B&B £60–£80 per person. Dinner £29.50.

WINCHESTER Hampshire   Map 2:D2

Lainston House, Sparsholt, SO21 2LT. *Tel* 01962-776088, www. exclusivehotels.co.uk. 'Lovely country house hotel.' 'High-quality food.' Managed by Cliff Hasler: 17th-century building in 'superb' 63-acre grounds (12th-century chapel ruin; dovecote; sundial garden), 2½ miles NW of city by B3049. Wood panelling; four-poster beds; smart bathrooms; elegant, traditional style. Drawing room, *Cedar* bar, *Avenue* restaurant; terrace (alfresco dining); gym; tennis; croquet; function/ wedding facilities. No background music. Children welcomed. Fishing packages (River Test). 50 bedrooms (4 in courtyard or stables; some suitable for &): £62.50–£170. Breakfast from £17.

Hotel du Vin Winchester, 14 Southgate Street, SO23 9EF. *Tel* 01962-841414, www.hotelduvin.com. Grade II listed Queen Anne house near cathedral: original Hotel du Vin, now part of Marylebone Warwick Balfour group (also owners of Malmaison hotels). Managed by Phillip Lewis. Drawing room, bar, terrace. No background music. 24 bedrooms (4 quietest ones in walled garden): £135–£175. Breakfast £9.95–£13.50.

WINDERMERE Cumbria   Map 4: inset C2

1 Park Road, 1 Park Road, LA23 2AW. *Tel* 015394-42107, www. 1parkroad.com. 'Home comforts, but more luxurious' at Mary and Philip Burton's small guest house in residential area 2 mins' walk from centre. Lounge (grand piano), dining room (locally sourced food; 'well conceived, delicious dinner'). Background music ('a key point of life here') at dinner, sometimes at breakfast. Picnic hamper/rucksack available. Wi-Fi. Children welcomed. 6 bedrooms. B&B £48–£80 per person; D,B&B £70–£107.

WOODSTOCK Oxfordshire   Map 2:C2

The Feathers, Market Street, OX20 1SX. *Tel* 01993-812291, www. feathers.co.uk. 17th-century inn, now smart hotel, privately owned, managed by Luc Morel. 'Comfortable, peaceful.' 'Delicious food, excellent service.' Rambling interior, lots of steps. Antiques, paintings, log fires. Drawing room, study, bar, restaurant, bistro (background music);

function facilities; beauty treatments; garden/patio (alfresco dining). 20 bedrooms. B&B £84.50–£139.50 per person; D,B&B £40 added.

YORK North Yorkshire   Map 4:D4

Bar Convent, 17 Blossom Street, YO30 6BL. *Tel* 01904-643238, www. bar-convent.org.uk. Georgian building (Grade I listed) near Micklegate, managed by Joanne Dodd: England's oldest active convent (sisters of the Congregation of Jesus). Sitting rooms, licensed café, meeting rooms, museum, shop, 18th-century domed chapel (weddings); function facilities, garden. Lift to 1st/part of 2nd floor. No background music. Garden. Simple accommodation (communal self-catering facilities, sitting area on each floor). 18 bedrooms (some suitable for &; beds upgraded this year). B&B (continental) £32–£37.50 per person. Full English breakfast £3.50.

The Bloomsbury, 127 Clifton, YO30 6BL. *Tel* 01904-634031, www. bloomsburyhotel.co.uk. B&B in Victorian house in leafy area, 12 mins' walk from minster. New owner/managers in 2008, Dawn and Paul Fielding. Bright, sunny dining room; vegetarian/special diets catered for. No background music. Wi-Fi. Courtyard. Parking. 9 bedrooms. B&B £30–£65 per person.

Dean Court, Duncombe Place, YO1 7EF. *Tel* 01904-625082, www. deancourt-york.co.uk. Opposite minster ('one of best hotel room views in the country'), Best Western hotel managed by David Brooks. 'Comfortable, enjoyable; good dinner and breakfast.' Contemporary style. Ramp, 2 lounges, bar, *D.C.H.* restaurant, *The Court* cafe/bistro/bar; background music; lift; conference/function facilities. Wi-Fi throughout. Children welcomed. Valet parking. 37 bedrooms (some family; 3 suitable for &). B&B £47.50–£104 per person; D,B&B £77.50–£134.

Hotel du Vin York, 89 The Mount, YO24 1AX. *Tel* 01904-557350, www.hotelduvin.com. Former orphanage, 19th-century Grade II listed building in tranquil area just outside city walls. Now Hotel du Vin (opened Nov 2007), managed by Donna Penberthy. Atmospheric, dark decor; lots of wood, candles; freestanding baths. Bar, bistro; courtyard (alfresco dining); background music; function facilities, 3-acre grounds. Limited parking. 44 bedrooms (some suitable for &): £130–£395. Breakfast £9.95–£13.50.

SCOTLAND

ABERDEEN   Map 5:C3

The Marcliffe Hotel and Spa, North Deeside Road, Pitfodels, AB15 9YA. *Tel* 01224-861000, www.marcliffe.com. Owned by Stewart Spence, managed by John Davidson, refurbished this year: large, luxury hotel in lower Dee valley, 20 mins' drive from airport/centre. Country house decor. Drawing room, lounge, snooker room, bar, conservatory restaurant ('excellent dinner'), terrace (alfresco meals), 24-hour room service; lift. No background music. Spa; gym. Function facilities. 8-acre wooded grounds; putting. 42 bedrooms (1 adapted for ♿). B&B £107.50–£215 per person; D,B&B £127.50–£245.

ABERFELDY Perth and Kinross   **Map 5:D2**
Fortingall Hotel, Fortingall, PH15 2NQ. *Tel* 01887-830367, www. fortingall.com. 'Scotland should be proud of this hotel.' Handsome Victorian Highland country house, managed by Ellie Miles. By church in historic Arts and Crafts village designed by architect James M MacLaren, surrounded by Glen Lyon estate. Lounge, library, bar (meals served), 2 dining rooms (*Yew* the cosier). Live fiddle music. Drying facilities. 10 bedrooms (plain: soft shades with touches of tweed). B&B £70–£95 per person; D,B&B £95–£120.

ALYTH Perth and Kinross   **Map 5:D2**
Lands of Loyal, Loyal Road, PH11 8JQ. *Tel* 01828-633151, www. landsofloyal.com. Victorian mansion in 7-acre grounds, overlooking Vale of Strathmore. Traditionally furnished (panelling, stags' heads, chandeliers, open fires); run by Howell family owners. Great hall (modelled on lounge of *Mauritania* steamship), lounge, bar, dining room; background music; conference/wedding facilities. 14 bedrooms (3 in coach house). B&B £65–£95 per person; D,B&B £95–£125.

ARISAIG Highland   **Map 5:C1**
Cnoc-Na-Faíre, Back of Keppoch, PH39 4NS. *Tel* 01687-450249, www.cnoc-na-faire.co.uk. Jenny and David Sharpe's small hotel with 'gorgeous views', 1 mile from village, on Road to the Isles. 'Simple but good; very well run; jolly bar; good dinner and breakfast.' Lounge/bar/café (Internet, light lunches, suppers; views across sea to Skye), restaurant (Scottish theme); background music; wedding facilities (marquee); house parties. Substantial breakfast (can be in bed). Dogs welcomed (by arrangement; small charge). 6 bedrooms (plaid fabrics). B&B from £55 per person.

ASCOG Argyll and Bute   **Map 5:D1**
Balmory Hall, PA20 9LL. *Tel* 01700-500669, www.balmoryhall.com. On Isle of Bute, Tony and Beryl Harrison's elegant B&B in secluded

Victorian mansion overlooking Ascog Bay. House party atmosphere. Reception hall, drawing room, dining room. No background music. No stiletto heels. 10-acre grounds (deer, owls, hawks). 5 mins' walk to beach (seal colony). 4 bedrooms (plus self-catering lodge). B&B £65–£80 per person.

AYR South Ayrshire   Map 5:E1

Fairfield House, 12 Fairfield Road, KA7 2AR. *Tel* 01292-267461, www. fairfieldhotel.co.uk. On seafront (views across Firth of Clyde to Isle of Arran): former home of Victorian Glasgow tea merchant, now hotel with both modern and traditional furnishing. Owned by George Martin, managed by Stuart Maxwell. Reception area, *Martin's* bar/grill; leisure club (gym, indoor swimming pool, spa, sauna, steam room); background music throughout; Wi-Fi; function facilities. 44 bedrooms (some in modern extension). B&B £61.50–£89 per person.

BOWMORE Argyll and Bute   Map 5:D1

Harbour Inn and Restaurant, The Square, Isle of Islay, PA43 7JR. *Tel* 01496-810330, www.harbour-inn.com. Neil and Carol Scott's old white-washed inn by harbour of village on E side of Loch Indaal. Refurbished throughout this year. Light, fresh, predominantly blue decor. Conservatory lounge, *Schooner* bar, restaurant (seasonal specialities; 'mellow' background music). Wi-Fi. Small garden. 11 bedrooms (some in neighbouring guest house, *The Inn Over-by*). B&B £57.50–£72.50 per person.

BRACHLA Highland   Map 5:C2

Loch Ness Lodge, Loch Ness-side, IV3 8LA. *Tel* 01456-459469, www.lodgeatlochness.com. 'Wonderful ambience, food and service.' Overlooking loch, managed by owners Scott and Iona Sutherland, traditional white lodge with smart interior in modern neutral tones. Drawing room, snug, restaurant (Franco-Scottish cuisine; organic, local produce); background music; spa (hot tub, sauna, treatments). Wi-Fi. 18-acre grounds. 15 mins' drive from Inverness. 7 bedrooms (1 suitable for &). B&B £90–£140 per person. Dinner £45.

CASTLEBAY Western Isles   Map 5: inset A1

Castlebay Hotel, Isle of Barra, HS9 5XD. *Tel* 01871-810223, www. castlebayhotel.com. On main settlement of Barra, most southerly of the Western Isles, small hotel managed by John Campbell. Convenient for ferry; overlooking Kisimul Castle, harbour and island of Vatersay. 'Clean, comfortable; easy access when arriving from Oban.' Ramp.

Sitting room, cocktail bar, dining room (fish and seafood specialities), conservatory/sun porch; background music. Garden. Children welcomed. Lively pub next door. 15 bedrooms (1 suitable for &). B&B £39.50–£70 per person; D,B&B £15 added.

The Craigard Hotel, HS9 5XD. *Tel* 01871-810200, www.craigardhotel. co.uk. On hillside above town, small white hotel with huge terrace with 'breathtaking views' of bay and southern islands. Lounge, 2 bars, restaurant (local seafood specialities). Parking. 'Very friendly, helpful owner [Julian Capewell] and staff.' 7 bedrooms. B&B from £40 per person.

DUNDEE   Map 5:D3

Apex City Quay Hotel & Spa, 1 West Victoria Dock Road, DD1 3JP. *Tel* 01382-202404, www.apexhotels.co.uk. In city quay development with 'stunning' views over River Tay, 5-storey modern dockside hotel managed by Marcus Kenyon. Unprepossessing exterior; stylishly contemporary inside. *Metro* bar/brasserie, *Alchemy* restaurant; spa: gym, sauna, hot tubs, treatments; conference/events centre; background music throughout. Wi-Fi; free local calls. 153 bedrooms. B&B £47.50–£65 per person.

Duntrune House, Duntrune, DD4 0PJ. *Tel* 01382-350239, www. duntrunehouse.co.uk. Family history enthusiasts Barrie and Olwyn Jack's B&B in lovingly restored stately home (1826). Part of Green Business Tourism Scheme. In 5-acre grounds and woodland, 5 miles NE of city; views over River Tay. Sitting room, breakfast room. Dinner by arrangement. No background music. Wi-Fi. Parking. 4 bedrooms (all with garden view). B&B £35–£50 per person.

DUNOON Argyll and Bute   Map 5:D1

The Enmore, 111 Marine Parade, Kirn PA23 8HH. *Tel* 01369-202230, www.enmorehotel.co.uk. Handy for car ferries to Western Isles, 18th-century 'gentleman's retreat' overlooking Firth of Clyde, 2 miles E of centre. 'Charming, obliging' owners, Robert and Wendy Thomson. 2 lounges, bar, dining room (background music). Veranda. 2 squash courts. 1½-acre garden; private beach. 10 bedrooms (1 suitable for &). B&B £45–£69 per person; D,B&B £67.50–£91.50.

EDINBURGH   Map 5:D2

Acer Lodge, 425 Queensferry Road, EH4 7NB. *Tel* 0131-336 2554, www.acerlodge.co.uk. Gillian and Terry Poore's homely B&B in suburban house 3 miles W of centre ('wonderful bus service: 15 mins' to Princes Street'); ample parking. No background music. Children welcomed. 5 bedrooms (some on ground floor). B&B £25–£60 per person.

Apex City Hotel, 61 Grassmarket, EH1 2JF. *Tel* 0131-243 3456, www. apexhotels.co.uk. 'Good facilities, helpful staff' at large, contemporary hotel in Old Town (castle views). *Agua* bar, restaurant; background music; conference facilities. Spa at *Apex International* hotel next door (pool, sauna, gym). Parking. 119 bedrooms (Internet, wide-screen TV, free local phone calls; power shower). B&B £44.50–£109.50 per person.

Glenora Guest House, 14 Rosebery Crescent, EH12 5JY. *Tel* 0131-337 1186, www.glenorahotel.co.uk. In Haymarket district: refurbished Victorian town house with original features (elaborate cornices, plaster-work, brass servants' bells and speaking tubes). Morag Thomas is manager. Reception, breakfast room (organic produce). No background music. 11 bedrooms. B&B £35–£75 per person.

The Howard, 34 Great King Street, EH3 6QH. *Tel* 0131-557 3500, www.thehoward.com. Discreet luxury hotel (Town House company), managed by Johanne Falconer. Composed of 3 Georgian houses in cobbled New Town street. Dedicated butler; chauffeur; planned itineraries. Drawing room, small *Atholl* restaurant ('traditional Scottish fare'); room-service meals. No background music. Parking. 18 bedrooms: B&B £82.50–£197.50 per person; D,B&B £112.50–£205.

Malmaison, 1 Tower Place, Leith, EH6 7DB. *Tel* 0131-468 5000, www. malmaison.com. Overlooking Leith harbour: boldly converted 19th-century seamen's mission, managed by William Verhoeven. Strong colours and stripes; photographs; abstract art. Café/bar, brasserie; terrace (alfresco dining); meeting/function facilities; fitness room; background music. Wi-Fi. Free parking. 100 bedrooms: £75–£295. Breakfast £11.95–£13.95.

Prestonfield, Priestfield Road, EH16 5UT. *Tel* 0131-225 7800, www. prestonfield.com. Restaurateur James Thomson's flamboyantly decadent hotel (see also *The Witchery*, below), managed by Alan McGuiggan. Splendid 17th-century mansion 1½ miles from centre. Sumptuous decor. Good views to Arthur's Seat. 20-acre garden/parkland (croquet, putting; bicycles), surrounded by golf course. 3 drawing rooms, 2 bars, *Rhubarb* restaurant; 4 private dining rooms; background music; Wi-Fi; lift; function facilities. Terrace; 'gothic' tea house. Dogs welcomed. Parking. 23 bedrooms (1 suitable for &). B&B £112.50–£175 per person. Dinner £25–£50.

Rick's, 55a Frederick Street, EH2 1LH. *Tel* 0131-622 7800, www. ricksedinburgh.co.uk. Chic bar/restaurant-with-rooms in basement of neo-classical house in Georgian New Town. Managed by Murray Ward. Eclectic modern cooking; background 'soul/funk' music. Some street noise. 10 bedrooms (custom-designed furniture, CD/DVD-player, Wi-Fi), across covered courtyard. B&B £65–£129.25 per person.

Ten Hill Place, 10 Hill Place, EH8 9DS. *Tel* 0131-662 2080, www. tenhillplace.com. In Georgian terrace facing garden square, ultra-modern hotel, done in heather hues. Owned by Royal College of Surgeons (adjacent to Surgeons' Hall complex; income generated helps provide surgical skills, education and training to needy areas of the world), managed by Neil Pinkerton. Bar (snacks)/breakfast room; 24-hr room service. Wi-Fi. 78 bedrooms (4 suitable for &). B&B (buffet) from £50 per person.

Tigerlily, 125 George Street, EH2 4JN. *Tel* 0131-225 5005, www. tigerlilyedinburgh.co.uk. 'Friday evening and the place was buzzing.' Hip hotel in Georgian house, managed by David Hall. Colourful, glamorous design. 2 bars (opulent *Lulu* bar and club below), restaurant. Wi-Fi. 'The food was good. A fantastic location.' 33 bedrooms. B&B £92.50–£172.50 per person.

The Witchery by the Castle, Castlehill, EH1 2NF. *Tel* 0131-225 5613, www.thewitchery.com. Gothic-style restaurant-with-suites in 2 adjacent 16th-century buildings at top of Royal Mile, by castle. Owned by restaurateur James Thomson (see *Prestonfield*, above), managed by David Wright. Ornate red and gold paintwork; decadent drapery; sybaritic bathrooms. 2 restaurants (Scottish produce; background music); terrace. 7 suites (in 2 buildings): £295 (includes continental breakfast and bottle of champagne).

ELGIN Moray   Map 5:C2

Mansion House Hotel & Country Club, The Haugh, IV30 1AW. *Tel* 01343-548811, www.mansionhousehotel.co.uk. 19th-century baronial mansion in mature woodland on River Lossie, 5 mins' walk from centre. Owned by David Baker, managed by Lynn Macdonald. Country house interior. Piano lounge, snooker room, bar, restaurant, bistro; leisure club (indoor swimming pool, sauna, steam room; treatments; gym); function/business facilities; background music. Parking. 23 bedrooms (some interconnecting). B&B £71.50–£90 per person; D,B&B £94–£112.50.

FORT WILLIAM Highland   Map 5:C1

Inverlochy Castle, Torlundy, PH33 6SN. *Tel* 01397-702177, www.inverlochycastlehotel.com. Baronial pile (built 1863) in foothills of Ben Nevis, 3 miles NE of Fort William. Managed by Calum Milne. Lavishly embellished interior: Great Hall (Venetian chandeliers, frescoed ceiling); front hall, drawing room, restaurant (live music at dinner), billiard room; terrace; weddings, conferences, etc. 500-acre grounds: tennis, loch, fishing. Children welcomed. 17 bedrooms. B&B £150–£350 per person. Dinner £65.

FORTROSE Highland   Map 5:C2
The Anderson, Union Street, by Inverness, IV10 8TD. *Tel* 01381-620236, www.theanderson.co.uk. Lively, award-winning restaurant-with-rooms in 1840s building in seaside village on Black Isle. American owners, Jim and Anne Anderson. Public bar (real ales), *Whisky* bar (*tapas* menu; over 200 single malts), dining room. Background music. Wi-Fi. Beer garden. Parking. Sandy beach 1½ miles. 9 bedrooms (redecorated in 2008). B&B £40–£49 per person. Dinner £33.

GATEHOUSE OF FLEET   Map 5:E2
The Bank of Fleet, 47 High Street, DG7 2HR. *Tel* 01557-814302, www.bankoffleet.co.uk. Small hotel run by chef/manager Ian Hogg, on edge of Galloway Forest park. Much blue in decor. Bar/restaurant (inglenook fireplace) overlooking walled garden; small function facilities; background music. 6 bedrooms. B&B £32.50–£35 per person.

GLASGOW   Map 5:D2
Malmaison, 278 West George Street, G2 4LL. *Tel* 0141-572 1000, www.malmaison.com. In financial district, chic conversion of Greek Orthodox church with magnificent Art Nouveau central staircase. Managed by Scott McKie. Bold colours and stripes, prints and black-and-white photographs. Bar, lounge; lift. Background music. Dogs welcomed. 72 bedrooms: £160–£210. Breakfast £13.95. Dinner £23–£30.
Hotel du Vin Glasgow, 1 Devonshire Gardens, G12 0UX. *Tel* 0141-339 2001, www.hotelduvin.co.uk. Spread over 5 town houses in West End (on busy, tree-lined road; double glazing). Managed by Garry Sanderson. Original features (stained glass, grand staircase, oak panelling); subdued colour scheme; atmosphere of gentlemen's club. Bar, bistro; gym; treatments. No background music. Walled garden. 49 bedrooms: £145–£315. Breakfast £14.50–£17.

GRANTOWN-ON-SPEY Highland   Map 5:C2
The Pines, Woodside Avenue, PH26 3JR. *Tel* 01479-872092, www.thepinesgrantown.co.uk. On edge of town, down quiet lane, elegant Victorian Highland home in 1-acre landscaped gardens and woodland. 'Immaculately kept and faultlessly run' by owners Michael and Gwen Stewart. Family portraits, original watercolours, oil paintings, antiques, *objets d'art*. 2 lounges, 2 dining rooms, library. No background music. 'Excellent evening meals and unimprovable breakfasts.' Parking. 7 bedrooms (1 on ground floor). B&B £63–£70 per person. Dinner from £35.

Ravenscourt House, Seafield Avenue, PH26 3JG. *Tel* 01479-872286, www.ravenscourthouse.co.uk. Former Church of Scotland manse (1905) in quiet location on edge of Cairngorms national park. Run by owners Andrew and Sheena Williamson and son Mark ('no prescriptive rules'). Traditionally furnished. 2 lounges, conservatory restaurant (classical background music). Small garden. 8 bedrooms. B&B £25–£87.50 per person; D,B&B from £50.

INVERNESS Highland   Map 5:C2
Dunain Park, IV3 8JN. *Tel* 01463-230512, www.dunainparkhotel. co.uk. 'Perfect base for a holiday in Inverness.' Secluded 19th-century Italianate country mansion (part of Classic British Hotels organisation; managed by Sue Leslie). 2 lounges, restaurant (modern Scottish cuisine); drying room. No background music. 6-acre grounds: 2 walled gardens, woodland, croquet, badminton. 'Delicious food. Much to praise.' 13 bedrooms (2 in garden cottages). B&B £70–£112.50 per person.

KELSO Borders   Map 5:E3
The Cross Keys, The Square, TD5 7HL. *Tel* 01573-223303, www. cross-keys-hotel.co.uk. Becattelli family's hotel in old coaching inn (built 1769) on cobbled town square. 'Delightful owners and staff. Straightforward, well-prepared food.' Lift. Lounge, *No. 36* bar, restaurant (Scottish and international dishes); background music. 28 bedrooms. B&B £35–£63 per person; D,B&B £50–£78.

KINROSS Perth and Kinross   Map 5:D2
Roxburghe Guest House, 126 High Street, KY13 8DA. *Tel* 01577-862498, www.roxburgheguesthouse.co.uk. Modest guest house on high street of old market town. Traditional Scottish cooking by owner/ managers Sandy Ferguson and Steve Wrigley; vegetarian/special diets catered for. Dining room (background music), patio (barbecue). Award-winning garden. Children, walkers, cyclists welcomed (drying facilities). Off-street parking. 5 bedrooms. B&B £25–£50 per person; D,B&B £40–£65.

KIRKCUDBRIGHT Dumfries and Galloway Map 5:E2
The Marks, DG6 4XR. *Tel* 01557-330854, www.marksfarm.co.uk. Sheila Watson and Chris Caygill's B&B in 16th-century dower house cradled by Galloway hills, 4 miles E of town. Drawing room, study, breakfast room. No background music. Rambling gardens (woods, loch, walks, stabling). By working farm with sheep, dairy herd, worms (for

organic waste management, fishing, composting). 3 bedrooms. B&B
£30–£35 per person. Dinner £15.

LOCHEPORT Western Isles   Map 5: inset A1
Langass Lodge, Isle of North Uist, HS6 5HA. *Tel* 01876-580285,
www.langasslodge.co.uk. In isolated position, white-painted, extended
sporting lodge, 10 mins' drive from Lochmaddy ferry harbour, 25 mins'
from Benbecula airport. 'Lovely view; sight of Skye on a good day.'
Owned and run by Niall and Amanda Leveson Gower, with John and
Anne Buchanan in charge of cooking and hospitality. Sitting room/
library, bar, restaurant (fish, seafood, game specialities). Background
music. Garden. Popular with birdwatchers, anglers, walkers. 11 bedrooms (6 in 'hillside' rooms, 'spacious, beautifully furnished'). B&B
£45–£65 per person. Dinner £29.

LOCKERBIE Dumfries and Galloway   Map 5:E2
The Dryfesdale, Dryfebridge, DG11 2SF. *Tel* 01576-202427, www.
dryfesdalehotel.co.uk. Useful staging post near the border: Best
Western hotel, managed by owner Glenn Wright, in former manse,
1 mile from centre, near M74, exit 17. Lounge, *Malt* bar, *Kirkhill* restaurant; conference/function facilities; background music. 5-acre grounds.
Children and pets welcome. 28 bedrooms (some patio rooms suitable
for &). B&B £55–£75 per person; D,B&B £82.50–£100.

LYBSTER Highland   Map 5:B3
The Portland Arms, KW3 6BS. *Tel* 01593-721721, www.portlandarms.
co.uk. Handsome granite coaching inn (1850s) on outskirts of fishing
village, 15 mins S of Wick; ½ mile from sea. Convenient stopover for
Orkney ferry. Managed by Craig Williamson. Traditional furnishing.
Lounge, library, bistro/bar, *Kitchen* restaurant (local produce); wedding/
function facilities. No background music. Small front garden. 22 bedrooms. B&B £37.50–£50 per person.

MELROSE Borders   Map 5:E3
Burts, Market Square, TD6 9PL. *Tel* 01896-822285, www.burtshotel.
co.uk. Listed 18th-century building (black-and-white facade; window
boxes) on square, owned by Henderson family for more than 35 years.
Lounge, bar (over 80 malt whiskies), restaurant. Background music (classical). Garden. 20 bedrooms. B&B £58–£60 per person; D,B&B £84–£87.
The Townhouse, Market Square, TD6 9PQ. *Tel* 01896-822645,
www.thetownhousemelrose.co.uk. Opposite Henderson family's other

hotel, *Burt's* (above). Smartly renovated house with white-painted exterior, in town square. Brasserie, restaurant (Scottish fusion food), conservatory; background music; patio; wedding/function facilities. 11 bedrooms. B&B £62–£100 per person. Dinner £29.50.

NORTH BERWICK East Lothian   Map 5:D3
The Glebe House, Law Road, EH39 4PL. *Tel* 01620-892608, www. glebehouse-nb.co.uk. In secluded garden overlooking town, Gwen and Jake Scott's B&B in listed, elegantly proportioned, Georgian manse (1780). 2 mins' walk to beach and town. Sitting room, breakfast room. Parking. 3 bedrooms. B&B £45 per person.

PEEBLES Borders   Map 5:E2
Cringletie House, off Edinburgh Road, EH45 8PL. *Tel* 01721-725750, www.cringletie.com. 2 miles N of town, pink stone, turreted Victorian mansion on 28-acre wooded estate, run as luxury hotel by Jacob and Johanna van Houdt. 'Rolling views. Good food in nicely decorated restaurant.' Lounge, library, bar, dining room; lift; background music. Wi-Fi. Walled garden; woodland paths. Outdoor chess; *pétanque*. Dogs welcomed. 13 bedrooms (1 suitable for ♿). B&B £145–£255 per person.
Park Hotel, Innerleithen Road, EH45 8BA. *Tel* 01721-720451, www. parkpeebles.co.uk. Centrally located (McMillan Hotels) in gabled, white building, with views of Peebleshire hills. Managed by Donald Innes. Lounge, bar (background music), restaurant; lift. Garden, putting; access to sports/health facilities at large sister hotel, *Peebles Hydro* (700 yds: swimming pool, sauna; tennis etc). 24 bedrooms. B&B £65.50–£91.50 per person; D,B&B £81–£107.

PERTH Perth and Kinross   Map 5:D2
The Parklands, 2 St Leonard's Banks, PH2 8EB. *Tel* 01738-622451, www.theparklandshotel.com. Run by owners Scott and Penny Edwards, well-equipped hotel overlooking South Inch Park: views across River Tay to Kinnoull Hill. 5 mins' walk to town. Lounge, bar, *Acanthus* restaurant, *Number 1 The Bank* bistro; function facilities; light background music. Wi-Fi. Terrace, garden leading to park. 15 bedrooms. B&B £49.50–£119 per person; D,B&B £59.50–£149.
Sunbank House, 50 Dundee Road, PH2 7BA. *Tel* 01738-624882, www.sunbankhouse.com. By River Tay, Remigio (chef) and Georgina Zane's Victorian house in landscaped gardens, 2 miles E of centre. 'Nice, homely atmosphere.' Italian-influenced dishes using Scottish produce. Lounge/bar, restaurant (light classical background music).

Traditional decor. Wi-Fi. 9 bedrooms (some ground floor). B&B
£32.50–£89 per person. Dinner £27.50.

PITLOCHRY Perth and Kinross   Map 5:D2
Craigatin House & Courtyard, 165 Atholl Road, PH16 5QL. *Tel* 01796-
472478, www.craigatinhouse.co.uk. In secluded wooded grounds, Martin
and Andrea Anderson's B&B in 1820s house 5 mins' walk from town. Stylish, contemporary rooms. Conservatory breakfast room; terrace, courtyard.
Garden. 13 bedrooms (some suitable for &). B&B £32.50–£50 per person.
Green Park, Clunie Bridge Road, PH16 5JY. *Tel* 01796-473248, www.
thegreenpark.co.uk. 'Couldn't ask for more – comfortable rooms, warm
welcome, excellent food.' McMenemie family's country house ('superb
position') in 3-acre garden on Loch Faskally (putting, fishing, boat hire),
on N edge of town. No background music. Children welcomed. 3 lounges,
library, bar, restaurant. No background music. 51 bedrooms (16 on ground
floor; 6 suitable for &). B&B £59–£68 per person; D,B&B £69–£92.

POOLEWE Highland   Map 5:B1
Pool House, IV22 2LD. *Tel* 01445-781272, www.poolhousehotel.com.
On Loch Ewe in village at mouth of River Ewe, 5 miles N of Gairloch:
Peter and Margaret Harrison's luxury lodge, managed by Elizabeth
Miles. Suites named after famous warships. Weddings a speciality.
Drawing room/library, *The Rowallen Room* (collection of single malt
whiskies; billiard table), *North by North West* dining room (nautical theme
in blue and gold; hand-painted starry ceiling, zodiac fresco; seafaring
charts). 1-acre garden, pergola, terrace. Environmentally friendly. 7 bedrooms (all with sea or river views; 3 ground floor). D,B&B £127.50–£245
per person.

PORTREE Highland   Map 5:C1
Cuillin Hills Hotel, Isle of Skye, IV51 9QU. *Tel* 01478-612003,
www.cuillinhills-hotel-skye.co.uk. Gabled, white-walled traditional
hotel (former Victorian hunting lodge; owned by small Wickman group,
managed by Peter Sim) in 15-acre wooded grounds overlooking Portree
Bay. 'Very friendly; good atmosphere; great views.' Lounge, bar,
restaurant; background music. 26 bedrooms (some on ground floor; 7 in
annexe). B&B £100–£225 per person. Dinner £35.

ST ANDREWS Fife   Map 5:D3
Rufflets, Strathkinness Low Road, KY16 9TX. *Tel* 01334-472594,
www.rufflets.co.uk. Ann Murray-Smith's turreted, white, baronial-style

mansion (built 1920s), managed by Stephen Owen. In award-winning gardens just outside 'home of golf'. Drawing room, music room/bar, *Terrace* restaurant (modern Scottish; local, seasonal produce); background music; wedding/function facilities; 10-acre grounds. 24 bedrooms (3 in Gatehouse; 2 in Lodge). B&B £92.50–£157.50 per person; D,B&B £130–£195.

SCARISTA Western Isles   Map 5:B1

Scarista House, Isle of Harris, HS3 3HX. *Tel* 01859-550238, www. scaristahouse.com. Facing sea, handsome white Georgian manse, 15 miles SW of Tarbert, managed by Tim and Patricia Martin (co-owners with Neil King). Children welcomed. 5 bedrooms (3 small ones in house, 2 suites, and 2 self-catering units adjacent). Drawing room, library, dining room. No background music. 1-acre garden: trampoline. 3-mile sandy beach nearby. B&B £87.50–£140 per person. Dinner £39.50.

SCOURIE Highland   Map 5:B2

Eddrachilles Hotel, Badcall Bay, IV27 4TH. *Tel* 01971-502080, www.eddrachilles.com. Isabelle and Richard Flannery's white-painted old manse above bay ('wonderful location'; 'spectacular views'), 2 miles S of village. 'A gastronomic delight in a wild area.' Reception, conservatory, bar (125 single malt whiskies), restaurant (French/Scottish food, extensive wine list); classical background music. Children welcomed. 4-acre garden; 60-acre grounds. 11 bedrooms. B&B £44–£67 per person; D,B&B £60–£84.

Scourie Hotel, IV27 4SX. *Tel* 01971-502396, www.scourie-hotel.co.uk. Overlooking Scourie Bay: Patrick and Judy Price's fishing hotel (old coaching inn). 2 lounges, 2 bars, *table d'hôte* restaurant; no background music. 7-acre grounds leading to sea (5 mins' walk to sandy beach); 36 fishing beats exclusive to guests, plus 3 beats on lochs Stack and More (sea trout and salmon). 20 bedrooms (bay or mountain views; 2 family rooms in garden). B&B £35–£49 per person; D,B&B £56–£71.

SWINTON Borders   Map 5:E3

The Wheatsheaf at Swinton, Main Street, TD11 3JJ. *Tel* 01890-860257, www.wheatsheaf-swinton.co.uk. Chris and Jan Winson's old stone-built inn (managed by Craig Dickson) on roadside opposite village green. 10 miles SW of Berwick-upon-Tweed. Fresh, simply furnished rooms. 2 lounges, 2 dining rooms; background music; conservatory; small garden. Children welcomed. 10 bedrooms (1 suitable for &). B&B £46–£75 per person; D,B&B £69–£105.

TAYNUILT Argyll and Bute   Map 5:D1
Roineabhal Country House, Kilchrenan, PA35 1HD. *Tel* 01866-833207, www.roineabhal.com. Smart country guest house near Loch Awe in family home of Roger and Maria Soep. Lounge, dining room (5-course dinners: special needs catered for; background music at night); veranda. Garden. Afternoon teas. Pick-up service from Oban/Taynuilt. 3 bedrooms (1 on ground floor). B&B £45–£60 per person. Dinner £40 (including wine).

TOBERMORY Argyll and Bute   Map 5:D1
The Tobermory Hotel, Main Street, PA75 6NT. *Tel* 01688-302091, www.thetobermoryhotel.com. On Mull, quirky hotel owned by Ian and Andi Stevens in row of colourful converted fishermen's cottages 'perfectly situated' on waterfront. Sitting room, bar, *Water's Edge* restaurant; drying facilities. Background music. Packed lunches available. 'Cosy rooms, good restaurant.' 15 bedrooms (most with sea view; 1 suitable for &). B&B £47–£59 per person. D,B&B £77.50–£89.50.

ULLAPOOL Highland   Map 5:B2
The Sheiling, Garve Road, IV26 2SX. *Tel* 01854-612947, www.thesheilingullapool.co.uk. Iain and Lesley MacDonald's 'value-for-money' B&B. Modern, white, low-roofed building 5 mins' walk from town. Light, contemporary interior. Lounge (log fire), breakfast room. Background radio. 1-acre garden down to shore: lochside patio; mountain views across Loch Broom; trout fishing free to guests. *Sportsman's Lodge* in grounds (laundry, drying room; sauna, shower). 6 bedrooms. B&B £30–£45 per person. `

WALES

BRECON Powys   Map 3:D3
Cantre Selyf, 5 Lion Street, LD3 7AU. *Tel* 01874-622904, www.cantreselyf.co.uk. Sandstone 17th-century town house near St Mary's church, informally run as B&B by friendly owners Helen and Nigel Roberts. Lounge, dining room (traditional Welsh/continental breakfast; organic produce), 1-acre garden. No background music. 3 bedrooms (moulded, beamed ceilings, Georgian fireplaces, cast iron beds). B&B £31.50–£37.50 per person.

CAERNARFON Gwynedd   Map 3:A2
Plas Dinas Country House, Bontnewydd, LL54 7YF. *Tel* 01286-830214, www.plasdinas.co.uk. 'Perfect mix of tranquillity, history and

luxury.' Grade II listed gentleman's residence with extensive Victorian additions, former country home of Armstrong-Jones family. Now 'wonderful' hotel run by 'enthusiastic' owners Andy and Julian Banner-Price. Elegantly furnished; antiques and royal memorabilia. Drawing room, dining room (closed Sun/Mon; background music). Wi-Fi. Wedding/small function facilities. 15-acre grounds. Dogs welcomed (£10 charge). 10 bedrooms (1 suitable for &). B&B £44.50–£149 per person. Dinner £39.95.

CARDIFF   Map 3:E4

The Big Sleep, Bute Terrace, CF10 2FE. *Tel* 02920-636363, www. thebigsleephotel.com. Friendly budget B&B hotel (former British Gas office building) ½ mile from station. Owned by Cosmo Fry with consortium including John Malkovich; managed by Claire Musa. 'Minimalist kitsch' decor (much formica). Good views over city from top floors. Lift. Residents' bar, breakfast room; background music, meeting room. Wi-Fi. Limited parking. 81 bedrooms (some family, some suitable for &). B&B (continental) £22.50–£85 per person.

CRICKHOWELL Powys   Map 3:D4

The Manor, Brecon Road, NP8 1SE. *Tel* 01873-810212, www. manorhotel.co.uk. At foot of valley, in Brecon Beacons national park, ½ mile from town: white-painted 18th-century manor house managed by Roger Francis. 'Smashing' views over valley and River Usk. Bar, bistro ('food very good'; locally reared organic meat). Background music. Leisure suite (sauna, steam room, whirlpool, gym). Conference facilities. 22 bedrooms. Large expansion planned Oct 2008 in separate building (28 more bedrooms; new leisure suite). B&B £37.50–£90 per person; D,B&B £67.50–£120.

ERWOOD Powys   Map 3:D4

Trericket Mill, LD2 3TQ. *Tel* 01982-560312, www.trericket.co.uk. Environmentally considerate, 'cosy, not luxurious' guest house in converted corn mill (Grade II listed) run by owners Nicky and Alistair Legge. Interesting interior (grain bins, gear wheels, chutes, shafts). Lounge (wood-burning stove), dining room. No background music. 'Delicious' vegetarian cooking (vegans catered for). 3 simple bedrooms in *Veggie Guest House* plus 3 basic rooms in bunkhouse; also riverside campsite. 9 miles SE of Builth Wells. B&B £28–£37 per person. Dinner £17.50.

HARLECH Gwynedd   Map 3:B3

Castle Cottage, Y Llech, LL46 2YL. *Tel* 01766-780479, www.
castlecottageharlech.co.uk. Near castle, Jacqueline (manager) and Glyn
(chef) Roberts's informal restaurant-with-rooms in 2 old buildings (one
a Grade II listed former coaching inn). Recently refurbished: contemporary interior alongside wooden beams, sloping floors, log fires. 'Stone-
floored bathrooms, lots of storage.' Lounge/bar, dining room (castle
views; background music; 'delicious dinners; reasonably priced wines').
7 bedrooms (4 in annexe; 2 on ground floor). B&B £53–£75 per person;
D,B&B £85–£105.

HAVERFORDWEST Pembrokeshire   Map 3:D1

Crug-Glas, Abereiddy, Solva, SA62 6XX. *Tel* 01348-831302, www.
crug-glas.co.uk. 1½ miles inland from Pembrokeshire coast: Perkin and
Janet Evans's country guest house ('like an upmarket *chambres d'hôte*')
on 600-acre mixed working farm. Traditional decor (family heirlooms).
2 drawing rooms (videos, books), bar; dining room (classical background
music). 1-acre garden. 5 bedrooms. B&B £40–£65 per person.

College Guest House, 93 Hill Street, St Thomas Green, SA61 1QL.
Tel 01437-763710, www.collegeguesthouse.com. Georgian town house
B&B (Grade II listed former college for Baptist ministers), 5 mins' walk
from centre. Run by owners Colin Larby and Pauline Good. Lounge,
dining room. Welsh breakfast using Pembrokeshire produce. No background music. Wi-Fi. Parking. Swimming pool 100 yds away, beach
6 miles. 8 bedrooms (some family). B&B £34–£50 per person.

HAY-ON-WYE Powys   Map 3:D4

The Old Black Lion, Lion Street, HR3 5AD. *Tel* 01497-820841, www.
oldblacklion.co.uk. Managed by owner Dolan Leighton ('she and her
staff are so friendly'): 400-year-old coaching inn near Lion Gate, 3 mins'
walk from centre. Simply decorated; beams, uneven floors, low ceilings.
Bar (oak timbers, scrubbed pine tables, comfy armchairs), restaurant. No
background music. Garden. 10 bedrooms. B&B £45–£52.50 per person;
D,B&B from £67.50.

LAMPETER Ceredigion   Map 3:D3

Tŷ Mawr Mansion, Cilcennin, SA48 8DB. *Tel* 01570-470033, www.
tymawrmansion.co.uk. 'We felt pampered.' Peaceful retreat, 4 miles E
of Aberaeron, in Grade II-listed country house restored by owner/
managers Catherine and Martin McAlpine. Ramps, 3 lounges, library,
restaurant (Welsh produce, mainly from garden/within 10-mile radius;

'easy-listening' background music); panelled snooker room. 12-acre mature grounds. 9 bedrooms (1 suite on ground floor). B&B £70–£120 per person; D,B&B £99.50–£145.

LLANARMON DYFFRYN CEIRIOG   Map 3:B4
The West Arms, LL20 7LD. *Tel* 01691-600665, www.thewestarms. co.uk. In hamlet 7 miles SW of Llangollen, 16th-century building by River Ceiriog, owned by Lee and Sian Finch and Grant Williams. 'Excellent food and service.' Ramp, lounge, 2 bars (meal service), restaurant; 'mellow' background music; conservatory; conference/ function facilities. Garden facing Berwyn mountains. 15 bedrooms. B&B £43.50–£118 per person; D,B&B £65–£144.

LLANDUDNO Conwy   Map 3:A3
The Lighthouse, Marine Drive, Great Orme's Head, LL30 2XD. *Tel* 01492-876819, www.lighthouse-llandudno.co.uk. Two miles from centre, in Great Orme country park: Fiona and Ray Kilpatrick's B&B in disused clifftop lighthouse, built in castle style in 1862. Keeper's Hall with unique pitch pine panelling and gallery; Victorian dining room (Classic FM during renowned Welsh breakfast), from which visitors can look down over 100-metre vertical drop. 3 bedrooms, all with lounge or sitting area (Lamp Room has panoramic views). B&B £75–£95 per person.
Osborne House, The Promenade, 17 North Parade, LL30 2LP. *Tel* 01492-860330, www.osbornehouse.co.uk. Richly decorated seafront hotel, managed by Elyse and Michael (also chef) Waddy. Lounge, bar, café grill (chandeliers, portraits; bistro-style cooking). Background music. 6 suites (sea views, gas fire). B&B £65–£200 per person. Dinner £30.

LLANGOLLEN Denbighshire   Map 3:B4
Gales, 18 Bridge Street, LL20 8PF. *Tel* 01978-860089, www. galesofllangollen.co.uk. 'Hotel, Food and Wine Bar' in 18th-century town house 20 yds off main street. Owned for 30 years by Gale family. Wine/gift shop adjacent. Informal atmosphere. Chunky wood furniture, carved bedheads, beams. Wine bar (background music), conference facilities, small patio area, car park. Wi-Fi. Children welcomed. 15 bedrooms (7 above shop, others in much older building; 1 suitable for &). B&B £40–£60 per person (£5 supplement for cooked breakfast). Dinner £30.

LLANRWST Conwy   Map 3:A3
Meadowsweet, Station Road, LL26 0DS. *Tel* 01492-642111, www. wales-snowdonia-hotel.co.uk. In small Snowdonia market town, Mary

and Nelson Haerr's refurbished hotel ('Victorian grandeur with a modern twist') in large, yellow-painted house (views of open countryside). Lounge, bar, *Lle Hari* restaurant. Background music. Courtyard. Hearty Welsh breakfasts. Free Wi-Fi. Children welcomed. 10 bedrooms. B&B £35–£65 per person. Dinner £28.

LLANWRTYD WELLS Powys   Map 3:D3
Lasswade Country House, Station Road, LD5 4RW. *Tel* 01591-610515, www.lasswadehotel.co.uk. In UK's smallest town, in foothills of Cambrian mountains, managed by owners Roger and Emma Stevens ('a good team'): eco-friendly, traditionally furnished, 'unassuming' Edwardian building. Local organic food. Drawing room, library; conservatory/function room (panoramic views); restaurant. No background music. Garden: kennels. Parking. 8 bedrooms. B&B £37.50–£65 per person; D,B&B £55–£93.

MUMBLES Swansea   Map 3:E3
Patricks with Rooms, 638 Mumbles Road, SA3 4EA. *Tel* 01792-360199, www.patrickswithrooms.com. Owned by Catherine and Patrick Walsh, Sally and Dean Fuller: restaurant-with-rooms (beautiful views), 5 miles SW of Swansea, on bay. Lounge/bar; restaurant (fresh fish; vegetarian options); background music. Children welcomed. Sea 200 yds. Expansion planned (8 more bedrooms and gym/leisure suite). 8 colourful bedrooms. B&B £55 per person. Dinner £30.

PENARTH Cardiff   Map 3:E4
Holm House, Marine Parade, CF64 3BG. *Tel* 029-2070 1572, www.holmhouse.com. Susan Sessions (manager) and Margaret Hewlett's glamorous renovation of 1920s mansion behind esplanade; views over Bristol Channel. Stylish wallpaper, mirrors, chandeliers and furniture. 15 mins' drive from Cardiff. Lounge/bar, restaurant; background jazz; indoor 25-ft swimming pool; ½-acre garden. 12 bedrooms (2 on courtyard, 1 suitable for &). B&B £72.50–£210 per person; D,B&B £100–£240.

RUTHIN Denbighshire   Map 3:A4
Manorhaus, Well Street, LL15 1AH. *Tel* 01824-704830, www.manorhaus.com. Boutique hotel/art gallery (exhibitions of contemporary Welsh artists), in Grade II listed Georgian building off main square. Tastefully refurbished by owners Christopher Frost and Gavin Harris. Lounge, *à la carte* restaurant, library; 'easy-listening'

background music; cinema; fitness room, seminar/meeting facilities. Parking nearby. 8 bedrooms. B&B £52.50–£110 per person; D,B&B £72.50–£130.

The Wynnstay Arms, Well Street, LL15 1AN. *Tel* 01824-703147, www.wynnstayarms.com. In centre: contemporary comforts within historic half-timbered coaching inn (established 1549), owned by Kelvin Clayton (manager) and Jason Jones (chef) and their wives. Lounge, café bar, *Fusions* brasserie (local ingredients); background music. Parking. 7 bedrooms. B&B (continental) £32.50–£65 per person; D,B&B £49.50–£85.

ST DAVID'S Pembrokeshire   Map 3:D1

Old Cross Hotel, Cross Square, SA62 6SP. *Tel* 01437-720387, www. oldcrosshotel.co.uk. 'Simple, unspoilt' stone-built hotel, owned by Alex and Julie Babis. 'Friendly, efficient staff.' Lounge, bar (popular with locals; background radio), restaurant. Garden: alfresco meals in summer. Children welcomed. Parking. 16 bedrooms. B&B £35–£65 per person; D,B&B £55–£85.

SWANSEA   Map 3:E3

Morgans, Somerset Place, SA1 1RR. *Tel* 01792-484848, www. morganshotel.co.uk. Converted Regency Port Authority building (Grade II* listed) in centre, owned by Martin and Louisa Morgan, managed by Christine Owen. Modernised, with many impressive features. Bar, *Plimsoll* restaurant; background music; lift; function room; wedding facilities. Courtyard. Parking. 41 bedrooms (21, cheaper, in *Morgans Townhouse* opposite). 'Daring double showers.' B&B £40–£250 per person. Dinner £22.50–£35.

CHANNEL ISLANDS

BRAYE Alderney   Map 1: inset D6

Braye Beach Hotel, Braye Street, GY9 3XT. *Tel* 01481-824300, www.brayebeach.com. Converted from several old pirates' warehouses, stylishly modernised beachfront hotel near harbour, 15 mins' walk from Alderney's main town, St Anne. Owned by Derek Coate, managed by Scott Chance. Lounge, bar, restaurant (local and French produce); decked terrace; private cinema; Wi-Fi; background music. 'Generous package deals. I was bowled over by both accommodation and food.' Special-interest breaks. 27 bedrooms (some with balcony, sea views). B&B £40–£120 per person.

KINGS MILLS Guernsey   Map 1: inset D5
Fleur du Jardin, Grand Moulins, Castel, GY4 7JT. *Tel* 01481-257996, www.fleurdujardin.com. 'Charming' shabby-chic hotel (bleached wood walls, sandstone bathrooms) owned by Ian and Amanda Walker (see also *Bella Luce*, St Martin, below). 10 mins' bus ride to town; 10 mins' walk to beach. Bar, restaurant ('tremendous evening meals'). Background music. Garden: heated swimming pool. 14 bedrooms (2 garden suites). B&B £43–£84 per person; D,B&B £22 added.

ST HELIER Jersey   Map 1: inset E6
The Club Hotel & Spa, Green Street, JE2 4UH. *Tel* 01534-876500, www.theclubjersey.com. 'Though "funky", it has a relaxing and peaceful ambience. Exceptional staff.' Managed by Tim Phillips, contemporary, understatedly luxurious hotel in convenient location in town. Library, *Club* café, adjacent *Bohemia* restaurant (*Michelin* star). Background music. Spa: saltwater pool, sauna, hydrotherapy bench, treatments. Free Wi-Fi. Beaches nearby. Parking. 46 bedrooms (suites have sitting room and balustrade). B&B (continental) £97.50–£212 per person. Set menus £20–£49.

ST MARTIN Guernsey   Map 1: inset E5
Bella Luce Hotel, La Fosse, GY4 6EB. *Tel* 01481-238764, www.bellalucehotel.guernsey.net. Hotel, restaurant and spa in manor house (11th-century origins), in scenic area 2 miles SW of St Peter Port. Recently upgraded (traditional features retained) by Ian and Amanda Walker (see *Fleur du Jardin*, above). Lounge, *Lucifer's* bar (revived 1960s look: painted flames, deep red walls, low-lit booth seating; light meals), restaurant; background music. Wi-Fi. Garden; heated swimming pool (summer months). Rock beach 5 mins' walk. 31 bedrooms (some family, 1 suitable for ♿): £90–£128. Breakfast £7.

ST PETER PORT Guernsey   Map 1: inset E5
The Clubhouse @ La Collinette, St Jacques, GU1 1UT. *Tel* 01481-710331, www.lacollinette.com. Near seafront and centre, 'friendly, welcoming' hotel run by Chambers family for almost half a century, recently much revamped. Bar, *Kashmara* North African restaurant (colourful decor). Gym. Garden; heated swimming pool. No background music. Children welcomed: children's pool; play area. Self-catering accommodation in grounds. 30 bedrooms. B&B £55–£95 per person.
La Frégate, Les Cotils, GU1 1UT. *Tel* 01481-724624, www.lafregatehotel.com. High above town (harbour views), refurbished 18th-

century manor house with contemporary interior, 5 mins' walk from centre. Managed by Chris Sharp. Bar, restaurant; terrace; function facilities. No background music. Small, secluded garden. 22 bedrooms (all with sea views; some with balcony). B&B £76.50–£350 per person.

ST SAVIOUR Guernsey · Map 1: inset E5
The Farmhouse, Bas Courtils, GY7 9YF. *Tel* 01481-264181, www.thefarmhouse.gg. David and Julie Nussbaumer's country hotel, former farmhouse (part 15th-century). Sophisticated modern interior; luxurious bathrooms. 'Fantastic, good-sized room; large bed; heated bathroom floor, great shower.' Bar, restaurant (background music, live music at weekends); courtyard; wedding/conference facilities. Wi-Fi. Large garden; outdoor swimming pool. 14 bedrooms. B&B £60–£125 per person. Dinner £28.

IRELAND

BANGOR Co. Down · Map 6:B6
Cairn Bay Lodge, 278 Seacliff Road. *Tel* 028-9146 7636, www.cairnbaylodge.com. B&B with characterful interior, serving 'gourmet' breakfasts. Overlooking Ballyholme beach, white pebble-dashed home of Chris and Jenny (a beauty therapist) Mullen and daughter Poppy. 2 lounges (views of bay), oak-panelled dining room; beauty salon; small shop selling local products. No background music. Mature garden. ½ mile from town. Children welcomed. Adjacent, self-catering luxury villa (sleeps 8). 5 bedrooms. B&B £37.50–£50 per person.

BELFAST · Map 6:B6
Culloden Estate & Spa, Bangor Road, Holywood, BT18 0EX. *Tel* 028-9042 1066, www.hastingshotels.com. Overlooking Belfast Lough, 6 miles E of city, former bishop's palace with Scottish baronial architecture and modern extension. Owned by Hastings Hotels group, managed by Kem Akkari. Lounges, *Cultra* inn, *Culloden Mitre* restaurant; background music; spa health club (indoor swimming pool; whirlpool, steam room, fitness suite); lift; wedding/conference facilities. 12-acre grounds: *Cultra Inn*. 105 bedrooms: £190–£670. Breakfast £18. Dinner £40.

Malmaison, 34–38 Victoria Street, BT1 3GH. *Tel* 028-9022 0200, www.malmaison-belfast.com. Converted from two 1860s red brick seed warehouses near River Lagan in Cathedral Quarter (edge of centre). Managed by Helen Caters. Iron pillars, beams and gargoyles. Lounge, bar, brasserie; background music; gymtonic; small business centre.

Wi-Fi. 64 bedrooms (bold colours, shiny fabrics, moody lighting): £135–£320. Breakfast from £12.

The Merchant Hotel, 35–39 Waring Street, BT1 2DY. *Tel* 028-9023 4888, www.themerchanthotel.com. In Cathedral Quarter, former head-quarters of Ulster Bank, owned by Bill Wolsey, managed by Adrian McLaughlin. Extravagant Victorian Italianate interiors; distinctive striped carpets. Lifts. 2 bars (*Cloth Ear* the more informal), *The Great Room* restaurant (stained-glass domed ceiling); club; background music; function facilities. Bentley car for hire. 26 bedrooms (2 suitable for &). B&B £80–£225 per person. Dinner from £30.

Old Inn, Main Street, Crawfordsburn, Co. Down, BT19 1JH. *Tel* 028-9185 3255, www.theoldinn.com. Ancient coaching inn (1640), in village 10 miles E of city. On edge of wooded country park that sweeps down to sea. Old-world charm: part thatched, beamed ceilings, wood-panelled walls. Gallery lounge, *Parlour* bar, conservatory-style *1614* restaurant; background music; Wi-Fi; conference/function facilities. Small garden. 30 bedrooms (1 suitable for &). B&B (buffet) from £60 per person.

BLARNEY Co. Cork   Map 6:D5

The Muskerry Arms, *Tel* 00 353 21-438 5200, www.muskerryarms. com. Lively *craic* at this public house with rooms in village centre, owned by 'hard-working' O'Connor family for 25 years. Wood flooring; soft colour scheme. Lounge, bar (large plasma TV screens), *Tavern* restaurant; live music. Wi-Fi. 7 bedrooms (some in *Lodge*, connected to hotel by walkway). B&B €49–€108 per person.

BUSHMILLS Co. Antrim   Map 6:A6

Bushmills Inn, 9 Dunluce Road, BT57 8QG. *Tel* 028-2073 3000, www.bushmillsinn.com. Traditionally the last stop for visitors to the Giant's Causeway; owned by Alan Dunlop, managed by Stephen Ball. On River Bush: old coaching inn and mill house joined together; atmos-pheric, maze-like; popular with locals. Peat fires, wooden booths. Draw-ing room, 'secret' library, gallery, loft, 2 bars (1 lit by gaslight), restaurant in 4 sections; 'New Irish' cooking; classical background music. 'Service smiling but erratic.' 3-acre garden. Parking. 32 bedrooms (1 ground floor). Major extension work planned. B&B £69–£158 per person.

CLONES Co. Monaghan   Map 6:B6

Hilton Park, Scothouse. *Tel* 00 353 47-56007, www.hiltonpark.ie. 'The ultimate Irish country house experience.' Ancestral home of Madden family (since 1734): imposing Italianate mansion run house party style by Lucy, Johnny and younger generation, Fred and Joanna. Imposing interior, furnished with antiques. Drawing room, sitting room, TV room, games room, smoking room, breakfast room, dining room (home-grown herbs, salads, most fruit and vegetables). No background music. 4 miles S of town, on wooded estate: 600-acre landscaped park and gardens with lakes and fine old trees. 6 bedrooms. B&B €125–€190 per person. Dinner (by arrangement) €55.

DERRY Co. Londonderry   Map 6:B6

Serendipity House, 26 Marlborough Street, Bogside, BT48 9AY. *Tel* 028-7126 4229, www.serendipityrooms.co.uk. Cosy, good-value B&B run by owners Paul and Stephen Lyttle, on hill in Bogside overlooking city walls. Original modern art. Lounge; sun deck (panoramic views). Background music at breakfast. 5 bedrooms. B&B £25–£50 per person. Dinner from £10.

DINGLE Co. Kerry   Map 6:D4

Milltown House. *Tel* 00 353 66-915 1372, www.milltownhousedingle.com. Overlooking harbour, on peninsula 3 km W of town: Tara Kerry's friendly B&B in white, 19th-century gabled house. Lounge, conservatory/breakfast room (light meals available). No background music. 1½-acre garden. Golf driving range, pitch and putt behind house. Parking. 10 bedrooms (some with views of garden or sea). B&B €60–€145 per person.

DONEGAL Co. Donegal   Map 6:B5

Harvey's Point. *Tel* 00 353 74-972 2208, www.harveyspoint.com. Gysling family's much-extended country hotel in secluded position on Lough Eske. Plush, spacious accommodation. Lounge, bar, restaurant; ballroom; resident pianist; classical background music; wedding/ conference facilities; indoor heated pool; beauty treatments. 1-acre garden. 71 bedrooms. B&B €99–€320 per person. Dinner €65.

DUBLIN   Map 6:C6

Leixlip House, Captain's Hill, Leixlip, Co. Kildare. *Tel* 00 353 1-624 2268, www.leixliphouse.com. 8 miles NW of Dublin (20 mins by motor-way to centre/airport): traditionally furnished Georgian house over-looking village. Lounge, bar (background music), *Bradaun* restaurant (modern Irish cuisine); wedding/function facilities; Wi-Fi. Golf packages. Parking. 19 bedrooms (4 in coach house). B&B €55–€180 per person.

Merrion Hall, 54–56 Merrion Road, Dublin 4. *Tel* 00 353 1-668 1426, www.halpinsprivatehotels.com. In Ballsbridge, S of city, Pat Halpin's extensively refurbished, creeper-covered Edwardian hotel (see also *Aberdeen Lodge*, main entry). 2 drawing rooms, dining room/conservatory; background music. Free Internet. Small garden. 28 bedrooms (2 suitable for &). B&B €74.50–€129 per person.

DUNGARVAN Co. Waterford   Map 6:D5

Powersfield House, Ballinamuck West. *Tel* 00 353 58-45594, www.powersfield.com. 1 mile outside Dungarvan, on little peninsula, Eunice Power's (award-winning cook) B&B and cookery school in symmetrical white neo-Georgian house. Colourful, smart interior. Background CDs/radio if wanted. Wi-Fi. Garden. Fly fishing on Blackwater River nearby. 6 bedrooms (1 suitable for &). B&B €55–€75 per person. Dinner (by arrangement) €27.50–€35.

GALWAY Co. Galway   Map 6:C5

The g, Wellpark. *Tel* 00 353 91-865200, www.theg.ie. Overlooking Lough Atalia, luxury hotel designed by milliner Philip Treacy. Owned by Gerry Barrett (Monogram Hotels), managed by Niall Kerrins. Vibrant jewel colours (pink, cerise, purple; swirling black-and-white striped carpets); 'decadent' furnishings; arresting black marble lobby, 3 lounges, champagne-drinking area, *Riva* restaurant (traditional Irish cuisine); lift; spa (indoor heated pool); Zen garden; function facilities; background music; live pianist at weekends. 'A most enjoyable stay.' 101 rooms. B&B €200–€1,250 per person. Dinner €55.

KENMARE Co. Kerry   Map 6:D4

Sheen Falls Lodge. *Tel* 00 353 64-41600, www.sheenfallslodge.ie. Overlooking waterfall: extended manor house in 300-acre mature woodlands. Former summer residence of Marquis of Lansdowne, now luxury hotel (Relais & Chateaux), owned by Bent Hoyer, managed by Alan Campbell. 2 miles SE of town (off N71). Lift. Lounge, sun lounge, library, 2 bars, *Oscar's* bistro, *La Cascade* restaurant; background music; billiard room; terrace. Health club (pool, whirlpool, sauna, treatments); tennis. 66 bedrooms: €310–€1,870. Breakfast €25, dinner €65–€90.

KILLARNEY Co. Kerry   Map 6:D4

Dunloe Castle, Beaufort. *Tel* 00 353 64-71350, www.dunloecastlehotel.com. Large, modern 5-star hotel facing ruins of medieval keep (views of Gap of Dunloe and River Laune: salmon fishing). 5 miles SW of town.

Lounge, bar, garden café; *Oak Room* restaurant; background music/live pianist; indoor swimming pool; wedding/function facilities. Children welcomed. 65-acre parkland: 20-acre subtropical garden; heated swimming pool, sauna, steam room, fitness room; 2 indoor tennis courts, putting, horse-riding; children's playground. 110 bedrooms. B&B €105–€170 per person. Dinner from €45.

KILLYBEGS Co. Donegal   Map 6:B5
Bay View, Main Street. *Tel* 00 353 74-973 1950, www.bayviewhotel.ie. Modern 3-star hotel, owned by Bernie O'Callaghan, in town centre, by pier. 'Good value. Good room overlooking harbour.' Lounge, 'pleasant' *Wheel House* bar/carvery, *Captain's Table* restaurant (overlooking harbour; 'catch of the day'); background music sometimes; leisure/fitness centre: indoor swimming pool, gym, sauna. Conference facilities. 40 bedrooms. B&B €65–€155 per person.

KINSALE Co. Cork   Map 6:D5
The Old Presbytery, 43 Cork Street. *Tel* 00 353 21-477 2027, www.-oldpres.com. In quiet street near centre, Philip and Noreen McEvoy's rambling red-doored Georgian house, once home of priests at nearby church of St John the Baptist. 'All ups and downs'; sitting room ('Victorian in every detail'), dining room. Classical/Irish background music. 9 bedrooms (including 3 self-catering suites). B&B €45–€130 per person.

LAHINCH Co. Clare   Map 6:C4
Moy House. *Tel* 00 353 65 708-2800, www.moyhouse.com. Flat, white, tower-topped building (18th-century), converted 'with panache' by owner Antoin O'Looney. Drawing room (honesty bar), library, dining room (background music). Popular with golfers (Lahinch has championship course). 15-acre grounds; access to beach. 1 km S of town. 9 bedrooms. B&B €92.50–€160 per person. Dinner €55.

LONGFORD Co. Longford   Map 6:C5
Viewmount House, Dublin Road. *Tel* 00 353 43-41919, www.viewmounthouse.com. James and Beryl Kearney's handsome Georgian house ('welcoming, comforting and homely') surrounded by 3½-acre segmented gardens adjoining Longford golf course. Courtyard; Japanese garden (waterways, hill, tunnel, path); upper patio and pond; orchard; herbaceous border; knot garden, etc. Interesting interior, furnished in period style. Sitting room, reception room, library,

restaurant; 'easy-listening' background music. 13 bedrooms (7 in modern extension; some on ground floor; garden views). B&B €65–€95 per person. Dinner €55.

RATHMULLAN Co. Donegal   Map 6:B5

Fort Royal, Letterkenny. *Tel* 00 353 74-9158100, www.fortroyalhotel. com. Owner/chef Tim Fletcher is the 3rd generation of his family to run this rambling white house with 'magnificent grounds' and fine views over Lough Swilly. 2 lounges, bar, dining room. No background music. ½ mile N of village; 18 acres of gardens and lawns (1 leading down to beach); tennis, pitch-and-putt golf. 11 bedrooms (plus 4 self-catering cottages). B&B €65–€75 per person. Dinner €45.

STRANGFORD Co. Down   Map 6:B6

The Cuan, 6–10 The Square, BT30 7ND. *Tel* 028-4488 1222, www.thecuan.com. Family-run (Peter and Caroline McErlean) licensed guest house in conservation village on S tip of Strangford Lough. Green-painted, flower-decorated building on village square. Modern bedrooms. A good stopover (ferries to Portaferry). Bar, restaurant (food served all day; seafood specialities at weekends); background music; conference/function facilities. Children welcomed. 9 bedrooms. B&B £37.50–£52.50 per person; D,B&B £52–£67.

WATERFORD Co. Waterford   Map 6:D5

Granville Hotel, The Quay. *Tel* 00 353 51-305555, www.granville-hotel.ie. Large, traditional hotel run by owners Liam and Ann Cusack in Georgian building overlooking waterfront and marina. Lounge, bar, *Bianconi* restaurant; wedding/conference facilities; background/live music. Wi-Fi. 100 bedrooms (penthouse suites have wide views). B&B €47.50–€80 per person.

Alphabetical list of hotels

(S) indicates a Shortlist entry

Roslyns Little Easton 214
Rothay Garden Grasmere (S) 504
Rothay Manor Ambleside 83
Roundwood House Mountrath 472
Roxburghe Guest House Kinross (S) 538
Royal Truro 309
Royal Ventnor (S) 528
Royal Oak East Lavant 162
Royal Park London (S) 488
Royal Seven Stars Totnes (S) 528
Rufflets St Andrews (S) 541
Russell's Restaurant Broadway 129
Rylstone Manor Shanklin 287

S

Sablonnerie Sark 439
St Brelade's Bay St Brelade 436
St Enodoc Rock (S) 522
St Ernan's House Donegal 458
St Martin's on the Isle St Martin's 281
St Michael's Manor St Albans 277
St Tudno Llandudno 415
Salthouse Harbour Ipswich (S) 509
Salville House Enniscorthy 463
San Domenico London (S) 488
Sanctuary House London (S) 488
Saracen's Head Wolterton 327
Sat Bains Nottingham (S) 519
Scarista House Scarista (S) 542
Scotsman Edinburgh 349
Scourie Scourie (S) 542
Seafood Restaurant Padstow 257
Searcy's Roof Garden Rooms London (S) 488
Seatoller House Borrowdale 111
Seaview Seaview 285

Seaview House Ballylickey 444
Serendipity House Derry (S) 552
Shaftesbury London (S) 489
Shallowdale House Ampleforth 84
Sharrow Bay Ullswater 311
Sheedy's Lisdoonvarna 470
Sheen Falls Lodge Kenmare (S) 553
Sheiling Ullapool (S) 543
Shelburne Lodge Kenmare 466
Shelleys Lewes 212
Shelley's Lynmouth (S) 515
Ship Chichester (S) 498
Sign of the Angel Lacock 201
Simpsons Birmingham 108
Skirling House Skirling 386
Smart and Simple Tunbridge Wells (S) 528
Soar Mill Cove Soar Mill Cove 290
Soho London (S) 489
Spire House Salisbury (S) 524
Spread Eagle Midhurst (S) 516
Stafford London (S) 489
Stagg Inn Titley 306
Star Castle St Mary's 282
Star Inn Harome 183
Starr Restaurant with Rooms Great Dunmow 178
Steam Packet Inn Whithorn 394
Stella Maris Ballycastle 443
Stock Hill House Gillingham 174
Stoke Lodge Stoke Fleming 295
Stone House Rushlake Green 274
Strand House Winchelsea 322
Strattons Swaffham 298
Summer Lodge Evershot 165
Sun Inn Dedham 159
Sun Inn Kirkby Lonsdale (S) 510
Sunbank House Perth (S) 540

[2009]

To: *The Good Hotel Guide*, Freepost PAM 2931, London W11 4BR

NOTE: No stamps needed in UK, but letters posted outside the UK should be addressed to 50 Addison Avenue, London W11 4QP, England, and stamped normally. Unless asked not to, we shall assume that we may publish your name. If you would like more report forms please tick ☐

Name of Hotel_____

Address _____

_____

Date of most recent visit   Duration of visit
☐ New recommendation   ☐ Comment on existing entry
Report:

Please continue overleaf

I am not connected directly or indirectly with the management or proprietors

Signed _____

Name (CAPITALS PLEASE)

Address _____

_____

Email address _____

[2009]

To: *The Good Hotel Guide*, Freepost PAM 2931, London W11 4BR

NOTE: No stamps needed in UK, but letters posted outside the UK should be addressed to 50 Addison Avenue, London W11 4QP, England, and stamped normally. Unless asked not to, we shall assume that we may publish your name. If you would like more report forms please tick ☐

Name of Hotel_____

Address _____

_____

Date of most recent visit   Duration of visit
☐ New recommendation   ☐ Comment on existing entry
Report:

Please continue overleaf

I am not connected directly or indirectly with the management or proprietors

Signed _____

Name (CAPITALS PLEASE)

Address _____

_____

Email address _____

[2009]

To: *The Good Hotel Guide*, Freepost PAM 2931, London W11 4BR

NOTE: No stamps needed in UK, but letters posted outside the UK should be addressed to 50 Addison Avenue, London W11 4QP, England, and stamped normally. Unless asked not to, we shall assume that we may publish your name. If you would like more report forms please tick ☐

Name of Hotel_____

Address _____

_____

Date of most recent visit   Duration of visit

☐ New recommendation   ☐ Comment on existing entry

Report:

Please continue overleaf

I am not connected directly or indirectly with the management or proprietors

Signed _____

Name (CAPITALS PLEASE)

Address _____

_____

Email address _____

[2009]

To: *The Good Hotel Guide*, Freepost PAM 2931, London W11 4BR

NOTE: No stamps needed in UK, but letters posted outside the UK should be addressed to 50 Addison Avenue, London W11 4QP, England, and stamped normally. Unless asked not to, we shall assume that we may publish your name. If you would like more report forms please tick ☐

Name of Hotel_____

Address _____

_____

Date of most recent visit   Duration of visit
☐ New recommendation   ☐ Comment on existing entry
Report:

Please continue overleaf

I am not connected directly or indirectly with the management or proprietors

Signed _____

Name (CAPITALS PLEASE)

Address _____

_____

Email address _____

British Isles maps

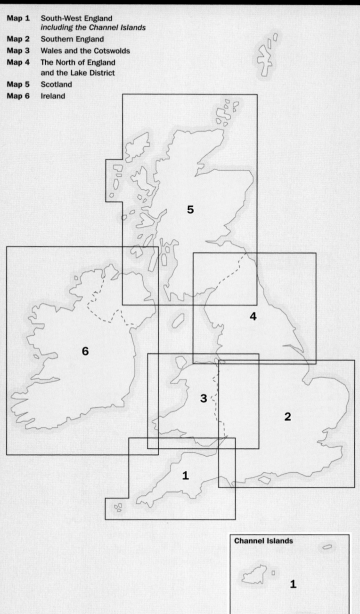

Channel Islands

1

Not to scale

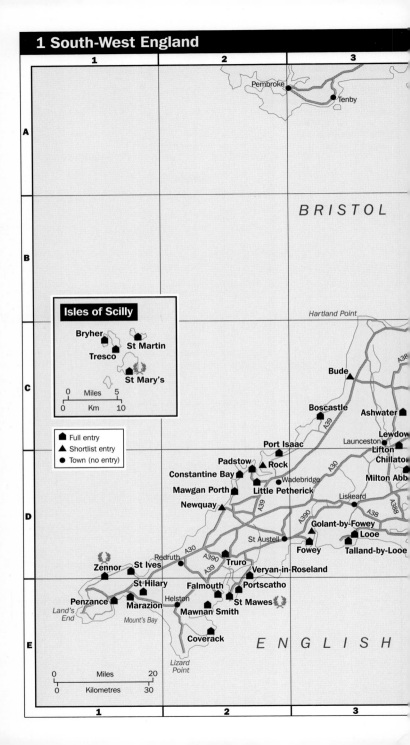

1 South-West England

Isles of Scilly

Bryher
St Martin
Tresco
St Mary's

0 Miles 5
0 Km 10

- Full entry ⬠
- Shortlist entry ▲
- Town (no entry) ●

BRISTOL

Pembroke
Tenby

Hartland Point

Bude
Boscastle
Ashwater
Lewdow
Launceston
Lifton
Chillato
Port Isaac
Padstow
Rock
Milton Abb
Constantine Bay
Wadebridge
Mawgan Porth
Little Petherick
Newquay
Liskeard
Golant-by-Fowey
Looe
St Austell
Fowey
Talland-by-Looe
Zennor
St Ives
Redruth
Truro
Veryan-in-Roseland
St Hilary
Falmouth
Portscatho
Penzance
Helston
St Mawes
Marazion
Land's End
Mawnan Smith
Mount's Bay
Coverack
ENGLISH
Lizard Point

0 Miles 20
0 Kilometres 30

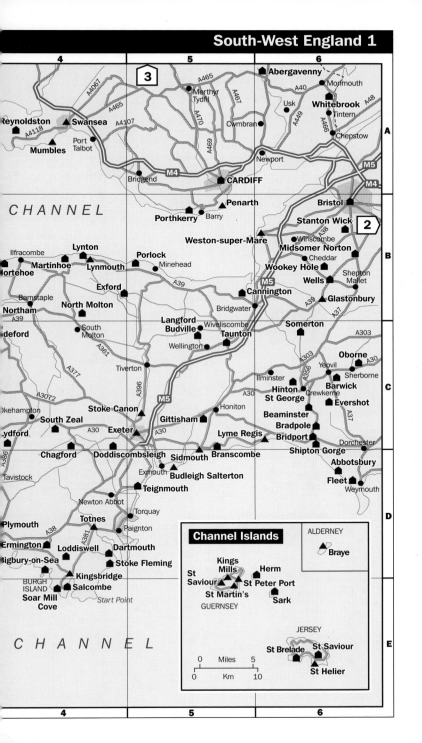

4   **5**   **6**

3

Abergavenny
Monmouth
Merthyr
Tydfil
A465
A467
Usk
Whitebrook
A40
A449
A48
Tintern
A466
Chepstow

Reynoldston
A4118
Swansea
A4107
A465
A4067
A470
A469
Cwmbran
Newport
M5
M5
M4

Mumbles
Port
Talbot
Bridgend
M4
CARDIFF

A

CHANNEL

Penarth
Barry
Porthkerry

Bristol

Stanton Wick

2

Weston-super-Mare
Winscombe
Midsomer Norton
Cheddar
Shepton
Mallet

Ilfracombe
Lynton
Porlock
Minehead
A39
Wookey Hole
Wells

Martinhoe
Lynmouth
Mortehoe
Exford

B

Barnstaple
Northam
North Molton
A39
South
Molton
Langford
Budville
Wiveliscombe
Cannington
Bridgwater
Somerton
Glastonbury
A39
A37

deford
A361
Tiverton
A396
Wellington
Taunton
A303
Oborne
A30
A303
A356
Yeovil
Sherborne

Okehampton
South Zeal
A3072
A30
Stoke Canon
M5
Honiton
Ilminster
A30
Crewkerne
Hinton
St George
Barwick
Evershot
A37

C

Lydford
A386
Chagford
Exeter
A30
Gittisham
Lyme Regis
Beaminster
Bradpole
Bridport
Dorchester

Tavistock
Doddiscombsleigh
Sidmouth
Branscombe
Shipton Gorge
Abbotsbury

Exmouth
Budleigh Salterton
Teignmouth
Fleet
Weymouth

D

Newton Abbot
Torquay
Plymouth
A38
Totnes
Paignton

Ermington
Loddiswell
Dartmouth
Bigbury-on-Sea
Stoke Fleming
BURGH
ISLAND
Kingsbridge
Salcombe
Soar Mill
Cove
Start Point

Channel Islands

ALDERNEY
Braye

Kings
Mills
Herm
St
Saviour
St Peter Port
St Martin's
Sark
GUERNSEY

JERSEY
St Brelade
St Saviour
St Helier

0   Miles   5
0   Km   10

CHANNEL

E

4   **5**   **6**

2 Southern England

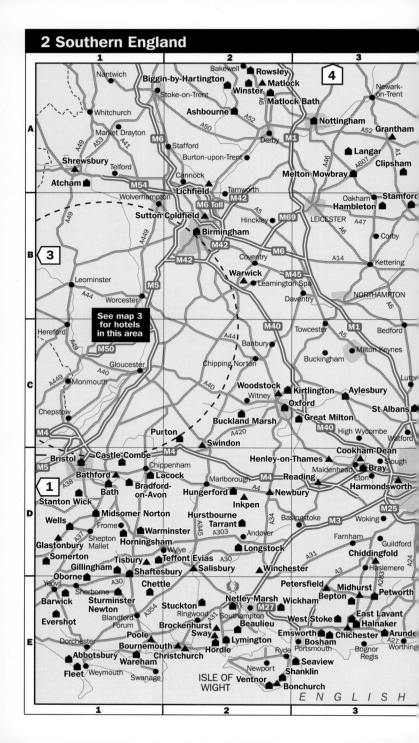

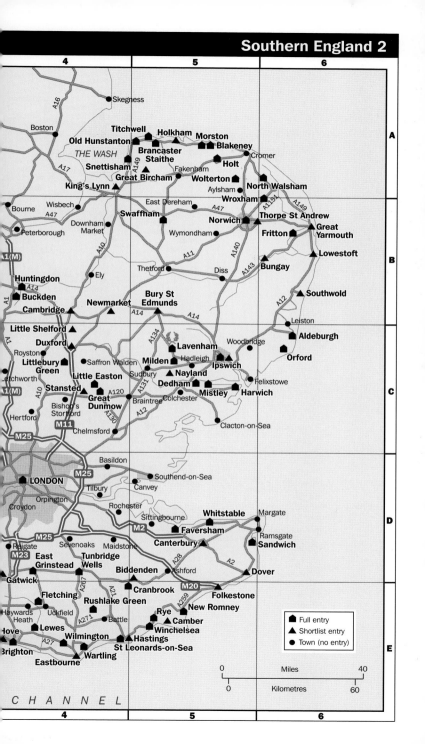

4   **5**   **6**

Skegness

Boston

Titchwell   **Holkham**   **Morston**

Old Hunstanton   **Blakeney**

THE WASH   **Brancaster**   Cromer

Staithe   Fakenham   **Holt**

Snettisham   **Wolterton**

Great Bircham   Aylsham   **North Walsham**

King's Lynn   **Wroxham**

Bourne   Wisbech   East Dereham   **Thorpe St Andrew**

A47   **Swaffham**   **Great**

Peterborough   Downham   **Norwich**   **Yarmouth**

Market   Wymondham   **Fritton**

Lowestoft

Thetford   Diss   **Bungay**

Huntingdon   Ely

Buckden   **Southwold**

Cambridge   **Bury St**   Leiston

Newmarket   **Edmunds**

Little Shelford   **Aldeburgh**

Duxford   Woodbridge   **Orford**

Royston   **Lavenham**

Littlebury   Saffron Walden   **Milden**   Hadleigh

Green   Sudbury   **Ipswich**

Little Easton   **Nayland**   Felixstowe

etchworth   **Stansted**   **Dedham**

A120   Braintree   **Mistley**   **Harwich**

Bishop's   **Great**   Colchester

Hertford   Stortford   **Dunmow**

Chelmsford   Clacton-on-Sea

Basildon

LONDON   Southend-on-Sea

Orpington   Tilbury   Canvey

Croydon

Rochester   **Whitstable**   Margate

Sittingbourne   **Faversham**

Reigate   Sevenoaks   Maidstone   **Canterbury**   Ramsgate

Sandwich

East   **Tunbridge**

Grinstead   **Wells**   **Biddenden**   Ashford

Gatwick   **Dover**

Haywards   **Fletching**   **Cranbrook**   **Folkestone**

Heath   Uckfield   **Rushlake Green**   **New Romney**

Hove   **Lewes**   Battle   **Rye**   **Camber**

Wilmington   **Winchelsea**

Brighton   **Hastings**

Wartling   St Leonards-on-Sea

Eastbourne

■	Full entry
▲	Shortlist entry
●	Town (no entry)

0   Miles   40

0   Kilometres   60

C H A N N E L

4   **5**   **6**

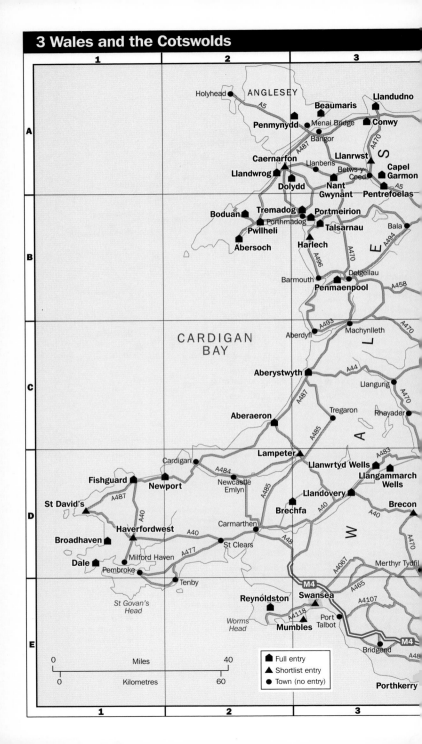

1 **2** **3**

A

Holyhead ● ANGLESEY

A5

Llandudno

Beaumaris

Penmynydd ■ Menai Bridge ● **Conwy**

Bangor ●

A487

A470

Caernarfon ■ **Llanrwst**

Llanberis ● Betws-y- **Capel**

Llandwrog ■ Coed ● **Garmon**

Nant

Dolydd ■ **Gwynant** ▲ A5

Pentrefoelas

B

Boduan ■ **Tremadog** ■ **Portmeirion**

Porthmadog ● **Talsarnau**

Pwllheli ■ Bala ●

A496

A494

Abersoch ■ **Harlech** ▲

A470

Barmouth ● Dolgellau ●

Penmaenpool ■ A458

C

CARDIGAN
BAY

A493

Aberdyfi ● Machynlleth ●

A470

Llangurig ● A470

Aberystwyth ■ A44

A487

Tregaron ● Rhayader ●

Aberaeron ■

A485

A

D

Cardigan ● **Lampeter** ▲

A484 A483

Fishguard ■ Newcastle **Llanwrtyd Wells** ■

Emlyn ● **Llangammarch**

Newport ■ A485 **Wells**

St David's ▲ A487 **Llandovery** ■

A40 **Brechfa** ■ A40 **Brecon** ▲

Carmarthen ● A470

Haverfordwest ▲ A40

Broadhaven ■ W

A477 St Clears ● A48

Dale ■ Milford Haven ● A4067

Pembroke ● Merthyr Tydfil ●

Tenby ● A465

M4 A4107

St Govan's **Reynoldston** ■ **Swansea** ▲

Head

A4118 Port A48

Worms **Mumbles** ▲ Talbot ● M4

Head

E

0 Miles 40 **Bridgend** ●

■	Full entry
▲	Shortlist entry
●	Town (no entry)

0 Kilometres 60 **Porthkerry**

1 **2** **3**

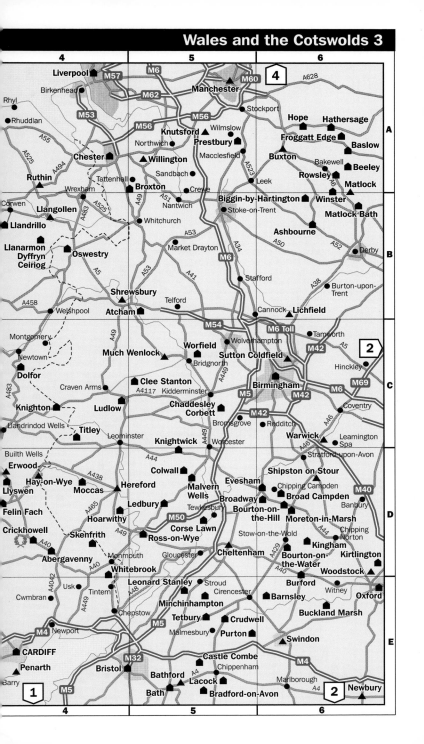

4 The North of England and the Lake District

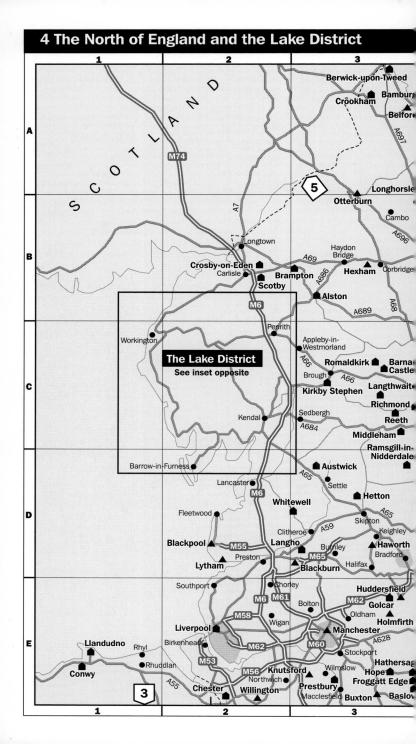

SCOTLAND

M74

Berwick-upon-Tweed
Bambur
Crookham
Belfor

A697

5

Longhorsle
Otterburn
Cambo

A7

A696

Longtown
Haydon
Bridge
Crosby-on-Eden
Carlisle
Brampton
A69
Hexham
Corbridge
Scotby
A686
Alston
A689
A68

M6

Penrith

Workington

Appleby-in-
Westmorland
Romaldkirk
Barna
Castle

The Lake District
See inset opposite

A66
Brough
A66
Langthwait
Kirkby Stephen
Richmond
Kendal
Sedbergh
Reeth
A684
Middleham

**Ramsgill-in-
Nidderdale**

Barrow-in-Furness
A65
Austwick
Lancaster
Settle
M6
Hetton
Whitewell
Fleetwood
A65
Skipton
Keighley
Clitheroe
A59
Blackpool
Langho
Burnley
Bradford
Haworth
M55
M65
Lytham
Preston
Blackburn
Halifax
Southport
Chorley
Huddersfield
M6 M61
Bolton
M62
Golcar
M58
Oldham
Holmfirth
Wigan
Liverpool
Manchester
Birkenhead
M62
M60
A628
Llandudno
Rhyl
Stockport
Hathersag
Conwy
Rhuddlan
M53
Wilmslow
Hope
Froggatt Edge
A55
M56
Knutsford
Chester
Northwich
Prestbury
Baslov
3
Willington
Macclesfield
Buxton

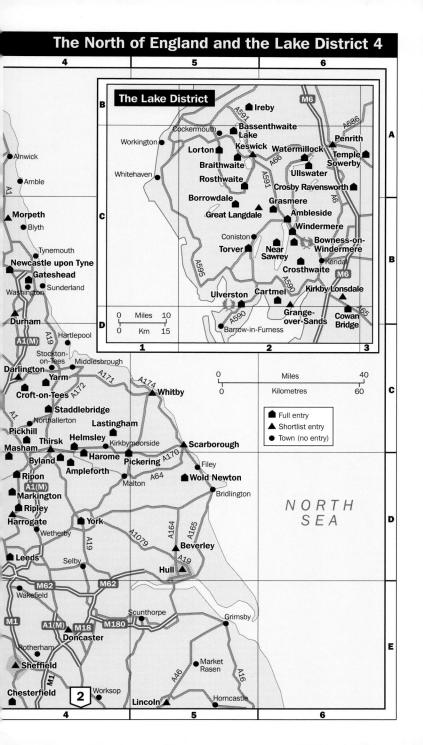

The Lake District

Ireby
Cockermouth
Bassenthwaite Lake
Workington
Lorton
Keswick
Watermillock
Penrith
Temple Sowerby
Whitehaven
Braithwaite
Ullswater
Rosthwaite
Crosby Ravensworth
Borrowdale
Grasmere
Great Langdale
Ambleside
Windermere
Coniston
Torver
Near Sawrey
Bowness-on-Windermere
Kendal
Crosthwaite
Ulverston
Cartmel
Kirkby Lonsdale
Grange-over-Sands
Cowan Bridge
Barrow-in-Furness

0   Miles   10
0   Km   15

Alnwick
Amble
Morpeth
Blyth
Tynemouth
Newcastle upon Tyne
Gateshead
Washington   Sunderland
Durham   Hartlepool
Stockton-on-Tees
Darlington   Middlesbrough
Yarm
Croft-on-Tees
Whitby
Staddlebridge
Northallerton
Lastingham
Pickhill
Thirsk   Helmsley
Masham   Kirkbymoorside
Scarborough
Byland   Harome
Ampleforth   Pickering
Filey
Ripon   Malton
Wold Newton
Markington   Bridlington
Ripley
Harrogate
Wetherby
York
Leeds   Beverley
Selby   Hull
Wakefield
Scunthorpe   Grimsby
Rotherham
Doncaster
Sheffield   Market Rasen
Chesterfield   Worksop
Lincoln   Horncastle

NORTH SEA

0   Miles   40
0   Kilometres   60

■ Full entry
▲ Shortlist entry
● Town (no entry)

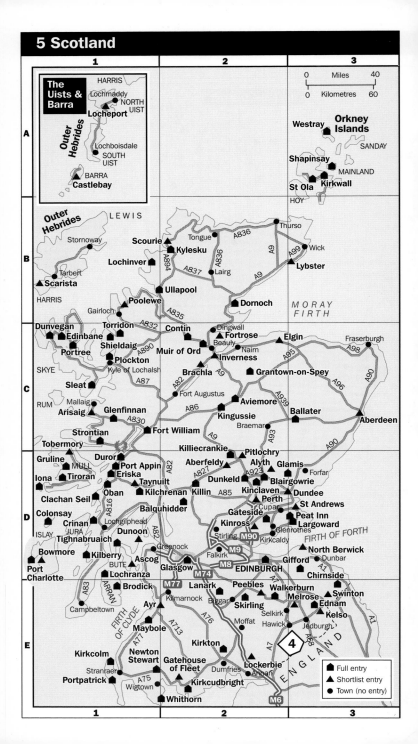

5 Scotland

The Uists & Barra

HARRIS
Lochmaddy
NORTH UIST
Locheport
Outer Hebrides
Lochboisdale
SOUTH UIST
BARRA
Castlebay

0 Miles 40
0 Kilometres 60

Westray **Orkney Islands**
SANDAY
Shapinsay
MAINLAND
St Ola **Kirkwall**
HOY

Outer Hebrides
LEWIS
Stornoway
Scourie
Tongue A836 Thurso
Kylesku
A9 A99 Wick
Lochinver A894 A836 **Lybster**
Lairg
A837
Tarbert
Scarista **Ullapool** A9
HARRIS A835
Gairloch **Dornoch**
Poolewe MORAY FIRTH
Dingwall
Dunvegan Torridon A832 Contin **Fortrose** Elgin Fraserburgh
Edinbane Beauly Nairn A95 A98
Shieldaig A890 **Muir of Ord** **Inverness** A90
Portree Plockton **Grantown-on-Spey** A96
SKYE Kyle of Lochalsh **Brachla** A939
Sleat A87 A82 A9
RUM Fort Augustus **Aviemore** **Ballater**
Mallaig **Glenfinnan** A86 **Kingussie** **Aberdeen**
Arisaig A830 Braemar A93
Strontian **Fort William** A9 A90
Tobermory
Killiecrankie **Pitlochry**
Gruline **Duror** **Aberfeldy** **Alyth** **Glamis**
MULL **Tiroran** **Port Appin** A827 **Dunkeld** A923 **Blairgowrie** Forfar
Iona **Eriska** **Kinclaven**
Taynuilt **Killin** A85 **Perth** **Dundee**
Clachan Seil **Oban** **Kilchrenan** **St Andrews**
Colonsay **Balquhidder** **Gateside** Cupar **Peat Inn**
Crinan A816 Lochgilphead **Kinross** **Largoward**
JURA **Dunoon** A82 Stirling M90 Glenrothes FIRTH OF FORTH
Tighnabruaich Greenock Kirkcaldy
ISLAY **Ascog** Falkirk M9 **North Berwick**
Bowmore **Kilberry** BUTE **Glasgow** M8 **Gifford** Dunbar
Port **Lochranza** ARRAN M74 **EDINBURGH** A1 **Chirnside**
Charlotte **Brodick** M77 **Lanark** A7 **Walkerburn**
Kilmarnock **Peebles** **Melrose** **Swinton**
Ayr Biggar **Skirling** Selkirk **Ednam**
Campbeltown FIRTH OF CLYDE A76 Moffat **Kelso**
Maybole A713 Hawick Jedburgh A1
A77 **Kirkton** A7 A68
Kirkcolm **Newton** A7 ENGLAND
Stewart **Gatehouse** **Lockerbie**
Stranraer of Fleet Dumfries Annan
Portpatrick A75 **Kirkcudbright**
Wigtown M6
Whithorn

■ Full entry
▲ Shortlist entry
● Town (no entry)

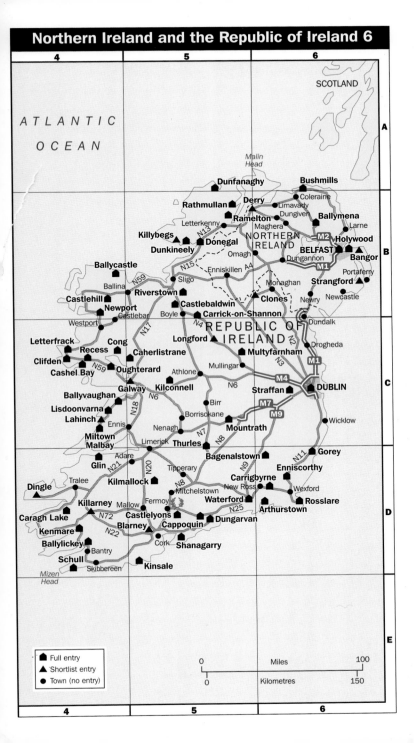

Northern Ireland and the Republic of Ireland 6

ATLANTIC

OCEAN

SCOTLAND

Malin
Head

Dunfanaghy

Bushmills

Rathmullan

Derry

Coleraine

Limavady

Dungiven

Ballymena

Larne

Letterkenny

Ramelton

Maghera

NORTHERN
IRELAND

Holywood

Killybegs

Donegal

Omagh

BELFAST

Dunkineely

Enniskillen

Dungannon

Bangor

Portaferry

N15

A4

Monaghan

Strangford

Ballycastle

Sligo

Clones

Newry

Newcastle

N59

Riverstown

Castlebaldwin

Dundalk

Castlehill

Ballina

Boyle

Carrick-on-Shannon

Newport

Castlebar

N4

REPUBLIC OF

M1

Westport

N17

Longford

IRELAND

Drogheda

Letterfrack

Cong

Caherlistrane

Multyfarnham

N2

Recess

Mullingar

N3

Clifden

Oughterard

Athlone

M4

Cashel Bay

N59

N6

Straffan

DUBLIN

Galway

Kilconnell

Ballyvaughan

N18

Birr

M7

Wicklow

Lisdoonvarna

N6

Borrisokane

M9

Lahinch

Ennis

Nenagh

Mountrath

Miltown
Malboy

Limerick

N7

Thurles

N8

Gorey

Adare

Bagenalstown

N11

Glin

N21

Tipperary

N9

Enniscorthy

Dingle

Tralee

N20

Kilmallock

Carrigbyrne

N8

Mitchelstown

New Ross

Wexford

Killarney

Mallow

Fermoy

Waterford

Rosslare

Caragh Lake

N72

Castlelyons

N25

Arthurstown

Kenmare

Blarney

Cappoquin

Dungarvan

N22

Cork

Ballylickey

Shanagarry

Schull

Bantry

Kinsale

Skibbereen

Mizen
Head

■ Full entry

▲ Shortlist entry

● Town (no entry)

0   Miles   100

0   Kilometres   150

4   5   6